KT-473-794

COUNTY REPORTS
To The
BOARD OF AGRICULTURE

THE REVIEW AND ABSTRACT

of the

COUNTY REPORTS

to the

BOARD OF AGRICULTURE

Vol. 5.   Sothern and Peninsular.

by

WILLIAM MARSHALL

DAVID & CHARLES REPRINTS

7153 4369 6

This edition first
published 1817

Printed in Great Britain by
Clarke, Doble & Brendon Ltd Plymouth
Published by David & Charles (Holdings) Limited
South Devon House Railway Station Newton Abbot

THE

REVIEW AND ABSTRACT

OF THE

COUNTY REPORTS

TO THE

BOARD OF AGRICULTURE;

FROM THE SEVERAL

AGRICULTURAL DEPARTMENTS OF ENGLAND.

By Mr. MARSHALL.

~~~~~~~~~~~~~~~~

IN FIVE VOLUMES.

~~~~~~~~~~~~~~~~

VOLUME THE FIFTH;

(Which was first Published, in 1817, and is now combined with the other
Volumes of the same Work;)

Comprizing those from the

SOUTHERN AND PENINSULAR
DEPARTMENTS.

Which include

HERTFORDSHIRE,	HAMPSHIRE,
BERKSHIRE,	SURREY,
MIDDLESEX,	KENT,
SOUTH ESSEX,	SUSSEX,
SOUTH WILTSHIRE,	CORNWALL,
SOUTHEAST SOMERSET,	DEVONSHIRE,
DORSETSHIRE,	WEST SOMERSETSHIRE.

York:

Printed by Thomas Wilson & Sons,

FOR LONGMAN, HURST, REES, ORME, AND BROWN, LONDON; CONSTABLE,
AND CO. EDINBURGH; AND WILSON AND SONS, YORK.

1818.

THE

CONTENTS

OF THE

SOUTHERN and PENINSULAR DEPARTMENTS.

SYSTEMATICALLY ARRANGED.

NATURAL ECONOMY.

POLITICAL ECONOMY

CONTENTS. V

RURAL

RURAL ECONOMY.

TENANTED ESTATES.

WOODLANDS.

WOODLANDS.

AGRICULTURE.

Farms.

Farm Fences.

Homesteads.

Cottages and Grounds.

Rural Profession.

Objects, State of Husbandry, and Plan of Management.

Occupiers.

Workpeople.

Surrey,

viii   CONTENTS.

Southeast

ADVER-

ADVERTISEMENT.

In the INTRODUCTION to the Work which I have now concluded, I traced the origin and progress of the Board of Agriculture;—showed its illegitimacy and deformity;—yet augured the benefits that it might, eventually, afford the parent stock, from which the scion was surreptitiously, and unskilfully, taken.

In developing those public benefits, and adapting them to the permanent uses of the Rural Science, I have, I find, expended ten years of unremitted and pretty close attention.——The labors of seventy or eighty public Writers, (many of whose Works have never been published) and the sentiments of some hundreds of Annotators, Correspondents, and parole Contributors,—concerning an important and, with me, a favorite branch of human knowledge,—were not to be allowed to sink, unprofitably, into oblivion; even though the task might cost some years of *time;* and no inconsiderable *sum,* to boot. The agents of the Board I have ever considered as MY ASSISTANTS,—as laborers in MY OWN FIELD.

Notwithstanding, however, this interruption to my original design,—which, during the last forty years, I have held constantly in view, as my leading object in life,—I despair not to accomplish it. The most important, and by far the most difficult part of it,—the registry of the existing practices of England, at the commencement of the nineteenth century,—IS NOW FINISHED.

WILLIAM MARSHALL.

April 1817.

SOUTHERN DEPARTMENT

OF

ENGLAND.

THE NATURAL DISTINGUISHMENTS of this Department are strong. Its prevailing SUBSTRUCTURE is CHALK,—of which peculiar fossil it comprizes, I apprehend, nine tenths, or a larger portion, of the whole quantity which this island discloses at its surface. The Wolds of Yorkshire and Lincolnshire are the only specimens of Chalk hill that I have observed, in England, Scotland, or Wales, which are not included within the boundary lines of the SOUTHERN DEPARTMENT of ENGLAND.

Another peculiarity of the SOUTHERN DEPARTMENT, in regard to its substrata, is also observable. There is not, I believe, a mass of noncalcareous rock (unless loosely cemented sand may be deemed such); nor even a stone! (other than flints), unless in a confined district of Kent,—to be found within its limits. *

The AGRICULTURAL DISTINCTIONS, observable in the SOUTHERN DEPARTMERT, are numerous.

The CHALK-HILL HUSBANDRY is peculiar.

The

* THE GREY WEDDERS of MARBOROUGH DOWNS.—These may be mentioned as another exception to the foregoing position.—The stones which bear that name I have seen and strolled among as a botanist : but without any other view.—They are scattered over an extent of surface, or partially bedded beneath it. Their sizes (to convey a general idea) may be said to vary from the size of a wedder to that of an ox.

But on the theory which I recently suggested (in the *Midland Department*, p. 14.) those stones might be considered as *atmospherical ;* or, more appropriately, of *cometic origin ;* and not as a native production of the SOUTHERN DEPARTMENT.

The " STONAGE" of SALISBURY PLAIN has been supposed to have been brought to that place, from a distance (of course from a very great distance) by human exertions. But it appears to me more rational to consider the materials of that striking work of art, as a DEPOSIT of SPACE; their present arrangement being the result of DRUIDICAL INGENUITY ; the fragments and minor masses having been removed, the more to astonish (as Stonehenge seldom fails to do) the posterity of those extraordinary times.

The HOP CULTURE,—tho not wholely confined to this quarter of the island,—is principally carried on with it. The Hop grounds of Worcestershire and Nottinghamshire are of inconsiderable extent, compared with those of Kent and Surrey.

IRRIGATION.—The practice of watering low-lying meadow grounds, with calcareous water, belongs, almost exclusively, to this Department.

HAY FARMS;—Farms consisting solely of *mowing grounds,* may be said to be peculiar to the Southern Department.

Ewe flocks kept for the purpose of producing HOUSE LAMB;—and herds of cows solely for that of furnishing the London markets with VEAL;—occupy no inconsiderable part of the lands, within fifteen or twenty miles of the metropolis;—whose markets draw various other articles of FARM PRODUCE, in a summary way, to that attractive center:—thus giving, to a still greater extent, a peculiarity of character to the rural profession.

MY OWN KNOWLEDGE of this Department of the island may be said to be universal. There is scarcely a square mile of its surface which I have not *seen;* nor a district of it that I have not *examined.* *

The REPORTS to the BOARD OF AGRICULTURE, from this Department, that require to be appreciated, and the useful information they may contain to be extracted and b ought together, in this CONCENTRATION of PRACTICAL KNOWLEDGE, are these:—

Counties.	Originals.	Published.
Hertfordshire	Walker	Secretary.
Berkshire	Pearce	Mavor.
Middlesex	Foot	Middleton.
South Essex	{ Griggs { Vancouver	} Secretary.
South Wiltshire	Davis	Davis.
Southeast Somerset	Billingsley ...	Billingsley.
Dorsetshire	Claridge	Stevenson.
Hampshire	{ Drivers { Warner { Secretary	} Vancouver.
Surrey	James &c. ...	Stevenson.
Kent	Boys	Boys.
Sussex	Young	Young.

It may be proper to mention, in this place, that, in reviewing

---

* See my Register of the RURAL ECONOMY of the SOUTHERN COUNTIES. Also MINUTES of AGRICULTURE, in Surrey.

viewing those several works, the requisite labor will be less than that which has been bestowed on the former volumes of this undertaking. There are *few* writers of high consideration, in *agriculture*, whose sentiments and dictations will, I conceive, be liable to warp the minds of practical men, or to lead the novitial amateur, or the unpractised student, into the labyrinths of error:—saving those, I mean, whose erroneous opinions, and dangerous maxims of management, have already been brought out, and held up to public view; and some of them, I trust, placed in a light sufficiently clear, to render them inoffensive.

The line of proceeding, in the present case, will be to examine, with unremitted attention and perseverance, the several Works, as they pass in Review; and to arrest every idea, whether practical or theoretical, which shall strike me as being capable of adding to the accumulation of valuable materials that I have already drawn together.

But while performing this task, it is my intention to avoid noticing the errors and incongruities which they may contain; excepting in such flagrant cases as I may judge to be altogether unfriendly to the progressive rise of Rural Science.

HERTFORDSHIRE.

HERTFORDSHIRE;

THE COUNTY of HERTFORD covers much of those calcarious grounds, which extend, in a southwesterly direction,
from the northwest point of Essex, through parts of Cambridgeshire, Hertfordshire, Bedfordshire, Buckinghamshire,
and Oxfordshire, to the southeast point of Berkshire.

In Hertfordshire, the chalk rarely rises to the surface;
being principally buried under soils and substrata of different qualities and depths:—a circumstance, this, which
belongs more or less to almost the entire range: thus
giving character to a peculiar species or variety of ENGLISH
TERRITORY.—The other chalk hills of the kingdom mostly
rise, abruptly, above the adjacent noncalcareous lands;—
calcareous *soils* being exposed on the surface; as they are
toward the two extremes of the range now under notice.

This NATURAL DISTRICT, " one and indivisible," is unfortunately *allotted* among the seven Counties above named;
and is, of course, more or less noticed,—in fourteen Reports
to the Board !

In the Reports from three of those Counties, principally
situated within the *Midland Department,*—namely Oxfordshire, Buckinghamshire, and Bedfordshire,—I found some
useful information relating to the natural district now in
view, and the extracts I took from them may be considered
as prefatory to that which the Hertfordshire Reports may
furnish.

THE SOUTHERN MARGIN OF HERTFORDSHIRE combines
with the upper grounds of the County of Middlesex; there
being no natural, nor agricultural, line of distinction between
them.

" GENERAL

" GENERAL VIEW

OF THE

AGRICULTURE

OF THE

COUNTY OF HERTFORD,

WITH

OBSERVATIONS ON THE MEANS OF ITS IMPROVEMENT.

By D. WALKER,

NO. 14, UPPER MARYBONE STREET.

DRAWN UP FOR THE CONSIDERATION OF

The Board of Agriculture and Internal Improvement.

1795."

THIS is the " original Report," on quarto paper, from that County. It has not, consequently, been *published.*

Judging from the matter and manner of this sketch Report, Mr. Walker is a *professional man* of superior intelligence in many particulars relating to rural concerns. His QUALIFICATIONS, therefore, as a Reporter of rural information, are admissibly good; and had he appropriated sufficient length of time to a survey of the County, and paid due attention to the revision and digestion of the materials collected, he would, I doubt not, have been able to send up to the Board of Agriculture a satisfactory Report of its practices.

The performance before me, however, bears no evidence of such a proceeding having taken place. The topics touched upon are few, and the information concerning them is mostly *general.* A very small portion of the few pages which constitute the Work, relate, especially, to " the County of Hertford;"—excepting some valuable observations on *soils* and *manures.*

The *dissertations* are in general superior, in their *manner,* to the flippant and futile remarks that are found in most of the productions with which the shelves of Agriculture

have

have been loaded during the last half century. They elicit,
however, little that is *new*. They are frequently common-
place, observations, which apply not, particularly, to the
established practice of the County under Report.

Some instances of *individual practice* are noticed; tho
seldom in a way that entitles them to a place, here. On
the *established practice* of the County, in regard to the OPE-
RATIONS of AGRICULTURE, scarcely any thing worthy of
notice appears.

The number of pages eightysix. No map or other engraving. Yet, in the letterpress, the plan of a farmyard
is referred to.

NATURAL ECONOMY.

SURFACE.—P. 9. "The uneven surface of the county,
varied through its whole extent with hill and dale, affords
natural drainage, and all the various aspects under heaven."

WATERS.—P. 7. " The principal rivers are the Lea and
the Colne; and these are composed of many inferior streams,
most of whose sources lie within the county, and join the
principal rivers at different distances from their source."

SOILS.—P. 10. "The prevailing soil is a strong, red,
shelvy clay, intimately mixed with flints covering chalk,
generally of an excellent quality, which lies at different
depths from the surface, and points out to the husbandman
a never-failing and unrivalled source of improvement."

" The remaining soils consist of the various gradations of
loam from the strongest to the weakest kind, more or less
intermixed with gravel, principally of the flinty sort, and
with chalk, which (though there are exceptions to this
general rule), may be said every where to obtain, and no
where to predominate: a small portion of moor, or peat
earth, in the beds of some of the rivers and low meadows
adjoining thereto, the quantity and depth of which has not
yet been ascertained, nor, as far as I have been able to learn,
converted in any one instance to the valuable purposes for
which it is adapted: and a soil widely differing from all the
rest, very fortunately of no great extent, and confined to
one corner of the county, consisting of a hungry clay or
loam, full of small blue pebbles, and only fit for the growth
of underwood.

" These soils (the two last excepted) have been indiscriminately scattered by the hand of sportive nature all over
the face of the county; and frequently, very frequently,
they

they may all be found in the small compass of a field of four
or five acres. Uniformity of soil is scarce any where to be
met with, except in the low flat lands by the river sides,
and in dells, the staple thereon, frequently to a great depth,
having been washed down from the uplands by the heavy
rains from time to time for ages past, and there deposited."

Having described the nature of the substructure of the
Soils of Hertfordshire (as under the next head) the Reporter
adds,—p. 11. " This general rule admits, however, of many
exceptions ; the chalk, in several parts of the county, is
covered for many acres together with a great depth of earth,
which often renders the question of a chalk basis uncertain ;
and the downs skirting the county towards Cambridgeshire,
are for the most part a continued bed of hurlock, or bastard
chalk, covered with a very thin staple, producing sweet but
scanty herbage for sheep, and incapable of any further improvement."

For the rental value of the Hertfordshire soils, see the
article *Rent*, ensuing.

SUBSTRUCTUE.—P. 10. " Having thus attempted to give
the only general description of the infinitely varied and
mixed soils of Hertfordshire which the nature of the case
will admit, the now prevailing practice of sinking pits, for
the purpose of chalking the surrounding land therefrom,
enables me to give a tolerable idea of a section of the soil,
to the depth of 40 or 50 feet. In general, the basis of such
section will be found to consist of a deep bed of chalk ; the
superstructure, an irregular indenture of chalk and earth-
pillars; the earth-pillars broadest at top, and narrowing as
they descend; the chalk-pillars broadest at the bottom,
rising conically, and narrowing as they ascend to the surface :—the chalk-pillars frequently ascend to the surface,
make part of the staple, and the whole extent of the apex
is visible in ploughed lands. The earth-pillars have been
found to descend 50 feet and upwards,* to the no small
mortification of the chalk-pit diggers, who are frequently
obliged to abandon a pit which they have sunk in an earth
pillar, to the depth of 20 feet and upwards, and sink in a
fresh spot with better hopes of success :"—a loss of labor
which a boarer might have prevented.

POLITICAL

* GEOLOGY.—This is an interesting fact, well described. The
chalk, probably, was first molded, and the earth deposited among the
roughnesses of its surface. But not, I think we may safely conclude,
in their present situation, which is far above the reach of alluvial
deposit.

POLITICAL ECONOMY.

APPROPRIATION.—*Common Fields.*—P. 48. " The land is generally inclosed, though there are many small common fields, or lands lying intermixed in small pieces, the property of different persons, which are cultivated nearly in the same way as inclosed lands; the larger common fields lie towards Cambridgeshire."

Common Pastures.—P. 50. " There are several small commons and wastes from 20 to 50 acres, and some considerably larger, the whole may contain 4500 acres: great part of these are the sheep downs skirting the county next Cambridgeshire, and other similar sheep downs producing sweet pasture on a very thin staple. These sheep downs, if not overstocked, are valuable in their present state, as they afford pasture for sheep in the spring and summer, and the sheep are folded every night on the light land fallows adjoining, and manure them with their dung. It is the opinion of woolstaplers that the wool of sheep so fed, is longer in the staple (?) and finer in the thread, than of those fed in inclosures and better land."

" *Crown Lands.*"—Mr. Walker speaks, at some length, on these *waste lands.* But his remarks cover the crown lands of the kingdom, and have no particular relation to the County of Hertford. He properly recommends the sale of those lands.

To the *appropriation* of common lands Mr. W. has assigned several pages; in which the effects of inclosures, on cottages, are more particularly dwelt on. Among a variety of less important remarks, we find the following general, well conceived, and not easily controvertible, observations:

P. 53. " As the county of Hertford is by far too narrow and unproductive a field on which to investigate the actual state, and determine the claims of cottagers at large, I must beg leave to refer to what experience has taught me of the actual state of cottagers, as far as my experience has reached. Where wastes and commons are most extensive, there I have perceived the cottagers are the most wretched and worthless: accustomed to relie on a precarious and vagabond subsistence, from land in a state of nature, when that fails they recur to pilfering, and thereby become a nuisance to their honest and industrious neighbours; and if the father of a family of this sort is withdrawn from society for his crimes, his children become burthensome to the parish. It may truly be said, that for cottagers of this description the game

game is preserved, and by them destroyed; they are mostly beneath the law, and out of the reach of detection, and while they can earn four or five shillings, and sometimes more, in a night by poaching, they will not be satisfied with 10d. or 1s. per day for honest labour. A reform here is absolutely necessary, whether by consent or otherwise, and an inclosure of the commons and wastes will afford these cottagers an honester livelihood, if they think proper to embrace it; if not, brighter prospects will thereby accrue to the rising generation, who may not be so hardened as their progenitors."

PROVISIONS.—P. 70. "In all the counties round London provisions are dearer than in the metropolis, and much of the provisions with which the poor are fed, are brought from thence, independent of groceries. Yorkshire bacon, generally of the worst sort, is retailed to the poor from little chandlers shops, at an advanced price; bread is retailed to them in the same way."

MANUFACTURES.—P. 73. "The commerce of Hertfordshire is in the produce of the soil, and the only manufacture, properly so called, therein, is perfectly analogous thereto, and confined to the women and children of Dunstable, Luton, and that neighbourhood. It is the straw manufactory. Great quantities of malt is made about Ware, Hertford, and that neighbourhood, principally for the London consumption."

TITHE.—This is a subject to which Mr. Walker repeatedly reverts;—an impost on improvements in Agriculture, of which he is a decided adversary. The following extracts may be worth preserving.

P. 33. "The average rent of land in these parishes" (Coddicot and Kimpton) "is about 8s. per acre, though that rent is certainly too little; the rector impropriate of part of the land which Mr. Hill occupies, formerly let his tithes on lease, and the composition exacted by the lessee never exceeded 2s. and 3d. per acre for all the land under the plough; this lease expired in 1793, and the rector employed a surveyor to value the land in his tithing, and to settle the future compositions to be paid to him for seven years. Some land which Mr. Hill had lately purchased, lay in half acres and small pieces intermixed in a common field with the lands of a farmer, who was as competent to farm as the surveyor to value, and had beggared himself and his farm, though his own property. The surveyor fascinated by the appearance of the crops produced by Mr. Hill's management and spring dressings, valued the tithe thereof at 6s. and 4d. per acre, and his neighbouring farmer's at 1s. 6d. though there is not a shadow of difference in the natural quality of the

the soils in each; and some of Mr. Hill's lands of the same
quality, which he had not then dressed, were valued at 1s.
and 6d. also. The farmers of lands within this tithing have in
consequence rejected these strange compositions, and are determined in future to slacken in their improvements thereof,
leaving it to the rector to resort to tithes in kind, till experience has taught him to be more reasonable."

P. 36. " I valued a farm in the parish of Ashwell, and
in an adjoining parish in the county of Cambridge, the 12th
and 13th of May, 1794, in the occupation of an industrious
and improving farmer, who kept his lands in as good condition as they could reasonably be expected in a common
field state; about 260 acres of this land is in Ashwell, for
which he paid Mr. Whitbread, the rector impropriate, a
composition of three shillings per acre; about 20 acres in
the adjoining parish of Great Morden in Cambridgeshire,
did not appear to me to have equal justice done to them : the
farmer's man who attended me gave the following very satisfactory reason. ' The rector of this parish has for some
years taken tithes in kind, and my master has never since
suffered the dung cart to travel over the shire baulk.' "

Under the head " Obstacles to Improvement," we find
this Reporter powerful in fight against Tithes.—P. 77. " If
the rector, or his tithe-renter, or gatherer, is of a litigious
and troublesome disposition, which the tithe laws, as they
now stand, put it too much in their power to indulge, the
evil of tithes in kind is increased to an alarming magnitude.
In rainy and uncertain harvest weather, when prudence
dictates the housing or stacking the crops immediately from
the scythe or sickle, to avoid the consequences of the season, they must be shocked or cocked before the farmer can
give the rector, or his petty tyrant of the parish, notice to
set out the tithe ; he must wait a reasonable time for his
arrival on the spot, before he will venture to decimate *ex
parte;* in the mean time a sudden and heavy rain outstrips
the slow-paced tithing-man, and both crop and tithe are
much injured or totally ruined thereby. If the tithing-man
does not arrive in the usual time allotted to him, the farmer
leaves the tenth shock or cock, and carries the rest of the
crop at the risk of a lawsuit. How frequently in such seasons do the tithes, rotting on the ground, meet the eye of
the traveller in every part of England."

P. 78. " The Hertfordshire farmers set the example of
spring or top dressings, which are brought from distant parts,
principally from London, and therefore expensive : they
are peculiarly applicable to light lands, and their effects
end with the crops on which they are sown. This accounts
for the moderation of the Hertfordshire rectors in general,
and

and these dressings would no doubt produce good crops on all light, sandy, or gravelly thin lands, and soils barren to the generality of seasons, but if a tenth thereof is taken from the grower, he will soon be ruined."

P. 80. " The consequences of tithes in kind taken by the clergy, are continual disputes and bickerings between them and their parishioners; the farmers grumble, slacken in their improvements, give their spiritual guide all the trouble in their power while collecting his tithes, and cheat him if they can ; he recurs to law, and soon becomes the most unpopular man in his parish; the church is deserted, the flock rapidly emerge into a state of nature, or are led away by the cant of knaves and blockheads."

CANALS.—P. 8. " The grand junction canal, from Branston wharf on the Coventry canal to Old Brentford, where it joins the Thames, enters the county of Hertford above Berkhamstead, and follows the course of the Bulburn and Gade to Rickmansworth; and from thence the course of the Colne, till it leaves the county."

ROADS.—P. 86. " Good roads in a corn country facilitate the agriculture thereof, as the crops are thereby conveyed to market, and foreign manure returned by back carriage. The roads in Hertfordshire are in general excellent, good materials to mend them abound every where ; the sections of the great roads are curved, and rise in the middle about one foot in thirty ; the timber trees and hedges towards the south sides thereof are lopped and kept low, that the sun may dry the roads."

RURAL ECONOMY.

TENANTED ESTATES.

DRAINING ESTATES.—P. 66. " If a pit is sunk 20 or 30 feet deep, in the middle of a field, through the Hertfordshire red, flinty, and impervious clay, into the chalk below; when the usual quantity of chalk is taken out, the pit shaft is filled up with the flints taken out of the chalk and clay, and the top drainage of this part of the field much shortened for ever afterwards, by making principal drains from the part of the field above the level of the top of the pit, terminate therein, and the superabundant moisture will escape through the flints in the pit shaft to the chalk below."

IRRIGATION.—On this valuable operation (when rightly performed) the Reporter has bestowed ten pages,—no inconsiderable

considerable portion of his work;—without furnishing a superiorly useful idea on the subject. Concerning the nature of waters, most suitable to the purpose, the best method of applying them, and the proper season for using them, he appears to have been,—at the time of writing,—equally uninformed.

RENT.—P. 30. " Hertfordshire is justly deemed the first and best corn county in the kingdom, though the soil therein is much inferior in point of natural fertility to many other counties; for notwithstanding its vicinity to the metropolis, its many large and populous market-towns and villages, famed villas, and great and much frequented roads, leading to the distant parts of the kingdom, the average rent of the lands therein does not exceed 12*s.* per acre."

WOODLANDS.

P. 68. " Where the soil varies so much, where the greatest part is under the plough, and where dressings are found to suit the poorest soils, this county may be said to be well wooded. Independent of the woodlands contiguous to the seats of gentlemen, nearly the whole county is interspersed with small woods and copses, and these generally occupy the most barren and gravelly spots, which are well adapted to the quick growth of underwood. The woods are well fenced in, when cut, and preserved from the bret of cattle, and also drained, if necessary. As the growth of hop poles is not attended to, the woods are cut in succession, about every ten years, and the straight sapplings of oak, ash, beech, sallow, birch, poplar, hornbeam, or any other wood, either from the stub or seed, are preserved till the succeeding fall, and then a due succession of the oak, ash, and beech seedlings are preserved, the rest are cut down and split for sheep flakes. Great part of the underwood is hazle."

AGRICULTURE.

FARMS.—P. 12. " A farm, should be of a sufficient size or greatness to afford constant employ to a team of adequate strength to plough the lands therein. There are many farms, particularly towards London, below this standard;

dard; and in general they do not exceed 100*l*. or 120*l*. per annum.—There are a few farms from 400*l*. to 600*l*. and upwards per annum."

HOMESTEADS.—P. 70. " 'The Hertfordshire farm houses and offices differ much : many of the houses are old buildings, and the *quondam* residences of the owners of the soil, constructed without taste or convenience, and situated at one side or end of the land held therewith ; the offices, and particularly the barns, are in general good, and some of them capital. It is much easier to describe and point out what farm houses and offices should be, than what they are."

Accordingly, the Reporter offers, in detail, the *requisites* of *Farm Houses* and *Cottages ;*—such as the " annexed sketch" represents. I happen, I know not why, to have two copies of this Report, in neither of which any sketch appears. The verbal description is *very well*. I find nothing in it, however, of peculiar excellence.

OBJECTS and STATE of HUSBANDRY.—P. 9. " Hertfordshire is deemed the first corn county in the kingdom ; and very properly so, for with the requisite advantage of climate, and of the various manures brought from London, to aid the production of the most valuable crops, nearly the whole of the soil is properly tillage land."

P. 12. " By far the greatest part being adapted to tillage, and not meadow or pasture, it is so occupied, except what is reserved for pleasure in the parks of gentlemen, and that part also would be more usefully employed in tillage."

PLAN of MANAGEMENT.—P. 24. " The rotation of crops in the county of Hertford, in common with those in all other counties in the kingdom, differ widely ; for instance, it is a common practice in some parts of the county of Hertford, to take after turnips two succeeding crops of barley ; the first without, and the second with seeds."—Indeed, from what appears in the unsatifactory sketch, on this head, Hertfordshire would seem to have no regularly established succession of crops.

WORKPEOPLE.—P. 83. "Great part of the labour of farmers is performed by annual domestic servants, whose labour commences and ceases at no stated hours. Day labourers work from six to six in the summer, and from seven to five in the winter ; their usual wages is eight shillings per week in the summer, and six in the winter."

WORKING ANIMALS.—P. 48. " Horses are in general made use of. Oxen are used by some gentlemen, and Mr. Casmajor in particular."—" He gives his bullocks not so much hay as they can eat at a time, and they chew the cud at the intervals of feeding, by which means their food

is

it better digested, and less hay is consumed, with equal or
more benefit to the bullocks." An accurate practice.

MANURES.—This is by much the most intelligent and
valuable article, in Mr. Walker's Report of Hertfordshire.
It comprizes various passages that are entitled to extraction.

Species in Use.—P. 28. " The manures brought from
London to the neighbourhood of Dunstable are scot, ashes,
furrier's clippings, horn shavings, and sheep's trotters."

P. 37. " The foreign manures are principally brought
from London. Spit or horse dung is not carried above 12
or 14 miles from thence; the market-towns in the county
supply the rest. The following are perennial or lasting
manures, and generally laid on light land; *viz.* boiled or
calcined bones, sheep's trotters, furriers' clippings, horn
shavings, leather cuttings, woollen rags, and soap boilers'
ashes: the unburnt bones are broke into small pieces, and
the woollen rags are also cut or chopped into small pieces,
and all, except the last, throw off an annual coat of manure:
the unburnt bones, which are generally boiled, and the fat
therein collected before they are sold to the farmers, are
said to last as a manure for 10 or 12 years."

Yard Dung.—P. 35. " The next species of manure to be
mentioned is that which is made in the farm-yards, from the
dung and stale of the cattle kept and foddered therein, and
the straw, helm, &c. with which they are fed and littered.
That this manure may have every advantage, the yard in
which it is made should be formed like the palm of the hand
when extended in a horizontal direction, lowest in the middle, the fluid part will thereby remain to assist in rotting
the solid part of the manure, and when absorbed thereby,
be carried together on the land intended to receive it. The
general practice of the Hertfordshire farmers is to throw up
the dung, which is, or ought to be, so made into heaps (or
clumps as they call them) till it has heated sufficiently in
their opinion to kill the seeds of weeds intermixed therewith, then to carry it on the land, and spread and plough it
in directly afterwards."

P. 36. " The spit-dung, if clear of the seeds of weeds, is
best calculated for strong heavy land, impervious strata the
effects of the London spit-dung, or dung equally good, may
be seen to an inch in such lands, for three or four succeeding crops."

Compost.—P. 36. " The mixens or mixtures of spit-dung
and good mould, or strong earth, are laid on light gravelly
land, or where chalk or sand is the predominant soil, on all
pervious strata. The mould is saturated with the fluid, and
mixed with the solid part of the dung, the seeds of weeds
                                                        therein

therein have vegetated and been destroyed by the turning the mixen, and the staple of the land is thereby thickened and mended for ever."

Sheepfold.—P. 37. "The last and not the least of domestic manures, is sheep's dung: this most important stock to the Hertfordshire farmer, let the breed be what it will, derive their subsistence in the spring, summer, and autumn, from the clover leys, hedge greens, meadows, and pastures (if any), fallows and crops on the ground, where they may be turned on without injury thereto; at night they are folded on the fallows and other lands to be manured by their dung, in the winter they are folded and fed on turnips, winter tares, and other food provided for them. The dung of sheep is considered to be among the best manures for light lands, and carried on at little expence. Without this aid the state of agriculture, even in the well cultivated county of Hertford, would be much inferior to what it now is."

Topdressing.—P. 39. "The spring or top dressings are the leading features of the Hertfordshire farming, and conconsist of soot *ashes,* malt dust, and oil-cake dust or pulverized oil-cakes.

"The soot and ashes are principally brought from London, the malt dust from Ware, Hertford, and other places where great quantities of malt are made, and the oil-cake dust from the different oil-mills in the county and neighbourhood."

P. 40. "These top dressings not only supply the want of previous manure, but also when crops are sickly and backward in the spring, occasioned either by bad seed times, frosts, or other causes, are attended with wonderful success, and enable the crops to vegetate quickly, and cover and protect the soil on which they grow from the ensuing droughts of summer. To their almost magical powers the Hertfordshire farmers are principally indebted for their never failing crops."

Chalk.—The following account of the Hertfordshire chalks, and the peculiar method of procuring and applying them, are highly creditable to Mr. Walker, as a rural Reporter.

P. 31. "This capital manure, for so it truly and incontestibly is, when applied to strong clay and binding land, differs widely in its qualities. The best chalk, when laid upon the land in large pieces and exposed to the frost, soon slackens or pulverizes, particularly if saturated with rain water, when the frost begins to act upon it, the dimensions of the pieces of chalk are much enlarged, and altered to the shape or appearance of the tops of fine large cauliflowers, and when handled fall into impalpable powder; when immersed

mersed in vinegar or the vitriolic acid, a strong and quick
ebullition ensues; the calcareous and efficient parts of most
marles will be found on analyzation to be chalk rubbish, or
fossil shells.

" The different gradations in the quality of chalk for the
purposes of agriculture, from the best sort above discribed
to the hurlock or bastard chalk, may be distinguished by
the above criterion. Where chalk can be found at any
reasonable depth, say 20 feet under the strong red Herefordshire clay, this single circumstance enhances the value
of the soil more than land owners are aware of, and the
most experienced Hertfordshire farmers agree, that chalking lands so circumstanced is the best mode of culture they
are capable of receiving.

" The method pursued in chalking such land is as under,
and the persons employed therein follow it as a trade : a
spot is fixed upon nearly centrical to about six acres of the
land to be chalked, here a pit, about four feet diameter, is
sunk to the chalk, if found within about 20 feet from the
surface; if not, the chalkers consider they are on an earth
pillar, fill up the pit, and sink in fresh places till their
labour is attended with better success. The pit from the
surface to the chalk, is kept from falling in by a sort of
basket work made with hazle or willow rods and brushwood,
cut green and manufactured with the small boughs and leaves
remaining thereon, to make the basket work the closer.
The earth and chalk is raised from the pit by a jack rowl on
a frame, generally of very simple and rude construction :
to one end of the rowl is fixed a cart wheel, which answers
the double purpose of a fly and a stop; an inch rope of
sufficient length is wound round the rowl, to one end of which
is affixed a weight which nearly counterbalances the empty
bucket fastened to the other end. This apology for an axis
in peritrochio, two wheel-barrows, a spade, a shovel, and
a pickaxe, are all the necessary implements in trade of a
company of chalkers, generally three in number. The pitman digs the chalk and fills the basket, and his companions
alternately wind it up, and wheel its contents upon the
land; when the basket is wound up to the top of the pit, to
stop its descent till emptied, the point of a wooden peg,
of sufficient length and strength, is thrust by the perpendi-
cular spoke in the wheel into a hole made in the adjoining
upright or standard of the frame, to receive it. The pit is
sunk from 20 to 30 feet deep, and then chambered at the
bottom, that is, the pitman digs or cuts out the chalk hori-
zontally, in three separate directions; the horizontal aper-
tures being of a sufficient height and width to admit of the
pitman's working in them with ease and safety. One pit
will

will chalk six acres, laying on sixty loads on an acre.—If
more is laid on, and to the full extent of chalking, viz. 100
loads, then a proportionable less extent of land than six
acres is chalked from one pit. Eighteen barrowfulls make
a load, and the usual price for chalking is 7*d.* per load, all
expences included; therefore the expence of chalking, at
60 loads per acre, is 1*l.* 12*s.* 6*d.*; and at 100 ditto 2*l.* 18*s.* 4*d.*;
as the chalk is considered to be better the deeper it lies,
and the top chalk particularly, if it lies within three or four
feet of the surface very indifferent, and only fit for lime, or
to be laid on roads, gateways, &c. the chalkers must be directed to lay by the chalk for the first three or four feet in
depth, to be applied to the above purposes, or if not wanted
therefore, again thrown into the pit when filled up, and also
to pick out the flints from the chalk before it is carried on
the land, for if they are not narrowly watched they will
chalk with both."

Clay.—P. 34. "Experience points out the strong red
clay as an excellent manure and mixture for burning gravel,
light sand, loam, or soils where the chalk predominates,
when found contiguous thereto. In sinking for chalk, and
particularly for water through this clay soil to depths of 40
and 50 feet and upwards, the heaps raised from the pits,
and of course covered with the lowest soil dug therefrom,
when exposed to and mellowed by the air for a short time
produce most luxuriant sow-thistles, rising like a thick
wood, and for some time checking the vegetation of other
plants, till the maiden strength of the soil is exhausted;
this proves that every inch of the soil is good and fit for
vegetation, from the top to the bottom, let it be ever so deep."

ARABLE OPERATIONS.—On this important department
of practical Agriculture, the Report under view is defective.
The ensuing passages comprize all the information, of
value, concerning the established practice of " the first and
best Corn County in the kingdom;" (p. 30.) and whose
arable processes ought, of course, to have been sedulously
explained.

P. 28. " On the strong lands, about two bushels and a
quarter of wheat, and four bushels of barley or oats, are
sown per acre. On light lands, from two and a half to three
bushels of wheat, and five ditto of barley or oats per ditto.
Rotation of crops.—Fallow, and dress or fold for turnips,
which are fed off by the sheep in winter. Barley on one tilth
sown about the 12th of March following. Barley and clover
about the same time next year. Depasture the clover from
harvest to Hollandtide. Sow ashes, and sometimes soot,
on the clover at or before Lady-day next; cut the clover
twice, and sow wheat in the autumn following on one tilth,
                                                        and

and harrow it in ; and oats or pease after the wheat. They
never sow the same land with pease but once in nine years,
and consider an interval of eleven years better. They fallow for turnips after oats, and sow wheat after pease.—If
the crop of turnips or pease fails, the rotation is of course
broke into. The following rotation is also practised, viz.
winter tares, turnips, wheat, barley, and clover ; then
wheat.

" Light lands, or such as in the language of farmers are
apt to run foul, are cleaned by fallowing, to get rid of
couch or black grass, which is the worst of the two if
possible."

P. 30. " While weeds continue to grow and increase in
the best cultivated lands, fallowing will be practised in
Hertfordshire and elsewhere, where farming is understood,
till a substitute less expensive and equally successful in destroying weeds is discovered."

ARABLE CROPS.—P. 24. " The grains principally cultivated
are wheat, barley, and oats; and I must here remark, that
there is scarce a farm of any extent in the county which
does not contain land peculiarly suited to each species."

GRASS LAND.—P. 13. " The pastures and meadows of
Hertfordshire are principally the *hedge greens* surrounding
the arable fields ; these are of different widths, from 15 to
20 feet, and upwards : the grass thereon is in general mowed
and made into hay; and when the fields to which they
belong are fallow, or after harvest, are depastured by the
cattle and sheep, and manured by their dung, when they
resort to the hedge greens for pasture, or the adjoining
hedges for shade or shelter."

In a district where permanent grass lands are few, and
where lands adapted to permanent herbage are equally un-
provided, by nature, the Hertfordshire practice of appropriating the margins of arable inclosures to the growth of
natural herbage, was, before the practice of cultivating
herbage, in the areas of arable fields became established,
entitled to imitation, in similar districts ;—more especially
in districts abounding, like Hertfordshire, with hedge-row
timber.

LIVESTOCK.—P. 13. " The stock of this county are horses
for the plough, milch cows, and sheep, principally ewes.
Working bullocks are kept by some gentlemen ; very few
of these are bred in the county ; nor are their breeds further
attended to than as they are found to answer the purposes
of those who purchase and keep them. A few cart horses
are bred in the more distant parts of the county, from mares
of the same description, and where a stallion of the draught
kind is in more repute than *Eclipse*. The black cattle are
                                                        the

the produce of the breeding parts of the united kingdom, Alderney, &c.; the working bullocks are principally bred and broke in Sussex; the sheep are in general from Wiltshire, and the west country: the Welch sheep are purchased for, and kept in parks only. The Hertfordshire farmers derive from the plough the surest and most ample source of advantage and compensation for their industry, experience, and capitals employed in husbandry; their live stock must therefore be bred, and that breed improved, before it comes to their hands."

" GENERAL VIEW

OF THE

AGRICULTURE

OF

HERTFORDSHIRE.

DRAWN UP FOR THE CONSIDERATION OF

THE BOARD OF AGRICULTURE

AND INTERNAL IMPROVEMENT.

BY THE SECRETARY OF THE BOARD.

1813."*

THIS is what the Board styles a " reprinted Report." It is in reality, however, an original Work; very little of Mr. Walker's sketch being incorporated with it.

To

* The title-page date of this Report (and we have no other) has puzzled me much. From various evidence, in the body of the work, it appears not only to have been written, but published, some length of time, before the year 1813. I first imagined that it was a new edition, and that, in the negligent way in which the Board's literary works are edited, the words " second edition" had been omitted. But, on further examination, I found that the *title-page, only*, is a reprint! It is, however, so neatly " guarded" that the deception is not readily discoverable. To what good purpose, or to what peculiar circumstance, can this unaccountable step have been taken? Being what it may, much of the work is thereby rendered in a degree abortive; for the want, *in these changeable times*, of an authentic standard to refer to; as will appear in the course of this article.

To speak of the Author, in this place, is not necessary
This is the sixth time I have had occasion to sit in judge
ment on the Secretary's Reports to the Board; and have
frequently spoken my sentiments, freely, on their merits
and demerits. Therefore, all that I have further to say
concerning the one which is now before me, is, that I will
draw from it such information as I conceive may add to the
useful knowledge, on rural subjects, which I have hitherto
been accumulating, for the instruction of the present and
future generations.

The number of pages two hundred and thirtysix.

A map of the soil of Hertfordshire; with engravings on
planting hedges and moveable sheep houses.

SUBJECT THE FIRST.

NATURAL ECONOMY.

EXTENT.—P. 12. " I have had a map of the county
carefully measured, by which measurement it appears, that
Hertfordshire contains 472 square miles."

SOILS.—*Species and proportional Extent.*—P. 12.

" The district of	chalk,	73
	clay,	141
	rich loam,	8
	loam,	223
	poor gravel,	27

472" square miles.

The Reporter opens his copious section " Soils," with
" notes that I took in the order in which they occur."—
These notes, of course, merely relate to the soils which
happened to fall within view, in making his " survey."—
They are mostly uninteresting. For, seeing the extraordinary intermixture of soils (mentioned not only by Mr.
Walker, but by his successor) those of opposite qualities
would necessarily lie within a few hundred yards of his
line of road, or the individual farm he might look over.
There is only one passage which appears to be entitled to
insertion here.

P. 6. " A clear distinction of soil from any hitherto described, is met with at Cheshunt; a very rich pale reddish
sand of an admirable texture, deep, moist, and friable, yet
so

so adhesive, as sometimes to bind. It lets at 40s. an acre, and may be considered as cheap; for it produces in favourable seasons and circumstances, five quarters of wheat an acre: it is viewed to advantage immediately out of Mr. Russel's garden." (!) " This noble vein of land continues to Hoddesdon, and to the hills before Ware. The vale is, for Hertfordshire, very wide, and is upon the whole the best land that I have seen in the county."

In the " Map of the Soil of Hertfordshire," prefixed to the Report, the County makes its appearance (notwithstanding its variegation of soils) under five *uniform* colors; blue, which denotes " loam," covering more than half the County.—The Author, however, very properly explains his plan; and, if the colors mark the *prevailing* soils, the map will have its use.

P. 8. " The soils traced in the Map may be termed:— 1. Loam,—2. Clay,—3. Chalk,—4. Gravel.

" But I should guard the reader against the idea that this is an accurate discrimination: the truth is, that the soils of this county mix and run into each other in a remarkable manner; so that, except, in the case of chalk, and that singularly unfertile land, which I term *gravel*, they are traced and named with a good deal of uncertainty; not for want, I trust, of attention in making the observations, but from the varying qualities of the respective soils."

SUBJECT THE SECOND.

POLITICAL ECONOMY.

APPROPRIATION.—The Secretary commences his chapter, " Enclosing," with journal memoranda, respecting the inclosures that have taken place, in sundry parishes of Hertfordshire.—Those minutes appear to have been the fruits of conversation. Many of them are uninteresting. They are not, however, entirely so. I transcribe the following, progressively, as they stand in the Report.

On the *Business* of Inclosure.—P. 44. " In the enclosure of Hartingfordbury, a plan was formed to escape the charges (so often very heavy) which are made by commissioners; that of naming in the bill three neighbouring gentlemen for commissioners: Mr. Byde, of Ware-park, Mr. Nicholson Calvert, and the Rev. Mr. Browne. By this mode, no other expense is incurred than is absolutely necessary; these

these gentlemen, of course, taking nothing, but acting as friends to the parties. If this plan could be more commonly pursued, which surely it might be, enclosing would not be so much complained of."

On *Fencing* new Inclosures.—P. 44. " In new enclosures, Mr. Irons, of Market-street, banks double quicks and rails, and cleans for eight years, when he engages to deliver up a complete fence, taking his rails away, for 10s. a rod."

Principles of Appropriation.—P. 45. " By the enclosure" (that of Cheshunt comprizing 8452 acres) " 86 acres are allotted for rectorial tithe of the common, and 167 for vicarial; and 100 acres are left, by direction of the act, as a stinted common for cottagers of 6l. a year and under, being vested in trust in the lord of the manor, vicar, and church-wardens. The improvement is likely to be very great; for the common was not fed by the poor, but by a parcel of jobbers, who hired cottages, that they might eat up the whole."

The *Reporter's Remarks.*—P. 48. " The preceding cases are sufficient to shew that enclosing has gone on as well in Hertfordshire as we have any reason to expect in a county so generally enclosed *of old time.* There remains, however, much to be done in the northern part of the county; and there are smaller scattered common-fields in many other parts, with extensive commons also in the western district. Many of these are too small to pay the expense of a distinct act of enclosure; but all would be properly cultivated under the sanction of a general act."

In the chapter " Wastes," we find further remarks on the *state of inclosure,* in Hertfordshire.—P. 148. " The quantity of waste land in Hertfordshire, compared with that in most other counties, is very inconsiderable. There are some small commons scattered about the county, which would pay well for improving, but the quantity is no where very great."

MANUFACTURES.—For some account of *straw-platting,* see *Workpeople,* ensuing.

POOR RATE.—P. 31. " Hertfordshire is free from any considerable manufactures, which, from depression on account of the war, or from other causes, might have left an increased population in distress; a case dreadfully experienced in the neighbouring county of Essex. It has also the advantage of being the residence of a great number of people of fortune, whose charitable attention to the poor must have operated in keeping down the poor-tax; her agriculture also affords a great and regular system of employment. The manufactures of this county are singularly beneficial, especially that of plaiting straw, in which the

earnings

earnings of the poor are very great; yet, with all these advantages, the poor-rates are high."

To these remarks succeeds a detail of the rates in twenty or thirty individual parishes. But, for want of the time when they were collected, and of the species of rent (whether real or nominal, unless in a few instances) they are not of consideration.

TITHE.—P. 30. " I am very happy to be able to premise, that I did not in the whole county meet with one instance of tithes being taken in kind; there may be such instances in Hertfordshire, but I no where heard of any; and I crossed the county in so many directions, that, if any exist, they must be extremely rare."

A list of thirty places is put down, with the compositions that are paid, by the acre, " for the tithe." Query, for the tithe of what? Of arable, meadow, pasture, or woodland? Separately, or jointly? The average comes out—" three shillings and five pence farthing." But at what period of time is not ascertainable.

CANALS.—This Reporter, having copied Mr. Walker's notice of the *Grand Junction*, (see p. 11, aforegoing)—says, p. 15. " I did not neglect inquiries into the effect which this canal has had upon the agriculture of the county: the following minutes throw some light upon the subject."

Those minutes are few and not important. The subjoined remark, by the Reporter, however, is striking, and may have its use in this register. I do not insert it, to throw a damp on *canals*, many of which are highly beneficial, not to agriculture, only, but to the country at large. My object, on this, as it has been on other occasions, is to shew that, in some instances, canals have failed to realize the too sanguine expectations of speculative men.

P. 17. " From the information which I could gain on this subject, several arrangements appear to be wanted, before this great work can be turned to all the advantage which the agriculture of Hertfordshire should derive from it. It appears by the preceding notes, that the benefit of bringing bulky manures, is extremely questionable at present; and the fact is, that vast quantities of hay and straw go to London, from the very banks of the canal, by land-carriage, the carts bringing dung back, which does not answer when brought by the navigation."

ROADS.—P. 221. " The roads of a county so near the Metropolis, can scarcely be bad: six great leading turnpikes passing through so small a district, would alone give this character, but there are many cross-roads nearly as good as turnpikes. The worst are found in the country between Pelham and Welwyn."

MARKETS.

MARKETS.—P. 134. " Hay and straw are carried to London from Bygrave, two miles beyond Baldock," (37 m.) "and ashes, soot, and sheep's trotters brought back : this is a vast exertion. The carriage is hired at Stevenage" (31 m.) " at 25s. for a load of hay, and 12s. for a load of straw."

SUBJECT THE THIRD.

RURAL ECONOMY.

TENANTED ESTATES.

ESTATES.—P. 18. " Property in Hertfordshire is much divided : the vicinity of the capital ; the goodness of the air and roads, and the beauty of the country, have much contributed to this circumstance, by making this county a favourite residence, and by attracting great numbers of wealthy persons to purchase land for building villas : this has multiplied estates in a manner unknown in the more distant counties. About 7000l. a-year is the largest estate in the county : there are six or seven from 3 to 4000l. ; more of about 2000l. ; and below that sum, of every value."

TENURES.—P. 19. " A large portion of the county is held by copyhold tenure, with a fine certain, or at the will of the lord ; but which fine never exceeds two years rent. Such land sells here at about six years purchase under the price of freehold."

PURCHASING ESTATES.—P. 18. " Freehold estates have of late sold at 28 years purchase, when any particular circumstances have not had an influence ; but much of the Watton Wood-hall estate sold at 30, and some at 31, and even at 32."

DRAINING ESTATES.—P. 154. " The importance of hollow-drains is no where better understood than at Sawbridgeworth and its vicinity, upon clay and strong loam. They vary the distance from five to ten yards, and fill the drains with bushes, or with straw ; Mr. Parris uses long pea-straw in preference, and has tried the twisting it into a rope, which answers perfectly. The expense in labour amounts to 2d. a rod. The effect is so great, that the improvement of the first crop has often paid all the expense."

SODBURNING.—P. 155. " I had little expectation relative
to

to this practice in Hertfordshire; and in the few cases I
found, it was quite of modern introduction."

IRRIGATION.—P. 178. "The county affords great opportunities for this important work; but it abounds also with
so many mills, as to impede it greatly."

Some instances of practice are noticed. But owing to
the Reporter's deficiency in knowledge (practical and
theoretical) concerning that subject, the information is unavailing.

RENT.—Some entries of the rate of rent, in different
parts of the County, are given. But the time or times of
collecting the information not being to be found, nor the
qualities of the lands sufficiently explained, no comparison
can be properly made between the rental values of lands, in
Hertfordshire, and those of other districts. The following
is the Reporter's retrospective, and apparently well considered, remarks, on the memoranda inserted.

P. 29. " From these notes, which apply to every part of
the county, it is clear, that the estimate of 15s. subject to
tithe, for the general average of rent, is nearly the truth.
Probably, the whole surface of the county included, the
rent is little less.

" In point of rent, therefore, it classes high amongst the
English counties; much higher than the mere soil would
permit, unconnected with the advantages of situation.
London is a market for hay and straw to every part of the
county; and manures are thence brought to every part,
which, with good roads, and a general attention to the
draining of most of the wet lands, and to improvements by
chalking, have so ameliorated the soil, as to enable the
farmer to pay perhaps 4s. per acre more rent on an average
of the whole, than he would be able to do under a less
favourable management."

WOODLANDS.

WOODS.—P. 146. "Much of the timber in Moor-
park * is of great antiquity; and no inconsiderable portion
of it is in a state of decay."

P. 147

* MOORE PARK was once a *show place* of high renown. It was laid
out, in the line-and-rule manner, by the celebrated COUNTESS of BED-
FORD; probably, in the beginning of the 17th century—about 200
years ago. It was extolled by Sir WILLIAM TEMPLE, and laughed
at by HORACE WALPOLE.

P. 147. " I have rarely seen finer trees than at Sir John Sebright's at Beachwood : it has the name in strict propriety, for the number of stately beeches is great ; but the soil agrees with all sorts of trees: the cedars are immense; the oak very large; the ash straight and beautiful; the larch, spruce, and Scotch fir equally fine, but the beech uncommon."

COPPICES.—P. 145. " The woods in the country between Hockerill, Ware, and Buntingford, are rented generally at about 12s. an acre, and cut at twelve years growth, when the produce is about 9l. an acre."

" Mr Rook, of Hertford, has hollow-drained many acres, and found it a very capital improvement."

" At Beachwood, the best underwood in Sir John Sebright's copses is black sallow, superior to all the rest; of this hurdles are made: hazel and ash are in the next estimation. When black sallow abounds, an acre at 12 years growth is worth 15l. paying better than the adjoining arable land, without including the timber that is taken ; but this is particularly valuable. Wherever Sir John cuts down a timber tree in a copse, he plants a black sallow set, not a cutting, as that will not grow ; the sallow takes well, and thickens the wood consequently with the most valuable of the copse tribe."

AGRICULTURE.

FARMS.—P. 23. " These are, in general, *small* in Hertfordshire. Not one in the county exceeds 1000 acres, and 500 form a large one ; perhaps the size most common is from 150 to 400 ; but there are many much smaller ;"—as there ever ought to be.

" Throughout the triangle of country formed by Hockerill, Ware, and Buntingford, and where the soil is generally strong, the farms are moderate; one of 400 acres is a large one ; and many are very small. At the Hadhams they are even as low rented as from 20 to 30l. a-year, and the farmers are worse off than day-labourers. This part is entirely arable."

P. 24. " At Albury, which is a large parish, farms rise from 100 to 500 acres ; in general, from 100 to 400; nor are there so many small ones of 30, 40, or 50 acres, as are common elsewhere."

From these and a few other notices adduced, the farms of Hertfordshire appear to be well varied, in size, to suit the

the capitals of the several orders of occupiers which the profession requires.

FARM FENCES.—P. 49. "Hertfordshire may be considered as the county where the plashing system is carried on to the greatest extent : it has been universally practised here from time immemorial. Scarcely can any county be worse situated for coals ; and the copses are not more extensive than common. These causes may have induced the farmers to fill the old hedges every where with oak, ash, sallow, and with all sorts of plants more generally calculated for fuel than fences, and which would form no kind of fence under any management but their own."

These conjectures appear, to me, to be instably grounded. The rough hedges of Hertfordshire, and of every other district that has been inclosed from the woodland state, have not, I conceive, been wholly formed by art ;—are not old hedges that have been filled up with oak, ash, &c. by the farmers ; but the natural hedges—the aboriginal fences themselves.

While wood continued to be the fuel of the Metropolis, Hertfordshire, with its other environs for several miles round, was necessarily kept, in great part, in a state of woodland. But, when coals became the prevailing fuel, the principal part of those woods were, in consequence, cleared for cultivation ; they having become unprofitable as a source of fuel. In the act of clearing,—lines of native coppice wood were very judiciously left ; not only as fences between inclosures, but as a supply of fuel, for the occupiers of the lands and their country neighbours.

Under these circumstances, it is more than probable, I conceive, that the art of " *Plashing*," like many other arts, was an invention of necessity. For it would be difficult, even in close thickset coppice woods, to find entire lines of natural wood, sufficient to form fences, against every species of stock, without the helping hand of the husbandman,—to " lay" the taller sapling shoots across the vacancies and thinner parts.

This being as it may, the art of laying live hedgewood, of rough uneven fences, is well understood in Hertfordshire:—a fact, this, of which the Secretary was so fully aware that he has entered upon a didactic discourse concerning the Hertfordshire practice ; and accompanied it with seven explanatory engravings. One of the first instances, this, in which I have recognized the Secretary of the Board in the character of a preceptor.

STATE OF HUSBANDRY. (Chapter, " Arable Lands.")— P. 55. " We are here come to the great object of the Hertfordshire husbandry. By far the greatest part of the county

county is under tillage, for which the county was singularly famous perhaps before the improvements in Norfolk were began; and it may not be improper to observe, before I enter on the particulars to be detailed here, that there are two opinions relative to the progress of husbandry in this county. Thirty years ago, when I resided in it, I often heard the Duke of Leeds remark, that the Hertfordshire farmers, through the period of his recollection (and he was an old man), had stood *still*, at least ; perhaps had declined in the merit of their agriculture ; and this appears from the writings of Ellis, who lived in this county, and whose books were published from 60 to 75 years since. There are at present scarcely any practices to be be met with in the county, that were not well understood at that period.

" Mr. Rooper, of Berkhamsted, informs me, that turnips and clover are supposed to have been introduced into this county in the time of Oliver Cromwell, who gave 100l. a year on that account to a farmer of the name of Howe. It appears also by old leases, that the course of crops, and the management in general, have experienced very little change in the last hundred years."

PLAN of MANAGEMENT.—In this, as in the other Reports of the Secretary. to the Board, we find page after page filled with " Courses of Crops." In the present instance however, only one sheet of paper is expended upon them.

OCCUPIERS.—P. 18. " In the more eastern counties, the farmers have been very considerable purchasers of land ; a circumstance that has not happened, except in very few instances, in Hertfordshire. The farms are not large, and the expenses of agriculture are higher than common ; which may account for the want of this sign of farming wealth."

WORKPEOPLE.—*Wages.*—By reason of the want of *dates*—the year or years in which the reported information was taken—this item, in the " Rural Economy"! of Hertfordshire, is rendered abortive.

At the time of writing (whensoever that happened) wages were exorbitantly raised, and farm workpeople rendered difficult to be procured ; owing to *the rage for straw bonnets*, which, at that time, would seem to have been at its height ;—when working women were able to " earn 5s a day," and girls (one at least) " a guinea a week."— " The farmers complain of it, as doing mischief, for it makes the poor saucy, and no servants can be procured, or any field-work done, where this manufacture establishes itself."—" There is so much plaiting at Hitchin, that they will not go to service ; boys are here also employed in it." They were of course rendered little fit for
farm

farm service. And, *now*, 1816, that the fervor has abated, and, especially, that the works of Agriculture are likewise on the decline! the old and the young, there is too much reason to fear, are crawling in crowds to the workhouses.

Straw being a species of *farm produce*, it may seem to be proper, in a work on Agriculture, to describe the method of raising it to the greatest perfection, as a *material* of *manufacture.*—P. 223. " The straw from stony and heavy land, like that of Essex, will not do for plaiting ; and if a crop produces much straw fit for plaiting, the produce of the corn is generally bad : weak straw under hedges and near trees, does best. They give 2*d.* 3*d.* and 4*d.* a pound for it, and sort it themselves."

A *grove*, therefore, let it be suggested, is the most elegible site for perfecting this high-priced production !

WORKING ANIMALS.—Under the head, " Horses," we find a few journal notices, respecting *farm* horses. But the only information that requires admission, here, relates to the practice of keeping them in the stable, throughout summer, and feeding them, there, with *green herbage*— sillily termed " soiling :"—a practice which, it is probable, had its rise in the Southern Counties.—The Secretary says, p. 199, " I found it general in every part of the county ; and it certainly forms a feature of uncommon merit in the husbandry of Hertfordshire : I know not any district where it is equally general. The farmers are clearly decided in the great advantages attending the practice ; not only in supporting the teams in the cheapest manner, but also in raising large quantities of very valuable manure."—The species of herbage, chiefly employed, in this practice, are tares and clover.

In a section, entitled " Horses and Oxen compared," is seen a lengthened string of opinions, respecting this disputed point of practice. But no instructive conclusion is drawn from that mass of information. The subjoined is the leading paragraph.

P. 199. " The use of oxen in husbandry is not a common practice in any part of the county ; in general, it is confined to gentlemen farmers, the case in many parts of the kingdom ; and a circumstance which tends to throw much doubt upon the question of comparison in ascertaining which is the more beneficial team."

I have carefully examined the contents of that section ; without having been able to discover any thing that is sufficiently new or excellent to require transcription.

IMPLEMENTS.—The same remark equally applies to the chapter bearing this title ;—the subjoined notice excepted.
                                                                P. 43.

P. 43. " *Oil-cake Mill.*—The Honourable Mr. Villiers has at Aldenham, a roller turning under a hopper, with stout teeth, for breaking oil-cake, in order to feed beasts, which answers its purpose well."

Manure.—P 157. " There is no part of the kingdom in which this branch of husbandry, every where so important, is more generally attended to ; or where exertions in it are more spirited. When the quality of the soil is compared with the products it yields, it will be apparent that manuring alone must occasion a disproportion so very great between the soil and the crops ; the latter being very superior to the soil. The fossil manure of the district, and the expensive additions from London, are used on a very extensive scale."

Chalk.—It is this valuabe species of manure that distinguishes the established practice of Hertfordshire. The other species, there in use, are common to the environs of the Metropolis. This, therefore, is the legitimate subject of report, concerning manures, from that County.

The different qualities of the Hertfordshire chalks, with the methods of raising and applying them, have been fully and satisfactorily given by Mr. Walker.—See p. 15, aforegoing.—What remain to be added, here, are the varying opinions of "gentlemen farmers," concerning the virtues of this fossil, as a manure, and the soils and crops to which it is most applicable. Some of those opinions are futile and others contradictory. The prevailing idea appears to be that chalk is beneficial to *gravelly* soils, by " cooling" them, and to *clayey* lands, by making them " work" better.

P. 161. " Mr. Whittington remarks, that chalk used as manure, is, for some time, bad for wheat, though good for every other crop ; and considerably the most useful on land that burns, as gravel : it is of little benefit on cold wet soils. * On land subject to sorrel, chalk is a sovereign cure, killing that weed speedily : a circumstance favourable to stock as well as to the soil, for it is very unwholesome for sheep : he has several times lost lambs by their eating it, as it gives them a cholic. He finds fifteen loads of chalk per acre, and repeated once in ten or twenty years, much better than a larger quantity at once."

P. 162. " Colonel Dorrien, at Berkhamsted, carts some hundred loads of chalk, in the autumn, into his farm-yard

---

* We are, however informed, in p. 163, that "chalk is much used about Beachwood, in the proportion of from 20 to 40 loads an acre : it lasts ten or twelve years, and does best on wet loamy land ; but this sort requires more frequent chalkings than any other. It does well on clay, and lasts longer."

yard, to fodder upon, and then mixes the chalk with the dung."

"Mr. Cotton, of Hempstead, thinks also, that it does most good on gravels: there is, however, much uncertainty in its effect. He once chalked a field of clay, and it did not bear a good crop of corn afterwards, for some years; but a neighbouring farmer did the same thing, and got a fine crop of wheat the first year; yet wheat is sometimes apt to be hurt, from the chalks being broken up by by the frost, and consequently, by the wheats being rendered light and root-fallen. It is agreed, that land chalked, wants the more dung on that account."

The retrospective observations of the Reporter, on this point of the Hertfordshire practice, are evidently the result of mature reflection on the subject.

P. 164. "Upon the whole, I must observe, that this husbandry, which is general through the county, has considerable merit; but the great singularity, is the long established practice of drawing it up by shafts, and barrowing it on to the land. Those who have been accustomed to the marle-carts of Norfolk and Suffolk, know what severe work to the teams, that business always proves; and what a most heavy expense attends it. Horses of great value are often lamed or destroyed, and the purchase of carts and harness, with the wear and tear of both, form very heavy articles. The Hertfordshire custom is therefore much to be preferred. One objection is obvious; so soft a substance as marle or clay (compared with chalk), could not be trusted to for chambering under-ground, without great danger to the workmen. The discovery of some plan to obviate this, would be of so much advantage as to render it an object of much interest to the public; nor do I conceive the thing difficult to be effected by moveable arches of timber-work, to be raised as the men advance. A good mechanic would easily contrive such, and the object highly deserves attention: marling and claying would be much promoted among many farmers, particularly small ones, who at present fear to undertake it. Two or three pounds an acre could be easily afforded by men who could not set any regular clay-carts at work for want of a scale of business proportioned to such teams, &c."

Concerning the catalogue of TOWN MANURES that are in use, in the several Counties adjacent to the metropolis, a large mass of memoranda is collected. I will insert here, such of the particulars as appear to be entitled to preservation.

Soot.—This would seem to be a prevailing topdressing of wheat, throughout the County.

P. 165.

P. 165. " About Barkway, they have a very high opinion of it ; 50 bushels an acre, brought 30 miles from London, is seen on wheat to an inch."

" I question whether there is a parish in it, in which some men are not in the habit of using this manure from London."

Lime.—P. 165. " I know from experience, and it seems " universally agreed, that chalk lime (ard no other can be " used in Hertfordshire) does not exceed chalk itself in " any proportion to it expense, so as to give encourage- " ment to burn it, unless it be in parts where chalk is far " distant*."

Ashes.—Here, as in Oxfordshire, Buckinghamshire, &c. ashes are sown over clover. But the species or quality of them is not mentioned by this Reporter.

P. 165. " Mr. Byde esteems ashes as a manure that acts by opening and loosening the soil, but that they do not feed a crop."

Bones.—P. 167. " This is a manure much esteemed in Hertfordshire ; but the price has risen so high of late years, as much to restrain its use. They were formerly 8s. or 9s. a chaldron ; but are now 16s. at London They are considered as best for pastures when burnt ; but for arable clay better when only boiled. This manure, especially when the bones are only boiled, is the most durable of those commonly used in Hertfordshire."

Nightsoil.—P. 171. " Of all the manures which Mr. Cassmajor, of North Mims, brings from London, none equal this : he lays three cart-loads an acre, at 10s. 6d. a load, and spreads it dry with a shovel. The effect is great. It is much used about St. Albans.

" Since the canal, this valuable manure has been introduced at Berkhamsted,"—twentysix miles from London.

Dung.—P. 173. " At St. Albans, Hatfield, &c. many poor persons employ themselves in picking up dung on the turnpike-roads, which they sell to the farmers at 2d. a bushel. Mr. Clarke, of Sandridgebury, buys large quantities, spreading 180 bushels per acre for turnips.

" Mr. Chapman, of Hitchin, has observed, that, about Baldock, they *carry out* their dung in a remarkably long state, without rotting, and yet they get as good turnips as any where. (!)

" Mr. Roberts, of King's Walden, would always, on every account, carry stable-dung long and fresh *to* the land, but thinks that farm-yard manure should be turned up once, yet not kept too long." In this there is much good sense.

Sheepfold

" * MS. Annotations, J. HUTCHINSON."

Sheepfold.—In the section Farms, p. 26, the Reporter says, " the general predilection for the application of the sheep-fold, is more universal in this county than in any other with which I am acquainted."

P. 168. " The best dressing (*compass,* as it is called in Hertfordshire) which Mr. Byde has ever observed for wheat, is top-folding even so late as May, with sheep fed with oil-cake in troughs."

P. 175. " Mr. Smith, at Clothalbury, at the distance of 39 miles from London, used to bring down much soot and trotters, not then keeping many sheep ; but he has since left it off, from being convinced that it did not answer so well as dressing by sheep ; and he has greatly increased his flock."

P. 194. " In the clay district of the county, Mr. Byde re-marks that sheep have been too much lessened. Of all the common manures, he considers the fold as the best ; and he has observed in many farms the general appearance of the crops decline, as the number of sheep kept has lessened.

" At the Hadhams, every man folds the sheep which he keeps : a little farmer will even set four hurdles, if he has not sheep for more.

" Good as the manure of the fold is, Mr. Chapman has found by trial in the same field, for turnips, that yard-dung was much better than both fold and malt-dust together.

" Mr. Roberts, of King's Walden, thinks nothing is equal to the fold : he never reckoned it worth less than 40s. per acre, corn being cheap ; but of late much more : he folds two poles of ground with 20 sheep.

" Mr. Sedgwick, of Rickmersworth, is clearly in favour of folding on all farms."

Atmospheric Melioration.—P. 174. " *Manuring in general.* —At Sawbridgeworth," (25 miles from London) " on the clays and strong loams, the farms are not large, and few sheep are kept. The cattle are by no means numerous, and chiefly cows for suckling ; nor do the farmers bring manures from London ; little is therefore effected by this branch of management. To make amends for its want, they exert themselves greatly in tillage, fallowing very often."

Here, *fallowing* seems to be considered as a species of *melioration ;*—as a substitute for *manuring !*

TILLAGE.—The Reporter's section " Tillage" is void of interest. In that of " Fallowing," we find the subjoined *moderate* remarks,—free from passion and prejudice,—cool considerate Report.—P. 61. " Under this head I am happy to have but a word to insert—The fallow system, except in a very small district, and in open fields, is not much pursued in this county. Wherever turnips can be sown, we find them ;

them; and consequently fallows, in a county containing but little real clay, are confined, as they ought to be, to the most difficult and impracticable soils. The observation must not, however, be taken as universal; for in every part of the county they accidentally take place, when land is got, by ill management, so foul as to make a complete fallow more advisable than turnips, as the means of cleaning it."

SEMINATION.—*Drilling.*—P. 126. " Hertfordshire, though a tillage county, has but little to offer towards forming a general mass of experience, so very earnestly to be desired on this head in particular, and which, when collected together, would be attended with such beneficial effects.

" At Westmill I had passed near 100 miles in the county, inquiring for drilled crops, but neither seeing nor hearing of any. Mr. Greg had tried, but gave it up as unprofitable on this soil.

" Mr. Bullock, of Bennington, tried the drill-husbandry for several crops: for two seasons he executed the work well, but gave it up from finding his soil improper for it.

" The following conversation took place relative to the drill-husbandry, between me and Mr. Marsh, of Simmonside, who made me the following answer to a question I asked, whether he drilled his corn?

" —' No: I have seen enough of it. I will shew you pre-
' sently as much barley as can grow out of the earth, broad-
' cast, and the land clean: what should I drill for?'

" Lady Melbourne, at Brocket-Hall, is one of the principal drillers in the county, where, however, this husbandry is very little practised. Her method is that of Mr. Ducket."

Several other instances of practice are drawn together; some of them making for, others against, the " new husbandry." The *cons* would seem to *have it* in Hertfordshire. But no matter as to those *flying reports;* the Secretary's own cool, considerate, dispassionate remarks are worth a volume of crude, contradictory, conversational opinions of inexperienced occupiers.

P. 131. "Such are the *experiments* I met with in this county; and upon the whole, they leave the subject pretty much as I found it: a conclusion, however, is fairly to be drawn, that a method of putting in crops which has failed with several intelligent cultivators, and only partially succeeded with some others, cannot be generally necessary as a means of profit. The observations relative to barley and oats are against the practice. I allude here to nothing done or talked of in other counties, as my business is with Hertfordshire; and certainly in this county, the experiments made, by no means ascertain that any advantage whatever may really exist; nor will the point be cleared up in this
county

county, till some capital farmer, by means of drilling, shall exceed the crops and profit which a Young of Hurral, a Whittington of Broad-water, and a Doo of Bygrave, gain by the common method."

ARABLE CROPS, and their INDIVIDUAL MANAGEMENT.— Ample room for instructive information is allowed by the Secretary, for this most important compartment of a County Report; especially that of Hertfordshire, which has been long famed for its arable management.

WHEAT.—The Reporter treats of this crop, in some considerable degree, *analytically* :—and, in speaking of the minor crops, a few traits of analysis are observable. But instead of meeting, even in the section, Wheat, with an intelligent detail of the established practice among professional men of the higher class, who, or whose ancestors, raised the Hertfordshire husbandry to its acknowledged state of superiority and celebrity, we perceive little more than prompt memoranda put down, as it were incidently, on the practices, or incidents in practice, or perhaps the conversational opinions,—not of hereditary, legitimate occupiers; but of more *recent* practitioners.

Some of those incidents, in " modern husbandry," are interesting, and might have been instructive, if the ATTENDANT CIRCUMSTANCES (the nature of the given land, its state as to tillage and weediness, the quantity and quality of the manure which it had recently received, and the crop or crops which preceded the one spoken of) circumstances out of which they severally grew,—had been fully declared. But, insulated as they mostly are, they convey, to the experienced practitioner, little useful information ; and may tend to lead the inexperienced into serious errors.

I will place before my readers, in the progressive order in which they stand in the Report, whatever may appear to be entitled to their attention.

Tillage and *Treading* of Wheat.—P. 81. " Mr. Young, of Hurral, in loose land subject in any degree to cause wheat to root-fall, takes care to plough the ley some time before the sowing, and he treads it well with stock.

" When Mr. Hale's wheat shewed signs, in November and December, of being loose at the root, he drove his flock over, to tread down the land ; and it did a great deal of good."

Topdressing Wheat.—P. 82. " In no district of the kingdom is wheat more generally top-dressed in the spring, with soot, ashes, and various other dressings ; and I may add, that the farmers have a high opinion of this husbandry, and entertain no doubt of its answering well. But it deserves attention at the same time, that the small comparative
quantity

quantity of natural grass which is found in the county, renders live-stock a very inferior object, and consequently the farm-yard dung much less than in counties abounding more in grass, and where hay and straw are in less demand for sale."

Topfolding Wheat.—P. 85. " Mr. Young, of Hurral, top-folds his wheat after it is up, with much success, even on land that does not particularly demand treading. Mr. Biggs, near St. Albans, top-folds after sowing, but desists just at the moment of its coming up; and thinks this practice on dry loam very advantageous.

" Mr. Sedgwick, on light lands, always folds after sowing, and till Christmas, and finds great benefit from it. After very wet nights, and the ground has been poached, he has scolded his shepherd, but the wheat has been the better." (!) "When he observes a piece of wheat failing, from red worm or grub, &c. he spreads turnips on it, and brings the flock to eat them, and tread the land; and it has always answered well."

Mildew of Wheat.—P. 86. " Mr. Whittington always cuts mildewed wheat as early as possible ; for it improves nothing by standing."

Produce of Wheat.—P. 87. " Mr. Whittington estimates the produce of all farms, on an average, as 23 bushels per acre."

Stubbles of Wheat —P. 91. " I know no district in which they are so attentive to cutting stubble as in Herts, carting it carefully to the farm-yards to make manure."

BARLEY.—*Soil.*—P. 95. " Barley is very uncertain on chalk ; for if sown late in spring, it fails, if the season be not very favourable indeed." This, as a general position, is erroneous. The abundant supply of the far-famed Thanet barley is grown on chalky lands. Applied to *shallow* calcarious soils, there is some truth in it.

Tillage for Barley.—P. 93. " The general practice, to which exceptions are very few, is to plough turnip land but once for this grain."

Species of Barley.—P. 94. " Zealand winter barley has been sown at Albury, and produced nine or ten quarters an acre ; but the grain so bad, as to be good for nothing but pigs and poultry. It is sown in autumn, and harvested much earlier than the common sort."

Produce of Barley.—P. 95. " The average crop, extracted from seventeen minutes made of crops, gives 32 bushels and a small fraction."

OATS.—*Quantity* of *Seed.*—P. 96. " The common quantity amounts to *five* bushels per acre."—" To multiply minutes would be useless ; for the general practice through the county is to sow *four* bushels."

Produce

Produce of Oats.—P. 97. " We find four quarters to be the general average."

Nothing is said of the *cultivation* of oats in Hertfordshire. We are informed, however, in p. 96, that " they are commonly mown either with the naked scythe, or a cradle added, and carted loose."

PEAS.—*A new mode of Culture.*—P. 97. " Mr. Leach has found pease a very hazardous crop; but, for these two years past, has ploughed in the seed in the beginning of February; and, when the plants have been four inches high, he has harrowed the ground in a dry season twice, across and across, and rolled it immediately. His crops are good, and of the Berkshire dun."

TURNEPS.—*History.*—P. 102. " This most useful plant was cultivated very early in Hertfordshire, as a general article of husbandry; and I believe, before they were commonly introduced in Norfolk: it is natural, therefore, to expect to find them in great perfection : this, however, is not the case in one very material point."

Semination.—P. 103. " A circumstance in the culture of this crop, which Mr. Byde has found of very great consequence, is that of ploughing in the seed, instead of harrowing it in on the surface : he has found in this management, that it is not nearly so liable to be destroyed by the fly. He ploughed it in on half a field, and harrowed it in on the other half; and the difference was so considerable, as to convince his bailiff, whose opinion was adverse to the practice. When the season proves too dry, it makes the difference of crop or no crop."

" Mr. Biggs, of Bursten, near St. Albans, has ploughed in turnip-seed shallow, and found it sometimes advantageous."

Hoing Turnips.—P. 104. " From these notes it appears, that the general practice is to hoe but once."

BULBOUS RAPE.—*History* in Hertfordshire.—P. 105. "This is an article of culture which gives me much pleasure to register, for it manifests an uncommon degree of merit. In other parts of the kingdom, these turnips are met with in the farms of gentlemen, but rarely in those of tenants; but in Hertfordshire, they have so rapidly made their way, as to be found in the usual management of great numbers of the common farmers: no trivial proof of their observation, knowledge, and good sense."

Expenditure of Bulbous Rape.—P. 106. " Mr. Keate has fed horses with them, entirely to his satisfaction; and cuts the roots with a very simple, effective turnip-slicer: each horse had a bushel every day, with chaff, but no oats; they did their work very well, but in spring-sowing had a few

oats

oats added: they throve well, and became fat while they
were eating this turnip. Cows also do well on it ; nor does
it give their milk or butter any taste, but increases their
milk considerably."

Disadvantage of Bulbous Rape.—P. 107. " The Marchio-
ness of Salisbury has many acres in great perfection, and
finds them of incomparable use. But Mr. Stephenson remarks, that their most important use is so late in the spring,
that it is difficult to introduce them in a regular course, and
sow spring corn in time : he thinks them rather applicable
to a few fields out of a regular rotation for sowing some
other crop than barley or oats after them ; such, for instance,
as winter tares."

" Mr. Deerman, of Astwick, is a great friend to them ;
but observes, that they throw the land out of course ; as
they are most useful so late in the season, that spring corn
cannot be sown after them, he thinks the best way is to
sow common turnips for the next crop, by which means also
the land would be brought into remarkably high order.
Mr. Marsh, his neighbour, makes the same observation, but
has, however, always sown spring-corn after them."

Soil for Bulbous Rape.—P. 108. " Mr. Chapman, of
Hitchin, is of opinion that this root demands a richer and
stronger soil than the chalks and loams about Hitchin; for
they have been cultivated some years, dunged for, and twice
hoed, but the success has not been great."

General Remarks on Bulbous Rape.—P. 111. (by the
Reporter).—" From this detail, it is sufficiently evident that
the cultivation of the Swedish turnip is thoroughly introduced into the husbandry of this county, and not likely to be
neglected in future. The farmers have great merit, in so
soon adopting a new plant. It already makes a considerable
figure."

These are certainly two serious *inconveniencies* belonging
to the cultivation of this crop. Namely, that arising from
early sowing, which prevents, at a critical season, the spring
tillage that a fallow crop requires. The other is that of re-
tarding the succeeding corn crop; *or* that of depriving
the crop itself of one of its most valuable properties ;—
that of filling up the chasm which too frequently takes place
between the decay of *turneps ;* and the spring shoot of
herbage.

The former of those disadvantages, however, may be
alleviated, or removed, by transplanting ; and the latter by
mowing off the spring shoots, for immediate use, and storing
the roots for a supply of late spring feedage,—for sheep and
cattle, until their pastures be fit for them ; or as summer
                                                        provinder

provinder for horses and hogs.—See the *Northern* and *Midland Departments,* under the head *Bulbous Rape.*

CLOVER.—Its *History,* in Hertfordshire.—P. 115. " This noble plant, the introduction of which has wrought a greater improvement in English agriculture than that of any other, has been cultivated in this county, probably as long, or longer, than in any part of the kingdom ; and it yields, from its vicinity to the Capital, a greater profit here than is commonly experienced elsewhere."

P. 116. " Mr. Keate and Mr. Stephenson, at Hatfield, assured me that all that vicinity has cultivated clover so long and so repeatedly, that the soil is, as the farmers say, sick of the plant. It matters not how fine a crop may be in autumn, it dies off in the winter gradually, so that little is left in May ; and it dies even so late as in that month. Mr. Keate had a proof of the benefit of not sowing it in one or two courses consecutively."

LUCERNE.—P. 124. " Mr. Doo, at Bygrave, has a field of ten acres broadcast, which is at present ten or twelve years old. He gave the land (a strong loam on a chalk bottom) a complete summer-fallow, on which he sowed barley *half seeded,* or *two bushels* an acre, and the lucerne twelve pounds an acre with it : he regularly mows it thrice a year, and feeds 23 horses with it from May-day to Michaelmas. He sows 50 bushels of soot per acre upon it every year, at 1s. per bushel, having previously harrowed it completely in March, with a heavy drag-harrow, as much as six oxen can well draw ; and this across the field in various directions, till the field has the appearance of a summer-fallow. He has a very high opinion of it ; and esteems it to be excellent for horses, and better than tares, except for a very short time while they are in full bloom : he can drive or ride horses 40 or 50 miles a day on it without any inconvenience. It never gives them a looseness."

TARES.—Their *History,* in Hertfordshire.—P. 125. " In the heavy land districts, I found tares very generally cultivated for soiling the teams ; a husbandry that cannot be too much commended It appears by the writings of Ellis, that this branch of agriculture was common in Hertfordshire above 60 years since, before it was at all practised in many other counties ; and I was glad to find it held its place steadily in the management of the present period."

P. 126. " Every farmer, at least nineteen in twenty, have tares for soiling their horses. It is one great feature of Hertfordshire merit, being more general than in any other county with which I am acquainted."

GRASS LANDS.—*Extent.*—P. 133. " The quantity of grass-
land

land in the county is extremely small, compared with that
of arable land : there is no grass district in it, except a very
narrow margin in the south line, in the vicinity of Barnet,
which being near to London, is made artificially productive,
by means of manures brought back by the hay-carts."

" Wherever the residence of a gentleman is found (and
Hertfordshire abounds with their seats), there is a tract of
grass kept artificially productive, whatever may be the soil ;
the expense of which is not easily ascertained. And on the
rivers, the flat bottoms of the vales" (valleys) " in general
very narrow, are, as every where else, in natural meadow :
these exceptions being made, the rest is arable."

ORCHARDS.—P. 143. " In the south-west corner of the
county, and particularly in the parishes of Rickmersworth,
Sarret, King's Langley, and Abbot's Langley, Flaunden,
Bovington, and partly in Watford and Aldenham, there are
many orchards : apples and cherries are their principal produce. Every farm has an orchard ; but the larger the farm
the smaller the orchard. Orchards are found chiefly in
farms of from 20 to 50 acres. The apples are most profitable ; but cherries very beneficial to the poor, in the
quantity of employment which they require in gathering the
crop, for which the poor are paid from 4d. to 8d. per dozen
pounds."

LIVESTOCK.

P. 182. "This subject, which, in so many counties, from
the modern improvements made in it, has so greatly occupied the public attention, and claimed the first consideration from the Reporters, is, perhaps, as barren a one in
Hertfordshire as any that can be named. It is merely an
arable country ; and the quantity of clover-hay carried to
London is so great, and forms so profitable a husbandry,
that live stock must be a very inferior object. I did not
neglect to make inquiries, and the reader will find some particulars, which merit his attention."

CATTLE.—*Breed.*—P. 182. " Hertfordshire having no
breed of its own, the cattle kept in it are of various sorts."

Cows.—P. 185. " Mr. Calvert, at Albury, when oil-cake
was much cheaper than at present, found it the most advantageous and profitable food that he could give his cows :
three cakes a day, with eight or ten pounds of hay, or four
cakes and good straw, were the usual allowance ; two were
given to cows in calf and to growing heifers : he practised
this till cake advanced beyond 9l. a thousand. How far it
may answer at much higher prices, hay and butter having
both greatly advanced, careful experiments will alone ascertain,

certain, which he himself should have made; but Swedish turnips being introduced, and answering uncommonly well, he lost the inducement to go on with the other food. Cake gave very good butter; and, at 6*l.* or 7*l.* a thousand, was the cheapest food that could be given."

Fatting Cattle.—P. 184. " In stall-feeding beasts, Mr. Chapman, of Hitchin, has remarked the advantage of changing the food, for instance, clover-hay for meadow-hay, and meadow for clover-hay; and he is clear in this point."

Sheep.—What the Reporter has said of the cattle, may be said of the sheep of Hertfordshire. Formerly, the tall, white-faced, horned breed of *Wiltshire,* and the large, greyfaced, hornless breed of *Berkshire,* were prevalent, in Hertfordshire. Of later years, different varieties of the *longwooled breeds* have been introduced; and, still more recently, the *Southdown* sort has become fashionable.

Having placed before his readers eight or ten pages of minutes, on the practices and opinions of individuals, none of which is sufficiently interesting to be placed in this register, the Secretary makes the following retrospective remarks.

P. 195. " The most interesting feature of these minutes is the comparison of the Wiltshire and South Down breeds. Amongst very practical and reasonable men, the notion of the former doing best on turnips, and the latter on grass, has gained such ground, that I can scarcely conceive it to be a mere prejudice; and I ought to remark, that I have in other counties, and on various occasions, met with so many instances of Wiltshire wethers paying greatly for turnips, that I am inclined to think there is much truth in the Hertfordshire notion."

Deer.—P. 213. " The Earl of Clarendon, justly considering that there is no more impropriety in converting one animal to profit than another, makes deer an object of husbandry. As soon as the rutting season is over, or usually about the 10th of November, his Lordship selects from the herd the weak ones, some of which would probably die in the the winter, and keeps them in a small yard that has a shed on one side, and a net over the whole against pigeons, &c.; the spot very warm, and well sheltered. Their horns are immediately sawn off, the place is well littered, and they are fed at a very small expense on pea-straw, hay, &c. warmth making up for the want of better food. At times, during the winter, they have clover-hay cut into chaff, and if they do not eat it well, a little salt is added. They have always plenty of water, and are kept perfectly clean: much attention should be paid by the keeper to make himself
familiar

familiar with them, that he may enter the place without disturbing them. The first week in March he gives them oil-cake, about half a cake each a day with chaff, which fattens them so quickly, that all are gone in May. Before killing, they have some green meat given, to take away any ill flavour from the cake, supposing such to be the effect of the food, for it is certain that the venison is exceedingly good."

BERKSHIRE.

BERKSHIRE.

THIS County is aptly separable into four DISTRICTS.

1. *North Berkshire* is, in *surface,* pretty uniformly, a Vale Land District; excepting a range of hillocks, near its northern margin—fragments of the Cotswold hills of Glocestershire.—But it is not such in the nature of its *soils.* The northwest quarter of the County enjoys a deep rich loam—old grass land—rich grazing or dairy grounds;—naturally, an extension of the vale lands of North Wiltshire; which fortuitously reach within the political limits of Berkshire. The main body of this district is covered with soils of a different description;—mostly of a dark color and a fertile nature; arable land of a superior quality.—*Some* part of North Berkshire goes by the popular name of the " Vale of White Horse." But its limits, I believe, are indeterminate.

2. In the midland part of the County, an extent of Chalk Hill—the easternmost swell of the Marlborough or North Wiltshire Downs—occupy more than one fourth of its area. *The Chalk Hill District.*

3. Along the southern margin of those hills lies a fertile valley of flat and much of it waterformed lands, among which the Kennet, a calcarious brook of size, with difficulty finds its way.—The *vale* or *valley* of *Newbery,*—or the *valley* of the *Kennet.*

4. At the east or lower end of that rich valley, rises East Berkshire,—a peninsular part of the County,—mostly a woodland district, or more barren heathlands;—aptly named the *Forest District**. It is bounded on the south by the heathlands of Surrey, and on the east by the vale of London.

On the northern margin of the last district stands the *western termination of the line of Chalk Hills,* described in p. 4, aforegoing.

" GENERAL

---

* Windsor forest forms a part of it.

" GENERAL VIEW

OF THE

AGRICULTURE

IN

BERKSHIRE,

WITH

OBSERVATIONS ON THE MEANS OF ITS IMPROVEMENT.

By WILLIAM PEARCE.

DRAWN UP FOR THE CONSIDERATION OF

The Board of Agriculture and Internal Improvement.

1794."

THIS is an " original," unpublished Report.

Mr. Pearce (if living) is a nephew. and was a pupil (and I believe a partner) of the late Mr. KENT*. His QUALIFICATIONS, therefore, as an *Estate Agent*, must not be doubted. And he evidently possessed, at the time of writing, the same kind of *general* knowledge of *agriculture*, which his relative and tutor possessed; with, unfortunately, the like prejudices.

Mr. Pearce's MODE of SURVEY—his method of collecting information—does not, in any way, appear. His selection of it, however—his PRINCIPLE of REPORT—is highly judicious, and appropriately defined.—P. 16. " It must be admitted, that Berkshire has to boast, of as many of these enlightened agriculturists as any county; but the minute methods followed by them, or any particular system not generally practised, would here be misplaced, and improper. I shall therefore proceed in reporting, in a general way, the present husbandry of the county."—This, I conceive, is the true principle of Report.

Mr.

---

* The Author of a *Report* from *Norfolk*. See EASTERN DEPARTMENT.

Mr. P's PLAN of REPORT is likewise peculiar. Instead of blending his own opinions, and his proposals for improvement, with the practice, or incidents of practice, collected,—as most others of the Board's Reporters have done,—he first gives the established practice of the County, and then makes his own " observations," distinctly, at the close of each head or division of the work.

Those observations are many of them judicious, and mostly well written; and what may be grateful to some men's minds, they evince a kindness of heart, and an amiableness of disposition.—A few of them are entitled to a place in this register But, more generally, they are the remarks of a man possessing good natural abilities, and an ordinary knowledge of rural affairs; but without a sufficient depth of *experience* in *Agriculture* to improve the knowledge of men of practice.

At the end of his little work, Mr Pearce has given a description of WINDSOR GREAT PARK, and the many IMPROVEMENTS that have been effected within it,—since the rangership, " on the death of the late Duke of Cumberland, some few years ago, reverted to his Majesty."

P. 63. " It then consisted of about 3,800 acres, of which about 200 acres were covered with water, 200 plantation, 300 meadow, and 200 in arable; the remainder in park. The arable land was ill selected and disposed; and instead of lying compact, was scattered in pieces, a mile or two apart; some of it was in single parcels, surrounded with high pales, separating fine vallies, and concealing ground, of the most beautiful shape. The greatest part of the park, was covered with high ant-hills, moss, fern, or rushes, and abounded in bogs and swamps, which, in many places, it was dangerous to cross. There were about 3,000 deer, in very bad health and condition, kept in it."

P. 64. " The park is now reduced to 1,800 acres. The detached pieces of arable, which intersected, and concealed, some of the finest parts of it, are laid down and thrown into it. The wet parts are rendered firm and sound, by the Essex mode of under-ground draining. The rushes are weakened and destroyed, by draining and rolling; the moss, and small hillocks extirpated, by harrowing; the large ant-hills cleared, by the scarifier; the fern weakened, by mowing; the irregular banks levelled; pits filled up; the vallies opened, and smoothed; the hills ornamented with new plantations; and the stiff lines of trees, the vestiges of former hedge-rows, judiciously broken; by which means, great beauty is produced in all parts; and it is apparent, that the park thus reduced, supports the same number of deer

it

it did before; and that they are in much better health, and condition."

Beside those well conceived improvements, of the deer park, two farms,—one of them after the manner of a " Flemish Farm,"—the other of a " Norfolk Farm,"—have been laid out and cultivated, within that magnificent royal demesne.

The whole of this grand establishment, says the Reporter, p. 69, " was formed, and is carried on, under His Majesty's personal, and gracious attention, for the most laudable purposes; and the operative management of it, is delegated to my uncle, Mr. Kent ;"—not merely, as his nephew intimates, with a view to rational recreation; but as a " practical school, from which the most rational, and praise-worthy lessons in agriculture, may be taken ;"—as an " example, upon a great and extensive scale, for the purpose of effecting, in this particular district, such desirable benefits, on which the comfort and happiness, of the community so much depends;—An example well entitled to general *attention*, *imitation*, and *adoption*."— pp. 63 and 64.

Nothing, however, in Mr. Pearce's general observations, concerning the management of those farms, nor in the general economy of the establishment at large, conveys to the reader any resemblance of a RURAL INSTITUTE!

As a faithful account (I believe) of well executed improvements, on an extensive scale, that were prosecuted, if not planned, by " the most illustrious character in the kingdom,"—it is superiorly interesting. The public, therefore, have to regret that it should be confined to an unpublished Report.

There are three plates annexed to this Report; all of them pertaining to Windsor Park ; namely, one of cottages, one of ploughs, and the third representing a moveable barn.

The number of pages of letterpress, relating to the Report of the practice of Berkshire, sixtyone,—to the improvements in Windsor Park, twelve.

NATURAL ECONOMY.

EXTENT.—Mr. Pearce furnishes an " alphabetical table, shewing the number of acres in each parish, in the county of Berks," p. 11. The total amount, as estimated by Mr. Rocque, who published a map of Berkshire, is nearly 439,000 acres.

P. 13.

P. 13. " From the foregoing table and my general observations, I consider,

	Acres.
The inclosed lands, parks, and woods to contain about	170,000
The common fields and downs	220,000
The forests, wastes, and commons	40,000
Roads	8,977
Total	438,977."

SOILS.—P. 9. " The predominant soil of Berks, is a kind
and fruitful loam, in some parts mixed with gravel, and in
others with sand ; pleasant to work, and grateful in its
produce.

" The vale of White Horse, by general acceptation, is confined to a few parishes west of Wantage, which is a rich
deep soil, equal to the best parts of England. I shall not
exaggerate however, if I state, that the whole of the county
lying north of the Downs, (with the exception of a small
district near Oxford,) is likewise of an excellent quality ;
and though not so rich as the Vale, is certainly a well
adapted country, not only for the production of corn, but
for the turnip system of fatting off cattle.

" The greatest part of the southern side of the county,
from Hungerford, to Windsor, (except a part of Kentbury
Hundred, and some land on the south side of the Kennet,
and the greatest part of Windsor Forest), consists chiefly
of a gravelly loam; and though it may not admit, of so
profitable a course of husbandry, as the north side of the
county, may nevertheless be applied, to great advantage
by the turnip system.

" The hills, and downs, are chalk, with a thin soil on the
surface, in some places inclined to gravel, in others to a
blackish sand."

POLITICAL ECONOMY.

APPROPRIATION.—*Common Pastures.*—P. 59. " The
waste lands of Berkshire are very extensive and occupy a
great proportion of the county. The Forest of Windsor,
Maidenhead Thicket, Tylehurst Heath, Wickham Heath,
and the numerous commons that are to be found in all directions, contain, without exaggeration, at least 40,000
acres.

" In their present wild and uncultivated state, little or nothing

thing is returned by them to the community : except some deer, in the Royal Forest, we generally see on all the COM-MONS and WASTE LANDS, a number of miserable cattle, sheep, and horses, which are a disgrace to their respective breeds, and the cause of many distempers, which I am persuaded, have their origin, from the animals, who are doomed to the impoverishing subsistence, of grazing on them."

Common Fields.—P. 49. "A moiety, at least, of the arable land in Berkshire, is still lying in common fields ; and though it is not divided into such very small parcels, as in some other counties, the farmer labours under all the incon-venience of commonable land ; and by that, is withheld, from improving or treating his land, so, as to return the produce which it would do, if entire, and under a good course of husbandry."

Principle of Appropriation.—P. 49. " With respect to *Tithes,* the practice generally followed, in the present me-thod of inclosing, of ' allotting land in lieu of them,' is cer-tainly a good one."

POOR RATE.—P. 41. "The Poors Rate is very moderate, in most parts of the county : not above 2s. 6d. in the pound, upon an average ; except at Newbury, where it is now so high as nine shillings in the pound, upon the rack rent. But this, may in some measure, be accounted for, by the failure of the manufactory of broad cloth, which is now at a very low ebb ; and, as the parish is small, and the popu-lation great, unless some new branch of trade is struck out, for the employment of the poor, the land-owners in this parish, will lose half the income of their property, by the decline of the manufactory."—What an instructive lesson is this to men of landed property, not to listen to the flatter-ing proposals of men of manufacture.

MARKETS.—P. 38. " Berkshire, with respect to situation of markets, is peculiarly fortunate. They are distributed so well, that a distance of ten miles to a market, is difficult to be found.

" Newbury, Reading, Abingdon, Wallingford, and Wind-sor, have all the advantage of water-carriage to London, and the interior parts of the kingdom. The two former send a prodigious quantity of flour to London ; and the others barley and malt, to a considerable amount.

" Ilsey has also, of late, become a sheep market, of the first importance, not only to Berkshire, but its neighbour-ing counties. Not less than 20,000 sheep have sometimes been sold in one market day ; and it is computed, that the annual average is not under 250,000, comprising lambs, tags, wethers, and ewes ; but they are chiefly lean sheep.

" Newbury has, time out of mind, been justly con-sidered

sidered a most excellent corn market; and still retains some
customs, that would be of great use were they observed, in
all other markets. Here the grain is pitched in open market, is ingenuously offered to the public, in small, as well
as large quantities: thus defeating, as much as possible,
the artifices of monopolizers; and holding out to the industrious lowly hand, the chief nourisher of his existence, at a
fair market price."

P. 39. " The laudable custom that still exists at Newbury,
of a pitched market, is so conducive to the comfort of the
lower classes of mankind, that it is to be wished, it may be
long continued; and much to be lamented, that monopolizers in most other parts of the kingdom, have contrived
to draw, from this most valuable class, a profit of at
least 20 per cent. to themselves, without any benefit resulting from it, even to the farmers."

I will here repeat what I have more than once intimated—
that because " pitched markets" may be a " comfort of
the lower classes," who are resident in their respective
neighbourhoods, by enabling them to purchase a single
bushel, or a sack, of corn of the grower, it does not follow
that quarters, loads, and lasts of corn, that are indispensibly
destined to supply distant towns, or the Metropolis, through
the media of corn merchants and flour makers, should be
dragged bodily to a market which is situated, perhaps, in
a direction opposite to the place of its delivery.—I mention
this the rather, here, as we are now in the pitch-market
department.

RURAL ECONOMY.

TENANTED ESTATES.

TENURES.—P. 17. " There are many estates, held
by leases on lives, under corporate, collegiate, and ecclesiastical bodies, and some few still existing of a similar tenure,
under lay-lords."

IRRIGATION.—P. 51. " The tract of meadows, contiguous
to the river Kennet, from Hungerford in the west, to
Reading east, are all of them watered in a masterly style;
and the burthens of hay, cut from them, independent of the
very early feed, evince the great improvement that arises,
from this simple method:" The Reporter unfortunately
adds—" of creating fermentation in a soil, which, in many
places, is sullen and torpid."!

TENANCY

TENANCY.—P. 17. " I am sorry to find, that the same prejudice, which of late years has so much influenced the minds of gentlemen of landed property, against the practice of granting their tenants leases, has too strongly rooted itself in this, as well as most other counties ; which is certainly very detrimental to all good husbandry, and a great check to many improvements, which would otherwise, have been long since effected.

" There are, it is true, some Estates granted on terms of seven, fourteen, and twenty-one years; but from the best information I could obtain, the quantity of land so demised, bears but a very small proportion, to the extent of the county."

P. 20. " The usual custom of the county, is, for the landlord to put the buildings into good repair on the tenant's entering ; and afterwards to find all materials, except straw for thatching. The tenant after his entry, pays all workmen's wages, and fetches the materials for repairs gratis."

WOODLANDS.

WOODS.—P. 54. " The south, and east sides of Berkshire, have a large proportion of wood land appertaining to them : and, as the parochial taxes are generally very light, on this part of landed property, and the demand for faggot, and hurdle wood, very great, they pay the landlord, in general, much better than his cultivated land.

" The predominant wood in the county, is hazle : sometimes, however, it is mixed with ash, oak, beech, willow, and alder. There are also, some few beech woods to be found entire ; which, when in a proper course of falling, are certainly a very productive wood, particularly as they may be planted on chalk, or rocky hills, where there is but little surface, and where other wood does not prosper.

" Hazle-wood, in a country where great quantities of hurdles are wanting, is of course very profitable. In a good soil, it is cut from seven to ten years' growth ; and will fetch, from ten to fifteen pounds an acre. In other places, it must stand twelve, or fourteen years, to be worth so much.

" The chief purposes, to which this wood is applied, is making hurdles, faggots, hoops, and bundles of stakes.

" Close hurdles are from six shillings to nine shillings a dozen.

" Bundles of stakes, seven pence each.

" Hoops,

" Hoops, 3s. 6d. a bundle of 60 hoops.

" The beech woods in this county are exceedingly well managed, by continually clearing, (which they call *drawing out,)* the beech stems, from eight, down to three or four inches girt, where they stand too thick, or appear unthrifty and dead. The best of this stuff is sold to coachmakers, wheelwrights, farmers, &c. at 7d. per foot, for making and repairing carriages, and agricultural implements ; the other is generally cut up into billets, and faggots, for the bakers of the country ; and a great quantity is also sent down to London, for the bakers there, as well as for packing in the holds of ships. The woodman marks the billets, according to their size, with one, two, or three notches, which are considered, as so many farthings-worth, when the billets are sold ; and by this means, he is enabled, not only to ascertain the value of the wood cut up, but pays his workmen accordingly, at the rate of sixpence, for 255 notches: which is construed a load.

" Those who take good care of their wood lands, permit their labourers, during the winter months, to take up the old roots, from which no heir or teller is rising ; on condition that the workmen plant new sets, in a proper manner ; and in case they do not strike the first year, are to replant them the next winter. By this excellent method, a constant succession is kept up, and is a plan worthy of adoption in all beech wood counties.

" The scrubby stuff, is often burnt into charcoal, which pays extremely well, from its vicinity to so good a market, as London.

" Ash, withe, and birch wood, are also very productive, and valuable, for hoop stuff, which is sent down the Thames, in great quantities. Instances have been known, of an acre of withe and ash, in an aquatic situation, at seven years' growth, selling for twenty-five pounds.

" Very little timber, is of course, encouraged to grow in these woods, as their shade, and roots, would be detrimental to the underwood. But, in many parts of the county, there is a great quantity of timber standing ; particularly at the eastern extremity, and the parts adjacent to the rivers Thames, and Kennet. The prices" (in 1793-4) " vary, in different parts, according to its vicinity to water carriage, &c.

	£.	s.	d.		£.	s.	d.	
" From	3	0	0	to	5	0	0	per load, for Oak.
	2	5	0	to	3	13	6	———— for Ash.
	1	15	0	to	2	12	6	———— for Elm.
	1	10	0	to	2	2	0	———— for Beech."

PLANTING.—In Mr. Pearce's " observations" no *Woods*

(tho

(tho mostly judicious) I find nothing of novelty or excellence which was not, in 1794, before the public. The following *incident* in *planting* shows, in a striking manner, the utility of covering the soil of young coppice grounds;—agreeably to the *practice* of the *district* of *Maidston.* See my Southern Counties.

P. 56. " The ashe, withe, and birch plantations, paying so remarkably well, are an object, which I conceive worthy of great consideration. An experiment, made by a Kentish farmer, on an ash plantation, has succeeded so well, that I recommend every person having this kind of underwood, to make some trial like it; conceiving many substitutes may be found out, in lieu of the hop binds which he used.

" Having a small shaw, or wood of ash, that was planted in beds, and having a great quantity of hop binds, which he could not make serviceable in his farm yard; a thought struck him, that by laying them on his ash beds, he could do no harm, and it might tend to smother the weeds and rubbish, which grew up amongst the stems. He therefore, covered every other bed with the binds, when the whole plantation was three years old.—I saw this shaw, when it was five years old, and the hop binds were then, in a perfect state, and no weeds appearing. The wood was full six foot higher, on those beds where the binds were laid, than on the others; and the farmer supposed it would be better stuff, and more fit to cut, at seven years' growth, for hop poles, than the other beds would be, at ten years."

AGRICULTURE.

FARMS.—P. 19. " The greater proportion of this county, is divided into what may be deemed large farms: for unless it is from some local circumstance, it is very rare to find a farm, under one hundred pounds a year. In the Vale of White Horse, indeed, some smaller dairy, and grazing farms are found; but I doubt there are more farms, from two to five hundred a year, than of any other size."

HOMESTEADS.—P. 20. " It may be said, that the farm buildings all over the county, are respectable, and convenient: and their ox-stalls and yards, in the grazing parts, judiciously arranged for the fatting of cattle."

PLAN of MANAGEMENT.—P. 28. " The mode of cropping followed by the fair and best farmers, on the south side of the county; is divided into five shifts, thus; first year, a crop of wheat (which has been manured for), next year, barley,

barley, then turnips fed off.—The fourth year, barley or
oats, laid down with clover; and the fifth year, clover mowed
only once. After which, wheat comes round again."

P. 29. " In the Vale of White Horse, and the country
adjacent, where the soil is a rich deep loam, the general
practice is, to take, 1st. wheat, 2d. beans, 3d. barley, or oats
with seeds, 4th. clover one year, 5th. fallow, vetches, or
turnips. After which, the wheat crop comes in succession."

In Mr. Pearce's " observations" on this subject, tho they
are of considerable length, I perceive nothing of superior
value. Yet the " Course of Cropping" is of all other subjects, in *agriculture*, the most requisite to be well understood by an estate agent. His remarks, however, show
that he had not, at the time of writing, been inattentive to
that point of his profession. Some of them are just; but
not important.

WORKPEOPLE.—P. 40. " The husbandmen of this county,
are well-disposed, tractable, and honest; and, when their
powers are called forth by fair encouragement, skilful, and
industrious.

" Their daily pay, in the winter, is from one shilling to
one shilling and three-pence. They come to work about
seven, and stay till five; and are allowed an hour in the
day for meals.

" In the summer, their labour commences at six, and
ends at six. They are then allowed two hours for meals;
and the pay is increased to one shilling and two-pence, and
more, according to the goodness of the hand, up to one
shilling and sixpence."

P. 41. " Some few farmers in this county, pay their labourers in kind; viz. with wheat and barley, when they
choose to take it."

In his " observations" on this head, Mr. P. humanely recommends, to landholders, to bestow due attention on the
comforts of the workpeople who reside on their estates;—
intimating (and in some cases the intimation is, unfortunately, too well grounded) that " at present, they are too
much left to the management and controul of the farmer,
whose situation being only temporary, is too often induced
to consider them merely as instruments, subservient to his
interest, so that the poor man's spirit is depressed, as he
sees himself abandoned by the landlord, who, having a permanent interest in the country, is, and ought to be, his Natural Protector." p. 41.

WORKING ANIMALS.—See *Tillage*, ensuing.

IMPLEMENTS.—Mr. Pearce speaks in high prai of the
waggon and the *cart* of Berkshire; but condemns its *plow*
and

and minor implements. He does not, however, enter on a description of either of them.

MANURE.—*Yard Dung.*—P. 24. " Among the best far-mers, the general custom is, to ' pot-dung' for their wheat crop, and feed off their turnips with sheep; so that each piece of land gets well manured every other year, besides occasional foldings, on the stubbles, as the course is pro-ceeding.

" The downs, from the great distance they usually are from the homestall, have but little pot-dung* bestowed on them; all their support arises from that quiet, generous animal, the sheep, which periodically bears to its fold, the nourishing means for future crops."

Sheep-dung Compost.—The following instance of practice, at WINDSOR, is entitled to an entry, here.—P. 66. " Eight hundred Wiltshire wethers are kept as a folding flock on the Norfolk farm, with the assistance of which, the land will be either mucked, or manured, twice in five years; viz. for wheat and turnips. The flock is constantly penned upon the fallows, or some of the meadow land, except when the sheep are foddered, in the hardest part of the winter, and then they are penned in a fixed fold, made large, and di-vided into two parts; this is generally done, during the months of December, January, and February. This fold, which is pitched in some sheltered spot, and is first laid a foot thick with maiden earth, is daily littered with leaves, moss, fern, stubble, or any litter that can be collected; and the fold is made use of at opposite ends, alternately every other night; hay being given in cribs, which are moved into the respective folds, as used. When the sheep leave this fold, the beginning of March, a layer of lime, chalk, or peat ash, is put upon the top, and the whole being mixed up together, makes excellent manure for the suc-ceeding turnip crop. It is astonishing what advantages may be deduced, from a steady adherence to this practice.—Six hundred loads of excellent compost, were made the first year of this experiment, in three months, from 600 sheep."

Peat Ashes.—The following notice of the NEWBURY PEAT WORKS, tho not so intelligent as might have been ex-pected, is also admissible.—P. 51. " I was informed, by a gentleman, that has concerns in this peat country, that he
last

---

* This is a West of England term, for *yard dung;* which was here-tofore, universally, and, in the more hilly parts of Devonshire and Cornwall, is to this day, carried to the land in " dung pots" or panniers, on horseback. In Berkshire it would seem to be used, at present, in contradistinction to sheep's dung, or *the fold.*

last year sold the peat, on one acre of land, for 300*l.*"!!!
" where the purchaser was limited,

" First, to cut no deeper than six feet.

" Secondly, to cut and clear off the whole in the course of the year.

" And lastly, he was to pare off the sward, that was on the acre at the time of agreement, and relay it, in a proper manner, on the surface, after he had got out the peat ; in order that it might, when returned to the landlord, be in a state for meadow land again.

" The reader, unacquainted with the properties of peat, may, with reason, exclaim, for what purposes can this earth be applied, to make it so very valuable ?

" First—It is, like all other putrid vegetables, an excellent fuel.

" Secondly—It has a property, that the peat of no other country has," (?) " in the virtues of its ashes ; which in Berkshire, and other parts, are used with great success, in dressing young crops, whether of wheat, barley, oats, or turnips.

" It is also an excellent improver of grass lands, particularly clover lays, and sainfoin ; which shew to an inch where the peat-ash has been bestowed on them. The quantity necessary to dress an acre, is reckoned from 15 to 25 bushels, according to the condition of the land, and which may be bought on the spot, from 2*d.* to 4*d.* a bushel, according to the strength and goodness of the ash.

" This cheap and striking improvement, has not been known in Berkshire more than seventy or eighty years. For a long time, like all other new methods, it had to combat the prejudices and obstinacy of many. But it seems now universally approved, and adopted by every cultivator, who lives within a reasonable distance, to procure the same."

TILLAGE.—P. 22. " To facilitate the operations of agriculture, and to adopt a system of economy in its necessary labour, are very material, and obvious advantages, and such as the farmer, for his own sake, ought to listen to, since his interest is highly connected with their adoption.

" I cannot, therefore, withhold censuring, not only the plough at present used in Berks, but the mode of working it. Four horses, and two men, employed a whole day, in turning up an acre of land, even if it be a third tilth, is so extravagant, and unnecessary, on land, such as I have described the greater part of Berkshire to consist of, that I cannot but consider it as a NATIONAL DRAWBACK and LOSS. I am persuaded, a Norfolk, or Suffolk farmer, would never, in the strongest soil of this county, put more than two horses to a plough, with one man, and he would do as

much

much work, if not more, than four horses, and two attend-
ants now do, in many parts of Berkshire."

The Reporter, afterward, comments on this *extravagant*
practice ; showing its mischievous effects, in a private and
in a public point of view.

On *fallowing*, it is no wonder that a pupil of Mr. KENT
should speak irreverently ;—not only as its being an *unprofitable*, but as a " slovenly" practice!! p. 26.

ARABLE CROPS, and their MANAGEMENT.—On this main
branch of *Agriculture*, the Report under view affords a
very scanty portion of information ;—either concerning the
general works of aration, or the culture of individual crops.
The few paragraphs that follow are what I find entitled to
extraction.

The Times of Sowing Arable Crops.—P. 25. " The wheat
sowing, is necessarily very early on the downs, and light
land. Some persons put their wheat in, so soon, as the
first week in August, and their turnips, in May ; but about
Old Lammas, is the general time for sowing wheat, in the
hill country. The Lent-corn, in the same situations, is got
in, during the months of March and April, and unless the
season is very backward, is completed before the middle of
April, and the turnip sowing, about the middle of June.
In the loamy, cohesive, and strong land, the periods of
sowing differ, according to the tendency of the soil. The
general busy time in these parts for wheat sowing, appears
to be, from the middle of September, to the middle of October ; and of the barley sowing, from Lady-day, to May-
day."

The Quantity of Seed.—P. 25. " The quantity of seed
sown on a statute acre, is on an average, in the most parts
of the county, nearly as follows:

Wheat	3	Bushels.
Barley	4	Bushels.
Oats	$5\frac{1}{2}$	Bushels.
Beans, or peas	$3\frac{1}{2}$	Bushels."

Harvesting Arable Crops.—P. 35. " From the nature of
the soil, it is to be expected, the harvest is forward in most
parts of Berkshire ; which is generally the case.

" The usual practice of the county, is, to let the harvest
work by the great ; and many of the women are employed
in reaping, as well as the other labour, necessary for getting
in crops.

" About Lammas, the reaping of wheat commences."

SAINFOIN.—P. 52. " There is another obvious improvement, which, I understand, was introduced many years
since into Berkshire ; but not much attended to, till of late
years ; viz. the cultivation of sainfoin.

                                        " On

" On the downs, and hilly land, where the predominant strata" (stratum) " is chalk, and the surface not naturally inclined to grass, this most excellent substitute for meadows, flourishes with vigour."   Mr. P's theory, concerning the proper species of *land* for the sainfoin crop is laughably erroneous.

GRASS LAND.—Had it not been that the Reporter touched on the subject of irrigation, the reader might have been left to conjecture whether or not permanent herbage is a product of Berkshire.   The grazing and dairy grounds in the northwest quarter of the County, the sheep downs in its more central parts, and the marginal meadows on the Thames and the Kennet, are not, however, inconsiderable.

LIVESTOCK.

WHAT we find on this important object, likewise, occupies only a small portion of this brief Report.   Berkshire, it is true, is not a favorable passage of Country in which to study and report the management of grass lands, or the general economy of livestock.   It is, emphatically speaking, neither a breeding, nor a fatting County ; excepting of sheep and swine ; for the latter of which, more particularly, it has long been celebrated.

HORSES.—P. 45. " The Berkshire farmer considers his profits from horses, no inconsiderable part of his farming, and this, in some degree, accounts for the unnecessary number of horses, we see kept in every part of the county. Some breed their own stock, and others buy in suckers, which they put to work very early ; and after using them for two or three years, sell off, to the brewers in London, and the stage waggons, at such high prices, as to make eight, or ten pounds per annum of each horse ; considering his work equal to the expence of his keep."

CATTLE.—The *Dairy* is the principal object of cattle keeping.   The following is a sketch of the Berkshire practice.—P. 45. " The cows most esteemed in this county, are those of the North country breed ; they are excellent milkers, and well adapted for the grass land of the Vaie, where the dairy farms are managed, with much skill, and judgment.   The dairymen keep up the succession, partly by rearing, and partly by buying heifers in calf, at Lambourn, and other fairs in the county."

The *fatting* of cattle, I believe, is chiefly confined to *stall* fatting, in the Glocestershire manner, and is chiefly practised in the Glocestershire margin of the County.   The Berkshire practice is thus described.—P. 44. " The *neat* cattle, fatted off in this county, are generally the Herefordshire, Shropshire,

Shropshire; Glamorganshire, and other parts of South Wales, bought in at the spring, and fall. The system of fatting with turnips, is not however, much known, and in the grazing part of the White Horse Vale, where a great quantity of beasts are annually stall-fed; they are generally fatted with hay, bean, and barley meal, oil-cake, &c. Linseed, both dry and steeped, is given by some graziers, and found to answer exceedingly well; but this practice, though a good one, is not common."

P. 48. "The method of stall-feeding cattle is exceedingly well understood in this county; and the plan of forming the stalls, so as to give each beast a separate walk, is worthy of being copied, in all counties, where winter fatting is practised."—For a description of those sheds, and the method of fatting with hay and oil cakes, see my GLOCESTERSHIRE.

SHEEP.—*Breed.*—P. 44. " Berkshire has, and ever must have, from the nature of the soil, a great quantity of sheep kept upon it. Its present breed are certainly not only a very useful, but handsome stock, and are in great reputation in the neighbouring counties. They are well adapted for folding; being strong and agile, they travel long ranges during the day, and from their size and weight, are good folding sheep at night."

" Various are the sizes, and weights, of the Berkshire sheep, so much depending on the breed and keep. A full sized Berkshire sheep, however, thirty months old, when fat, weighs seldom less than 20 lbs. a quarter, and are sometimes increased to 25 lbs. or 30 lbs."

" A fleece of 4 lbs. is reckoned a good produce; the general average of the county will not, however, be so high. Eight sheep to a tod of 28 lbs. is about the usual allowance."

Fatting and *Market* of Sheep.—P. 44. " Great numbers are now annually drawn out of the flocks, and fatted off, by the introduction of the turnip system; and a still greater number are bought at Ilsley, to fat in the counties nearer London."

The following " observations," on the *Improvement* of Sheep, *I* of course consider as judicious.—P. 46. " That ' every soil has its own stock,' is an accurate observation of a very judicious and sensible writer on agriculture. Improvements may, no doubt, be effected in the breed, of almost all kinds of sheep; but crosses, where two very opposite breeds are to be combined, can never, in my opinion, be advantageous to either.

" A Berkshire sheep, will certainly be improved in its wool, by the cross of a South Down; but perhaps it will not be so good a folding sheep. In short, it appears to me, most

most rational, and most beneficial, to every sheep county, to strive to the utmost to improve its native breed;—foregoing the little advantage that may be derived from the improved quality of the wool, for the more permanent and solid one, of having a thrifty breed, congenial with the soil."

SWINE.—P. 45. " The quantity of swine fatted in Berkshire, is certainly very great. In the small town of Faringdon only, 4000 are slaughtered for the London, and Oxford markets, between the beginning of November, and the beginning of April. This however, is in a part of the county, where the dairy farms are situated; but nevertheless, when it is considered how many store pigs, are sent annually to the distillers and starch-makers, in the vicinity of London, Berkshire receives no inconsiderable return, from this profitable kind of stock."

POULTRY.—P. 45. " At the east end of the county, the poultry becomes very profitable from its vicinity to London. A great number of hucksters are constantly employed, in purchasing them, and the number weekly sent away is prodigious. At the northern, and western sides, the farms running large, these useful and necessary articles, which the little farm rears up, are overlooked, or rejected, and perhaps will account for the dearness of this kind of provision."

" GENERAL VIEW

OF THE

AGRICULTURE

OF

BERKSHIRE.

DRAWN UP FOR THE CONSIDERATION OF

THE BOARD OF AGRICULTURE

AND INTERNAL IMPROVEMENT.

By WILLIAM MAVOR, LL. D.

1813"!*

DOCTOR MAVOR is known to the public, as a " literary man." His QUALIFICATIONS, as a *public writer*, require

---

* A prefix, by the author, is dated November 1808, and, by incidental mentions made in the course of the work, the materials of it would seem to have been principally collected in 1807.

quire not to be spoken of, here. His acquirements as a *Reporter* of *Rural Practices*, are to be looked for in his performance. They will be seen in the ensuing extracts.

The MATERIALS of this Report appear to have been obtained by some considerable portion of personal examination; by enquiries and incidental communications; and, probably, through the more efficient assistance of a FRIEND†; who, as a zealous and veteran amateur of the Rural Science, was well enabled to supply Dr. M. with valuable information;—as well as to guard him from the errors and impositions into which inexperience is ever liable to be led, by the ignorance, and the interested views, of informants.

In addition to the materials, collected as above, we find a paper of Mr. Kent (formerly presented to the Society of Arts &c.) on the improvements in WINDSOR PARK*.—Also a paper of Mr. Page, concerning the best means of perfecting the navigation of the Thames.

Those papers, together with a list of indigenous plants, and other details not connected with the subjects given out, in " the Plan of the Board," afford sufficient matter to furnish an octavo volume of nearly five hundred and fifty pages; among which are interspersed thirtyseven engravings;—none of which require to be noticed, here.

In a prefatory " advertisement," which I transcribe, we read Doctor Mavor's own account of his work.—P. iii. " It is now upwards of three years since the Report of Berkshire was delegated to me; and I feel that some apology is due to the Honourable Board of Agriculture and to my numerous friends, for this apparently long delay. Had not ill health clouded many of the intervening days, had not various avocations, as well as the duties of an active profession occupied many more, the undertaking would probably have been completed in a much shorter space.

" This, however, I can aver, that though I have been almost wholly engaged for the last eight months in arranging and drawing up the materials, previously collected, I could have spent as many more on the composition, before I could have pleased myself.

" It was my attachment to Berkshire, and my wish to oblige a most respectable and kind friend†, that first induced me to enter into this engagement. To that friend, who was ever ready to encourage my endeavours, to obviate my difficulties, and to satisfy my doubts, this Report owes whatever

---

† " Edward Loveden Loveden, Esq. M. P. one of the Vice-presidents of the Board."

* Varying, in many particulars, from that furnished by Mr. Pearce, in his original sketch of Berkshire; which is, I think, a *plainer* account.

whatever merit it may be found to possess. Should I have unfortunately failed in doing some degree of justice to the subject, let the fault be ascribed to my own want of knowledge, not to my want of industry and zeal.

"For the County, which has been the scene of my present labours, I had long borne a partial regard; and I have every reason to retain my attachment, now that I know it better. To its gentry and yeomanry in general, I can only express my gratitude for their kindness, and assure them that the impression of it will be indelible. Particular acknowledgements in this place would be ill timed, where so many have claims to receive them; but I cannot withhold my best thanks from Frederick Page, Esq. of Newbury, for the valuable information with which he favoured me on the subject of the Berkshire Navigations; and for his readiness to assist my enquiries, in every way that his extensive local knowledge could suggest.

W. M.

WOODSTOCK,
November 20, 1808."

SUBJECT THE FIRST.

NATURAL ECONOMY.

EXTENT.—P. 3. "From astronomical observations which have settled the longitude of Oxford, and the trigonometrical survey by government, makes Berks, including its insulated parts, to contain about 464,500 acres, according to the following distribution:

	Acres.
Arable land about - - -	255,000
Meadows and dairy land in the vale	72,000
Sheep-walks, chiefly uninclosed, on the chalk-hills - - - - -	25,000
Other dry pastures, parks, &c. - -	25,000
Wastes, chiefly barren heaths - -	30,000
Woods, copses, &c. - - -	30,000*
Other space, occupied by buildings, courts, fences, roads, rivers, &c. - -	27,500
	464,500"

CLIMATURE.

* Dr. M. thinks the quantity of Woodland is somewhat underrated.

CLIMATURE.—P. 19. " In a track of such considerable
extent, with a surface and a soil so various, there must be
some diversity of climate ; but in almost every part of Berkshire, the air is pure and salubrious, and this is more particularly the case on the chalky and gravelly soils which
prevail through the greatest part of its limits."

WATERS.—P. 36. " The principal rivers and streams of
Berkshire are the Thames, the Kennet, the Loddon, the Lambourn, the Ock, the Aubourn, the Emme, and the Broad-
water."

DISTRICTS.—(Section " Divisions.")—P. 16. " The four
grand *natural* divisions of Berkshire are :—

" 1. The *Vale*, beginning at Buscot and terminating at
Streatley. It is bounded by the Thames on one side, and
by,"—

" 2. The *Chalky Hills*, which run nearly through the
centre of the lower part of the county."

" 3. The *Vale of the Kennet*."

" 4. The *Forest Division*, which commences on the
east of the Loddon, and extends the breadth of the county
to Old Windsor."

SOILS.—Of the *Vale Lands.*—(Section " Soil and Surface.")—P. 22. " The prevailing soil of the Vale is ' a strong
grey calcareous loam, which evidently owes it excellence
to the intimate mixture of vegetable mould with cretaceous
earth.' In fact, a considerable portion of it is alluvial land;
and its fertility differs according to the various proportions
of the component materials."

Of the *Chalk Hills.*—P. 25. " The downs are chiefly
composed of a blackish light earth.

" On the south side, these hills throughout their whole
extent gradually descend to the vale of the Kennet, and
contain some intermediate tracks of considerable fertility,
of flint, chalk, loam, and gravel, with occasional beds of
clay, but almost wholly with a chalky substratum."

Of the *Valley* of the *Kennet.*—P. 27. " In the soil of the
vale of the Kennet gravels predominate, but they vary considerably in their qualities, admixtures, and depths from
the surface. On the north side of the river the soil is generally a reddish loam, with a gravelly substratum, easily
tilled, and, with proper management, not much inferior in
the produce of some kinds of grain to the vale of White
Horse. On the south side of the Kennet, between Hungerford and Newbury, the soil is of gravel, loam, and clay
near the river; but towards Inkpen, Shalbourn, and West
Woodhay, we come to a track of deep, white maumy land,
well adapted for the growth of wheat, beans, and oak timber."—Doubtlessly, the base of the Chalk Hills of Hampshire,

shire, which there breaks out.—Other remarks on the same peculiar species of soil will appear in the course of this volume.

Of the *Forest District.*—P. 29. " The more northern parts of this division, towards Maidenhead, Bray, and Clewer, is gravel, strong loam, and clay; in the central parts, about Old and New Windsor, Winkfield, and Warfield, a tenacious clay prevails; and in the southern parts of the forest, sand and gravel. In many spots, however, within these limits, I found a good kind loam, in others a stiff loam mixed with clay."

FOSSILS.—P 32. " Berkshire possesses no minerals of considerable value, nor any uncommon variety of curious fossils. The chalk hills in general contain nothing very remarkable, as far as excavations have been made. The substance in general is too much mixed with heterogeneous matter to be applied to any useful purpose; but it is nevertheless found sufficiently pure in some places, particularly in the eastern direction of the stratum, to be dug for manure, and occasionally for building."

P. 34. " The Sarsden stones or grey wethers, as the country people call them, are irregularly scattered over the Wiltshire and Berkshire downs. They are pretty numerous in a valley near Ashdown park, in the road from thence to Lambourn, and seem as if they had been showered from heaven in some convulsion of nature, being totally unconnected with the soil on which they lie, which is here chalky; whereas, towards Compton Beauchamp, where they are likewise found, it is clayey. The Honourable Daines Barrington has made some observations on these stones in the Archæologia. They are composed of a fine siliceous grit, and are frequently blasted with gunpowder, and used for pitching; but they resist the mason's tools."

See the note, p. 1, aforegoing; which was written, some considerable time, before I saw the work that is now before me.

SUBSTRUCTURE.—P. 32. " At Catsgrove, near Reading, a stratum of chalk has been found, thirty feet in thickness, below which no experiments have been made in sinking, because a stratum of flint, where the water accumulates, lies immediately under. Above the chalk is a stratum of sandy clay, of about a foot thick, on which rests a layer of oyster shells, two feet more. Above the shells, is a stratum of sandy clay, one foot and a half thick; then four feet of greenish sand, and over this three feet of coarse fuller's earth. Above all, is a very deep bed of clay, fit for tiles and bricks."

SUBJECT

POLITICAL ECONOMY.

APPROPRIATION.—On this subject, Dr. Mavor speaks at some length, in three distinct sections; namely, 1. "Enclosing" &c., wherein is included a list of parishes, with the different states in which they were, in 1807;—thus furnishing valuable data for future topographers. 2. "Wastes." 3. "Common Fields."

In these separate divisions of the work, we find many ingenious remarks,—without much practical information.—The subjoined passages are what appears, to me, eligible to be inserted, here.

Common Pastures.—P. 324. " Though Berkshire may be considered as a well cultivated county, the wastes are by far more extensive than in others which are infinitely behind it, in their general agricultural improvement. Including the sheep-walks, on the chalks hills, chiefly uninclosed, and which amount to about 25,000 acres, the whole quantity of land, in a comparatively unproductive state, cannot amount to less than 60,000 acres, or nearly one-sixth of the whole area.

" The forest of Windsor, Maidenhead thicket, Bulmarsh heath, and many smaller wastes, the downs from Ilsley to Ashbury, and a track of common and waste lands, beginning at Inkpen, about eight miles to the south-west of Newbury, and running east, with a few intermission, as far as Windsor forest, of the breadth of two or three miles, and forming the Hampshire boundary, are incontestable proofs of what still remains to be done, in order to render Berkshire as rich, fertile, and productive as it might be made."

For a disadvantage of *Common Meadows,* see Irrigation, ensuing.

Common Fields.—P. 492. " The want of a general inclosure, and the enormous expences attending private bills of this kind being carried into execution, are not only checks on agricultural improvement, but in many instances render it impossible. A common field bargain, in which many have an interest, but no one can be said to have an exclusive property, can neither be cultivated, drained, manured, or managed with any degree of spirit or effect. As for wastes, however productive they are susceptible of being made, they

they are inevitably devoted to sterility and neglect, till allotted to individual owners; and it may be said in regard to all property, not in severalty,—

> The lands that many owners share,
> Can never know an owner's care."

On the *Difficulties* of Appropriation, by *separate Acts.* —P. 141. " In courts of law, I have more than once seen the parties obliged to produce a written copy of a bill of enclosure; and in one instance, I am well assured that the solicitor in a suit of this kind, being pressed for time, and finding the clerks otherwise engaged, was glad to copy the act himself, and only received the usual attestation, for which they were paid as if they had done the whole business. Even admitting the distinction between public and private bills, might not the subject be relieved, and the revenue increased, by affixing a stamp of five guineas to every private printed act, in order to give it the validity required? I throw out these hints to country gentlemen, members of parliament, whose interest and whose duty imperiously call upon them to bring forward some regulations in this respect.

" But it is not only in obtaining an act of parliament that the proprietors of land have to lament a wanton waste of money. The grand system of fleecing only commences with the circuitous and protracted manœuvres of solicitors and commissioners, who are to put it in force. Summonses are sent to every individual proprietor by the attorney, on the most trifling occasions, in order to swell his bill; and meeting is held on meeting by the commissioners, that they may come in for their full share of the spoil. When an act of parliament is passed, it must be a matter of notoriety to the proprietors of land, and an advertisement in the provincial papers ought to be the only further notice to parties interested in subsequent arrangements.

" At length the award is made out and signed; but this instrument, so far from defining every thing with a precision that will allow no scope for future litigation, has been known to contain *accidental* or *intentional* omissions, which furnish the lawyer with a future job, and involve the proprietors in new expences.

" But supposing every thing adjusted as it ought to be, which I will hope is frequently the case, it is alway expressly ordered that a copy of the award shall be deposited in the parish chest; and as a further security, that another copy shall be lodged with the clerk of the peace, or in one of the courts at Westminster. This wise provision, however, of rendering what concerns all easily accessible to all, at a trifling

trifling expence, is not unusually defeated by the interested
policy of the solicitor, who perhaps keeps the only copy of
the award in his own possession, as long as the proprietors
will submit to it : and charges for information and extracts,
according to his own fancy. I speak of practices that have
fallen under my personal notice elsewhere."—*excellent!*

MANUFACTURES.—" Berkshire," we are told, p. 472, " cannot be considered as a manufacturing County."

Under the Head, " Markets," the manufacture of each
market town is noticed. *Sack cloth* appears to be, at present, a principal object. Formerly, different articles of the
woolen trade were manufactured at

Newbury.—P. 460. " Newbury was formerly famous for
its woollen manufactures; but these are now nearly lost,
and hence a numerous poor.

" In the town and its vicinity, however, some kerseys,
cottons, callicoes, linen, and damask, are now manufactured. Blankets are likewise made by some persons from
Witney, in Oxfordshire; and it does not appear that they
produce an inferior article.

" A paper-mill, on a large scale, does much business in
its line. The paper is excellent, and applicable to almost
every purpose of printing or writing."

Oakingham.—P. 462. " Three silk manufacturers have
establishments here. One is for spinning, and two for
weaving. Hatbands, ribbands, watch-strings, shoe-strings,
sarcenets, figured gauzes for ladies' dresses, &c. are manufactured here."

Reading.—P 465. " Large quantities of malt are made
here for the London market; and not less than 20,000
sacks of flour are annually sent from hence to the same
mart. The Abbey mills remain."

PUBLIC TAXES.—P. 494. " I am fully aware that the
necessities of the state require, and I trust the patriotism of
the subject will ever incline him to pay the very large
aggregate sums now imposed, for the defence and support
of all that can be dear to men; but in apportioning the
taxes in such a manner as may be least oppressive, and produce the best effect, all the wisdom of legislators and states-
men should be brought into action. With the greatest part
of our rulers, for the last century or two, commerce has
been the idol to which every thing has been sacrificed. A
national debt of five hundred millions, an annual expenditure so enormous as almost to stagger belief that it could be
raised, attest this truth, without the necessity of a single
argument : for it will never be contended, that of the millions of debt which are ready to overwhelm us, one-fiftieth part
was ever incurred by agriculture and internal improvement.

                                        Manufactures

Manufactures and agriculture go hand in hand, and encourage each other; but foreign commerce and colonial possessions are certain drains on the mother country, for the benefit of comparatively few; as they must be supported by wars and taxes, beyond their relative worth."—*Hear! Hear!*

LOCAL TAXES.—POOR RATE.—*Assessing.*—In the section, "Size of Farms," Dr. Mavor elicits a novel and good idea (susceptible I conceive of improvement); namely, that of assessing the occupiers of lands, toward the maintenance of the poor,—not simplexly according to the rental value of the lands in occupancy, but jointly with the sizes of farms; as " for instance, a farm of 50*l.* a year should be assessed at 6*d.* in the pound, rent; 100*l.* at 7½*d.*; 150*l.* at 9*d.*; 200*l.* at 10½*d.*; 250*l.* at 1*s.*; 300*l.* at 1*s.* 1½*d.*; 350*l.* at 1*s.* 3*d.*; 400*l.* at 1*s.* 6*d.*; and so on in proportion." p. 79.

It appears to be evidently unjust that a *working farmer*,—a man who cultivates his farm by the labor of his own family—by himself, his wife, and his children—should pay in equal proportion with one who cultivates his, by the means of hired *servants* and *laborers;* who and whose children may be liable to become burdensome.—A law to assess to the poor, in proportion to the number of workpeople employed,—not in AGRICULTURE, only, but in MANUFACTURES and TRADE in general,—would, in my opinion, be founded in right reason. The working farmer, however, ought not to be wholly exempt; inasmuch as some part of his family might eventually become chargeable to the parish.

P. 101. " Moveable property, as far as I have obtained information on the subject, is seldom assessed. In Abingdon, however, where the rates in St. Helen's parish now average about 6*s.* 6*d.* on a three-fourths value, and in St. Nicholas' about 7*s.* 6*d.*, on a two-thirds value, stock is charged in a moderate proportion; and in towns where the poor is numerous, from the decline of manufactures or other causes, it seems not only just, but expedient, that the poor's rate should be assessed on moveable as well as immoveable property.

" Instead of this, I have to lament, that in some parishes, the proprietor of a cottage and a garden, who lives by his daily labour, and ought to be an object of respect and indulgence, because he keeps himself from being chargeable to the parish, is assessed in his full proportion; while a person who is making hundreds a year by trade or a profession, pays only to the poor for the premises he occupies."

Average of Poor Rate.—P. 101. " From a variety of calculations, and taking a number of averages from accurate data, I find that the poor's rate on the actual rents throughout

throughout the county, does not exceed 3s. 4d. in the pound."

P. 108. " The poor's rate, on the nominal, but not on the real rent, in most parishes which are not very populous, and where there is a considerable quantity of land, pretty much divided in occupation, averages about 4s. 6d. in the pound."

In a section entitled " Poor," in the chapter " Obstacles to Improvements," a series of well intentioned remarks appear. The following are worthy of transcription.

P. 475. " The characters of men are influenced by circumstances, and are formed by habits; and the only effectual means, in my opinion, of ameliorating the condition of the labouring poor, and of giving them honorable feelings and impressions, is to assist and direct their endeavours in the path of *independence*.

" The first step is to render their cottages comfortable, and to give them an interest, if possible, in this kind of property, which is dear to every mind not wholly lost to sensibility and reflection. In a former section I have delivered my sentiments on this subject, and I wish to enforce them here. Nothing would more tend to make men good labourers, good husbands, good fathers, and good subjects, than a property in their homes, or an assurance that they would not be dispossessed, except by their own misconduct, with such a portion of land for a garden, &c. as would employ their leisure hours, without drawing them off from their regular engagements."

P. 479. " The number of public houses is unquestionably a nuisance ; and that country is in a lamentable state where the Machiavelian principle of ' private vices being public benefits,' is acted on, however much it may be disguised. The poor, however, not only require, but are entitled to comforts and occasional relaxations ; and if they cannot brew their own beer, it would be a humane and charitable action if the persons by whom they are employed, would allow them from time to time a certain quantity of table beer at prime cost, without being subject to any duty. To the gentleman or the farmer, the trouble of brewing a few bushels or quarters of malt extra, would be but trifling—to the poor the accommodation would be great."

" Connected with the amelioration of the condition of the poor, a virtuous education is also indispensably requisite. Their duty to God, to their neighbour, and themselves, they should have an opportunity of knowing, not by accident, but by systematic arrangements. Where the parent is unable, the parish officers should see that every child be taught by some competent person, to be paid by them, the principles of religion, and the practice of morals."—This is a
valuable

valuable suggestion,—well entitled to the consideration of legislators.—For the close of those remarks, see *Workpeople*, ensuing.

TITHES.—This subject is repeatedly brought forward, in the Report under review. We reach, however, nearly the close of the work, before we fully discover that the writer of it is personally interested in the subject.—P. 490. " Neither popular prejudice nor the *esprit du corps* have, I trust, biassed my sentiments."—This impels us to admire, the more, the candor with which he has treated it.

But waving the doctor's sentiments concerning the *nature* and *tendency* of tithes, I will here attend to their *operation*, in the County under Report.

P. 91. " The highest composition for vicarial tithes in this district being only 3s. per acre in dairying farms, and the highest rectorial no more than 7s. in the most productive and well cultivated parishes; while several vicars, to my knowledge, have only the very low composition of 9d. in the pound rent, and rectors 4s. : so that, taking the average of vicarial compositions, they do not exceed 1s. 3d. in the pound, nor great tithes 5s. This must obviously be extremely reasonable ; and I can add, from a very minute investigation of the fact, that not one rector in ten takes his tithes in kind; and I heard only of one or two vicars who did so, and who were probably driven to this measure, by the stubborn opposition of their parishioners*. Yet notwithstanding this indulgence, I will not disguise that complaints exist of the hardship of tithes from the farmer, and of the unpleasant situation in which the incumbent is sometimes placed, by trying to raise his humble benefice to two-thirds, or even one-half of its real worth. Hence there must be something radically wrong in a system, which excites prejudices in the most liberal and enlightened minds, and which equally militates against the interests of religion and the interests of agriculture."

Under this liberal impression Dr. M. adverts to a COMMUTATION of TITHES.—His thoughts on the subject are clearly expressed in the subjoined extract.—P. 94. " A corn-rent alone is found to be an inadequate mode of commutation ; but taking the three great articles of life in every family, *bread, meat,* and *malt,* the clergyman would be secure

" * I will candidly own, that except in extreme cases, it is seldom beneficial to the clergy to take up their tithes. The expence of servants and horses, and the charge of poor rates, to which they are thus rendered liable, must inevitably absorb all the profits which can accrue, over and above the terms of a fair composition, while the chance of being unpopular or unhappy, must be increased in a tenfold degree."

cure from injury, and the farmer paying only in proportion to the value of his produce, would have no reason to complain. It will be observed, however, that I wish the laws uniformly to act for the benefit and security of the parochial minister, without subjecting him to the necessity of coming forward in a personal and partial light. By these means, what he might lose in the influence of fear, would be amply compensated for on the principle of love; without which he can seldom be happy himself, or discharge the duties of his sacred office with effect and satisfaction.

"Where lands have been exonerated from tithes by an act of parliament, and an allotment made in land in lieu of them, even where an adequate value has been given, which in no instance that has fallen within my notice is really the case, it is throwing too much land into mortmain, it is subjecting the incumbent to all the cares and incumbrances of landed property, and driving him to the necessity of becoming a farmer, for which he is often ill qualified, or of letting his lands, according to the existing laws, on such conditions, that improvement must be checked, and industry languish."

Tithe of *Wood.*—P. 99. "Vicars are usually entitled to the tithe of woods. At Hurley, a composition, under a decree of chancery, which has been hitherto acquiesced in, though certainly not binding, is paid in lieu of nine loads of billet wood, at the rate of 12s. per load, though the fair value is from 36s. to 42s. per load. Even the nine loads of billet wood seem to have been a still more ancient composition, in lieu of the value of the tithes, on cutting the woods formerly belonging to Lord Lovelace."

Other *ancient Customs,* in Berkshire, relating to Tithes.—P. 99. "The parishioners who pay tithes to my respected friend, the vicar of Cumner, formerly one of the largest parishes in the county, have a claim of being entertained at the vicarage, on the afternoon of Christmasday, with four bushels of malt brewed into ale and beer, two bushels of wheat made into bread, and ½ cwt. of cheese. An allowance in money is now made in lieu of this singular entertainment.

"At Southmoreton, where there are four tithings, one of them belongs to the rector *solely,* and another *jointly* with a layman, in which the tithes are taken in kind, and their produce being divided into five parts, the rector has two of them. The other tithings are in lay hands."

INLAND NAVIGATION.—The Reporter appears to have paid particular attention to this important branch of political economy, in a populous Country. In the section, " Navigable Rivers and Canals," we find interesting accounts of the

the navigations of the *rivers Thames* and *Kennet; of the Kennet and Avon Canal,* and of the *Wiltshire and Berkshire Canal.*

The subjoined extracts convey an interesting account of the INLAND TRAFFIC of a rich and populous line of Country.

P. 427 " Berks, though an inland county, has peculiar advantages in respect to its navigations. The river Thames, which forms its boundary on the north and north-eastern side; the river Kennet, and the Kennet and Avon canal, which pass through the most southern parishes for nearly three-fifths of its extent; and that part of the Wilts and Berks canal, nearly executed, within its limits, on the north-west, have precluded the necessity of projecting any future increase of navigations within the county. Upon inspection of the map, it will be perceived, that in the western division of it, no part of the area of the triangle formed by the Thames on the north-east, by the Kennet on the south, and by the Wilts and Berks canal on the west, is distant more then twelve miles from water carriage; and in the east and south-eastern parts, when we consider that the Basingstoke canal is carried in a line nearly parallel to, and only about eight miles distant from its southern boundary, we find in that division of the county no place more than twelve miles distant, either from that navigation, the Thames, or the Kennet.

" Of all these navigations, the first in importance is the river Thames, almost the whole of whose navigable stream, not within the jurisdiction of the corporation of the city of London, washes the borders of this county in a circuitous course of nearly 105 miles. For neither Lechdale, to the west, where it first becomes navigable, nor Staines, to the east, where the city jurisdiction commences, are far from the limits of Berkshire.

" The antiquity of the navigation of this river may be traced beyond any records of parliament, to the reigns of Henry II. and III., at which time it appears, that barges *(naves)* brought down wood for firing from the upper part of the Thames to London. For the passage of these barges, a custom or toll, called 'avalagium,' was paid, which having been farmed, appears to have been part of the royal revenue."

P. 431. " From Lechlade to Staines stone, the distance is 108 miles, the fall being 225 feet; and as the fall from Staines to the tide-way at Brentford is 45 feet, the total height of Lechdale above the sea appears to be about 270 feet."

P. 433. " The exports from the country adjacent to this river consist of corn, wool, timber, and woodland produce. Corn is conveyed principally in its manufactured state, as flour,

flour, meal, or malt; there being many considerable mills seated on the river, and supplied by its stream. The principal mills subservient to manufacturing purposes are the Temple copper mills, near Marlow, and several paper mills, seated on the short but rapid stream of the Wye, which flows into the Thames, at a little above Cookham, and below Marlow. Beech in timber, plank, and billet for the bakers in London, and various other uses, makes a large proportion of the downward trade, from the Oxfordshire and Buckinghamshire wharfs.

"From Lechlade and Abingdon are sent considerable quantities of cheese, the produce of the rich pastures of Gloucester and North Wiltshire, as well as of the dairying parts of Berks.

"The imports, or upward freight to the above places, consist of those commodities which now form so large a proportion of the necessaries and comforts of a British population—Such are the productions of the East and West Indies, the Baltic, the Mediterranean, and the South Sea, through the port of London. Newcastle coal is conveyed upwards as far as Abingdon and Wallingford; but at these places, and at Reading, its consumption is now limited, by the Staffordshire coal brought down the Oxford canal, and by Shropshire and Welch coal brought down the Thames and Severn canal. There are, however, express statutes to prevent coal, brought down the Oxford or Wilts and Berks canal, from being carried down the Thames lower than Reading. No kind of manure seems to have found its way generally up the Thames, except woollen rags, which are sold in considerable quantities at Reading, Henley, and Marlow. Coal ashes have scarcely ever been brought up higher than Maidenhead or Marlow, peat ashes, which will be particularly mentioned hereafter, being more generally sold as a manure at the wharfs between Maidenhead and Wallingford, a distance of nearly forty miles. Exclusive, however, of the produce and manufactures of the county more immediately adjoining, by its communication with other navigations, the division of the Thames, which we have been describing, conveys the produce and merchandize of very distant counties, to and from London. The Thames and Severn canal connects it with the river Severn, and consequently with all ports, upwards as well as downwards, on that river:— with Wales, and circuitously with Bristol. The Oxford canal unites it with the various navigations of the North, with Birmingham, Manchester, and Liverpool."

In the "conclusion" of the body of the Work is inserted a paper of Mr. PAGE,—on the "System of Improvement by Pond Locks, as practised on the Thames;"—together with

remarks

remarks (by the Reporter?) on facilitating the passage, by water, from the Thames, above Windsor, to the Metropolis *.

ROADS.—This is another favorite topic of the Reporter; and the only one, I think, on which he speaks as a *practical man.*

P. 422. " On the facility of communication, and consequently the goodness of the roads, not only the comforts of residence, but agricultural improvements and advantages materially depend. Few places in this county are above three miles from some good turnpike road; yet it is necessary to limit this commendation of *good.* Indiscriminate censure or praise is generally unjust. If much has been done, much more might be effected towards the improvement of the public roads, as the materials are generally excellent, and the revenues ample. Throughout the greatest part of Berkshire we find fine gravel, flints, or calcareous stone near at hand; and it is therefore the fault of the trustees if the roads are not put and kept in the most perfect repair. But in many places, even in the line of the great roads, they are not sufficiently raised in the middle, the water tables † are neither regularly made, nor with proper outlets towards the ditches; and the ditches themselves are not scoured, or the hedges cut, where it might be equally beneficial to the roads and to the contiguous grounds.

" In some places, I believe the baneful practice of letting the roads by contract per mile prevails. Where this is the case, the contractor will do as little as he can help for his money; he must naturally be expected to make a profit by his engagement; and that neatness, which is so cheap under a better system, and those improvements which mark attention, and are so delightful to the eye of the traveller, are either wholly neglected, or but slovenly performed."

P. 423. " From long observation, and taking an active part in the management of a particular road of great travelling, I am convinced that the only effectual means of improving or keeping up roads, is to have an honest and intelligent surveyor, at a suitable salary, whose business it is to superintended the whole line, to pay the labourers, to call out the statute duty, observe the directions of the commissioners, and to be responsible to them. It is proper, likewise, that he should have a kind of foreman, at the increased

---

* See my observations on the VALE of LONDON; prefixed to the 8vo Edition of the MINUTES of AGRICULTURE, in the Southern Counties, on this interesting topic.

† *Water Table* is a west of England term (rather ill chosen) for the draining channel, on the side of a barreled road, to convey away the rain water that may fall upon it.

POLITICAL ECONOMY.

creased pay of 1s. 6d. or 2s. extra per week, over every groupe of four or five men along the road, who is to labour with them, to see that they do their duty, and to report from time to time to the surveyor, whose utmost vigilance will often be ineffectual without such assistance. I have seen the beneficial effects of this plan, both as to the quantity of labour performed, and the mode in which it is done, and I humbly beg leave to recommend it where it has not hitherto been acted on."

Not even a well experienced Road Surveyor, retiring from business, could have dictated more appropriate directions, on the management of roads, on a large scale. They are evidently tne dictates of much thought and experience. They might well be brought forward in evidence that, had the writer of them turned his attention to practical agriculture, for a due length of time, he might have demanded a place among the first class of cultivators.

MARKETS.—In a *compound* section (a tough morsel for an analyser to digest)—entitled "Towns, Fairs, Weekly Markets, Commerce and Maufactures,"—the several market towns of Berkshire are topographically, but briefly, described; and their specific differences spoken of, under the above named heads.

Ilsley.—Fairs.—P. 455. "August 26; usually called lamb fair, the largest in the year. At this fair, upwards of 30,000 sheep, of various breeds and ages, and many from a great distance, have been exposed to sale. Stationary pens for sheep line the streets, at all times of the year.

"An All Hallows tide fair was mentioned to me; but I do not find it noticed in the almanacks.

"Markets. The market-day is on Wednesday. Little business done, except in sheep. The grand sheep markets begin at Easter, and continue every fortnight till shearing time. Twenty thousand sheep have been collected at one of these markets, which are six or seven annually: the average number during their continuance may be taken at 15,000, as I learned from the principal proprietors of the pens."

Newbury.—P. 458. "The weekly market is on Thursday, and is one of the largest for grain, in this part of the kingdom. The quality, as it arises from various soils within the distance of 20 miles in some directions, is adapted for every purpose that can be required. One sack out of a parcel is pitched; the rest is delivered into granaries, erected near the wharf. The corn-porters, a body of men who are much trusted, though under no particular responsibility, transact the greatest part of the business. They probably owe their origin and support, to the indolence and opulence of the farmers.

"Though

" Though a pitched market, small quantities of corn are not easily procured. The market commences about eleven o'clock, and is over by one. After dinner, the sales are paid for; the waggons return with the sacks, and the farmer with his money.

" Tolls are taken at the rate of a quart in a quarter, or eight bushels. They are now let for 365 *l.* per ann. and probably produce double that sum in gross to the renter; which may give some idea of the quantity of grain sold here."

Reading.—P. 464. " The principal market-day on Saturdays. Corn pitched. Not less than 100 loads of wheat sold weekly, and other grain in proportion. Begins at nine o'clock, and is finished in about an hour and a half, when the farmers return with their money and sacks. Toll a quart per quarter. The Winchester bushel used here.

" The wheat sold at Reading market is peculiarly excellent, and the flour is much esteemed."

Windsor.—P. 470. " The weekly market by charter is on Saturdays, and is well attended. Corn is pitched, but it is said that too much is sold privately, by sample. The tolls are a pint out of every sack."

In all other markets of Berkshire, corn is sold by sample.

An evil of pitching markets appears in a note, p. 398. (section " Horses")—" The *first* teams, as they are called, which may be seen every market day at Newbury and Reading, are a most wanton expence. These pampered animals seem only intended for pomp and parade; and the *first* carter, who attends them, is probably equally useless. But why, it will be asked, may not state horses be kept for a waggon as well as for a coach? I confess the question is not easily answered."

SOCIETIES of AGRICULTURE.—P. 498. " An Agricultural Society was established in this county in 1794, on a scale so extensive, and for purposes so multifarious, that if its objects could have been accomplished, a parochial report of Berkshire would have long since been in its archives, from which the most valuable and minute information might have been obtained. Unfortunately the wheels of the machine were too numerous and complicated, to act by voluntary motion. Sub-committees were appointed in eight different districts, consisting of the chief proprietors and practical farmers in each, with their separate local clerks; and queries were circulated, and premiums proposed with judgment and discrimination, but without producing the intended effect. Subscribers were to pay a guinea or half a guinea annually; and a general committee, consisting of the most intelligent and respectable gentlemen, selected from the sub-committees, was to carry on the correspondence, and to convene the subscribers when they judged it expedient."

P. 499.

P. 499. " At length, in 1800, many gentlemen who had belonged to the original institution, and others who felt the propriety of supporting such an useful establishment, and who were animated, by royal example, to give a new stimulus to agricultural pursuits, agreed to subscribe in the same proportions as before, to simplify the mode of conducting business by having only one committee and one clerk."—An institute, this, which, it appears, continued at the time of the Reporter's survey.

SUBJECT THE THIRD.

RURAL ECONOMY.

TENANTED ESTATES.

ESTATES.—P. 49. " On a moderate calculation, the landed property, including houses, mills, and other productive revenue, arising from, or attached to the soil, cannot amount to less than 500,000l. per annum. Of this sum, the largest possessor in the county may probably have about 8000l. a year ; a few more may have estates to the value of 5, 6, or 7000l.; but great land owners are rare, either among peers or commoners: of the former Earl Craven has the largest possessions ; of the latter E. L. Loveden, Esq. In the lower part of the county, indeed, property is least divided, though every where we find a respectable number of yeomanry ; in the upper part, we see several handsome seats with land not exceeding 100 acres."

PURCHASE of Estates.—P. 51. " It is difficult to say, with any degree of accuracy, what may be the present value of freehold estates. An old, or an improved rent, exoneration from tithes or from land tax, the advantages of situation, and the magnitude of the purchase, are all to be taken into the account, and considerably influence the price. According to circumstances, the minimum may be about twenty-six years purchase, and the maximum thirty-five, at a fair nett rent. The average, however, will not exceed twenty-eight years."

TENURES.—P. 52. " By far the greatest part of the land is freehold, a kind of tenure which possesses the most numerous advantages with the fewest inconveniences.

" I have found, however, in different parts of the county considerable portions of copyhold lands, held by different tenures, according to the customs of the respective manors. In some places, the lords are disposed, on equitable terms, to enfranchise their tenants. Lord Kensington has done so
at

at Cholsey, and the practice is to be commended; as holding courts is seldom beneficial to the lord, and is often attended with expences and disadvantages to the tenant."

P. 54. "Leases on lives, and leases renewable every seven
years under deans and chapters, and other corporate bodies,
are not unfrequent in this county."

"Some few estates are held by leases of 1000 years:
others are leased on single or on three lives, by individual
land owners; but this practice is not common, and renewals,
where it exists, are generally refused."

EMBANKMENT.—For a *want* of it, see *Grass Lands*, ensuing.

IRRIGATION.—P. 370. "About Abingdon are some water
meadows; and the practice on a small scale has been introduced in other places; but on the long line of the
Thames winter floods are the principal fructifiers of the soil,
and they sometimes lie too long. Common meadows, which
are frequent, are the best excuse for the neglect they
they experience.

"On the Kennet there are several hundreds of acres of
water meadow, more especially between Hungerford and
Newbury; between the last named place and Reading they
are less frequent*."

TENANCY.—*Leases.*—This subject is twice brought forward; and treated of at some length. The Reporter's
remarks upon it however, tho sometimes ingenious, are
altogether unavailing, *under existing circumstances.*—Having repeatedly offered my sentiments on this topic, in the
course of my present undertaking, I will confine my attention, here, to what is reported of the present practice of
Berkshire.

P. 112. "Except some old leases of twenty-one years,
nearly expired, I found few recent instances of so long a
term, certain. Fourteen years appears to be the longest
term granted within the last seven years, and I heard of
several leases for only five, seven, or ten years certain.
The prevailing practice undoubtedly is determinable leases,
at the option of either party, for seven, fourteen, and
twenty-one years."

P. 90. "Many instances occur where the same race of
tenants, and the same race of proprietors have for generations maintained an unbroken connection, which is equally
creditable to both."

RENT.

"* Were Theale meadow, in the parish of Tilehurst, thrown into
severalty and watered, it would be astonishingly valuable. In many
other parishes, irrigation is rendered impossible from the nature of the
tenure. It is the want of a general inclosure, not the farmer that is to
be blamed, for many apparent neglects in improvement."

RENT.—In the section, " Size of Farms," the average rent, in each parish, in every district of the County, is set down.   The general average " of land of every description" is put (p. 88.) " at about 1*l.* 1*s.*"

RECEIVING RENTS.—P. 89. " According to the best information, they allow from three to six months rent in hand."

WOODLANDS.

I HAD vainly hoped that I should have passed through the volume now under review, without being subjected to the painful task of censure; until I entered on the chapter " Woods and Plantations;" where my approbation was forcibly arrested, by the following passage.

P. 307. " Oak, elm, and ash, within the last twenty years, are nearly doubled in price;* yet this has not operated in favor of new plantations, in any degree equal to the consumption of the old.   The cause is obvious, and nothing but legislative authority can check the evil.   When neither the interests of descendants, nor the public welfare, have any effect on the conduct of proprietors of woodlands, it is time that the controul should be delegated to other hands, and that the sanctions and inflictions of laws should be called in as auxiliaries to produce what a sense of duty fails to do.

" On private estates in general, no sooner is a difficulty felt, or an incumbrance to be wiped off, than the axe is applied to the patrimonial groves, and the fond hopes and prudent cares of a virtuous ancestry are sacrificed to some temporary accommodation of their posterity.   It is nothing unusual, indeed, for a father to join his next heir, even when estates are entailed, and waste cannot be safely committed by either singly, in cutting down timber, and dividing the produce, in order to support their respective extravagance and love of dissipation.   But no sooner does a young man come to the possession of his estate, than he commonly strips it of its woods; and lets in the light, as it is termed, on his native mansion, in order to discharge the debts he has often wantonly contracted.   A law, therefore, to restrain any person from cutting down trees, not arrived at *perfection*" (*!*) "and to oblige him to plant *two* in a *suitable situation*

* The market value of money had, at the time of reporting, been reduced, during that period, in nearly equal proportion.

situation" (*!!*) " in the room of each felled, could neither be arbitary nor unjust."!!! *

The chapter under notice occupies twentyfour pages of the volume; chiefly with an elaborate detail of " Forest Trees" growing in various parts of Berkshire; each species being separately treated of. In that detail, however, we meet with little that is interesting.—The *Beech* appears to be a prevailing species, and we are told the woods of it are generally well managed.

The subjoined extract conveys a concise yet intelligent sketch of the *natural woods* of the County under Report.— P. 312. " The best wooded tracks in Berkshire, exclusive of the Forest, are to the south of the Kennet, several parishes on the north, and along the banks of the Thames, at intervals, and some miles interior, from Streatley to Cookham, where there are entire woods of beech. Bagley wood, near Oxford, likewise deserves to be particularized. Except in hedge rows, or in parks, the greatest part of the standard trees grows in those districts. The whole quantity of wood land exceeds 30,000 acres."

Planting.—On this operation, not much is said. Berkshire is not, emphatically speaking, a planting County. Dr. M. names some few gentlemen planters; particularly Mr. Loveden, who has planted about 200 acres.

AGRICULTURE.

FARMS.—*Sizes.*—In the legitimate section, " Size of Farms," the annual rents of farms, and the rental value of land, by the acre, in the several parishes of the County— classed according to its natural districts,—are noted. By that list, the sizes of farms in Berkshire rise from 40 or 50 to 300 or 400*l.* a year. A few to 500 or 600*l* The Reporter at the close of it, says, p 88, " on the whole, I think I am warranted in taking the average rent of farms throughout the county at 150*l.* a year."—Hence, let it be said, Berkshire is fortunately circumstanced, regarding the sizes of its farms.

HOMESTEADS.—Of *Yeomen.*—P. 62. " In passing through a part of Berkshire where yeomanry abound, and where their residences have an air of gentility, and frequently of elegance,

* For the mischievous tendency of such a law, see almost every volume I have written. See, also, James and Co.'s Hampshire, ensuing.

elegance, a youth who accompanied me, and who belonged to a county not remarkable for good farm houses, several times asked me, as he came in sight of a Berkshire farmer's habitation, ' What gentleman's seat is this?'

" I do not, however, mean from this to infer that these houses are too good; but I wish to mark the impression their appearance made, when contrasted with a neighbouring county. A yeoman possessing from 200*l.* to 600*l.* a year in landed property, and who occupies his domain himself, may well rank with a gentleman of three times the nominal income, who lives solely on his rent, and is entitled to every corresponding accommodation."

Of *Tenants.*—P. 65. " The farm buildings belonging to the rack-renters and lifehold tenantry, and more especially such as have no leases, are generally inferior to those of the yeomanry, and the tenure may in some measure be discovered by the style of the accommodations."

Some *gentlemen's* farmeries—particularly Mr. Loveden's—are noticed.

Materials of Farm Buildings.—P. 67. " In the eastern parts of the county, and along the line of the Kennet, the farm buildings are commonly of brick, tiled, and possess some degree of elegance. In the north-western parts they are chiefly of stone, covered with Oxfordshire slates; and on the whole are inferior in appearance and accommodations. Too many of the outhouses and barns are still thatched, a mode of covering not less dangerous than expensive, if the frequency of repairs be taken into the account. The practice, however, is gradually discontinuing, and in another age will probably become obsolete."

OCCUPIERS.—*Proprietors.*—P. 113. " From the most accurate calculations I have been able to make, about one-third of the whole county is occupied by the proprietors of the soil."

Yeomen.—P. 50. " In the parish of Winkfield, consisting of nearly 10,000 acres, the largest estate is under 400 acres; nor is this moderate distribution unusual in many other parishes of Berkshire. Hence, a high spirited and independent yeomanry, actively engaged in agricultural pursuits, and each forming a circle of connection around him, is the distinguishing character of the county. The gradations of society have here no broken links: from the highest to the lowest, there is a gradually ascending or descending scale. In such a state we may look for patriotism without interest, and a display of generous feelings without the dread of offence. It is here that the influence of love can do much; the influence of power or property, little. It was observed on a particular occasion by the late lamented Mr. Pitt, and I quote

quote the *dictum* on the authority of a highly respectable gentleman to whom it was made, ' that no minister of this country could command ten votes in Berkshire.' This sufficiently marks the independence of the county, and is the highest eulogium that can be paid to it."

Tenants.—P. 89. " Without any partial praise, the character of the Berkshire farmer unquestionably deserves to stand high. The yeomanry have already been mentioned with due applause; and the influence of their example descends to the rack-renters," (tenants) " many of whom are not inferior in point of education and manners, and in the spirit with which they carry on agricultural improvements, when circumstances allow them to exert their native energies.

" In short, a hospitable style of living, liberality of sentiment, and independence of principle, are characteristic of the Berkshire farmer, to which he unites persevering industry and integrity in his dealings, which render him worthy of the comforts he enjoys."

PLAN of MANAGEMENT.—The Reporter of Berkshire, in conformity, it would seem, with other Reporters to the Board, has allowed ample space in which to enumerate the " Rotations of Crops." Dr. Mavor's plan of collecting matter for this section differs widely, however, from that of many or most of his fellow-laborers. Instead of listening in conversation to the crude plans of novitial amateurs,—without enquiring as to the soil, situation, or other circumstance,—the Doctor has given us the established practices of professional men; not only in every district of the County, but in several particular parishes in each district; and, in most instances, has informed his readers of the nature of the lands on which the several practices have been established. His own explanation of his plan here follows.

P. 165. " From the variety of soils of which Berkshire consists, a different course of crops, as well as a different mode of tillage, must of necessity be introduced; and on this important point I have studied to inform myself as minutely as possible. Without, however, presuming to censure or applaud every particular practice, I shall lay the rotation of crops at present usually adopted by the best agriculturists before my readers; and in order that others may judge of the propriety or impropriety of the system pursued, shall briefly notice the distinction of soils in the spots brought under review."

As a specimen, I insert the Report of the parish of *Reading*, in the *Valley* of the *Kennet*.

P. 176. " Soil gravel, rich mould, strong clay, and some sand, with chalk as a substratum in several places. Rotation

tion of crops various. Occasionally, 1. Clean fallows; 2. Wheat, with clover in the Spring; 3. Beans; 4. Oats; or if the land is clean, and in good heart, the skim is sometimes used, and with two or three plowings, wheat sown again. On the light gravelly soil, however, another course is in practice. 1. Turnips; 2. Barley and grass; 3. Wheat; 4. Barley, or oats. Spring wheat is sometimes sown after turnips."

I will also insert what is reported of another parish, for the sake of the note appending to it.—P. 175. " Shalbourn✳. Strong deep soil, some flint and gravel. Well adapted for beans and wheat, which are the staple produce. The same applies to *Inkpen*, &c."

WORKPEOPLE.—*General Character.*—P. 481. " The lower classes are a hardy and personable race, patient of labour, but impatient of control, when they think it improperly exerted. In a word, they have a laudable pride, which, properly regulated, might be productive of the best consequences, and would lead to that *love* of *independence*,† which I assume as the foundation of all moral excellence; because it cannot be separated from industry, frugality, and honorable conduct !"

Labourers.—P. 415. " A day labourer is paid from 9s. to 12s. per week, according to situation : the more remote from the metropolis, and from towns, the lower the wages in general. In towns, a labourer will sometimes have 14s. per week allowed him. A woman will occasionally earn 3s. or 4s., and a boy from 2s. to 3s. 6d."

Servants.—P. 416. " Farmers in general keep no more servants in the house than they can possibly help. A carter is paid from nine to twelve guineas a year; an under carter from

" ✳ Prosperous Farm, in this parish, was the spot where Mr. Jethro Tull carried on and perfected his interesting experiments in the horse hoeing husbandry. He died in 1740."

† *Love of Independence.*—These might be deemed dangerous words, when speaking *in a general way* of the laboring classes. It is a love of independence, among those whom circumstances have doomed to labor for a scanty living, that breeds Poachers, Smugglers, Highwaymen and Housebreakers.

It is, nevertheless, a cardinal virtue in a farm workman, in the first instance, to do his best endeavor to render himself and his family *independent of charity.* His next virtuous pride is that of inhabiting a cottage and garden which he can call his own : and the highest, to occupy a small tenement, as a working farmer.—Such, I conceive, are the sorts of independence which ought to be *expressly* held out, as belonging to servants and workmen in husbandry. These remarks are not particularly pointed at Dr. Mavor. Others of the Board's Reporters have conveyed similar sentiments, in a less guarded manner.

from four to seven guineas; a shepherd from eight to ten
guineas, and the run of a few sheep; a boy from two to three
guineas; a dairy maid from five to ten guineas, according
to her qualifications; a house maid from five to seven
guineas."

" *Nurseries* of *Servants.*—P. 416. It is greatly to be lamented, that good servants every year become more scarce
and difficult to be found. The best domestics used to be
found among the sons and daughters of little farmers; they
were brought up in good principles, and in habits of industry; but since that valuable order of men has been so
generally reduced in every county, and almost annihilated in
some, servants are of necessity taken from a lower description
of persons, and the consequences are felt in most families."

There is much truth in those remarks. But they more
closely apply to the servants of gentlemen, clergy, and
others, than to mere farm servants.

WORKING ANIMALS.—For the Breed of Working *Horses*,
see that article, ensuing.

For the folly attached to *Horse Teams*, see *Markets*,
p. 75, aforegoing.

Plow Team.—N. P. 121. "With the heavy Berkshire two
wheel plough, four horses, two abreast, are commonly used
when the land is pretty dry; or four at length, when wet,
sometimes five!"

Comparison of Horses with *Oxen.*—I find nothing under
this head that requires notice, here, expecting the opinion
of "Mr. Frost, his Majesty's Bailiff" on this unsettled point.
—P. 403. " I am clear in my opinion, that if oxen were
properly attended to, we should be able to maintain one-
third more people in England, and feed them with more
animal food."

IMPLEMENTS.—To this popular subject, among men of
genius and inexperience, some considerable share of attention has been paid, in the Report now under consideration. Twenty pages of letterpress, and twentyseven engravings have been *expended* on its elucidation.—In examining
the Reporter's chapter " Implements of Husbandry," with
wonted solicitude, my attention was rarely stayed. The
few short passages that follow were the only ones which employed my pencil in marking my approval.

Waggon.—P. 118. "Mr. Loveden, whose name is so often
mentioned with deserved respect in this Report, puts narrow fore-wheels to his *waggons*, and broad behind, in order
to prevent injury to tender grass land. The hind wheels
roll over the track made by the fore, and cancel the mischief they have done."—This happy thought I register,
here, with peculiar interest.

Plows.

Plows.—P. 121. " On the authority of well informed men in different parts of the county, I am able to state, that this implement is now as much used to humour the prejudices of the plowman, as because his master thinks it necessary to till his land properly.   With a *two wheel plough*, the holder may stare round him, crack his jokes with the plowboy, or even occasionally ride on the stilts, that the horses may have still a stronger draught; while with a swing or a chain plough, his attention must be constantly directed to his business."

Mole Plow.—P. 124. " Mr. Loveden, of Buscot Park, who is distinguished for the variety and utility of his agricultural implements, has a plough of this kind, by Lumbert, and improved by himself, which is drawn by one horse, and sometimes by women, as occasion requires."*

Thrashing Mills.—P. 129. " Within the last two or three years a considerable number of threshing machines, on different principles, and of different powers, have been erected in Berkshire."

Winnowing Mills.—P. 128. " The common flap winnower, which from its rudness seems to have been invented within a century of the Deluge, is not yet discarded."

MANURES.—*Yard Dung.*—P. 358. " Yard or pot dung is generally preferred when rotten."

Chalk and *Lime.*—P. 361. " About Hurley, Wargrave, and other places in the eastern part of the county, chalk pits of a good quality are to be found; and chalk is frequently in use as a manure."

" Lime made from chalk would probably answer where the raw material will not."—This seems to indicate that chalk lime is not in use, as a manure, in Berkshire.

Marl.—P. 362. " Though marl is probably abundant in this county, it does not appear to be much used.   Sir John Throckmorton has found it very serviceable.   The shell marl, *over* the peat in the Vale of the Kennet, has not been employed, as far as I know, in manuring."

Peat Ashes.—Berkshire being the principal source of this extraordinary manure,—as set forth in the Reports from Oxfordshire, Buckinghamshire, and Hertfordshire,—an intelligent account of it becomes valuable; and the agricultural public are much indebted to Dr. Mavor for the following interesting particulars, concerning " Newbury Ashes."

Origin

---

* A man must be a Stoic whom this could not interest.   A valuable implement, whose only demerit, at the time of its being first in use, was that of its requiring eight or ten horses to work it, is now, through the *magic of invention*, drawn by one horse;—even by women!

Orign and *Nature* of the Berkshire *Peat Bogs.*—P. 28. " The vale of the Kennet is remarkable for producing a peculiar kind of peat ; and along the whole course of the river from Hungerford to Reading, a distance of nearly thirty miles, this valuable article, both for fuel and manure, is found at intervals in different states of perfection, or has been already exhausted. As the outlet of the Kennet into the Thames at Reading is confined by rising grounds, it is probable that the original channel was too narrow to allow the waters a free efflux, and thus being thrown back, they formed a morass for many miles above the obstruction. We learn likewise, from ancient records, that Windsor forest once extended up the vale of the Kennet to Hungerford, and that this track was disforested by charter, in 1226. Hence it is easy to account for the accumulation of peat, by the action of the water on decayed trees and other vegetable matter.

" It should, however, be remarked in this place, for the subject is too important not to be resumed, that this peat is very different in its nature from the fibrous mosses, which grow again, after a certain number of years, from the same causes that produced them at first. Here these causes no longer operate; and therefore when the peat land is once dug out, it must be applied to some other purpose, either to the formation of water meadow or osier beds, according to circumstances and situation. Much is already exhausted, and much more cannot be brought into use, from that bane to all agricultural improvement—the right of commons. The present digging commences within two miles of Hungerford, and is carried on at intervals to Woolhampton, where the stratum approaches close to the Bath road. Such is the value of good peat land, that Charles Dundas, Esq. M. P. assured me, in making some exchanges of property, fortytwo acres of this description belonging to him were estimated at 30,000*l.*"

P. 358. " Though it is probable that peat, nearly of the same nature as that along the Kennet, is to be found in other parts of the kingdom, its general application as a top dressing to clovers, and other artificial grasses, to turnips, to vetches, and even occasionally on wheat, is perhaps unique in this county :"—and its environs.

History and *Practice* of *burning Peat.*—P. 359. " In the year 1745 it was first burnt at Newbury, by a Mr. Thomas Rudd, who at the same time spread the ashes on clovers, for which they have ever since been famous. An acre of peat land at that period sold for 30*l.* : it has since sold, according to its quality, for 300*l.* and 400*l.*, and in one instance reached about 800*l.* per acre.

" Over

"Over the stratum of peat, which is about five or six feet deep is a good meadow soil, and under the peat is gravel. The peat varies in colour, but the blackest is reckoned the best, and is used for firing, the ashes of which are most esteemed, and have the reddest colour. What is burnt for sale only, is mixed with turf and other substances, which gives it a pale whitish hue.

"Peat is usually dug with a spade for that purpose, resembling those used in Scotland, from the middle of May to the end of June. It is conveyed from the spot where it is dug, in little wheel-barrows, to a short distance, where it is spread on the ground, and after lying about a week, the pieces are turned. This being three or four times repeated, a heap is made in the middle of the place where the peat is spread, and in the centre of this heap some very dry peat is put, which being lighted, the fire communicates slowly to the rest of the heap. When it is completely lighted, an additional quantity of peat is put upon the heap, and this operation is continued till the whole is consumed, which generally takes a month or six weeks, as quick burning is not approved of. Rain seldom penetrates deep enough to extinguish the fire. The heap is commonly of a circular form, and rather flat at top. At first it is very small; but at last it is sometimes two or three yards deep, and six or seven yards in diameter.

"The ashes being riddled, are conveyed away in uncovered carts, to a distance sometimes of twenty miles, and put into a house, or under a shade, to keep them from the wet, till they are wanted to be put on the ground."

P. 360. "The *price* at Newbury wharf is from fourpence to fivepence per bushel. At Reading, sevenpence or eightpence. With the distance, the price varies of course. Carried to Bisham, the expence of manuring an acre will be about 15s."

Sheepfold.—P. 358. "The folding of sheep continues to be almost the universal practice in this county; and on the hills, it is nearly the only manure attainable. On turnips, the sheep are hurdled, and the fold gradually extended for the future crop of barley. They are likewise folded at night on land intended for wheat, on all the light soils more especially; and in this situation it is calculated that their manure is worth 5s. per week per score. The horned sheep, or Wiltshires, and the native Berkshire notts, are most esteemed for folding on fallows."

TILLAGE.—*Fallowing.*—P. 160. (The Reporter's section "Fallowing") "It was the observation of the most distinguished personage in this kingdom, and which deserves to be written in letters of gold, "THAT THE GROUND, LIKE MAN,

MAN, WAS NEVER INTENDED TO BE IDLE; IF IT DOES NOT
PRODUCE SOMETHING USEFUL, IT WILL BE OVER RUN WITH
WEEDS."

I must not allow, even an L.L.D. to propagate false
doctrine, *in Agriculture.*—Error and inconsistency, with
some semblance of truth and common sense, were never
more intimately blended, than in the above quotation.—
For, be it known unto all men,—THE MAIN PURPORT OF
FALLOWING IS TO DESTROY WEEDS;—not to propagate
them; nor to give them an opportunity to propagate them-
seves—*in an " idle" hour!*

Try we to illustrate this truth, in a familiar, not a fastidious way.—Most men of negligent habits are liable, like
neglected lands, " to be out of order;" and to require a
puke or a purge, or both, to renovate their health, and enable them to perform their offices, with due effect. Most authors, I wot, and some of their readers, will feel the force
of this fact.

In like manner, when lands have been kept in a state of
aration, and have acquired a *foulness of habit*, it becomes
indispensibly requisite, to accurate treatment, that a
course of medicine should be persevered in, until a *radical
cure* be effected.

The renovating medicine—the sovereign remedy—in this
case, is FALLOWING; which is capable of doing more
service to agriculture, and of course to the community, in
six, twelve, or eighteen months (according to the inveteracy
of the case) than can be effected, in as many years, by
tampering with the " TULLIAN HUSBANDRY."

After a well directed course of TILLAGE has re-estab-
lished the wonted tone and exertion of a soil, and radically
cleansed it from weeds and vermin,—*then*, may the children
of Jethro amuse themselves, *for a while*, with their *superficial system.*

SEMINATION.—*Drilling.*—P. 126. (Section " Drills")
" Sir John Throckmorton, Bart , O. Williams, Esq. M. P.,
and some other gentlemen, use drill machines for grain as
well as pulse; but the practice is not common in this
county."—Yet Berkshire, we are informed, was not merely
the cradle of Drilling, but the theatre on which it was
" carried on and perfected." (!). Again,

P. 187. " Sowing broad cast has numerous advocates, and
is the prevailing practice in this county; but it is not exclusively so. It is the avowed opinion, however, of Mr.
Frost, his Majesty's baliff, that all kinds of grain produce
most by the acre when sown broad cast, and I found he was
not singular in this belief."

ARABLE CROPS.—Most of the crops that are cultivated,
in

in English husbandry, are touched upon, in the Report under notice.

WHEAT.—This crop is spoken of, at some length, and in a degree analytically.—But, after an attentive perusal of the section, I perceive but few practical ideas that are suitable for transplantation. Many ingenious theories are observable, and many useful practices are noticed; but very few that are singular, or particularly eligible.

Time of Sowing Wheat.—In the subsection, " Sort," we meet with the following passage.—P. 185. " It should be remarked, that the later any kind of grain is sown, the the greater quantity of seed will be required, as it has less time to tiller, and therefore the crop must depend chiefly on the principal stalk. This theory may apper novel; but it is offered with diffidence, and solely with the view of inviting inquiry and experiment."

I do not insert this passage as conveying a new idea to agricultural science; it being a received opinion, among practical men, in most districts, that two bushels of wheat, sown in September, are equal to three bushels, sown in November;—but to show Dr. Mavor's right way of thinking, and strength of mind, tempered by well-judged diffidence,—as a theorist.

P. 190. " From the diversity of soils and situations, the seed time varies considerably in this county.

" On the richer soils of the Vale of White Horse, it seldom begins before November, or the corn would be too far advanced before winter. About Faringdon, which, though in the same district, has a less strong soil, if the seed is not committed to the ground before November, it is thought advisable to wait till February, even for lammas wheat. About Buckland, where the soil is still lighter, wheat sowing begins about the middle of September.

" On the downs, it is sown about five weeks or a month before Michaelmas. On very light land as early as August. About Lambourne, which is near the centre of the downs, sowing of wheat is continued from a month before Michaelmas to a fortnight after, except on turnip land, where the vegetation of course is more rapid. That which is earliest sown on the downs and Chalk district in general, is found to be least obnoxious to the blight, and therefore the practice is regulated accordingly.

" In the Vale of the Kennet, wheat is commonly sown from Michaelmas to November.

" In the Forest district, the nature of the soil determines the season when the seed is to be committed to the ground; and it extends from the earliest to the latest period, already mentioned."—This I hesitate not to pronounce—masterly
Report:—

Report:—concise, intelligent, and instructive. Not only are the varying practices clearly described, in a few words, but the *reasons* of them given, as they pass in review.

Produce of Wheat.—P. 196. "From the averages of parishes in the different districts, it appears that the Vale of White Horse yields about four quarters per acre: the best soils five. The Chalk districts from two and a half to three and a half quarters; the light downs from two, to two and a half; the Vale of the Kennet from three to four, the best land more; and the Forest, including his Majesty's highly cultivated farms, from three to four quarters and a half per acre."

Surplus Produce of Wheat.—P. 198. "Besides the internal consumption, and the flour consigned to London, much seed wheat is sold, particularly from the Chalk district, into Gloucestershire, Oxfordshire, and some other counties. This seed has gained high and deserved reputation for its cleanness and its adaptation for other soils, and its sale adds in no small degree to the emoluments of the Berkshire farmer, while it is a source of future wealth to the neighbouring counties. The price of seed wheat being always higher than bread corn, every attention is paid to the goodness of the sample; and the demand is generally equal to the whole quantity that can be spared."

BARLEY.—On this crop, nor on that of OATS, do I find any thing that requires transcription.

BEANS.—*Semination.*—P. 210. "Beans are never sown broad cast in this county. In the eastern parts, or Forest district, and the bordering part of the Chalk district, they are not unfrequently drilled; but from the largeness of the seed, the machines in common use do not always drop them regularly, and therefore present objections to the practice. Indeed, Sir John Throckmorton, who drills all other kinds of grain, dibbles this; and throughout the greatest part of Berkshire, they are put in by the hand. Women and children, as well as men, are employed in this service, which costs about 3s. 4d. or 3s. 6d. per acre, on an average. This operation begins as early in February as the season will allow; but it may be performed as late as March. Early planting, it is thought, is a preservative against the black *aphis.*"

PEAS.—*Semination.*—P. 212. "In the eastern parts of the county, peas are commonly drilled; in others they are dibbled, or sown broad cast, which last is the prevailing practice."

WOAD.—P. 230. "This plant, which delights in a deep
fat

fat friable loam, used to be cultivated about Wantage ; but,
though found very productive, it seems is discontinued."

BULBOUS RAPE.—P. 224. " This species begins to become
a favorite in many parts of Berkshire, though a very few
years ago it was little noticed."

In the APPENDIX is inserted a paper " on *Transplanting*
Sweedish Turneps ; by a BERKSHIRE AGRICULTURIST."

By an incident in practice, the writer was led (as many
an attentive practitioner has fortunately been, in other instances) to a new method of propagating this valuable crop,
—a method which, as an expedient at least, may be found
profitable.   Transplanting this variety of the common rape,
or cole, is nothing new ; nor is the practice of equalizing an
uneven crop, by filling up the vacant ground with super-
numerary plants, drawn from the overstocked parts.   But
transferring such surplus plants to ground that has been
early freed from another crop, as tares or other green herbage, early peas &c., is an idea I have not met with, before.
Yet, in a moist season, and by distributing the fresh drawn
plants, in every *second* furrow,—as the ground is plowed,
in narrow plits or slices,—such a practice, I doubt not,
might frequently be found profitable.

P. 542. " The plants drawn were generally about the
size of a walnut.   I directed two children to follow every
third furrow of the plough, and lay down plants along the
furrow, at about six or eight inches apart; some women
and children followed, and with a planting stick, set the
plants in the furrow."

CULTIVATED HERBAGE.—In a section entitled " Artificial Grasses," the different species of herbage, usually cultivated in English husbandry, are enumerated, and their
several properties commented upon ; but without the looked
for intelligence.—Indeed, there is less of useful information, and more of mistaken suggestion, in this, than in
most other sections of the volume.

GRASS LANDS.—P. 235. " Berkshire being bounded and
intersected by rivers, must consequently have a large proportion of meadows; and if to this we add the dairying
land in the vale, and dry pastures and parks producing
natural grass, the whole quantity cannot be much less than
100,000 acres, or somewhat more than a fifth of the contents of the county, without including the sheep downs on
the Chalk district.

" But considerable as the proportion of grass land may
appear, before the introduction of artificial grasses, it bore
a much higher relative price than it does at present.   In
the reign of Charles II. a small portion of glebe meadow
belonging

belonging to the vicarage of Hurley, on the banks of the
Thames, yielded nearly the same rent as it does at the present time; and I have heard from Mr. Loveden, and other
gentlemen of the county who possess meadow lands, that,
except in the vicinity of towns, where, from the number of
horses kept, accommodation land will let at any price, the
rise of this kind of property has been very trivial, compared
with its intrinsic value, and the advance on arable lands.

"*Thames meadows.*—Along the meandering course of
the Thames, which washes this county for nearly 105 miles,
a track of meadow land, of various breadths, accompanies
its progress, generally of an excellent quality, and from
the fertilizing effects of the water, when accidentally flooded
at favourable seasons, rendered still more productive. But it
is to be lamented, that the facilities which are presented for
artificial watering, are very little attended to on the banks
of the Thames, and that by obstructions, or neglect, the
floods not unfrequently come in when they are least of all
desired, when the grass is far advanced, or when it is nearly
ready to be carried."

Sheep Downs.—P. 324. (Section Wastes.) "With regard
to the downs, however, I am not unaware that many intelligent persons think they ought to remain in their present
state. ' In the hilly part of this county,' says a remarker
on Mr. Pearce, ' those lands which are looked upon as
wastes, are in fact the very support of the farms, which
every good husbandman there will acknowledge. They are
fine healthy downs, which are occupied with the farms as
sheep-walks, the limits whereof are as well known by the
shepherds, and the common consent of the farmers, as if
bounded by hedges. The business done at Ilsley market
will pretty clearly demonstrate them to be the nursery for
sheep. It is the decided opinion of the principal farmers in
that neighbourhood, that the plowing such downs indiscriminately, would, after the first seven years, be the utter
ruin of the farms.'"

Natural Herbage of Grass Lands; and other *indigenous
Plants* of *Berkshire.*—P. 240. "For the following list of
indigenous plants, the most ample, by far, that ever has
been exhibited of this county, I am, in a great measure, indebted to the botanical researches and skill of Dr. Noehe-
den, of Windsor, and Mr. Bicheno, of Newbury. The con-
tributions of the former I owe to the kind attentions of the
Rev. Mr. Townshend, of Bray, to promote the object of
my enquiries."

That list occupies more than forty pages of the work.
The properties of some of the plants, and the habitats, or
locations, of others, are noted.

HOPS.

Hops.—P. 229. " Hops (the *humulus lupulus*) used to
be cultivated formerly in considerable quantities in Berks,
as I have ascertained from old books and records, and now
grow naturally in the hedges in many places, a proof that
the soil is well adapted for them, though at the present
period there are few hop grounds, and those generally in
small patches. The largest is at Faringdon, where ten
acres have long been devoted to the culture of this plant.
A ground of two acres is to be seen at Bisham, said not to
be very productive. At Bradfield, and a few other places,
hops are still cultivated; and formerly at Hurley they were
raised in some quantities."

LIVESTOCK.

P. 372. " The live stock in this county is large, and of
great importance ; but except in sheep and hogs, it has no
native or peculiar breeds."

On the folly of *over-fatting* Livestock.—The subjoined
remarks, on this " modern improvement," are highly creditable to the writer of them.—P. 297. " There has, for some
years been a prevailing rage, a ridiculous kind of competition among graziers, to produce the largest cattle and the
fattest meat. Not only cows and oxen have been loaded
with fat by unnatural food, but sheep have likewise been
commended, not for the sweetness and tenderness of their
flesh, but for their weight per quarter ; though the tallow-
chandler was chiefly benefited by the excess to which fatting has been carried. To produce the greatest quantity of
wholesome food for man in the least time, and at the smallest
expence, is the only criterion of merit in feeding ; it is the
only way to individual profit or public benefit; and I am
happy to find that this fact again begins to be admitted and
acted on. Reason and truth may be clouded for a time,
but they will burst out in brighter lustre than before."

Horses.—P. 396. " The native Berkshire horses are of
the common black race, very strong, and powerful, and
rather of full proportions than tall. In their legs they are
pretty short, in their bodies thick, and their whole figure
indicates strength rather than activity. More, however,
are bought in, from Northamptonshire, &c. as suckers, than
are bred."

P. 397. " Near the forest, and large commons, we find
a poor starved breed, scarcely applicable to any useful purpose, but which, nevertheless, are kept by as many as have
the power and ability, lest they should lose one iota of
their privileges."

Cattle.—*Breed.*—P. 372. " The cattle which are
almost

almost universally adopted here are of the long horned, or common county breed, and differ in nothing from those of Warwickshire, Oxfordshire, and other neighbouring counties."

DAIRY.—*History* of the Berkshire Dairy.—P. 23. " In the western part of this vale the land is chiefly devoted to pasturage, and dairying is carried on to a considerable extent, and with great success. It appears from the Doomsday Survey, that the land was then appropriated to the same purposes as now. At this period, in the parish of Coleshill, consisting of 1,820 acres, only 10 are in culture; and in some other neighbouring parishes, particularly Buscot, Eaton Hastings, Coxwell, Shrivenham, and Uffington, full two-thirds are in grass."

Sizes of Dairies.—P. 377. " Some of the dairy farms are large. Mr. Gearing, one of the Earl of Radnor's tenants in Coleshill parish, keeps about one hundred cows; but this is the greatest number I believe in the possession of one person. The usual number is between twenty and sixty; the last is reckoned a very considerable dairy. About ninety acres of good grass land will carry twenty cows."

Cows of Berkshire.—P. 372. " In the dairying district, many of the cows are brought out of Warwickshire, often with too little attention to their qualities as milkers."

P. 378. " Many calves are bred for stock; but suckling for the butcher is the prevailing practice."

Butter.—P. 374. " Much butter is sent to London. The best butter, or at least what is reputed as such, is made about Wytham, Radley, and other parishes on the Berkshire borders near Oxford, where the land is good, and yet cheese making is little followed. Fine butter, however, is made in most parts of the county."

Cheese.—P. 375. " In the dairying tract, properly so called, which lies at the western extremity of the Vale of White Horse, chiefly within the hundreds of Shrivenham and Faringdon, though partially extending to Ganfield and Wantage, very large quantities of cheese are made during the summer; and here butter making is less an object, except when the cows are at hay or straw.

" The number of cows kept in the parishes of Shrivenham, Coleshill, Buscot, Eaton Hastings, Faringdon, Shellingford, Uffington, Compton, and Kingston Lisle, which are among the principal dairying parishes, from a pretty accurate inquiry, do not amount to fewer than 3,000; and it is probable that the whole number is little less than 5,000, within the compass of the four hundred specified."

" The cheese made here is chiefly of that kind known by the name of single Gloucester. From six to ten cheeses go to a cwt.; usually eight, nine, or ten."

" The quantity made in the whole of the Berkshire dairying

ing tract alone, cannot amount to less than one thousand
tons annually, at the lowest calculation, allowing each cow
to produce four cwt."

Suckling.—P. 375. " In some places, suckling of calves is
so much the pursuit, that it is difficult to purchase even
milk or cream for tea and other purposes."

P. 378. " In the eastern parts of the county, they are
chiefly sent to London in carcase. Chalk or whiting is
allowed them to lick. In other respects the manner of
treating them presents nothing peculiar. ' Suckling is de-
clining about Hurst, as not being found sufficiently profitable.'—Mr. Nicholls."

SHEEP.—Doctor Mavor has paid much attention to this
valuable species of domestic animals, in husbandry ; more
especially to the various *breeds* that were propagated in
Berkshire at the time of his survey.

P. 381. " Berkshire has a *native breed* of sheep, strongly
marked, and though less valued than formerly, still acknowledged to possess many qualities which adapt them to
their situation. The pure race, however, is not so commonly to be met with as many would be apt to imagine.
By crosses, it has undergone several changes, though the
characteristic features of the Berkshire notts, are not easily
obliterated ; and the name continues to be given to the various mixtures, as long as they have black faces, Roman
noses, black or mottled legs, and long tails."

P. 387. " In order to do all the justice in my power to a
subject so essentially connected with the agriculture of
Berks, and to furnish a memorial of the existing breeds,
and the purposes for which they are kept, I shall give brief
miscellaneous extracts from my notes, in some of the principal parishes of the different districts."

On examining those extracts, which occupy eight or nine
pages, it appears that, at the time of writing, the favorite
breeds of professional men, in the several districts, were as
follow.

" Vale of White Horse."—There, the Berkshire and the
Wiltshire breeds were still, as they had long been, nearly
in full possession. A few *crossings* with Berkshire and
Southdowns.

" The Chalk District."—Here, the Wiltshire still remained the favorite breed. The Southdowns, very properly,
gaining ground.   Two parishes " chiefly Southdown."
Wiltshire and Southdown a favorite cross for early grass
lambs for the London market. Of this district the Sussex
breed will probably gain, in no great length of time, the
full possession. Chalk Hills are their natural element.

" Vale of the Kennet."—There, the Wiltshire still prevailed ; with here and there some Southdown. And many
crosses

crosses between those breeds. "Some Dorset ewes for forward lamb."

"Forest District."—In this district we probably discover the *aboriginal breed* of Berkshire:—one of the ancient breeds of the kingdom. I regret that Dr. Mavor has not more fully described it.

P. 394. "*Forest sheep*, or *heath croppers*, as they are vulgarly" (pertinently) "called; a small breed, ill shaped, and of little value, but producing very sweet mutton. They abound in the parishes which lie within the precincts of the Forest of Windsor. A quarter will weigh from twelve to fourteen pounds. About thirteen fleeces make a tod. The wool of equal value with the South down."

P. 395. "*Greensward sheep*, a breed somewhat larger and better than the heath croppers."

These are, more than probably, the same breed. The Greenswarders being an improvement of the Heath Croppers; through the means of better food and shepherding.— See the NORTHERN and the WESTERN DEPARTMENTS, on this subject.

Fatting Sheep.—P. 396. "Sheep are fatted most commonly on turnips and hay, or on good natural pastures. In some parishes, however, oil cake is given them."

Market for Sheep.—See *Markets*, p. 74, aforegoing.

RABBITS.—P. 406. "George Elwys, Esq. of Marcham, has a rabbit warren, which is well stocked. It has likewise been stated to me, on what I consider as competent authority, for I had not the pleasure of finding the gentleman at home, that Exuperius Turner, Esq, of Challow, near Wantage, has a breed of white tame rabbits, by which he clears a large sum annually. Their skins, which have lately been much used in trimmings, sell for a good price."

SWINE.—*Breed.*—P. 403. "Whatever may be said of the Berkshire native breed of sheep, the hogs of this county deserve, and have obtained, unqualified approbation from the best judges; and those who wish to improve their breed of swine, are desirous, from the most distant parts of the island, to obtain one of the genuine Berkshire race, which, for compactness, aptitude to feed, and the size they will reach, are not inferior to any that can be named."—Twenty or thirty years ago, the above might have been more justly said, than it can be, at present.

Food of Swine.—P. 405. "Mr. Nicholls, of Hinton-house, collects the shells of the ruta baga, after the sheep have done with them, and carts them to the yard for his store pigs, to which they appear to be as grateful and nutritious as corn."

Market for Swine.—P. 453. "No fewer than 4000 hogs, from

from 10 to 20 score each, and upwards, though the average is about 12 score, are killed and cured in this place annually; chiefly by two families, who have engrossed the greatest part of the business. The bacon, which is deservedly in high estimation, is disposed of in London, and along the line of country between this place and the metropolis. From the uncertainty attending the navigation of the Thames, it is obliged to be sent principally by waggons."

POULTRY.—*Fatting Fowls.*—P. 462. Oakingham "is particularly famous for fatted fowls, by which many persons in the town and neighbourhood gain a living. They are sold to the London dealers; and the sum of 150*l.* has been returned in one market day by this traffic. Twenty dozen of these fowls were purchased for one gala at Windsor, at the rate of half-a-guinea a couple. At some seasons of the year, 15*s.* is paid for a couple. They constitute the principal *commerce* of the place.

" They are put up in a dark place, and crammed with a paste made of barley-meal, mutton suet, and some treacle, or coarse sugar, mixed with milk, and are found to be completely ripe in a fortnight. If kept longer, the fever that is induced by this continued state of repletion, renders them red and unsaleable, and frequently kills them."

BEES.—P. 409. " In the gardens of middling farmers, and more especially in the gardens of moderate tradesmen and labourers, we frequently find a few hives, seldom a dozen in one place; though few kinds of stock would be so productive, without incurring any expence.

" A poor man, near Abingdon, in one year cleared 27*l.* by his bees. At West Ilsley, hives have been found to contain forty pounds of honey; but this is considered as a very extraordinary quantity, and only to be expected under favourable circumstances.

" In the Forest district, bee-hives are pretty plentiful. ' About Newbury,' says Mr. Bicheno, ' bees are not very productive, as a stock seldom yields more than twelve or fourteen pounds of honey.' "

FISH.—P. 46. " In the parishes of Oakingham, Hurst, Lawrence, Waltham, and Ruscombe, several gentlemen have natural or artificial fish ponds, which are let to tenants, and produce every third or fourth year a crop, if it may be so termed, of carp and tench. The occupier stocks with yearlings about two inches long, obtained chiefly from Yately, on the neighbouring confines of Hampshire. The breeders are about eight or nine pounds weight; but in the Berkshire ponds they are never suffered to breed, but are sold off to the inns at Henley and other places, when the ponds

ponds are drawn, which is generally once in four years, and weigh at that age about three or four pounds each."

This is an extention of the Surrey and Sussex practice; which will be noticed in this volume.

PROFIT of FARMING.—P. 114. "Though this county is distinguished for the number of its intelligent and independent cultivators, and though I was particularly anxious to obtain some accurate estimates of expences and profits, I found it impossible to succeed. Several keep a correct account of expenditure; but on a farm, it is scarcely possible to strike a balance annually, and without this, how vague must every calculation be!

"Besides, so much depends on judgment, industry, and capital, that one person will make double the profit, with those advantages, which another will, without them. It is not always the nature of the soil, or the quantum of rent, that makes a farmer successful or otherwise: under the most favourable circumstances there are failures, and under the worst, there are instances of doing well.

"By the most sensible men who occupied their own property, it was admitted, that an average clear profit of ten per cent. on the capital employed was a fair return."

The insufficiency of that percentage has been shown, again and again. See the NORTHERN DEPARTMENT, County of *Northumberland*. And the Review of Reports from other Counties.

RETROSPECT.

Before I put aside the volume now before me, I think it right to say, that, in the analysis and abstraction of it, I have experienced much gratification and satisfaction; and to express an opinion that it is one of the very few Reports to the Board which are entitled to a place in a gentleman's library:—in the library of a man, be it put, who reads for general information, on the useful arts, and who has not leisure and assiduity enough to dig into the depths of practice. He will *understand* Dr. Mavor, and will *rarely* be led astray by unguarded assertions, and ill grounded propositions.

MIDDLESEX.

MIDDLESEX.

THE NATURAL and AGRICULTURAL distinctions of this metropolitan County have been noticed, in speaking of the Department at large.

It contains within its outlines no entire DISTRICT. That part of the *Vale of London*, which is situated on the north side of the Thames, occupies the principal part of its area. The irregular range of rising grounds which form the northern banks of the Vale, assimilates, as has been said, with the southern margin of Hertfordshire.

" GENERAL VIEW

OF THE

AGRICULTURE

OF THE COUNTY OF

MIDDLESEX,

WITH

OBSERVATIONS ON THE MEANS OF THEIR IMPROVEMENT.

BY PETER FOOT,

LAND-SURVEYOR, DEAN-STREET, SOHO.

DRAWN UP FOR THE CONSIDERATION OF

The Board of Agriculture and Internal Improvement.

1794."

THIS is an original Report, from Middlesex, on quarto paper; and has not been published*.

The QUALIFICATIONS of its author, so far as his *profession* leads us, we see in the title page. His acquirements, as a Reporter of rural practices, in the several branches of Agriculture,

---

* I have some recollection of a meager Report of Middlesex being, previously to Mr. F's, sent in to the Board, by a Mr. Baird, whose name is mentioned by Mr. Foot.—Whether Mr. B's sketch was printed, or remained in manuscript, I do not remember.

culture, and its various relations, we can learn from his performance, only.—Neither on the subject of Agriculture, proper, nor even on that of Estate Agency, (abstractedly considered from Landsurveying); nor on Natural and Political Economy, as they are connected with agricultural science, do we perceive in this work any convincing evidence of much experience or mature judgement; excepting what appears on the subject of Soils, and on that of the Appropriation of Commonable Lands.

Mr. Foot's *manner* is sufficiently appropriate for the occasion; as will be seen in the extracts from his Report. Mr. F's *plan* of *Report* would seem to be all his own.

The number of pages—ninetytwo.

A map of the different states in which the lands of the County lay, at the time of Reporting,—whether in " arable"—" principally meadow or pasture,"—or in " nursery grounds and gardens,"—is prefixed to the work.

NATURAL ECONOMY.

EXTENT.—P. 7. " It extends about 23 miles in length, is nearly 14 miles in breadth, and 115 in circumference, and contains 240 square miles, or two hundred and seventeen thousand six hundred acres."

WATERS.—P. 8. " Besides the river Lea, and the river Thames, aforementioned, there are the rivers Brent and the New-River; the latter of which supplies the greater part of London with water."

SOILS.—In his " Introduction," the Reporter is *bold to say*, p. 8, " the soil of this county is abundantly fertile, and for pasturage, and grain of all kinds, is not excelled by any other county."

In his division, " 1. the Soil," Mr. Foot gives a sketch of the soils of each Hundred of the County, with the states in which they were, at the time of writing. I copy his section, entire.

P. 9. " The soil of the Hundred of Edmonton, including South Mims, the land of which is about one-third arable and two-thirds meadow; Enfield, the land of which is about three-fourths arable, and one-fourth meadow; Edmonton, the land of which is about one-half arable, and one-half meadow; and Tottenham, the land of which is chiefly meadow, consists of clay, strong-loam, and a small part gravel.

" The soil of the Hundred of Gore, including Hendon, Harrow, Edgware, Stanmore, and Wemley, the land of which

which is almost, without exception, meadow, consists generally of a stiff clay, with a small portion of gravelly loam.

"The soil of the Hundred of Oselston seems to be distinguished by five kinds.

"First. In the vicinities of Barnet, Finchley, Highgate, Hornsey, and Hampstead, the land of which is meadow, the soil consists chiefly of clay, with small portions of gravel and loam. Around Wilsdon a deep stapled soil clay, with a mixture of loam and gravel, prevails.

"Second. In the vicinity of Newington, Clapham, Hackney, Bethnal-Green, and Stepney, the land of which is meadow, intermixed with garden-grounds and nurseries, the soil is rich and mellow; but the vicinities of Hackney frequently partake of a strong loam, approaching to a clay of that species which is called brick-earth.

"Third. The soil around Islington, Pancras, and Paddington, which is almost wholly employed first in making hay, and then in pasturage, consists of a gravelly loam, tending in some parts, but in small portions, to clay.

"Fourth. In the vicinity of Kensington, Brompton, Chelsea, Fulham, and Chiswick, the soil varies from a strong, to a tender or a sandy loam, and from a black and fertile, to a white and sharp sand and gravel; and, in the parish of Chiswick, it is remarkable, that in the deepest soil the gravel lies within two feet of the surface. The land of these districts is, in a small proportion, devoted to the plough, but is chiefly employed in raising plants and vegetables for the London markets.

"Fifth. The two remaining places of this Hundred, Acton and Ealing, the lands of which are partly arable and partly pasture, seem to possess a soil in a great measure similar to that of Chiswick; about Acton, however, are sometimes discovered soils of lean gravel, and of a deep staple sandy loam. In the neighbourhood of Brentford the soil is of a deep gravel, and towards Greenford and Perival of a strong loam and clay. The lands of these districts, are, almost without exception, arable.

"The Hundred of Isleworth contains the places bordering on the river Thames, viz. Isleworth, Twickenham, and Teddington, the land of which is arable, meadow, and garden-ground, and consists mostly of a hazel loam, or rich mellow soil. The parish of Heston, the land of which is chiefly arable, contains a small portion of light gravel, but is, in general, a strong loam.

"The Hundred of Elthorne, in the vicinity of Cranford, Harlington, Hillingdon, Uxbridge, and Cowley, the land of which is for the greater part arable, consists of strong loam, and a small part gravel.

"The

" The soil in and around the parishes of Harefield and Riselip, the land of which is about three parts arable, and one part meadow, chiefly consists of strong loam, with a small part gravel. The soil of the parishes of Harmondsworth and Drayton, consists chiefly of light loam and gravel, and is almost entirely devoted to the purposes of the plough. The parishes of Northolt, Hayes, Southall, and Northcott, consist of a soil partaking of a strong loamy clay and gravel.

" In the Hundred of Spelthorne, the parishes of Teddington and Hampton, which are chiefly occupied by gentlemen, together with those of Sunbury and Shepperton, consist of a lean gravel, and of a light loam; Littleton, Laleham, Staines, and Stanwell, of a lean gravel and strong loam; Bedford, Feltham, Ashford, and Hanworth, of a lean gravel and light loam. The whole of the lands of these districts is chiefly arable."

POLITICAL ECONOMY.

Appropriation.—" *Waste Lands.*"—P. 30. " There are many thousand acres of land in the county of Middlesex, within a few miles of the capital, which at present lie waste, and are of little or no value to the individuals interested in them; an absolute nuisance to the public; and yet capable of very great improvement."

After speaking on the advantages growing out of the Appropriation of such Lands;—on the burdensomness of the present method of procuring separate Acts of Inclosure;—and on the benefit that would accrue from a general act,—Mr. Foot proceeds to enumerate the Commons in the County of Middlesex.

Common Pastures.—P. 32. " Among the commons, now uncultivated in the county of Middlesex, are Hounslow-Heath, Finchley-Common. The remains of Enfield-Chace.

" The commons in the parish of Harrow, are Harrow-Weald Common, Pinner-Common, Sudbury-Common, Pinner-Marsh, Roxhull-Green, Apperton-Green, Wembley-Green, Kenton-Green, Greenhull-Green.

" The commons in the parish of Hillingdon and Uxbridge are Uxbridge-Moor, Uxbridge-Common, Memsey-Moor, Hillingdon-Heath, Gould's Green, Peil-Heath.

" There are also Riselip-Common, Sunbury-Common, Hanwell-Common, Worm-wood shrubs, in the parish of Fulham, and between four and five hundred acres of waste-lands in the parish of Hendon, &c."

Common Meadows.—P. 69. " There is a large tract of excellent

excellent meadow land on the Middlesex side of the river
Lea, belonging to the parishes of Enfield, Edmonton,
Tottenham, &c. The canal is cut through these meadows,
and falls into the river Lea, near Old Ford. This tract
of meadows, containing about 1000 acres, is divided, as
appears by the stakes, to the different proprietors, in
allotments, from about *half* an acre, to *four or five* acres,
but in general in *two and three* acres. They are laid up
to be mowed every year on the 5th of April, and after
the hay is cut, and taken off, are opened again for commonage on the 12th of August: and this is what is called
‘ Lammas Tenure.’ Every inhabitant of the respective
parishes claims and exercises a right of turning into these
meadows what stock he pleases; there being no stint to
this right of common. Every horse, cow, or heifer, thus
turned in, is marked by the parish brand for one penny
each; and if any are found thereon unmarked, they are
taken to the pound, and are not released without paying
a fine of eighteen pence each, if they belong to a pa-
rishioner, and if otherwise the fine is three-shillings each.

“ These meadows are frequently flowed both in winter
and in summer, not only by the river Lea, but by the canal;
but it does not appear that any attention is paid, either by
keeping the ditches, or the other drains to carry off these
floods, open; by which neglect the water is suffered to remain, to the great injury of the meadows. The reason
assigned for this neglect, I understand, is, that the property is in small pieces, intermixed, and subject to Lammas tenure, which prevents any general system from being
pursued by one, as all must join in the expences for the
improvement required.”

Common Fields.—P. 72. “ The common fields in the
county of Middlesex, which are at present in a good
course of husbandry, form a large proportion as to the
number of acres, when compared to the cultivated inclosures in the county.”

On *Appropriating* common Pastures.—Mr. F. brings forward two instances of “ Inclosure;”—namely, that of the
parish of *Stanwell,* and that of *Enfield.*

Relating to the latter, some memorable circumstances
occurred.—I recollect its being said that in the inclosure
of ENFIELD CHACE, much money, even fortunes, had been
sunk*. The subjoined extracts show the twofold ignorance
through which those losses were brought on.

P 40.

---

* See the second edition of my Rural Economy of YORKSHIRE;
in which I noticed the subject here under view, and pointed out the
way by which those losses might, with certainty, have been avoided.

P. 40. "Enfield Chace, though it is now near seventeen years since it was inclosed, has not profited so much by management or exertion, as might have been expected.

"The original purchasers of the crown-leases were ignorant both of experimental and of practical agriculture, being, in general, gentlemen retiring from trade into the country, and who, from the former habits of their lives, were ignorant of that regular process of husbandry which new soil requires to bring it into a state of profitable cultivation.

"The ground of the Chace was covered with trees; and although the oak found a ready sale, the beech did not repay the woodman's labour. The grubbing and stocking up of the roots was a still farther impediment; and the industry of these inexperienced farmers was alarmed and checked by the considerable advance of money which was immediately required to clear the ground. Partial and penurious experiments made upon a raw and crude soil, that had been for ages shut up from the rays of the sun by the thickness of the surrounding foliage, were not likely to be crowned with success. It will not excite wonder, therefore, that the new soil sullenly and reluctantly yielded to the adventurers from the metropolis, the seed they sowed: The wood, however, at length encreased in price, and, by the monies it produced, opened a way to the farther improvement of the soil."

P. 41. "The rise in the value of wood evinced, that though the ground refused to repay the toils of husbandry in the produce of grain, it would, at least for a certain time, produce, by the value of its wood, sufficient to answer the call of the Crown for rent.

"The ground, therefore, though rapidly cleared of its wood, lay, for the most part, in an uncultivated state for many years; for the real intrinsic nature of this *soil* never having been properly tried, remained entirely unknown.

"Time, however, has lately discovered it to be of a strong *clay marl*, containing a great proportion of calcareous earth, effervescing with acids, and equal, if not superior, in its quality and effects to most of the marls in this country.

"A circumstance of so interesting a nature, not only caught the eye of speculation, but the more useful one of the practical farmer. The gravelly jejune soil, of which the Chace was originally supposed to consist, no longer imposed an insuperable obstacle to improvement; the marl soon produced its expected effect; and the rapid progress which, within these four or five years, has been made in the cultivation of the Chace is surprising."

PROVISIONS.—P. 68. " Bread, throughout the county of
Middlesex

Middlesex, appears to be, in regard to price, the same as regulated by the city magistrates, in proportion to the price of wheat. In the vicinity of London, all kinds of butchers meat are equally as dear as in the London markets. In the more remote part of the county, and in the market towns of Uxbridge and Brentford, pork, poultry, eggs, and vegetables, as well as milk, are to be had something under the London-market prices; but beef, mutton, veal, and lamb, are seldom to be had at a cheaper rate; and, I much question, if the coarse pieces of beef, &c. are not sold cheaper to the poor in London, than in any part of the country."

CANALS.—P. 8. "There is a navigable canal leading from Hertfordshire along the banks of the river Lea, with which it forms a junction in the neighbourhood of Bow, from whence the united streams run to Limehouse, and incorporate themselves with the waters of the Thames.

"The Branston canal also, which is now nearly finished, enters Middlesex near Uxbridge, passes by Drayton, runs near to Cranford, at a little distance from Osterley-Park, and forms a junction with the river Thames at Brentford."

RURAL ECONOMY.

TENANTED ESTATES.

IN passing through this Report, the work of a "Land-surveyor," I have not discovered a sentence, on the management of landed property, that requires particular notice, here.

WOODLANDS.

NOR on this interesting object of examination, to a landsurveyor, have I been more successful. Middlesex, it is true, is not *now* a woodland County.

AGRICULTURE.

PLAN of MANAGEMENT.—Mr. Foot reports the "System of Husbandry," in different districts of the County; very properly declaring the nature of the land, in each. I
perceive

perceive nothing, however, in any of the Middlesex systems,
that he has reported, which requires to be registered.

WORKING ANIMALS.—See *Horses*, ensuing.

IMPLEMENTS.—P. 75. "The Rev. Mr. James Cooke, of
Red Lion-square, London, has greatly simplified and improved his patent drill-machine, as well as its attendant
cultivator, &c.

"In my correspondence with this gentleman he furnished
me with the following account of these implements."—
This clerical mechanist's account occupies the principal part of Mr. Foot's section, "Implements of Husbandry," *in the County of Middlesex*.

The subjoined account of the prevailing wheel carriage,
used in husbandry, in the County under report, is entitled
to a place, here;—as it records a usage in English husbandry which now belongs, almost exclusively, to the more
immediate environs of the Metropolis;—most particularly
to the hay farms;—rather than, generally, to the County
at large.

P. 75. "There are but few waggons used; and the carts
mostly in use are the six-inch wheeled shooting-carts, with
iron arms of various sizes for their axis. These carts,
with the addition of movable head and tail ladders, carry
hay, corn, &c. and, when thus enlarged, are found more
convenient in the farming business than waggons, they
being less expensive, and standing in less space when
out of use."

ARABLE CROPS.—Concerning this subject, I have found
nothing of importance, in the Report under view.

GRASS LAND.—*Common Meadows.*—P. 70. "From Fulham
to Chiswick, and almost all along the margin of the river
Thames, as far as Staines, are meadows, to a great extent,
which are frequently flowed both by the tides and by the
floods. These inundations produce great quantities of
rush, and other coarse grasses, and render it extremely
difficult to make the produce into hay; and, indeed, when
this is accomplished in the best possible manner, it is but
little worth. Most of these meadows have open ditches
dug in the lowest part of them to take off the water
which remains after the tides and floods have retired;
but, the surface being in general nearly a dead level, the
water drains very slowly off; and in the winter season
the soil is so very tender that it will hardly *bare* the weight
of stock upon it."

P. 71. "Extensive and fertile meadows also adorn the
banks of the river Coln, from Staines to Harefield.—Those
at Harefield are known by the name of 'The Moor,'
and contain about 300 acres, which are watered by the
river

river Coln. Parts of these meadows are mowed twice a year, and other parts grazed. A more strict attention is paid to the keeping of the drains and ditches in these meadows in proper order, than in any of those before mentioned, adjacent to the rivers Lea and Thames."

Haymaking.—P. 55. "Hay-making in Middlesex is carried on by a process peculiar to the county, and which, if the weather be favourable, has, by a long course of practice and experience, been attended with almost invariable success. To state this process clearly to the Board, I shall particularly describe the operations of *each day*, from the first employment of the scythe, until the hay is stacked in the yard, or field."—And so, in truth, the Reporter has described the operation of each day;—without any regard being paid to the state in which the grass to be made into hay was cut; namely, as to whether it had been cut while in a growing state, in a moist time, and of course full of sap; or overgrown, in a dry season, and of course nearly made as it stood; or to the size of the crop, whether heavy or light; and but little as to the weather after the cutting,—whether it shall happen to be rainy or fair, cloudy or clear, hot or cold, calm or windy! Circumstances, these, which jointly and severally accelerate or retard the progress of making hay. They may fit the crop for the stack, in a few days, or may detain it as many weeks, in the field.

Neverthelss, Mr. Foot's account of the method of haymaking, which has, I believe been practised, time immemorial, by the hay farmers, in the neighbourhood of the metropolis,—by men who live by haymaking,—being the fullest and the most correct that I have seen in print,—in regard to the various *operations* there in use,—I will here insert it, entire.—Practical men, in almost every district of the kingdom, may gather something from it, to improve their own practices.

P. 56. " On the *first day*, all the grass mowed before nine o'clock in the morning is tedded, broke as much as possible, and well turned. This is performed before twelve o'clock, and, if hands are plenty, it will be of great advantage to turn it a second time. It is then raked into wind-rows; and afterwards made into small cocks.

" The business of the *second day* is, to ted all the grass which was mowed the preceding day, after nine o'clock, and to ted, and treat as above, all that was mowed on this day before nine o'clock. But before the grass of this day's work is turned, the small cocks of the preceding day, should be well shaken out into straddles, or separate plats, of five or six yards square. If the crop is so thin as to leave the spaces between

between the plats, or straddles, pretty large, the spaces must
be raked clean. The next business is to turn the plats or
straddles, then to turn the grass of the second day's mowing, as before directed. This should always be done, if
there are hands sufficient, before one o'clock, that the people
may, as the custom is, take one hour for dinner, whilst all
the grass mowed is drying. After dinner the straddles are
raked into double wind-rows; the grass into single wind-
rows; and the hay cocked into middling sized-cocks, called
bastard cocks: The grass is then cocked as before on the
preceding day.

" On the *third day* the grass mowed on the preceding
day, and on the morning of this day, is to be managed as
before directed. The grass made the preceding day, and
now in grass-cocks, is to be managed in the same manner as
on the first and second days. The hay now in bastard cocks,
is spread again into straddles, and the whole is turned before the people go to dinner, that is, the hay, though last
spread, is first turned, next that which was in grass-cocks, and
then the grass. If the weather should have been sunny, and
fine, the hay that was last night in bastard cocks, will on
the afternoon of the third day be fit to be carried; but if
the weather should have been cool and cloudy, no part of it
probably will be fit to carry; and, in that case, the first
thing done after dinner is to rake the second day's hay into double wind-rows; the grass into single wind-rows; to
make the first day's hay into cocks with a fork, putting only
one cock in a straddle; to rake the ground clean; and put
the rakings on the top of each cock. The hay raked into
double wind-rows is now put into bastard cocks; and the
grass which is in single wind-rows is made into cocks as before. Provided there be no rain, even though the weather
should have been cloudy, the hay now in great cocks ought
to be carried; the hay in bastard cocks put into great cocks;
the grass-cocks made into bastard cocks; and that tedded
this morning into grass-cocks.

" In the course of hay making the grass cannot be too
much protected from the night dews or rain by cocking.
Care also should be taken to proportion the number of hay-
makers to the mowers, so that there should be no more hay
or grass in hand at one time than can be managed according to the above direction.

" The hay thus made becomes the object of the *fourth
day's* consideration in order to get it into stacks. The
hay-farmer pays great attention to have the stack well tuck-
ed and thatched, and I may venture to assert, that, from
what I have seen in other counties, there are no hay-stacks,
when finished, that are so well secured, and nicely formed,
as those in Middlesex.

" In the neighbourhood of Harrow, Hendon, and Finchley, there are many hay-barns capable of holding from 50 to 100 loads of hay. They are found very convenient in a catching time in hay-making, and also at other times, when the weather will not admit the hay to be cut and trussed out of doors."

HORSES.—P. 59. " Few horses of any excellency are bred in the county of Middlesex. The farmers in general supply themselves with their cart-horses, which are compact and boney, at the different fairs in the neighbouring counties, and at the repositories and stables of the several dealers in and around the metropolis."

CATTLE.—*London Cows.*—P. 80. The " *number* of cows, kept by the London cow-keepers in the county of Middlesex, amounts to nearly 7,200; and in the counties of Kent and Surrey to 1,300. I have taken great pains to ascertain these numbers with as much precision as the nature of the subject is capable of."

Breed and *Management.*—P. 82. " The cows kept for the purpose of furnishing the metropolis with milk, are, in general, bred in *Yorkshire*, Lancashire, and Staffordshire.* The London dealers buy them of the country breeders when they are three years old, and in calf. The prices given for them are from eight guineas to fourteen pounds a cow. The different fairs and markets, which are held at Barnet, *Islington*, and other places around the metropolis, furnish the London Cow-keepers with the means of keeping up their several stocks. Many cows likewise are bought in Yorkshire in small lots, from ten to twenty, by private commission, and forwarded to the cow-keepers in and about London.

" During the night the cows are confined in pens or stalls. About three o'clock in the morning each cow has a half-bushel basket of grains. From four o'clock to half past six, they are milked by the milk-dealers, who contract with the cow-keepers for the milk of a certain number of cows, at the price of fourteen or fifteen pence for eight quarts. When the milking is finished, a bushel-basket of turnips is given to each cow; and very soon afterwards they have an allotment, in the proportion of one truss to ten cows, of the softest meadow-hay of the first cut that can be procured. These

* This is a palpable error. The established breed of Lancashire and Staffordshire is the longhorned : whereas the " cows kept for the purpose of furnishing the Metropolis with *milk*," may be said to be invariably of the shorthorned breed. The *suckling* farmers, in the neighbourhood of London, have their cows chiefly out of Staffordshire. Hence, probably, the mistake.

These several feedings are generally made before eight o'clock in the morning, at which time the cows are released from their stalls, and turned out into the cow-yard. About twelve o'clock, they are again confined to their different stalls, and served with the same quantity of grains as they had in the morning. About half past one o'clock in the afternoon the milking commences in the manner as before described, and continues till near three, when the cows are again served with the same quantity of turnips, and, about an hour afterwards, with the same distribution of hay as before described.

"This mode of feeding generally continues during the turnip season, which is from the month of October to the month of May. During the other months in the year they are fed with rowing, or second-cut meadow hay and grains, and are continued to be fed and milked with the same regularity as above described, until they are turned out to grass, when they continue in the field all night, and even during this season they are frequently fed with grains, which are kept sweet and eatable for a considerable length of time by being buried under ground in pits made for the purpose. There are about ten bulls to a stock of 300 cows. The calves are generally sent to Smithfield market at a week old.

"Good milkers are kept four, five, six, and sometimes seven, years; they are fatted by an encreased allowance of the same food as is given to them while in milk, and sold off."

The *Produce* of Cows, and the *Profits of Retailers.*—The following calculations are grounded on eight quarts of milk, a day, by each cow, " taken on an average the year round."

P. 84. " The account, therefore, of eight quarts of milk a day, will stand thus, supposing the milk of every cow to be sold to the milk-men, which is not the case:

" Each cow, on an average, eight quarts a day, £. s. d. for 365 days, 2,920 quarts, at 1¾d. a quart* comes to 21 5 10

" 8,500 cows, at 21l. 5s. 10d. *per ann.* each cow, or 24,820,000 quarts, at 1¾d. a quart, comes to 180,979l. 3s. 4d. *per ann.*

" The consumers, however, as before observed, pay 3d. a quart to the retailers, which, on 24,820,000 quarts, amounts to the sum of 310,250l. and makes a difference of 129,270l. 16s. 8d. in favour of the retailers.

" But

---

* The price of milk, to retailers, at the time of reporting.

" But, when the families leave London, the cow-keepers do not find a ready sale for all their milk; and in this case they generally set the unsold milk for cream, of which they make fresh-butter for the London markets, and give their butter-milk to the hogs."

P. 85. "The facts and observations above stated have been collected personally by myself, from those whose engagements in, or connection with the business of cow-keeping enables them to judge with accuracy and discrimination on this subject."

Calves.—P. 90. " The calves from the large cows do not so soon get fat, as they grow too fast, are coarser in the grain of their flesh, and not so white. To make them better, the cow-keepers have their cows served by a bull of the long-horned breed. Those that get their calves white and *bright in the fat* and flesh are very valuable."

Another and well judged motive, for employing long-horned bulls, is that of lessening the risk, in calving.

Suckling Calves, in Middlesex.—P. 67. " The practice of suckling calves prevails mostly in the western part of the county."

SHEEP.—*Breed.*—P. 60. " The county of Middlesex is not famous for the breed of sheep. Hounslow Heath, and its adjoining pastures, are the only places where flocks of sheep are kept, and this seems more for the sake of folding their lands than from the hope of sending a superior kind of mutton to market.

" The farmers buy them at the fairs at Burford, Wilton, Weyhill, and other fairs in Wiltshire and Hampshire. The flocks differ in their individual numbers in proportion to the right of common which the respective proprietors possess.

" The sheep in the parish of Harmondsworth amount, I believe, to nearly 2000, and from the best accounts I could collect about 6000 are fed on Hounslow Heath. The sheep are generally sold off between fair and fair; some few however are fatted. The hay farmers also, particularly in the neighbourhood of Hendon and Barnet, devote their after-grass to the agistment of sheep and other cattle, which they take in at so much a score or head."

House Lamb.—The Reporter offers an account of " the method of breeding house lamb in the County of Middlesex." But it is not sufficiently full to serve as a guide to the inexperienced, nor sufficiently accurate, I think, to be inserted in this register.

' VIEW

'VIEW

OF THE

AGRICULTURE

OF

MIDDLESEX;

WITH

OBSERVATIONS ON THE MEANS OF ITS IMPROVEMENT,

AND

SEVERAL ESSAYS ON AGRICULTURE IN GENERAL.

DRAWN UP FOR THE CONSIDERATION OF

THE BOARD OF AGRICULTURE,

BY JOHN MIDDLETON, Esq.

OF WEST-BARNS FARM, MERTON, AND OF LAMBETH, SURREY,

LAND SURVEYOR;

Member of the London Society for the Encouragement of Arts, Manufactors, and
Commerce, and Corresponding Member of the Board of Agriculture.

ACCOMPANIED BY THE

REMARKS OF SEVERAL RESPECTABLE GENTLEMEN

AND FARMERS.

1798."

THIS is one of the earliest of the "reprinted" Reports
of the Board.

The QUALIFICATIONS of its author as a *rural Reporter*, is
declared in the title page, only. It does not evidently
appear, in his work, that Mr. Middleton possessed, at the
time of writing it, a maturity of knowledge in *practical
agriculture.*—Nevertheless, throughout his extended volume,
there is abundant evidence to show that Mr. M. naturally
possesses a considerable compass of mind, amply stored,—*by
reading*, as well as *by professional observations* on the practices
of other men,—with general ideas on rural subjects.

Mr. Middleton's mode of COLLECTING the MATERIALS
which his volume contains, concerning the established
practices of the County of Middlesex, is not explained.

We

We perceive no evident traces of a regular SURVEY of the County, with a view toward the requisite groundwork of Report. The *fresh* matter, relating to its practices, might be deemed inconsiderable. And the quotations from the former reports are neither numerous, nor important (saving such as appear in the preceding article); nor do the marginal notes, made on those reports, convey much practical information.

Viewing the Work in the mass, it appears as a didactic essay, dissertation, or treatise;—a lecture on the Natural, Political, and Rural Economy of the island at large. Not only are its propositions frequently enforced by prompt assertions, but some considerable part of them is *marked by Italic types;* even to the length of long paragraphs.

This, however, is merely a matter of *taste*, and cannot lower, in the mind of a considerate reader, the many ingenious suggestions that are discernible in the book. It would, nevertheless, be unpardonable, in a *censor*, not to apprize the unpractised student, that the work is not free from misconceptions, and hazardous dictations :—a caution, this, which is the more requisite, as the forcible language, and impressive tone, in which they are generally conveyed, are such as may be capable of leading, not only students, but novitial practitioners, into error.

Having already refuted, in the course of my present undertaking, many or most of the ill grounded doctrines which the volume before me contains, I will here bring forward such particulars, only, as relate to the County which is now under view;—with, however, such new or important observations of the author, as I may think will enrich this concentration of useful knowledge.

The number of pages—five hundred and ninetyseven; including a copious index.

A map of the County (the same as that prefixed to Mr. Foot's sketch). No other engraving.

SUBJECT THE FIRST.

NATURAL ECONOMY.

EXTENT.—Mr. Middleton estimates, in p. 2, the extent of the County of Middlesex, at "280 square miles, or 179,200 acres." Hence, it ranks among the smallest of the English Counties.

SURFACE.—P. 22. "This county, from its gentle waving surface, is particularly suited to the general purposes of agriculture :

agriculture : it being sufficiently sloping, to secure a proper drainage, and at the same time without those abrupt elevations which in some places so much increase the labour and expence of tillage ; and from its being entirely free from large stones, those powerful enemies to the free operations of the plough."

P. 23. " All the land to the south of the road passing from Brentford through Hounslow to Longford, is so nearly level, as to have no more than a proper drainage, and much the greater part of it is less than ten feet above the surface of the river Thames at Staines-bridge, and not more than from three to five feet above the level of the rivulets flowing through this district.

" From Staines, through Ashford and Hanworth commons, to Twickenham, a distance of seven miles and an half, is a perfect level, and generally of from ten to twenty feet above the surface of the river Thames."

CLIMATURE.—P. 14. " The temperature of the atmosphere, except perhaps so far as the influence of the London fires extend, is nearly the same through the whole county, there being no situation so much elevated as to produce the cold and thin air that we find in mountainous countries."

WATERS.—The section, " Water," of this report, is rather uninteresting. The *rivers* named in it are the Thames, the Lea, the Brent and the Coln; and to those are added the " New River" (Sir Hugh Middleton's Aqueduct) and the " Serpentine River" (a fish pool in Hyde Park): also several *brooks* and *rivulets*. I find nothing in the section that requires transcription. The navigation of the Thames and the Lea is spoken of in another section,—" Rivers and Canals."

SOILS.—On this important subject of a provincial report, Mr. Middleton speaks with satisfactory intelligence, and becoming diffidence.

P. 16. " The following observations are offered in a very general way. To delineate the variety of soils, so as accurately to draw the lines between them, would require much more time, even supposing it possible to investigate every part of the county, than can be expected in a work of this kind.

" A surface of perfect sand, clean gravel, or pure clay, is not now perhaps to be found in any part of the county. The top soil has every where been ameliorated or changed by the operation of the elements, by manure and cultivation ; these powerful agents have made the surface of all the lands in this county assume, more or less, the appearance of loam.

" *Sand* and *Gravel.*—Hampstead-hill consists of eight or ten feet of yellow iron-stained sand, with some loam and rounded

rounded flints, on a pure white sand of many more feet; and at the depth of about 150 feet are springs. The surface is covered with furze, except where the ground is dug.

" The summits of most of the highest hills in the county consist of *sand* and *gravel*, though frequently intermixed with loam. I observed in the old inclosures, and on En-field-chase, in various places, that when the gravel is very near to the top, a full crop of yellow blossomed broom covers the ground, if in a state of grass; and when ploughed, an equally full crop of sorrel.

"*Loamy Sand*—Or dry turnip and barley land, will include all that portion of the county lying between the road lead-ing from Hounslow to Colnbrook on the north, and the river Thames on the south, containing in depth from one foot to three (though for the most part from eighteen inches to two feet), on a gravel of small flints, six, eight, or ten feet in thickness, with a subsoil of blue tile earth.

" On the east side of the county, the whole way from Tottenham to Enfield-wash, the superstratum is of the same light nature ; of from six inches to two feet in depth, on a gravel of small flints, which can only be dug for the repair-ing of roads to the depth of from two feet to five, owing to its then putting on the appearance of a quick sand, so filled with water as to prevent all deeper digging. There is some poor land about the extreme west end of Hounslow-heath, and doubtless in a few other places.

" *Sandy Loam*—Will include all the land between the Colnbrook and Uxbridge roads, on the west side of Han-well and Hounslow, of from eighteen inches to upwards of five feet in depth, on six or eight feet of the gravel of flints on a subsoil of blue tile earth.—Of this description is the south side of the parish of Harefield, and the parishes of Twickenham, Isleworth, Ealing, Chiswick, Kensington, Fulham, Brompton, and Chelsea : at the last place, this soil has been most highly enriched by cultivation and manure.

" *Strong Loam.*—All the land from Riselip and Icken-ham, on the west, to Greenford, Apperton and Harrow, on the east, and between Pinner on the north, and Northcote on the south, is composed of strong loam. The land about South Mims is also of this kind.

" The level between Islington, Highgate and Hornsey, is a strong but very productive loam."

FOSSILS.—P. 27. " The immediate subsoil of the county, for the most part, consists of a gravel of flints, which is also found in the beds of most or all of the rivers; and under that, for the most part, blue tile earth."

P. 26.

P. 26. " I have not met with any stratified-rock stone, such as freestone, limestone, slate, &c. in this county; nor are any pebbles of the like stone found in the rivers, except such as have come there fortuitously."

SUBSTRUCTURE.—N. p. 32. " At Mr. Munday's brewery at Chelsea, in this county, a well was dug about the year 1793, to the depth of 394 feet, within 20 or 30 feet of the edge of the river, mostly through a blue clay or marl. At the depth of about 50 feet a quantity of loose coal about twelve inches in thickness was discovered; and a little stratified sand and gravel was found about the same depth. The well digger usually bored about 10, 15 or 20 feet at a time lower than his work, as he went on; and on the last boaring, when the rod was about 15 feet below the bottom of the well, the man felt, as the first signal of water, a rolling motion, something like the gentle motion of a coach passing over pavement: upon his continuing to bore, the water presently pushed its way by the side of the auger with great force, scarcely allowing him time to withdraw the borer, put that and his other tools into the bucket, and be drawn up to the top of the well. The water soon rose to the height of 200 feet.—*J. M.*"

SUBJECT THE SECOND.

POLITICAL ECONOMY.

APPROPRIATION.—*Common Pastures.*—P. 98. " The commons of Middlesex are situate in the more remote parts of the county, and bear a much smaller proportion to the whole quantity of land, than those of most other districts in the kingdom.

" The names and computed quantities, are as follows, viz.

	Acres.
1. Hounslow-heath, which is said to contain about	6,300
2. Sunbury-common,	1,400
3. Finchley-common,	1,240
4. Harrow-weald, and part of Bushy-heath, commons,	1,500
5. Riselip-commons,	1,500
6. Uxbridge-common,	350
7. Harefield-common,	200
8. Hillendon-heath,	160

12,650 acres.

The

Brought forward   12,650 acres.

The remains of Enfield-chase, still uncultivated, from actual mensuration, are,

The allotment to Enfield parish, ...	1,532
Ditto to Edmonton parish,	1,231
Part of the allotment to the crown, ...	1,047
Ditto .... to Hadley parish, ...	190

———— 4,000

Making together,   16,650 acres, to which add, several smaller ones, under 100 acres each, such as Hampstead-heath, Pinner-common, Sudbury-common, Pinner-marsh, Roxhill-green, Apperton-green, Wembly-green, Kenton-green, Greenhull-green, Uxbridge-moor, Memsey-moor, Goulds-green, Peils-heath, Hanwell-common, and Wormwood-shrubs, which possibly may contain altogether 1,350 acres: then deduct for roads, ponds, and gravel-pits 1000 acres, and it will shew that the uncultivated soil of this county, capable of receiving improvement, is about 17,000 acres, or rather under one-tenth of the whole quantity."

P. 103. " On estimating the value of the commons in this county, including every advantage that can be derived from them, in pasturage, locality of situation, and the barbarous custom of turbary, it appears that *they do not produce to the community, in their present state, more than four shillings per acre!* On the other hand, they are, in many instances, of real injury to the public; by holding out a lure to the poor man—I mean of materials wherewith to build his cottage, and ground to erect it upon; together with firing, and the run of his poultry and pigs for nothing. This is, of course, temptation sufficient to induce a great number of poor persons to settle upon the borders of such commons. But the mischief does not end here; for having gained these trifling advantages, through the neglect or connivance of the lord of the manor, it unfortunately gives their minds an improper bias, and inculcates a desire to live, from that time forward, without labour, or at least with as little as possible.''

" Another very serious evil which the public suffers from these commons, is, that they are the constant rendezvous of gypseys, strollers, and other loose persons, living under tents which they carry with them from place to place, according to their conveniency. Most of these persons have asses, many of them horses, nay, some of them have even covered carts, which answers the double purpose of a caravan for concealing and carrying off the property they have stolen, and also of a house for sleeping in at night. They usually

usually stay a week or two at a place; and the cattle which
they keep, serve to transport their few articles of furniture
from one common to another. These, during the stay of
their owners, are turned adrift to procure what food they
can find in the neighbourhood of their tents, any the deficiency is made up from the adjacent hay-stacks, barns
and granaries. They are known never to buy any hay or
corn, and yet their cattle are supplied with these articles,
of good quality. The women and children beg and pilfer,
and the men commit greater acts of dishonesty: *in short,
the commons of this county are well known to be the constant
resort of footpads and highwaymen, and are literally and
proverbally a public nuisance.*"

Common Fields.—P. 114 " The *common arable fields* of this
county contain about 20,000 acres."

" Nearly half the foregoing quantity consists of a good
turnip and barley soil; the other half of a *bean soil.*"

P. 138. (Section " Tillage") " The *arable land* of this
county is, for the most part, confined to common fields.
The rest consists of such parts of the said fields, as have
lately been inclosed, under separate acts of parliament, as
at Stanwell and Enfield-chase; and of a field or two here
and there, seldom of more than ten or twenty acres together, in other parts of the county.

All the inclosed arable land is supposed to be under.................................... } 3,000 acres

I have before stated the quantity of common-field arable land at about .... } 20,000 acres

making together 23,000 acres."

PROVISIONS.—P. 387. " *Bread* throughout the county of
Middlesex, is at the same price as in the city of London.
In the vicinity of the metropolis, every kind of *butcher's
meat* is equally dear, or rather more so, than in the London markets. In the more remote parts of the county, and
in the market-towns of Uxbridge and Brentford, pork,
poultry, eggs, vegetables, and milk, are to be had something under the London market price."

FUEL.—P. 391. " *Coals* are in general use for the fires of
this county. The exceptions are only on the north side of
it, in cottages and small farm-houses, where the expence
of coals, and the carriage of them, induces the use of wood
fires."

POOR RATES.—P. 63. " The rates are from 6*d.* to 7*s.*—
perhaps 3*s.* 6*d.* would average the county "

Mr. Middleton's " Observations" on the present mode of
meliorating the condition of the indigent, are of some
length. Most of them are too *general* for a *provincial* Report.

port. Nevertheless, some of them are so pertinent that it
would be wrong to overlook them.

P. 64. " Agriculture occasions very few poor; on the
contrary, it provides them almost constant labour. It is
only the blind, the extreme old, the very young children,
and idiots, which become chargeable in a parish purely agricultural.

" A labourer in agriculture, is more likely to support his
family without assistance from the parish, at twelve shillings a week, than is a journeyman in any large manufactory, though his earnings should be a guinea, or a guinea
and an half.

" In the parish of Merton, in which is my country residence, we have several large manufactories of calicoes, and,
as a necessary consequence, many pattern-drawers, &c.
whose earnings are from one guinea to one guinea and a
half per week; but these are never assessed to the poor-
rates; the fear of their families becoming chargeable to the
parish, prevails over the vestry so much, as always to prevent persons of that description from being rated.—J. M."

P. 65. " All the really necessitous, and who only want a
part of their support, should be assisted in their own houses,
where five shillings will frequently go as far as twenty would
do in the work-house."

P. 67. " The funds raised for supporting the idle poor of
this county are so numerous, efficient and comfortable, as to
operate against the general industry of the labouring poor.

" Lodging and diet in the work-houses, in every instance,
are superior to what the industrious labourer can provide
for his family. It is obvious that this must have an influence over their minds, and become most injurious to the
interests of society. It holds out encouragement to prefer
the work-house to labour; and, by filling the poor-houses
with improper inhabitants, it reduces the amount of industry.

" In those parishes with which I am acquainted, the annual expence of each pauper is about fifteen guineas; a
stout healthy labourer in husbandry, with a wife and three
children, earns only thirty for the support of five persons.

" The earnings of the inhabitants of work-houses, on
an average of the whole of this county, does not amount to
eight shillings per head per annum; which taken from the
former sum, leaves fifteen pounds seven shillings, or near
six shillings a week, as the expence of supporting each
pauper."

P. 69. " Every institution which tends to make the poor
depend on any other support than their own industry, does
them great disservice, and is highly injurious to society."

TITHES.

TITHES.—P. 58. " In many parishes of this county, the tithes are taken in kind; and which is nearly the same, in others they are annually valued, and compounded for. In several parishes, a reasonable composition is taken; in some it has been very little advanced during the last twenty years; happily there are farms which pay a modus, and others that are entirely tithe-free.

" I doubt not but that I shall stand excused for relating the following oppressive cases of tithes. It is in order to shew more clearly than I could otherwise do, that tithes operate againt the improvement of the soil, and consequently against the interest of the nation."

After noticing some flagrant instances, Mr. M. thus reflects on them. P. 59. " A few instances equally oppressive with these, have happened in every county in England; and the necessary consequence is, that they have severally put a stop to some expensive, but promising improvement. Every matter of this kind becomes a subject of general conversation among farmers, and of course prevents their making the like attempts. *In short, an act of parliament to prohibit the improvement of land by any considerable expenditure, would not more effectually do it than the tithe-laws.*"

INLAND NAVIGATION.—P. 401. " The river *Thames* is rendered famous by the port of London, in every commercial part of the world; and is navigable, for ships, to London-bridge, and, for barges, along all the southern borders of this county. The *Lea*, on the east, is navigable from the Thames near Blackwall towards Tottenham, about eight miles, where a canal navigation quits that river, and runs nearly parallel to it through the meadows of Tottenham, Edmonton, and Enfield, accommodating the whole eastern border of the county with a water-carriage to Hertford on the north, and London on the south."

P. 403. " The Grand Junction *canal*, just finished to the extent of this county, from Brentford passes through a rich corn district near Hanwell, Norwood, Harlington, West Drayton, Cowley, Uxbridge and Harefield. It is already of great importance to the lands through which it passes, and particularly to the market of Uxbridge, and will daily increase in its consequence as it extends, till it reaches Braunston, in a length of ninety miles."

ROADS.—P. 395. " Most of the *parish highways* in this county, are superior to any other of equal extent, that I have ever seen. They are hard and clean in every sort of weather; so much so, that gentlemen may ride along them, even directly after rain, and scarcely receive a splash.

" The

" The *turnpike roads*, on the contrary, are, generally,
very bad; although at the toll-gates of this county there is
collected a very large sum of money, probably not less than
30,000*l.* a year; which is uselessly expended in sinking
wells, erecting pumps, building carts, and hiring horses
and men, to keep the dust down, by watering, instead of
more wisely scraping it off. By the folly of this practice,
the roads are kept many inches deep in mud : whereas, if
they were raked and swept clean, winter and summer, there
would neither be dust in such quantity as to offend, nor
any of the present obstructions. There is now double the
draught necessary for conveying every carriage on the
roads, along which there is no riding even in boots and
horseman's coat, during half of the year. The mud indeed
is so very deep all the winter, and so fluid after rain, as to
render it unsafe to meet horses, owing to their feet throwing the mud not only over an horseman's clothes, but also
into his eyes."

P. 396. " The road from Tyburn through Uxbridge, is
supposed to have more broad-wheeled waggons pass over
it than any other in the county. Therefore, if broad wheels
were advantageous to the roads, this would be in high
condition, as it certainly is sufficiently rolled ; and it has
also the advantage of lying on a bed of gravel. But these,
and the present management, are insufficient to keep it in
repair.

" During the whole of the winter 1797-8, there was but
one passable track on this road, and that was less than six
feet wide, and was eight inches deep in fluid mud. All
the rest of the road was from a foot to eighteen inches deep
in adhesive mud.

" This track was thronged with waggons (many of them
drawn by ten horses, and most of them having broad wheels,
even to sixteen inches wide) and farmers' six-inch-wheel
carts, which occupied almost the whole of this confined
space. It was therefore with great difficulty, and some
danger, that horsemen, and light carriages could pass.

" The road continued in this infamous condition during
the whole winter half year. No exertions were made
towards cleansing it, although an expenditure of such a
trifle as twenty pounds, in the employment of a *road-scraper,
drawn by one horse*, would have effectually kept it clean
and dry; and would also have prevented the unnecessary
destruction of upwards of three hundred pounds worth of
materials, that were reduced to mud by being soaked and
ground, for six months, in water mixed with pounded flints.

" The only labourers to be seen on the road, during several

veral succeeding months, were those of a neighbouring gentleman; and they were employed in carting the foot-path into his inclosures."

MARKETS.—P. 408. " At Uxbridge-market a great deal of corn is sold, and there is a large public granary over the market-place, for the purpose of depositing it from one week to another.—At Hounslow-market there is a consider-able show of fat cattle; such of which as are not disposed of there, are sent on to Smithfield-market."

P. 409. " The following is an account of the number of black, or neat cattle, and sheep, annually brought for sale to this market, from the year 1731 to 1795, being 63 years: which I have divided into seven averages of nine years each."

Those averages stand thus:—

1732 to 1741 —	83,906 Cattle	465,650 Sheep.
41 to 50 —	74,194 ———	559,892 ———
50 to 59 —	75,351 ———	623,091 ———
59 to 68 —	83,432 ———	615,328 ———
68 to 77 —	89,362 ———	627,805 ———
77 to 86 —	99,285 ———	687,588 ———
86 to 95 —	101,075 ———	707,456 ———

The source from whence this statement was drawn does not appear.

LAWS concerning AGRICULTURE.—Under a head, entitled, " Agricultural Legislation and Police," Mr. Middleton com-plains, and on good grounds, of the insufficiency and im-policy of the present laws relating to pilfering, or petty thefts. What he advances, however, is applicable to Lon-don and its environs, rather than to the County of Middle-sex and the kingdom, at large.

Mr. M. appears to be well versed in the polity of the Metropolis and its neighbourhood.—P. 460. " The fields near London are never free from men strolling about in pilfering pursuits by day, and committing greater crimes by night. The depredations every Sunday, are astonish-ingly great. There are not many gardens within five miles of London that escape being visited in a marauding way, very early on a Sunday morning, and the farmers' fields are plundered all day long of fruit, roots, cabbages, pulse and corn. Even the ears of wheat are cut from the sheaves, and carried away in the most daring manner in open day, in various ways, but mostly in bags containing about half a bushel each. It has been moderately estimated, that 20,000 bushels of all the various sorts are thus carried off every Sunday morning, and 10,000 more during the other six days of the week, or one million and a half of bushels in a year, which, if valued at so small a sum as six-pence each, would amount to 37,500 *l*.

" The

" The occupiers of many thousand acres round London, lose annually in this manner to the amount of much more than 20s. an acre. And all this is done, as it were, under the eye of 270 magistrates, 1000 constables, and upwards of 2500 watchmen and beadles. ' Men who are more attentive to their own emoluments, and more desirous of promoting their own interests, than putting a stop to these nefarious practices.' " Are not the above estimates much overcharged ?

That pilfering is practised, to a serious, if not an alarming extent, upon the occupiers of lands to the distance of some miles round London, is a well known fact ; and that the existing laws, respecting it, are rather an encoragement than a prevention of the crime, is not less obvious. The subjoined remarks sufficiently convey Mr. Middleton's general sentiments on the subject.

P. 458. " One great hindrance to comfort in a life of agriculture, and which drives liberal minded men, who are always the best friends to improvement, out of the profession, is the want of laws to put a total stop to the receivers of stolen goods. These are the wretches who encourage servants in agriculture, and others, to pilfer, by holding out the lure of buying every article which such servants can bring, without asking them any questions. Most things which are usually produced on a farm, from so small an article as an egg, to hay, straw, and grain of all sorts, are daily stolen, and sold on the sides of every principal road in this county.

" These thefts are carried on daily at every farm, in a small way, seldom exceeding a truss of hay, or a bushel of corn, by one man at one time ; and are generally of smaller articles. When one of these fellows is taken in the act of stealing to the amount of a shilling or two, who in his senses would prosecute, at the certain expence of 20l. in money, and loss of time ?"

Here rests the GREAT ERROR, or, be it put—the more to excite the consideration of those whom it may concern—the PROMINENT ABSURDITY, in the PENAL LAW and DOMESTIC GOVERNMENT of this country. How the Lawgivers of a civilized and enlightened nation can have so long deferred to abolish it, is not to be reconciled to reason or common sense; nor, I will venture to assert, to any sound principle of legislation.

It is well ascertained that wherever LOCAL ASSOCIATIONS for the PROSECUTION of FELONS exist, *there* the crime of theft is rarely heard of—comparatively, at least, with places in which no such wise regulations have been adopted.

Why

Why, then, have we not NATIONAL ASSOCIATIONS—guaranteed by a permanent law of the country, for the same salutary purpose?—Is it not enough for a man to lose his property—perhaps through the negligence of those who are paid to protect it—but that he must perform the office, and pay the whole, or some considerable part, of the expence of prosecution!—and moreover alienate his attention from *his own concerns*, and probably have to undergo an irritation of mind, in which an undertaking of that sort is ever liable to involve him.

I have long been waiting for a suitable opportunity to bring forward my sentiments on this subject,—so far as relates to country concerns;—and I cannot do less than thank Mr. Middleton, most cordially, for affording me one*.

Every individual, I conceive, who loses, by theft, property that had been placed, in *prudent security*, ought to be amply paid for his time and expences, in attending the officers of the executive government; and, for a reason that will be offered, ought further to be remunerated for some part, at least, of his loss.

The hundred, or other division of a County, is liable to remunerate individuals, for losses sustained by *day* robberies; provided negligence or other improper conduct cannot be proved against the losers. And, surely, it may be worthy of consideration whether it will not be sound policy to make, in like manner, some compensation for the loss of property, by *night* robbery; provided no neglect of its loser can be shown.

Such a regulation, would not be merely a measure of justice toward the unfortunate; but would radically tend to the SUPPRESSION of THEFT;—as it would make it the *interest* of every man of property, being an assessee within the district, to prevent it; and would consequently put every active man on the alert, to recover the property, and bring the offender to punishment. Thus would every *prudent* man's property be, in a certain degree, *insured* by the district.

On the contrary, no remuneration whatever can be due
to

* It is not to the stealing of a truss of hay, or a bushel of oats, that I am here soliciting the attention of the reader;—but to thefts in general. It is probable, however, that robberies of every degree of magnitude mostly originate in PETTY THEFTS; and suffering these to pass unpunished serves as an encoragement to the commitment of greater.

But how few INDIVIDUALS have public spirit and *nerve* enough to spend even twenty *shillings*, and moreover to enter within the *entanglements* of *prosecution*, for so trifling a loss? Yet such are the rootlets which require to be extirpated.

to the loser of property, *taken in a state of neglect*, or *wilful insecurity :*—rather should some *salvage*—some considerable percentage—on its value, be claimable by whomsoever shall recover it; and a penalty be moreover levied, for the CRIME of NEGLIGENCE,—in proportion to its flagrancy. In flagrant cases, let the whole be forfeited to the district.

NEGLIGENCE of PROPERTY is the parent of THEFT; and ought, I am clearly of opinion, to be punishable:—not as a crime against what, in feeble phraseology, is termed "good manners;"—but against INDUSTRY and HONESTY.

Perhaps, let the officers of each parish in the district be a COMMITTEE of INSPECTION; and, in cases of persevering neglect, let them make their report to the magistracy; the penalties, they may levy, to pass to the district fund; or go in aid of the poor rate, in the parish where the crime shall be committed; or be applied to the education of the children of the indigent parishoners:—not merely to make them more tractable and ready, as servants and workpeople; but to prevent early habits of IDLENESS and PILFERING.

Regulations of this nature, and making the punishment, for *receiving* stolen goods, *greater* than that for theft itself, would, I doubt not, reduce the crime within a narrow compass;—comparatively with the boundless range which it occupies, at present.

SUBJECT THE THIRD.

RURAL ECONOMY.

TENANTED ESTATES.

ESTATES.—P. 34. " An increasing wealth, among the more numerous classes of the community, has a direct tendency to produce the division and subdivision of landed property; and accordingly we find, that, as the number of this description of persons is larger, so estates are less extensive in this county, than in any that are remote from the capital."

TENURES.—P. 37. " There is much freehold, a considerable portion of copyhold, and some church, college, and corporation lands."

IRRIGATION.—P. 317. " In *Hanworth-park*, which contains 600 acres of land, there are about sixty acres of water-meadows. I have no knowledge of there being any more in the county."

MANAGEMENT

MANAGEMENT OF ESTATES.—P. 35. " Estates are, for the most part, under the management and direction of attornies-at-law, whose attention to these concerns seldom extend any further than to receiving the rents at their own houses or chambers, generally in London, and in drawing leases from old precedents: men who are not at all skilled in the business of agriculture ; which, from the nature of their profession, cannot be expected."

TENANCY.—P. 71. " It is, without doubt, a most un-reasonable prejudice which many proprietors entertain against granting leases of their estates; for the with-holding them certainly operates as a powerful bar against every improvement, and is as injurious to the interests of the landlord as to those of the tenant and the com-munity. For the same reason, it is perhaps equally bad policy to restrain the tenant from selling or assigning his lease." (!)

To those lines are added ten pages of a similar cast. It is true, that at the time Mr. M. wrote, the impropriety of granting leases of length was not so great as it has been of later years. Having already had occasion, in the course of my present Work, to speak, again and again, on this, now, threadbare subject, I pass over it, here, without further notice.—When the value of money shall become less rapidly fluctuating—much more stationary— than it has been, for several years past, long leases may, *in some cases*, be eligible*.

RENT.—P. 56. " The rent of land in this county, varies from ten shillings to ten pounds per acre; which great disproportion is here, as every where else, occasioned by a variety of circumstances: such as the natural quality and aspect of the soil; the distance from London and other markets; the goodness, situation, and convenience of the buildings; the state of the walls, hedges and ditches; the expence of conveying the produce to market, and of obtaining a supply of manure in return ; and also, whether it is by land or water that the products are to be carried : the state of the roads; the expence of toll-gates, weighing engines, and markets :"—together with a variety of other circumstances.

P. 57. " The method practised by some gentlemen, of estimating

---

* MARCH 1816.—The above was written before the late alarm among tenants in husbandry took place: that is to say, before the bubble burst. Or, let it be said,—before the morbid tumor, which I have, for a length of years, as proper occasions offered, been pointing out to my readers—broke.——May the distressing crisis save the Patient!

estimating the produce of land by trebling the rent, is very fallacious: three times the rent is not by any means equal to the value of the produce of the land under the best systems of husbandry now in use; though under the old exploded course of fallow, wheat, oats in the scanty produce of common fields, and when taxes, and the expences of living, were at one half of the present amount, it was not very distant from the truth. But under the more improved courses of husbandry on land at, and under, twenty shillings an acre, the produce is now more generally worth from five to seven times the rent."

See more on this topic, under the head *Profit*, at the close of this article.

On the *Rental* of the *County*, we find the following statement.—P. 57. " The rental of the whole county is about four million and an half, whereof 2,900,000*l.* was assessed to the county-rate to raise 12,000*l.* during the last year: the rate is at about two-thirds of the value, therefore the unassessed is 1,450,000*l.* Cottages not assessed 35,000, at 4*l.* is 140,000*l.;* total 4,490,000*l.*"

WOODLANDS.

PRESENT WOODS.—P. 273. " The *copses and woods* of this county have been decreasing for ages; and, in a few centuries more, they will probably be annihilated.

" There are, however, still a few acres so occupied on the north slopes of Hampstead and Highgate hills; about one hundred acres on the east side of Finchley-common; and two thousand acres on the north-west side of Riselip; together about three thousand acres (exclusive of near one thousand acres on the remains of Enfield-chase, which are accounted for under chapter vi, on inclosing)✻. Rather more than half the said quantity is wood, pretty well stocked with thriving young oaks; the rest is copse. I believe the whole is on a soil of yellow clay."

Diswooding.—P. 274. " The hills about Copthall and Hornsey

" ✻ The forests, woods, copses and commons of this county, are nurseries for thieves. The security which they apparently hold out against detection, has tempted hundreds of the ill-disposed to commence footpads and highwaymen; and has also been the occasion of numberless murders and robberies being committed, and some of the perpetrators being gibbetted.—*J. M.*"

Hornsey are now appropriated to the scythe; though, but a few years ago, they were covered with wood. They are already of five times their former value; and, after being ten years more in grass, their produce will be worth, to the community, ten times more than the produce of the same ground would have been in a state of wood." (?) " Near Bowes Farm, several hundred acres of underwood have been grubbed up within the last eight or ten years; and the improvement of the soil is going on in a proportion nearly similar to the foregoing."

AGRICULTURE.

FARMS.—*Sizes.*—P. 48   " The farms of this county are in general small, especially when compared with Sussex, Wilts, and other counties, where large downs or sheep-walks constitute a part of the farms. Mr. Willan's farm, at Mary-le-bonne-park, containing upwards of 500 acres, is probably the largest in this county; there are many of about 200 acres; but perhaps the average of the county would not exceed 100."

While speaking on the long continued dispute, about great or small farms, Mr. M. truly says, what every man of mature observation will allow, that " it is rather the larger farmers and yeomen, or men who occupy their own land, that mostly introduce improvements in the practice of agriculture, and that uniformly grow much greater crops of corn, and produce more beef and mutton per acre, than others of a smaller capital." p. 49.

Farm Fences.—P. 132. " The hedges are generally full of live wood, consisting mostly of hawthorn, elm, and maple, with some black thorns, crabs, bryers and damsons: the last frequently very fruitful, which is the cause of its being destroyed. All these are made anew once in ten or twelve years; at which time the whole is cut down to within a few inches of the bank. The scouring of the ditch is thrown up, a very thin stake and edder hedge is formed, and all the rest of the wood is made into bavins, and sold principally to bakers, at about a guinea a hundred delivered. In about two years, the live wood is grown so thick again, as hardly to be seen through."

HOMESTEADS.—P. 39. " The oldest farm-houses and of-fices now in the county, are built with timber, lathed and plastered" (or weather-boarded) " and the roofs thatched; which sufficiently indicates, that at some distant period they were generally so. These buildings appear to have
                                                                            been

been erected by piece-meal, merely to suit the immediate
and indispensible wants of the farmer. Of the houses,
many are in villages; others in low sheltered situations;
often on the side of a green lane; and frequently near a
pond. In the arable part of the county, the offices have
been added one after another, in proportion as the woods
were cleared, cultivation extended, and the requisitions of
the farmers increased. Being built with timber, they
will endure repairing, even after every vestige of the original materials is perished and gone.

"Those farm-houses that have been built within the present century, are generally erected with bricks; and, owing
to the high price of straw, and the great value of manure,
the roofs are now, for the most part, covered with tiles."

P. 40. "Many hay-farmers have only a stable for their
horses, and an open shed for loaded carts to stand under,
in addition to the dwelling-house and its offices. Others
have a shed for a cow, and a barn (without a threshing
floor) which they fill with hay, frequently the second crop.
Some of these barns are fitted up with deal linings, partitions and floors, in a very complete manner for the purpose of suckling house-lambs; and the second crop of hay
is either placed at one end of the barn, or adjacent to it,
for the especial use of these lambs.

"Many of the modern farm-houses, in the hay district
of the county, have pretty much the appearance of gentlemen's houses, both in construction and neatness, principally owing to there being no farm-yards with cattle.
And even in the arable part of the county, there are but
few yards of this description, as the straw is almost all
sent to market."

PLAN of MANAGEMENT.—Still we continue to find the
section, "Rotation of Crops," a favorite with the Board's
Reporters. Mr. Middleton has extended it to fourteen
pages; not by the means of pocket-book memoranda, put
down in conversation with novitial practitioners; but, chiefly,
with theoretic systems of the author's own invention.

P. 159. "When the commons, downs, and sheep-walks
are inclosed and cultivated (as in a few years they must
be), the old inclosed lands will, in consequence, be deprived
of the manure deposited in the sheep-folds, which they
now derive from those wastes. It will then very soon
be found, that *the wiser way*, if not absolutely necessary,
will be to grow two green crops for one of corn, as is
now practised over six thousand acres in this county, with
complete success.

"With these ideas impressed on my mind, *I venture to
recommend for the best land, alternate green and white
crops.*

crops. *For land of a full medium quality, three green
crops for two of white; for ordinary land, two green crops
for one of corn; and for the worst, or most exhausted,
land, downs and sheep-walks, three green crops to one
of white.*

" Cropping land in the foregoing ratio or proportion,
would keep it free from weeds, and in a high state of
cultivation ; and *under such management, might be continued in perpetual aration, with a constant succession
of large products.*"

Under this very *ingenious* system, how, let it be asked,
would the poor and the rich be supplied with corn, for
bread, beer, and other valuable purposes? And where
would a market be found for the cattle and sheep which
such a system would consequently produce? A surplus
of corn may be exported, or preserved ; but not so a
superabundance of beef and mutton.

P. 163. " There are several farmers of this county, who
have a field or two near their houses, of a few acres each,
cropped *one year with winter tares, then turnips, and
the next year wheat;* thus obtaining *three valuable crops*
every two years, averaging *a produce of fifteen guineas
per acre per annum.* *

" If this system could be extended to a whole farm, and
thence over the nation, what a wonderful scene of fertility
would this island exhibit! The entire kingdom, undoubtedly, could not be so cropped, but most of the light, dry
soils, are perfectly adapted to this mode of culture, even
in places the most distant from dunghills. Provided the
tares and turnips were one or both of them eaten on the
land, a continual productiveness might be ensured. The
cold clayey loams are exceedingly well calculated for the
alternate growth of tares and wheat, or, which is still
better, of wheat, clover, tares. The former rotation would,
in this county, average eleven guineas, and the latter
twelve guineas per acre.

" If it were either necessary or advisable, *clover, tares,
turnips, &c. might be grown and consumed on the land,
until it became too rich for wheat, in which case it might
be laid down to grazing pasture,* or again depreciated by
the growing of oats." O! fine, fine!

OCCUPIERS.—I have pleasure in copying the subjoined
well

* This is eligible. GARDEN FIELDS are most convenient appen-
dages, to farmsteads. I am gratified to hear of their being adopted
in the environs of the Metropolis. See my Minutes of Agriculture
in Surrey.

well drawn picture of Middlesex farmers.—P. 51. "The farmers, or cultivators of the soil of this county, may be divided into various classes, or descriptions of persons.

"In the vicinity of London, the ground is mostly rented by gardeners and nurserymen. The land lying immediately beyond the last, is occupied by the villas of wealthy citizens and others; and at a still further distance, by farmers, who are again divided, first, into persons with whom farming is but a secondary object (their primary occupation being generally in London), and who do not pay to it that attention which is necessary to make it profitable.

"Secondly, into persons who, having acquired an easy fortune in other pursuits, retire to farming, with the idea of uniting profit and amusement in their agricultural labours. There are many of this class, who know nothing either of the theory or practice of agriculture; but having hastily imbibed a notion that it is a very pleasant pursuit, enter into it with great expence and precipitancy, and generally quit it again in two or three years, after having suffered considerable loss, from having laid out large sums of money for the most part in useful improvements, without waiting to receive a return for their labour and expence. They then quit their farms in disgust, and leave them for others to reap the fruits of their industry.

"The third is a less numerous class, and consists likewise of persons ' who have been in a different line of business, yet have had such a strong inclination for rural occupations, that they abandon their former employments altogether, and betake themselves wholly, and without reserve, to farming of land, as a profession. This class forms the most intelligent and most accurate of husbandmen.'"

P. 52. "The number of cultivators of this description, is, however, very limited."

"The fourth and last class, is about equal in number to all the rest, and is composed of persons who are farmers by profession, and who have at no time been engaged in any other line of business: these, as a body of men, may justly be said to be industrious and respectable, and much more intelligent and enlightened than the generality of farmers in places more distant from the metropolis."

WORKPEOPLE.—P. 380. "The wages most generally paid" (in 1798) " to ordinary labourers in husbandry in this county, is ten shillings a week during the winter half year, and twelve shillings a week during the summer half year; but on most farms, there is one handy, confidential workman, at twelve shillings a week all the year round. Those who are only employed during hay-time and harvest, are paid fifteen shillings a week; they are
occasionally

occasionally allowed beer, and sometimes a dinner, which
makes it equal to their being paid twelve shillings a week
the year round.

"In summer, the hours of labour are from six o'clock in
the morning till six o'clock in the evening; and during
the winter months, from light till dark : but half an hour of
rest is always allowed at breakfast, and an hour at dinner.

" A great deal of labour, perhaps a moiety or more, of
the whole, is done by the piece."

P. 382. " The number of *women* (mostly from North
Wales) who are employed by the farmers and gardeners
round London, during every summer season, in weeding
and making hay, in gathering green peas and beans, in
picking fruits, and carrying strawberries and other tender
fruit to market, is astonishing."

P. 388. " The *servants* who are boarded by the farmers,
frequently consume more animal food than their masters.
There is no certain rule, but perhaps something like the
following routine may be near the truth, viz. bread, cheese,
and fat pork for breakfast; coarse joints of beef boiled,
with cabbages and other vegetables, or meat pyes, meat
puddings, &c. for dinner; cold pork, bread and cheese, &c.
for supper; and with every meal small beer.

" It is evident the expence of such a diet must be very
considerable; and the waste which the servants of this
county make, is shameful.

" This, together with their rude manners, induces most
farmers to pay them board-wages, especially as this method
greatly lessens the trouble of the mistress, and female
servants of the house."

Mr. Middleton's observations, and censure, concerning
chandler's shops and public houses, as grievances to laborers, are highly creditable to him, as a zealous moralist.

IMPLEMENTS.—Mr. M. has thought it fitting to bestow
nine or ten pages of general "Observations" on this head,
without conveying much useful information to his readers.
They are the remarks of an amateur—of a man of reading and incidental observation, rather than those of a
practised occupier.

MANURES.—In the section " Manuring," is comprized
some interesting intelligence, concerning the amelioration
of Soils, in the County of Middlesex.

Town Manure.—P. 301. " The greater part of the manure used in this county is carted from London; being
part of the sweepings of a surface containing *three thousand
acres of pavement, in streets and market-places, and the
dung produced by 30,000 horses, 8000 cows, and 650,000
inhabitants.*

" The

" The *whole* quantity thus produced is **probably not less** than *five hundred thousand cart-loads ;* about *one-half* of which is supposed to be annually spread on the land of this county. *Unfortunately, ninety-nine parts in an hundred of the soil of privies is carried, by the commons sewers, into the Thames ; which is a very great loss to agriculture, as night-soil is not only more quick in its operation than any other dressing, but is by far the richest manure that ever was laid on land.*"

Lime.—P. 307. " There is neither limestone nor chalk in this county ; nor is there any lime burnt in it ; though there are kilns for the burning of both chalk and limestone at Nine-elms, near Vauxhall, on the Surrey side of the Thames."

Chalk.—P. 303. " *Chalk* is brought by the same canal, from Ware-park, and its environs (Herts) a distance of about eleven miles, and delivered at Enfield, at the rate of 4*l.* for about thirty tons ; and is found to answer with tolerable success."

Shell Marl.—P. 312. " I have not heard of there being any *shell marl* near the surface in this county ; but, at the depth of many feet, a strata of four or five feet in thickness, consisting of oyster, and other marine shells, and sediment, has been dug through at Chelsea ; and it most probably extends over at least all the flat part of the county. The same strata has been met with in many places in the adjoining county of Surrey. I know not whether it has been used as a manure, except indeed in such small quantities as are usually dug on the sinking of wells ; nor has any one entertained an idea of raising it purely for the purpose of agriculture."

Sheepfold.—P. 303. " Sheep-folding is resorted to, in order to manure part of the land in different parishes round Hounslow-heath and other commons."

In the author's section, " Size of Farms," as well as in other parts of his Work, we perceive, pretty plainly, his decided opinion on this species of melioration ; as well as on the value of " sheep downs"—" sheep walks"—and other " wastes."

P. 50. " No waste, sheep-downs, sheep-walks, or pasture, should *by any means be permitted for the mere purpose of feeding dung-carriers, or of filling the bellies of lean sheep, which are intended to empty themselves at night in the fold on the arable land, to the ruin of all the grass land so used.*"

TILLAGE.—*Plow Team.*—P. 139. " It is not one time in fifty that they go to plough with so few as three horses ; but mostly for the lighter work using four ; on rather
stronger

stronger land, five, and sometimes even six: in every instance, drawing at length, or one before the other. In May 1796, I saw, in one day, two teams, with six horses in each, and three men to attend each team, namely, one to hold the plough, and two to drive the horses, ploughing with a wide furrow, about three quarters of an acre per day."

SEMINATION.—*Seed.*—P. 165. "The method I wish to recommend to those cultivators who desire to excel in the article of grain, is the following, namely, a few days before harvest, to walk through their fields of corn, to select and gather the prime samples of every species of seed, and ever afterwards to continue the same practice, by repeating the operation of *collecting the most perfect grain from the crops produced from such selected seed.*"

This recommendation is excellent, but not new. Nor does it go to the full extent of the advantage to be gained by a selection of superior individuals, among cultivated plants, as among domestic animals. Not only may a cultivator, by selecting prime plants, *from his own crops,* improve, from time to time, the particular sorts under cultivation, *as to a fairness of sample,* but he may, at the same time, and by the same ready mean, become possessed of a sort *superiorly adapted to his own soil, situation, and climature.* And moreover, by diligent search, may discover a NEW VARIETY of superior excellence to every other, previously known. See my YORKSHIRE; article *Wheat;* first published in 1788.

For Mr. M's thoughts on *Drilling,* see the head, *Wheat,* ensuing.

VERMIN.—The Reporter (in p. 476) "estimates the damage done, by vermin, on a farm of two hundred acres, one half of it arable, the other in grass, without sheepwalks," in manner following:

	£.	s.	d.
Mole-catcher	1	11	6
Rat-catcher	3	3	0
Mouse-catcher	3	3	0
Scaring sparrows and other small birds	6	6	0
More for rooks and jays	2	2	0
Mischief by magpies, carrion crows, ravens, kites, hawks, and dogs,	2	2	0
Damage by game	10	0	0
By hunters and shooters, "who prey upon game"	10	0	0
And lastly by "the slug only"	20	0	0

"Thus" says the estimator, p. 479, "the amount is upwards of fifty-eight pounds a year, or near six shillings
an

an acre, on the whole quantity of land; which sum will perhaps average the cultivated corn and grass land farms of Britain; and as there are thirty-nine millions of acres, these depredations amount to upwards of ten millions per annum."

Mr. M. may be assured that I do not insert, here, the above abridgement of his estimates, in ridicule; though the minuteness of the detail may excite an involuntary smile. In the mass, they exhibit a serious evil. I give them a place, here, to convey, to the minds of gentlemen of Mr. Middleton's profession, that "such things are." For I verily believe that but few of them, in estimating the value of tenanted estates, make any allowance, in rent, for the various depredations above set forth.

ARABLE CROPS.

Concerning this important branch of the rural art, we find very little, in the report under consideration, regarding the practice of the County whose name it bears, that can command particular mention, in this register; although the article, in the aggregate, is of considerable length. The matter it contains chiefly consists of didactic effusions, from the copious fund of agricultural lore, which would seem to have been stored up in the Reporter's own mind, previously to his survey of Middlesex. Some of them, on first sight, wear the semblance of superior worth. Few of them, however, will bear the test of mature examination. Such particulars of the section under view as I may judge, after due deliberation, will assimilate with the select materials of this work, I will incorporate with them; whether they arise out of the practice of Middlesex, or emanate from the writer's own sentiments on rural subjects.

WHEAT.—*Drilling.*—Mr. Middleton's ideas regarding this *infatuating* operation, accord with my own, *more* than do those of any other public writer.

P. 170. "Future experiments, I believe, will determine the comparative merits of the drill and broadcast methods of growing wheat, on light soils that are clean, in favour of the drill, owing to the single circumstance of earthing up the plants just before the shooting forth of the last set of roots."

P. 171. "On strong loams and clayey soils, however, if they are ever so clean, and on all lands that are foul with root-weeds, it does not admit of any argument to support the superiority of the broadcast over the drill. In the latter case, the drills cannot work; and in the former, the horse-hoes must be equally at a stand. The harrowing and rolling of strong land, aided by the usual
                                                            operation

operation of weeding, and, if needful, with top-dressings, will be found to promote the growth of the corn; whereas the horse-hoes in such a soil, in a dry season, would have so unsteady a motion, as to cut up part of the rows without being able to raise any mould towards earthing up the plants."

The *growing Crop* of Wheat.—P. 170. "After a frosty winter, the *crowns of the roots* of wheat are sometimes exposed for two or three inches in length above the mould; in that case, turning sheep in after a moderate shower, and driving them about, will tread the wheat into the moist ground, where it will abide, and produce fresh roots."—An admirable thought.

Market for Wheat.—P. 177. "The farmers sell their wheat to mealmen, who manufacture it, and sell the flour to the bakers, and the pollard to the farmers and others, for the food of horses, hogs, &c."

BARLEY.—*Quantity grown.*—P. 180. "There are about 3800 acres of land annually sown with barley in this county, the greater part of which is sown after wheat."

Produce of Barley.—P. 183. "*Produce*—Varies from fifteen to seventy-five bushels per acre. The average produce of the county is about four quarters of corn and two loads of straw per acre."

Market for Barley.—P. 184. "Much of the most ordinary barley is given to poultry: the rest is sold to the maltsters, except so much as is reserved for seed.

BEANS.—*Quantity grown.*—P. 188. "There are about 2800 acres of land annually cropped with beans in this county; and they are cultivated in the most clean and perfect manner."

The subjoined directions rank high among this writer's dictations.—*Manure, Tillage,* and *Semination* of Beans.—P. 189. "The preparation for this crop should be as follows: early in autumn lay the manure on, and immediately plough the land into ridgelets, of two feet six inches wide; in which state let it lie until the season for planting, when the seed may be dibbled in, one row of beans into the middle of each ridgelet, at the distance of about three inches from bean to bean. They should be immediately covered, which may be done by children, with a garden-rake or hoe; or, should the land be dry and crumbly, a horse and a bush harrow would do as well. In most places, it is advisable to set a boy with a rattle to frighten away the rooks, until the beans are up.

"The distance between the rows will not prevent the crop from completely covering the ground, especially if
the

the land was manured for them, as they will branch out
sideways, three or four stout stems from each root." (?)

In the established practice of Middlesex, the semination
of beans appears, by Mr. M's report, to have been, at the
time of reporting, similar to that of Glocestershire; namely,
dibbling them in, across the ridges.—P. 190. " The women
are paid 4*d.* a gallon for dibbling in the seed, which they
perform with astonishing rapidity, along a line stretched
across the ridges, leaving a space of fifteen inches between
each row; the seed is covered by a bush harrow, drawn
by horses who walk in the furrows."

Disposal of Beans.—P. 193. " All given to horses, except
what are preserved for seed, and such as are podded while
green, and sent to the London markets. When pigs are
fed with beans, the meat becomes so hard as to make very
ordinary pork, but good bacon. Also, it is supposed that
the meal-men grind many horse-beans among wheat, to
be manufactured into bread."

In Norfolk, it is well known that white peas are frequently ground, by flour makers, with wheat. This is
the first time I have met with any intimation of beans
being used in a similar way.

PEAS.—*Quantity grown.*—P. 193. " There are about
3000 acres of land annually cropped with peas in this
county; they are much on the increase, *and are cultivated
in the most clean and garden-like manner.*"

Succession and *Tillage* for Peas.—P. 193. " On upwards of 2000 acres they succeed a clean crop of beans:
in which case, the bean stubble is about January, and
during every dry time till March, ploughed up with a
thin furrow, and soon afterwards re-ploughed a full depth.
The water-furrows are kept open, and the land remains
in this state till seed-time."

Consumption of Peas.—P. 196. " About one-third of
them are eaten by human beings, and the rest by hogs."

POTATOES.—P. 197. " Most of the farmers in this county, and such of the cottagers who have gardens, grow
potatoes for their own use, but few or none for sale."

TURNEPS.—*Succession.*—P. 207. " In this county, there
is no such thing as turnip-fallow:" (?) " the land invariably
produces a crop in the spring, before the preparation
for turnips *."

Culture and *Market* of Turneps.—P. 204. " *The broad-
cast method* of growing turnips is the only one made use
of in this county. They are invariably twice hoed by
hand, and are mostly consumed by cows, whose owners
buy

" * Generally of tares, early peas, or rye.—*J. M.*"

buy them growing in the fields, at every distance short of twelve or thirteen miles from London, at prices varying from five to ten guineas per acre, according to the length of carriage and quantity of the crop. The cow-keepers are at the expence of pulling them up, loading and carting them home, which is generally done in waggons drawn by six stout horses, in loads, that, for their largeness, surprise every beholder."

CULTIVATED HERBAGE.—*Rye.*—P. 179. " There are a few acres of rye grown on many farms of the more sandy nature in this county, for spring green feed."

Tares.—P. 198. " Many of the farmers in this county grow a few acres of tares, and the culture of them is extended every year, from the circumstance of their importance becoming better understood. It is a considerable degree of gratification to me, to have been the first who sowed them on a large scale, and publicly recommended them to the notice of farmers, as highly deserving to be introduced into a regular rotation of crops."

This is speaking of tare herbage as *something new*, in Middlesex! Whereas, in the County of Surrey, not more than ten miles from the confine of Middlesex, nor above three or four from the Reporter's " country residence," both rye and tares have been grown, mixed as well as separately, by professional farmers, for "green meat,"— during the last half century. The former for cows, as affording not only much, but sweet, milk; the latter for cart horses*.

Clover.—Disposal.—P. 230. " Most of it is sold and delivered in London for the support of draught horses; and it is the general opinion, that it is more nourishing than any other hay, except sainfoin, and sells at about fifteen shillings a ton higher than meadow hay."

Sainfoin.—Disposal.—P. 233. " Sainfoin, is not grown in any part of this county; but the superior value of its hay is well known in the London markets: *it produces at least a guinea a ton more than meadow hay equally well cured.* It is brought from the chalk-hills of Surrey and Kent."

GRASS LAND.

The opening of this Reporter's chapter, " Grass," is altogether incomprehensible to ordinary understandings.
P. 219.

---

* For the culture of tare herbage; and a successful method of making it into hay;—see my *Minutes of Agriculture*, in *Surrey;*—those relating to tare herbage being written in 1775 and 1776; when tares and rye were, there, ordinary crops in husbandry.

P. 219. " *Natural meadows* are no where to be found, as all grass land which is in a state of nature, or uncultivated, is universally depastured.

" *Natural pastures* are, of course, the most wretched of all grass land; and, in this county, are only to be met with in commons."

Admitting that the world is natural,—that the atmosphere which involves it is natural,—that mountains and valleys are natural, and that rivers and the alluvial lands they have every where formed are natural,—surely, the herbage with which such lands have been covered, without the help of man,—some of them, possibly, before the being man set foot on the island,—ought to be deemed natural.

The author of the Report of Middlesex, however, arranges the river-formed grass lands of that County, under a conspicuous head (across the page)—ycleped " CULTIVATED MEADOWS and PASTURES"!! And, under that *monstrous head*, proceeds to describe them;—with satisfactory intelligence, and interesting information.

Border of the Lea.—P. 219. " There is some excellent grass land on the Middlesex side of this river, lying in the parishes of Enfield, Edmonton, Tottenham, &c. containing about one thousand acres; most of which is divided, by land marks, among a great number of proprietors, in pieces containing from a rood to four or five acres each. The meadows are opened for the reception of the cattle of every inhabitant of those parishes, from the 12th of August in every year, until the 5th of April in the following year. On the latter day the cattle are taken off; and soon afterwards the ground is prepared for a crop of hay, which it yields in July.

" This tract of land is occasionally flooded every winter; and also once in two or three years, in the summer, by water impregnated with manure, brought from the well-dressed and chalky lands of Hertfordshire. If these occasional floods were made to pass off in a few days, or so soon as they had deposited their enriching particles on the land, they would promote a very high degree of fertility; but unfortunately, the drainage is so interrupted from Stratford-le-bow to the Thames, that *the water is detained much too long on the land;* and, owing to the very nature of common meadows and pastures, the sewers, ditches, and drains, are so shamefully neglected, that *the soil is chilled, the best grasses destroyed, and a worthless herbage substituted in their place.*

" These meadows are said to produce about *a ton of ordinary hay per acre*, and are lett for about twenty-five shillings on an average. If they were inclosed and embanked,

banked, and a proper drainage obtained, they would be as well worth three or four pounds per acre."

Border of the Thames.—P. 220. " In many of the parishes on the Middlesex border of this river also, there are meadows and pastures, though of small extent, which are occasionally laid under water by floods in winter; and sometimes, though in a less degree, in summer. Perhaps there may be one hundred acres which are sometimes overflowed by particularly high tides. The water drains very readily off much of this land at the reflux of the tide, particularly so much of it as lies adjoining to the river. But some parts of it are situated rather more distant from the Thames, and the surface being nearly level, the water is more interrupted, and consequently runs very slowly off."

Borders of the Coln.—P. 221. " There are extensive meadows and pastures on the borders of this river, the whole way from Staines to Harefield. The soil is of a black, peaty, tender nature, and but little above the level of the river. Such of them as are inclosed and drained, are very fertile; but much the greater part of them are *Lammas-meads*, and one of the necessary consequences is, that *the ditches* are so much neglected as to be nearly grown up.

" The pastures are more than half covered with mole and ant hills; and, in some places, gravel has been dug from them in such quantities as to leave them under water.

" The drainage being wholly neglected, the land is consequently filled with water, and thereby rendered *unsound.* No farmer would hire it, if he were obliged to continue it in its present condition, *at any price;* but, if it were inclosed, and properly drained, the produce would yield from five to eight pounds per acre.

" The whole of the several tracts of grass land included in the foregoing description, contain about 2500 acres. They are subject to be flooded by sudden and heavy rains, even during the spring and summer months; and, when that happens early in the year, the water deposits among the growing grass quantities of sand, mud, slime, sticks, and weeds, which afterwards impede the operations of the scythe; and, above all, reduces the hay in value below the price of straw. *When such a flood takes place* after the grass is cut down, and before the hay is carried away, *it frequently floats the whole summer's produce on the surface of the water.* The occupiers of these lands have only the *entire* produce of them four months in a year; which, together with the risk of suffering such serious losses during that time, keeps down the rent and produce of this soil shamefully below that rank in the scale of productiveness, which

which, from its natural fertility, if aided only by a little art, it would be entitled to possess."

Isle of Dogs.—P. 223. "The isle of Dogs, containing about 1000 acres, lies at the south-east corner of this county, and would be overflowed every tide, were it not secured by an embankment. This ground is divided by ditches, which empty themselves through sluices, at low water, into the Thames, and keep this tract of land sufficiently dry."

" *Upland Meadows and Pastures.*—P. 223. "About seven-eighteenths of this county, or 70,000 acres, consist of grass land of this kind, great part, or nearly the whole of which, exhibits the usual marks of the plough."

Even where the surfaces of old grass lands are marked by the plow, the herbage is as natural, as where no such marks appear; and as it is on commons, sheep walks and wastes.

Man, it is true, can now *cultivate herbage,—can make* " *artificial grasses*"*!*—But if the soil be suffered to remain, only a few years, undisturbed, nature will not fail to treat silly man as a bungler; and cover the ground with a valuable assortment of natural plants which are better adapted to the soil, situation, and climature *.

Sheep Downs.—It has been shown, aforegoing, that the writer of the Report, under review, ranks sheep walks with wastes. In page 127, he opens a section on " Sheep Downs" alone; which he extends through five or six pages; without proving any thing (it will not to be too severe to say) but his own deficiency in correct knowledge concerning them.

MANAGEMENT of GRASS LANDS.—P. 225. "*Meadow land* in the occupation of *cow-keepers*, is generally mown two or three times in a summer. Their great number of cows enable them to dress it every year, *and they are studious to procure their hay of a soft grassy quality,* not letting it stand till the seedling stems rise, but mowing it two, three, or four weeks sooner than it would be advisable to do for the support of horses. This land lies near the town, as at Islington, Mary-le-bonne, Paddington, &c. and is usually mown the first time in each summer early in May."

HAYMAKING.—Mr. FOOT's systematic account of this operation

---

* For an ample proof of the correctness of the above position, see my YORKSHIRE; section, *Cultivated Herbage;* subsection, *mixed perennial Ley.* And for farther observations on the subject,—see the NORTHERN DEPARTMENT (of my present work); " County," *North-riding of Yorkshire.*—See also the ensuing article, *Young's Sussex,* in this volume.

operation is inserted, in p. 106, aforegoing. Mr. Middleton has copied much of it, without the accustomed marks of quotation; and has added to it some remarks of his own, and several notes from the margins of the former reports. I perceive nothing, however, among those additions, of sufficient interest to be noticed, here; saving an error of a learned annotator, concerning the *heating* of hay. This note-upon-note writer asserts, p. 247, that " it is the moisture received from the atmosphere, and not the sap of the grass, that is the general cause of the heating of hay. If the grass is dead, which it soon is in dry weather, and has not been wetted by rain, it may be early stacked with safety. But though it were never so dead and discoloured, if it has been drenched with rain, and stacked without being skin dry, it will most certainly heat."

No fact in rural affairs, I believe, is better ascertained than that it is the natural juice,—the sap of herbage—which generates heat—even unto flame; and that " water wet,"— as an unlettered hay farmer would say,—begets " mould and muck."

Mr. Middleton's leading remark, to the section under consideration, is perfectly just.—P. 237. " This branch of the rural art has, by the farmers of Middlesex, been brought to a degree of perfection altogether unequalled by any other part of the kingdom. The neat husbandry, and superior skill and management, that are so much, and justly, admired in the *arable* farmers of the best cultivated districts, may, with equal justice and propriety, be said to belong, in a very eminent degree, to the *hay* farmers of Middlesex."

The neighbourhood of London, where, and where only, hay farming, on a large scale, is a separate branch of business,—where hay fetches a price at market, according to its quality, and of course where the farmer's *profit* principally depends on the method of manufacture,—is certainly a proper place in which to study the process.

LIVESTOCK.

CATTLE.—*Breed.*—P. 327. " This county is not distinguished by any particular breed of *neat* cattle, as belonging peculiarly to itself; for most of the calves bred here are suckled till about ten weeks old, and then sold to the butchers, for the supply of the London and other markets, in the article of veal.

" In the pleasure-grounds of gentlemen, the Suffolk, Alderney,

derney, Jersey, Guernsey, Welsh, and Scotch breeds, are
mostly to be met with. The Holderness short-horned
breed are almost the only sort kept by cow-keepers for the
produce of milk for sale. The farmers in the more distant
parts of the county have a mixed breed, consisting of all
the foregoing kinds, which are employed by them in *suckling.*"

Cows for *Suckling.*—P. 327. " This practice is well
know to be more profitable than grazing, and less so than
the dairy. The latter is pretty nearly excluded from the
domestic economy of the farm-houses in this county, as the
farmers' wives, for the most part, have neither inclination,
industry, nor skill, sufficient for the management of a dairy;
and in suckling, the business is performed by men, as the
women (even the servants) will not go into a dirty cow-
house, and submit to the drudgery of milking, and attending the calves."

Cows for *Milk.*—Mr. Middleton has paid considerable
attention to this prominent subject of practice, in the metropolitan County. He has extended his article to nearly
a sheet of letterpress in length; including various extracts
from former Reports. The fresh matter, which is entitled,
I conceive, to a place here, as an addition to Mr. Foot's
account (p. 108, aforegoing) I here subjoin.

P. 329. " Mr. Baird says, ' that round Hackney, Islington, Paddington, and several miles thereabouts, the cow-
keepers engross every inch of land they can procure. Some
of these men have remarkable large stocks of cows. One
of them (Mr. West, of Islington), has, on different farms
which he possesses in that neighbourhood, very near eight
hundred.

" ' The cow-keepers breed very few cattle, and those
only from favourite cows (which become so merely from
their giving much milk), and with very little attention
to the choice of their bulls. Even in summer, and when
the grass is in the greatest plenty, the cows are regularly
fed with grains, which, though the quantity of milk is
thereby increased, by no means add to its quality.' The
general allowance is forty-five quarters of grains per week
(at 1s. 10d. per quarter) to every twenty-five cows. They
are given them twice a day, and they have, besides, two
meals of turnips and hay. ' Some cow-keepers have tried
salt mixed with the grains, more with a view to preserve
the grains longer in a sound state, than from any consideration as to the health of their stock, or the improvement
of the quality of the milk. It is acknowledged that the
cows eat the grains so mixed with great avidity; but the
proprietors

proprietors not getting an adequate return for their trouble and expence, I do not find that it is now much practised.'"

P. 335. " The milk is always given in its genuine state to the retail dealers; and, as it is sold to them by the cow-keepers after the rate of two-pence and 1-8th of a penny per quart, and is retailed by them at three-pence halfpenny per quart, the profit is surely so large as ought to prevent even the smallest adulteration.* But when it is considered how greatly it is reduced *by water*, and impregnated with *worse* ingredients, it is much to be lamented, that no method has yet been devised, to put a stop to the many scandalous frauds and impositions in general practice with regard to this very necessary article of human sustenance."

P. 336. " Five or six men only are employed in attending near three hundred cows. As one woman cannot milk more than eight or nine cows twice a day, that part of the business would necessarily be attended with considerable expence to the cow-keeper, where it not that the retailer, as before observed, agrees for the produce of a certain number of cows, and takes the labour and expence of milking on himself.

" Every cow-house is provided with a milk-room (where the milk is measured, and served out by the cow-keeper), and this room is mostly furnished with a pump, to which the retail dealers apply in rotation; not secretly but openly, before any person that may be standing by; from which they pump water into the milk vessels at their discretion. The pump is placed there expressly for that purpose, and indeed is very seldom used for any other. A considerable cow-keeper in Surrey has a pump of this kind, which goes by the name of the *famous black cow* (from the circumstance of its being painted black), and is said to yield more than all the rest put together.

" Where such a pump is not provided for them, things are much worse; for in that case the retailers are not even careful to use *clean* water."

P. 337. " A cow-keeper informs me, that the retail milk-dealers

---

* If the article were delivered, ready-milked, to the sellers, at their own homes, and retailed, *there*,—such a profit would indeed be exorbitant. But considering the laboriousness, or let it be put, the slavishness, of the trade of a London milk seller,—of a woman who can bear on her shoulders a limited quantity, only,—exposed in the winter season, at untimely hours, frequently in the severest weather,—her profit at those prices, with the privilege mentioned, may not be too great. It is not the material alone, but jointly with the labor bestowed upon it, that gives the fair selling price of a commodity. A few pounds of iron, when wrought into watch springs, may perhaps be worth a hundred guineas.

dealers are, for the most part, the refuse of other employments; possessing neither character, decency of manners, nor cleanliness."—This information I conceive to be incorrect.

" The same person suggests, *as a remedy for these abuses, that it would be highly proper for every retail milk-dealer to be obliged to take out an annual license from the magistrates:* which license should be granted only to such as could produce a certificate of good conduct, signed by the cowkeeper, and a certain number of their customers; and also on their being sworn to sell the milk pure and unadulterated:"—at, of course, an advanced price.—This would seem to be a practicable idea; and might become a valuable regulation.

Butter Dairy.—P. 338. " There is not, perhaps, a county in the kingdom, where a *smaller quantity* of this article is made, and certainly not any, where a *greater quantity* is consumed, than in Middlesex.

" As the farmers of this county employ their cows, for the most part, in suckling, the very small quantity of butter they make is principally for their own consumption; and what is made at the dairies of noblemen and gentlemen is, of course, intended solely for the use of their respective families: so that the astonishing consumption of this article in the metropolis and its environs, is almost entirely supplied from those counties where the dairy is more the object of the farmer; and from the sister kingdom."

The Reporter proceeds to describe the manner in which the Metropolis is supplied with this favorite luxury of its *native* inhabitants. His statement, however, is not well drawn up. The great supply of butter which is sent in, from Oxfordshire, Buckinghamshire, and Bedfordshire, under the name of " lump butter," and with which the middle classes of society in London are principally furnished, is not included in it. Fresh butter, we are told (p. 338.) comes from Norfolk, and salt butter from Cambridgeshire.

Fatting Cattle.—P. 327. " The wash of malt distilleries, which had for a considerable time been solely used for the purpose of fattening hogs, has of late years been applied to the fattening of oxen on a very extensive scale, both in this county and in Surrey. Mr. Liptrap, of Whitechapel, has fattened many beasts in this manner; and at a single house in Battersea (Surrey), stalls have been erected to accommodate 500 at a time. They have a little hay or straw given them once a day, to enable them to chew the cud; they both stand and lie on a framing (a kind of trellis) of woodwork, raised a little above the pavement, and are not allowed straw, or any substitute for it, for bedding. This beneficial

beneficial practice is extending itself very much, and is, as well as the feeding of hogs by the same means, a very considerable improvement, and must be of great advantage to the community."

SHEEP.—*Breed.*—P. 345. " There is not any particular breed of sheep distinguished from the rest, as exclusively belonging to the county. Indeed the farmers of Middlesex employ their land more profitably, than could be done by breeding and rearing sheep to any greater age than to be slaughtered either as house or grass lambs."

Purchase and *Number kept.*—P. 345. " The farmers buy their sheep at the fairs in Wiltshire and Hampshire, and of the jobbers of west-country sheep at fairs within the county. ' The flocks differ in number, in proportion to the right of common appertaining to the respective farms.' "

P. 346. " Sheep are kept in this county all the year round, only where there are common rights sufficient to support them from Candlemas till the after-grass is ready to receive them.

" On the commons above Riselip and Pinner, there are many kept, and folded on the arable land."

Diseases of Sheep.—The following suggestions appear to be worthy of attention.—P. 349. " *Sheep* that have been reared and constantly pastured *on chalk-hills*, such as the south and west country downs, *are free from the rot* so long as they are continued in those situations. I have heard the same remarked of salt marshes, and that sheep with diseased livers, brought from rotting gound, heal and become fat in these marshes. *Rotten sheep have in many instances been cured by feeding on the herbage growing in a thin soil on limestone rock.*

" Reasoning on these premises, I am inclined to think that *on all soils strongly calcarious, and properly drained, sheep will continue sound.*

" It seems to be highly probable, that *the most rotting soil may be cured of that defect, after it is well drained, by the addition of a proper quantity of calcarious matter; such as either lime, chalk, or marl.*"

HOUSE LAMB.—Nearly the same observation may be offered, concerning Mr. Middleton's account of producing fat lambs, in winter, as that which I have made on Mr. Foot's, p. 110, aforegoing. The practice, conducted on a large scale, is local. In the neighbourhood of the Metropolis, it may be considered as a branch of business, to which belongs many nice points of management; and much experience is required to render it profitable. A few un-

digested

digested particulars, even if accurately set down by a practitioner, would be of little value *.

POULTRY.—*Turkies.*—N. p. 359. " It is now found of the
greatest use, when young turkies come too early, or when
the season is cold, to bathe them every morning in cold
water, for eight or ten days, and to give them a pepper-
corn every day."

BEES.—P. 379. " There are no bees of any consequence
kept in the county. We rarely see a hive at a farm-house,
and perhaps not ten cottages in the county have any."

PROFIT of FARMING.—P. 83. " The *Profits* of farming,
under the old rotation of two crops of corn and a fallow,
have seldom afforded more than a mere subsistence to the
farmer, and the means of establishing his children to run
the same course. But even this is no proof against the
profits of farming at per cent. on the capital employed,
which is generally so small a sum, that the foregoing produce may be a large per centage, and with sedulous attention this has been the fact, as the accounts of particular
families, produced to me, have demonstrated a profit of 32
per cent per ann on the sum employed, for thirty-five
years in succession.† Indeed it seems to be evident, that
a man who employs only 500*l.* and with it brings up a large
family, and places them in a situation equal to his own,
while himself retires with an easy fortune, could not have
done it with a less return."

P. 84. " This account shall be closed with the following
statement of the produce and expence of 150 acres of good
grass land, at eight miles distance from St. James's hay-
market.

	£.
" Hedge-rows, and waste of the farm are 20 acres; the mowing ground is 130, which yields at one cutting 260 loads of hay, and which have been sold for five or six years to average 5*l.* is	1300
" The after feed sold for	65
" Total produce per annum	1365"
" Total expences	620
" Remains, for rent, and attention	£745

which is nearly equivalent to 5*l.* an acre. Suppose the
party

---

* In the octavo edition of my Minutes of Agriculture in Surrey, I
have attempted to convey the *rationale* of the practice.

† See the head, *Rent*, p. 125, aforegoing, on this topic.

party to pay 3*l.* an acre rent, it will leave 2*l.* which, on 150 acres, is 300*l.* a year profit, or 40 per cent. upon the capital employed."

This, I must not refrain from saying, is, in my opinion, deviating more widely, on one side of the true line of percentage, than ten percent. (including interest on capital) is on the other.

For discussions on this topic, see NORTHERN DEPARTMENT—County of *Northumberland;* and EASTERN DEPARTMENT—County of *Suffolk.*

SOUTH

SOUTH ESSEX.

IN REVIEWING the Reports from the EASTERN DEPART-MENT, I examined those from Essex; so far as its lands and their culture resemble those of *Suffolk*, and may be properly considered as a continuation of the soil and management of that County.

The principal line which I then drew, as the right boundary between the *eastern* and the *southern* Departments, were the ESTUARY of the BLACKWATER RIVER,—continuing the line of separation,—agreeably to the nature of the soils, and the established plan of management,—by MAL-DEN, DUNMOW, and SAFFRON WALDEN, to the confine of Cambridgeshire.—*That* portion of the County I named *Northeast Essex;* and assigned the remainder of it to the SOUTHERN DEPARTMENT*.

SOUTH ESSEX naturally separates into three Divisions, or DISTRICTS; namely, 1. The *Forest and Dairy District;* which occupies the southwest quarter of the County, bordering on Middlesex. 2. *The Vale Lands of Essex;* which fill the more central parts. And 3. *The Marsh Lands*, or " Hundreds of Essex;" which form the southeastern quarter; accompanying the northern bank of the Thames to near the Metropolis; whose more immediate environs form the lower extreme of the *Vale of London†*.

Four distinct Reports have been sent in to the Board, from the County of Essex; namely, the " original Report," by Messrs. GRIGG;—the *second original* (in the 4to form with broad margins, and has not been " reprinted,"—of course not published), by Mr. VANCOUVER;—the third, by the late Mr. HOWLETT (not printed);—the last, by the Secretary of the Board,—who has incorporated much of Mr. Howlett's MS. (it would seem) and some of Mr. Vancouver's remarks, with his own:—so forming two bulky octavo volumes.

" GENERAL

---

* My motives, for this division of the County, may be seen in the EASTERN DEPARTMENT; article, *Northeast Essex.*

† The northwest corner of Essex assimilates, in soil and management, with Hertfordshire.

"GENERAL VIEW

OF THE

AGRICULTURE

OF THE COUNTY OF

ESSEX,

WITH

OBSERVATIONS ON THE MEANS OF ITS IMPROVEMENT.

By MESSRS. GRIGGS,

OF HILL HOUSE, NEAR KELVEDON, IN ESSEX.

1794."

IN ABSTRACTING the Reports from the *Eastern Department* of England, a few extracts were taken from this diminutive sketch;—relating to the *northeast* or the Suffolk side of the County; and I here insert a few passages, which belong to the *southern*, or the Thames and Middlesex side.

POOR LAWS.—The Reporters, speaking of the " Obstacles to Husbandry," say (what has often been intimated by other writers)—P. 24. " Another circumstance which would aid the plough, it is conceived, is liberty to the poor to seek a livelihood where ever work offers, or inclination leads them to seek for it, instead of being subject to be taken up, if found out of their own parish, and carried to what is called to their place of settlement, at the caprice of an overseer, to sit at home, or what is worse, while they have any credit left, at the alehouse, for want of employ; labourers will then, it is presumed, naturally be led to reside, where they could render most service to the community, and have a prospect of supporting themselves and families, without being reduced to the mortifying application to an unfeeling parish officer."

PUBLIC DRAINAGE.—P. 25. " An object, not perhaps beneath the notice of this most useful institution, is thought to be a general commission of sewers, for the repairs and preservation of the sea walls along the coast, which protect the lands most capable of improvement, from the destructive inundations of the salt water, which is known to leave such fatal effects behind it, that the land is not worth the

tillage

tillage for several years after it has been overflown; besides, that the expence and trouble which may have been laid out upon it, are for ever lost. At present, it is common for the owners of land, to manage their own walls according to their own discretion, by which means, the neglect of an individual, may cause not only ruin to himself, but to many of his more careful neighbours, and spread a general distress around him."

ARABLE CROPS.—P.12. " In the southeast corner" (doubtlessly the Marshland District) " farming seems to be as near, if not nearer perfection, than in any other part of Essex. The land is in general of a deep, rich, tender, loamy quality, and, as in other parts, rather farmed than grazed. The crops of wheat, beans, oats, coleseed or rape, mustard, and in short of any thing that is sown, afford a great return, compared with the common produce of land. The wheat is not unfrequently found to rise to a load an acre; oats (particularly the Poland), to eleven or twelve quarters, and beans and other corn in proportion. Some of this land has been known to produce five or six of the most exhausting crops successively, without a fallow or other particular usage, affording large crops of each. Wheat has been sown three successive years upon the same field, and the crops, upon an average, have amounted to four quarters per acre, the first, from the too great richness of the soil, being the least."

This information is in praise of the *soil*, of Essex, not of the *management* of its *husbandmen!* I insert it, here, as it conveys an interesting fact (I take for granted) in English agriculture; tho not a singular one.

LIVESTOCK —P. 23. " If Essex fails in any part of husbandry, it is in the kind of stock it sends to market, which seem to be bought in without any sort of preference to this or that particular breed. In the course of a few miles ride, you will see North and South Wales, Irish and most other sorts of cattle, Norfolk, Hertfordshire, Lincoln, Wilts, &c. sheep, and not uncommonly two or three different kinds in the same field."

DAIRY.—P. 13. " Our largest dairy farms are at, or in the neighbourhood of Epping, so deservedly famous for the richness of its cream and butter. The farmer even here confines himself to no particular sort of cows, but keeps up a stock of promiscuous cattle, bought in as opportunities offer, though indeed the more provident of them say, where the land is particularly good, the Derby and Leicestershires have a preference. These in the summer are fed with the natural and artificial grasses, and in the winter with hay (which is in general of the best quality) and grains. The best

best dairies are built on the north side of the farm houses, calculated to be always cool; and are furnished with square troughs, lined with lead, sufficient to hold nine or ten gallons of milk, which is seldom suffered to be *more* than five or six inches deep; this, in winter, is skimmed four, and, in summer, two or three times; and the cream, after being kept three or four days, is churned into butter; and the milk, after it will afford no more cream, is given to the hogs, which it fattens to most delicious pork."

The dairy practice of Essex, and that of Buckinghamshire &c., appear, pretty evidently, to have risen from the same root.

"GENERAL VIEW

OF THE

AGRICULTURE

IN THE COUNTY OF

ESSEX;

WITH

OBSERVATIONS ON THE MEANS OF ITS IMPROVEMENT.

By CHARLES VANCOUVER.

1795."

ON the QUALIFICATIONS of this Reporter, as a writer on rural affairs, I have had repeated occasions to speak; namely, in the EASTERN DEPARTMENT, *Waterlands* of *Cambridgeshire*, and *Northeast Essex ;* and in the MIDLAND DEPARTMENT, *Uplands* of *Cambridgeshire.*—Suffice it, therefore to say, here, that Mr. Vancouver has evinced, especially in his Survey of Cambridgeshire, extraordinary exertion and perseverance; and that his knowledge of rural concerns, as well as his manner of communicating the information acquired, is superior to many or most of the Board's Reporters.

Mr. Vancouver's PLAN of *Survey, in Cambridgeshire,* was to examine every parish in the County, and to put down the extent, the soil &c., the state of appropriation, the state of drainage, and a few other circumstances, belonging

ing to the natural, political, and rural economy of each, *in detail;* and, at the close of each parochial journal, to insert a wide-spreading table, exhibiting several more minute, though not perhaps less important, matters, *at one view;*—afterward reporting, in a digested form, the general information relating to the County at large;—together with his own opinions and sentiments concerning the several subjects touched upon,—in a distinct part of the Work, termed " Part II."

His survey of *Essex,* though made on the same general principle, differs in its minutiæ. Instead of giving, in detail, the several particulars, as to soil &c. &c. &c. of *each parish,* he throws the County into fourteen *Districts;* and gives a cursory report of each; with a table of sundry particulars of information at the close of each district.

In the Essex, as in the Cambridgeshire Report, a " second Part" is added; stating, in many instances, the existing circumstances, and the prevailing practices, of the County at large, at the time of reporting; but setting forth, more generally, the Reporter's own sentiments on the subjects brought forward.

My mode of abstraction, in *this* case, has been to systematize, agreeably to the general plan of my present Work, the particulars which have engaged my attention in going through the volume (no matter whether in the " Journal," or the " second Part") and which, I conceive, will be conducive to its value.

Mr. Vancouver's districts from which I have selected the following particulars of information are the sixth (in part), the whole of the seventh, eighth, ninth, tenth, and eleventh, and the principal part of the fourteenth. These districts and parts of districts are principally included within the following outlines :—the sea coast, on the east :—the Thames, on the south:—the river Lea, on the west: and, on the north, an almost straight line, passing nearly by Walthamstow, Epping, Ongar, Chelmsford, the river Chelmar, and the Estuary of the Blackwater river, to the British sea. For the situation of each, see the next page.

The number of pages—two hundred and thirteen.

A map of districts.

SUBJECT

SUBJECT THE FIRST.

NATURAL ECONOMY.

SOILS.—On this subject of Report Mr. V. has bestowed great attention. At the head of each of his districts, he has given, in a few words, the specific qualities of the lands which they severally contain; and then leads his reader across the area of each; describing to him the particular sorts of soils and substrata, *that fell in his way.* The former statements being sufficiently descriptive, to convey a general idea of the lands of South Essex, I readily give them a place, here.

District seven;—situated between the Estuary of the river Blackwater and the river Crouch, nearly corresponding with the hundred of Dengy.—P. 64. "Temperate and heavy mixed soil, upon a brown tender clay, a gravelly loam, a brick and a tile earth."

District eighth;—comprizing the main land of the hundred of Rochford; being situated between the Crouch and the Estuary or mouth of the Thames.—P. 71. "Temperate mixed soil, upon a gravelly loam, a gravel, and a brick earth."

District ninth;—the islands in the Estuary, and at the mouth, of the Thames.—P. 77. "The islands of Foulness, Wallasea, Potton, Haven-Gore, New England, and Canvey.—All consisting of a deep rich hazel coloured loam, upon a fine sea sand or silt, ouze, or sea clay: the husbandry of which, equally applies to the embanked marshes, and all such lands as have been produced by, and enclosed at different times from the sea."

District the tenth;—a small tract, situated to the north of Canvey Island, within the hundred of Barnstable.— P. 83. "Strong heavy mixed soil upon a brown clay, or brick earth, a gravelly loam, and a tough red clay, or tile earth."

District the eleventh;—bordering on the Thames, on the south;—the towns of Romford, Brentwood, and Billerricay standing near its northern margin.—P. 86. "Being that of a temperate mixed soil, upon a sandy and a gravelly loam, a pure sand, a pure gravel, a chalk, a brick, and some tile earth."

District the fourteenth;—adjacent to the County of Middlesex; including the dairy and forest lands.—P. 109.
"Temperate

" Temperate mixed soil, upon a gravelly loam, a yellow
woodland clay, a brick, and a tile earth, and a chalky
clay."

SUBJECT THE SECOND.

POLITICAL ECONOMY.

APPROPRIATION.—P. 110. " The adjacent forests
of Epping and Henhault, are viewed as an intolerable
nuisance, and are equally regarded as such, at Chigwell
and at Loughton, where the farmers uniformly declare,
that the privilege of commonage is by no means equal
to the one tenth part of the losses they constantly sustain
from the deer in breaking down their fences, trespassing
upon their fields, and destroying their crops either ripe
or green. Against these depredators it is further alledged,
that there are no fences, however laboriously contrived,
expensive, and formidable against other animals, that will
in any wise avail : add to this, that the evil is continually
increasing from the annual increase in the stock of deer.

" These forests, so near the metropolis, are well known
to be the nursery and resort of the most idle and profligate
of men : here the under graduates in iniquity commence
their career with deer stealing, and here the more finished
and hardened robber secrets himself from justice, or retires for a time with his plunder from his haunts in London,
where his arrest is certain whenever it is determined by
the master robber, or the robber catcher, that the active
and actual robber is to be *done*."

The Improvement of which the County of Essex is capable of receiving, by the complete *Appropriation* of its
Commonable Lands.—P. 185. " A general statement of the
improvement, which by enclosing and laying into severalty,
may be annually made on the present rent or value of the
open common fields and waste lands, in this County.

" By a reference to the minutes taken on the
    survey, it appears, that the arable land in
    about forty parishes in the county, lies very
    much in open common fields ; and which,
    in point of quantity, is found to average
    about 1,200 acres per parish. This amounts
    in the whole to 48,000 acres ; the excess
    whereof in the annual rent or value from
    enclosure and laying into severalty, would
    according to the general average table, be
                                    4s. 6d.

4s. 6d. per acre, and consequently form an
annually increased income or revenue of £10,800 0   0
" By enclosing or embanking from the sea
4,600 acres of salt marsh, an acquisition to
that extent would be made to the national
territory, and yield to the individual owners
annually 15s. 6d. per acre, equal to 3,565 0   0
" By enclosing for cultivation 10,370 acres of
thicks or forest lands, unfit for the growth
of oak timber, thereby improving its rent
or annual value 12s. 6d. per acre 6,481 5   0
" By enclosing and laying into severalty
14,237 acres of waste or common land,
thereby increasing its annual rent or value
11s. 4d. per acre, equals 5,067 12 8
                                                                   ─────────────
                                                                   £25,913 17 8"
                                                                   ─────────────

For farther information, see the head *Summary*, at the
close of this article.

PUBLIC EMBANKMENT.—See above.

PAUPERAGE.—This Reporter of Essex is the first writer
whom I have heard to speak of the *revenues of the poor*.
Not in the way of modest intimation.   He boldly declares
that "as revenues of the poor, they may now with as much
propriety, as roundly and as correctly be asserted, as any
other revenue drawn from the subject, and attaching upon
the crown." p. 159.

And on this foundation he builds his plan of reform.
The first step of which is this:—p. 160. " Let the average
value of labour in every parish be correctly ascertained,
and let an argumentation thereon be made equal to the
annual amount of the *present poor's rates* in such parish."

Now, it has so happened, in the very County of Essex,
that what *was* the " present poor's rates" in a parish,
has lately been, and I fear *still is*, tenfold greater ; and
what is, *now*, may, in no great length of time, be tenfold less.

That the present " Poor Laws" of this Country are, as
a punster might say, poor indeed, every one seems to be
well aware.   I have not, however, found them more forcibly *satirized* than in the subjoined extract.

P. 161. " How different the whole design from the me-
lancholy experience of thousands, who in the present day,
and in the case of settlement only, are no longer treated
as sensible and rational beings, but are hunted like wild
beasts from parish to parish, not because they have of-
fended against the laws of their country, or otherwise
                                                              possess

possess evil, which ought to be avoided; but too often
because they may have piqued the parish officers; or that
some of those gentlemen may occasionally wish for a
frolick, at the expence of the parish, or for an agreeable
excursion in a post chaise: but this, together with the
immense sums annually expended in legal contests concerning the removal and settlement of paupers, and which
are necessarily charged to the account of the poor, would
on a certainty be saved, were an arrangement generally
adopted, somewhat similar in principle to that above
stated."

SUBJECT THE THIRD.

RURAL ECONOMY.

TENANTED ESTATES.

IMPROVING ESTATES.—Forming *Drinking Places*
for Pasturing Stock.—P. 78. (Marshland Islands.) " From
the situation, general structure, and materials, of which
these islands are formed; it is obvious, that they can
afford no springs of water; and consequently, that the only
supply for drinking, or for fencing, is to be obtained from
the rain, or from the melted snows: this forms but a precarious and scanty dependance, which in the summer season
is frequently dried up, or by putrefaction rendered extremely injurious to the health of the inhabitants, and too
frequently also to that of the horses and cattle: Hence
there are but few resident occupiers in the islands; and in
particular dry seasons, the larger stock are driven from
Foulness to Shoebury for water; and in like manner from
the other islands, and embanked marshes, the cattle are
driven at much expence and inconvenience to water upon
the higher lands."

These natural inconveniences, or shall we say distressing
circumstances, might surely be alleviated, or removed,
by art. An inclined plane of one eighth of an acre in
extent (more or less according to given circumstances,
and as experience would soon point out:—in ordinary
cases a few square rods would be sufficient),—with a
spacious receptacle on the lower side of it, would collect,
in the course of twelve months, rain water sufficient to
supply, with wholesome beverage, a numerous herd of cattle,
during the grazing season.

The method of forming artificial pools is now *known*,
and

and is in general practice, in different parts of the kingdom. See my YORKSHIRE. Also TREATISE on LANDED
PROPERTY.

The collecting surface might be *formed* with the natural
soil of the marshlands; and be *covered* in various ways. If
of great extent, *clay*, condensed as in pond-making, and
strewed, from time to time, with *clean sand*, to fill the
cracks, and render it impervious to *running* water, would be
sufficient. More confined slopes might be covered with
flags, *slates*, or *tiles*, applied as on a roof; and might be
found more effective than clay and sand. In either case,
the expence would be found inconsiderable, comparatively
with the benefit which would certainly arise from it.

For other serious evils, occasioned by a want of good
water in those marshes, see the article *Grass Land*, ensuing.

AGRICULTURE.

FARMS.—P. 167. " One very material error exists in the
present mode of occupying farms throughout this county;
which is that of one person monopolizing several farms, and
holding them as it is termed, ' off hand.' These farms lie
frequently detached and very wide of each other, and a
looker or superintendant, at ten or twelve shillings per
week, occupies the ruins of the old mansion or farm house,
which was heretofore the seat of hospitality, industrious
emulation, or modest virtue. In the course of the tour,
it was observed, with much indifference by an overgrown
farmer's wife, ' that her husband had *but* nine farms in his
occupation;' each of which upon further enquiry was found
to be equal to the care and capital of the same number of
equally skilful and respectable, although perhaps not such
wealthy and imperious families."

PLAN of MANAGEMENT.—By Mr. V's Journal, this varies,
minutially, in every district. But, viewing South Essex at
large, the following would seem to be the prevailing practice; and a better I believe is not at present known.

On the more absorbent, free-working lands, an autumn,
winter, and spring fallow, for turneps or rape; to be succeeded by spring corn and mixed herbage, is prevalent.
On the stronger, more retentive, less friable soils, an
eighteen months' fallow; to be followed by the same.

The subjoined passage evidences the lasting benefit,
which may arise, and which may reasonably be expected,
from an EIGHTEEN MONTHS' FALLOW; namely, a
                                                    fallow

fallow broken up soon after harvest, and continued, as the
given circumstances of the soil, the weather, and intervals
of leisure will point out, until the spring-twelve-month
following :—

P. 75. " Upon the temperate lands, first, thorough summer and winter fallow for oats or barley, with which sow
sixteen pounds of red clover, or in lieu thereof, six pounds
of white Dutch clover, and ten pounds of trefoil per acre.
Clover ley sown with wheat, the etches of which are
dunged, and sown with beans that are kept well howed
through the summer, and again sown with wheat; after
which, a crop of oats or barley is sometimes taken, but
most generally the wheat stubbles are haulmed, and sown
with winter tares for spring food, then dunged and prepared for coleseed, fed with hogs, left for a crop, and
succeeded with wheat; the stubbles of which, are dunged,
sown with beans, which are kept well hoed and fallowed by
a second crop of wheat; then fallow in course, for oats or
barley. In this routine of crops, a thorough summer and
winter fallow, and a short preparation for coleseed only
occurs once in twelve years :"—a succession of benefits,
these, which it might be said, are purchased for the pit-
tance of one twelfth of a year's rent, annually.

On the *marshlands*, that are embanked from the tide, the
following appears to be an established practice.—P. 80.
(Foulness Islands.) " The most approved husbandry in these
islands, and in those embanked marshes along the coast,
which have been enclosed a great length of time from the
sea, and have not been chalked; is first to apply chalk upon
the ley or swerd ground, about six waggon-loads, of ninety
bushels each, to the acre. This dressing is recommended
to lie upon the surface for three or four years; the marsh
then to be very neat and fleetly ploughed, and sown with
white oats upon the flag."

MANURE.—*Species*.—The favorite manure, in South Essex,
seems, by the report under view, to be *chalk rubbish*,—
from the quarries on the Kentish side of the Thames. A
native marl is also repeatedly spoken of, under the names
of " chalky clay," " blue and white clay," &c. The *dung*
of animals, it appears, was, in the richer parts, of the
County, considered, until of late years, a troublesome encumbrance on a farm.

Chalk.—This is conveyed, by water carriage, up the
Estuaries of the Blackwater and the Crouch, and other
creeks and inlets of the Thames and its mouth; where
wharfs have been formed to receive it; and, from these,
by land carriage, into the more interior parts.

P. 65.

P. 65. " A considerable expence is annually incurred through this neighbourhood" (Southminster) " in chalking the stiff heavy lands, and of which the following account may be taken as the average per ann.

" Eight waggons of 90 bushels each, costing at the
    wharf, or landing place, 11s. per load £4 8 0
Carting, filling, and spreading the same at 10s. 6d.
    per load 4 4 0

                               £8 12 0

Which dressing is supposed to act with an almost un-abating force for the first twenty years, following a lapse of three years (which time is allowed for the chalk to melt down and incorporate with the soil) from the time that it was first applied or spread upon the ground. The same expence frequently occurs in chalking the marshes; but its effects there, are neither so observable, or so permanent, as upon the stronger higher lands."

P. 190. (From an intelligent communication by the Rev. H. BATE DUDLEY.) " Chalk rubbish brought in vessels from the Kentish cliffs has been the principal manure, or rather *alterative*, to the ploughed lands here time immemorially. Horse, and other dung, till within a few years, were esteemed of no value, and therefore not carted on the land.—Eight waggon loads of chalk, value 11s. a load, without cartage, are a good dressing per acre which in fair husbandry will be productive twenty years.

" The universal opinion, that land once chalked would never receive benefit from rubbish a second time, is now found fallacious by daily experience; but the stiff-soiled old chalked lands, require that the second dressing should be previously mixed with bank or other earth."

Notwithstanding those and several other favourable ac-counts of the effects of chalk, Mr. V. in his " second Part," under the head " Manure," inserts the following observa-tions;—*as* from his own knowledge.—P. 144. " Where the length of carriage has not forbid the use of chalk, it has in-dubitably produced for a time upon the tough heavy clays in this county, very beneficial consequences; the practice however, begins to be much deplored, and that by very observing and able persons, on a supposition, that the old chalked lands, at this day, are equally obstinate, and far more steril than they otherwise would have been, if chalk had never been applied."

Marl.—P. 59. (In Widford near Chelmsford.)—" The chalky clay has been applied very successfully upon the gravelly soils in this parish, thirty loads of forty bushels each to the acre.

                                 " Stubbing,

" Stubbing, filling, and spreading the same, at 6s.
    per score £0 9 0
" Four horses, two tumbrells, and a driver, five
    days, at 15s. per day 3 15 0
" Allowance for beer upon stubbing, filling and
    spreading 0 1 6
" Ditto for the driver 0 1 3

                                £4 6 9."

Lime.—P. 84. "The length of carriage through the northern parts of this district," (10th) "has in a great measure precluded the use of chalk, and lime has there been substituted in its place, mixed with earth, and farm yard dung."

ARABLE CROPS.—For the *produce* of arable crops, see the close of the present article.

In his "second Part," Mr. V. has opened a section under the title "Crops." But it contains little more than theoretic intimations.

POTATOES.—Essex has long been noted as *a land of potatoes.* I find not, however, in this report of its practices, any resemblance of a regular detail of the established cultivation of that useful root.

RAPE SEED.—P. 94. (Neighbourhood of Romford.) "Rapeseed is transplanted at twelve inches square upon the potatoe land, costs a guinea per acre, generally stands for a crop, and is always found to answer extremely well. This practice is strongly recommended where wheat straw is in much demand, as the straw of the rape seed, affords an excellent substitute for littering the straw yards, the cow sheds, and the stall fed cattle."

RAPE HERBAGE.—P. 55. "The land belonging to the Borough of Malden, varies from a strong well stapled earth upon a brown tender clay, to a light gentle soil upon a gravel; upon the former a great deal of coleseed is sown for soil; mown and carried off to the cattle by the end of February, and succeeded with oats or barley."

P. 72. (Neighbourhood of Rochford.) "Coleseed is frequently sown and fed off green with *hogs*, and then left to stand for a crop, which is said to answer extremely well."

P. 73. "In this neighbourhood" (Pakelsham) "a great deal of coleseed is sown for sheep food, or mown and carried to the fattening cattle, to which it is given in the yard, or in the stalls, mixed with hay. The dung produced in this way, is esteemed particularly strong and good."

GRASS LAND.—In this report of South Essex, no other mention is made of its permanent grass lands, than what relates to the *marshes*, or waterformed lands.

                                    What

What strikes most forcibly, concerning those lands, is their want of fertility, comparatively with most other " salt marshes," in the island. In the want of sweet water they are not peculiar; tho, in this respect, they appear to be more than usually deficient. See *Drinking Places*, p. 156, aforegoing.

P. 67. " Whilst the marshes remain in pasture, their herbage is very indifferent, and incapable of fattening a beast of more than twenty-four score; and even not that, in a dry summer. Small Welsh runts, and Norfolk ewes, are the stock usually grazed; but the latter must be kept upon the clovers during the early part of the summer, or the lambs will not thrive."

P. 79. " About two and a half acres of the feeding marshes are usually allowed during the six summer months, to the grazing of a runt of about thirty-six score: horses, cows, and sheep are generally depastured in the same marshes for the remainder of the year, feeding them down as close, and as bare as possible by the end of January, at which time they are shut up for the spring, and for the early summer's growth."

P. 65. " The embanked marshes, which are here very productive and extensive, consist chiefly of a deep hazel-coloured loam, upon a very fine sea sand or silt. This property is extremely valuable; and would be much more so were it possible to command a supply of water during the dry season : so long as the springs are flush upon the higher country, the water continues tolerably abundant and wholesome; and is diffused through the different levels with great equality, judgment and œconomy: but when those resources fail, which unfortunately is too often the case in the summer season, the distresses in these marshes for drinking-water, and for fencing, are very great indeed."

P. 79. " The Scots and other cattle, brought from countries watered with lively and refreshing streams, are very subject to the red-water about Midsummer, but which being timely observed, the remedy is not very difficult. A scouring also frequently comes on about Michaelmas, which is only to be stopped by immediate removal and change of food; if long unobserved or neglected, it always proves fatal. The pole-evil and fistula are extremely troublesome among the horses, every effort to prevent their gathering has hitherto proved ineffectual, and to cure them after the ulcer is broke, is held to be a very uncertain and almost endless task. The young horses which are bred and depastured through these islands, in very dry seasons, are subject to a disease, which relaxes their whole frame, and occasions them to tumble and stagger about in a most
extraordinary

extraordinary manner. They are frequently found sitting upon their hind parts, like cats before a fire. This is referred to the badness of the water, and like the scouring among the bullocks, if taken in time, is to be remedied by an immediate removal to the higher lands, which gradually restores the use of the limbs; but there is no change of food, of situation, or of care afterwards, that can completely restore the animal to its natural vigour."

P. 87. "The commons and low grounds in these parishes, called the fen, though strong good land, and in general affording very good herbage, are, from their being subject to frequent inundations from the higher country, found to communicate the rot in sheep, and at such times very much to injure the cattle that depasture upon them."

P. 157. (The Reporter's own remarks in "Part II.") "The islands bordering upon the sea coasts, (Mersea excepted) and the lands which have been produced by, and embanked at different periods from the sea, were formerly under pasture, but of late years a considerable portion of them have been brought under the plough."

LIVESTOCK.

P. 117. (Part II.) "The great variety of soil in this county, and the consequent difference of herbage in a very small space, has doubtless contributed very largely to that intermixture of breeds among the sheep and cow cattle, with which the primest of the grass lands through the county are generally depastured: but though this observation applies to the county at large, it does not extend locally, and through those particular districts, where the herbage, from time immemorial to the present period, has neither degenerated or improved, and where, without question, the pastures employed for particular purposes, would favour the breed of one species of stock, rather than that of another.

"That these matters have hitherto been too much disregarded is plain, for in the richest and most luxuriant pastures, are too frequently found, an assemblage of the refuse stock, and cullings of the adjacent, the northern, and western counties of the kingdom."

CATTLE.—P. 118. "The stock of *cow cattle* in most parts of the kingdom (if we except the breeding counties) is chiefly appropriated to two purposes, viz. the dairy, and for grazing; in this county, a third may be added, that of suckling, or feeding calves for the London market. The rank which these different modes of appropriation holds in the

the estimation of the Essex farmer is, first, the dairy; second, suckling, and third, grazing.

" With regard to the first, so much depends upon the unwearied exertions of the mistress, both early and late, that unless the farmer's wife is able and willing to encounter such fatigue, little profit can accrue to the farmer therefrom."

DAIRY.—Cows.—P. 111. (In the Epping quarter.)—" As a large proportion of this country is laid into grass or pasture ground, the dairy, with some suckling business, is most generally pursued; but for either of these purposes there does not appear to be that necessary choice or general preference to any particular breed of cows, which it should seem that the soil, the herbage, and the peculiar appropriation of the milk, most essentially requires."

P. 118. " In the country about Epping and Ongar, this business is carried on extensively, but where in general there seems to be no particular choice or preference as to breed, or the stock of cows best suited to the purpose. The Norfolk, Suffolk, Derby, Lincoln, Leicester, Craven, Holderness, North and South Wales, and Galloway breeds, are indiscriminately mixed together, and constitute the principal dairies throughout that neighbourhood."

Diseases of Cows.—P 61. (Billericay.) " In this neighbourhood the cows are particularly liable to slip calf, which is generally ascribed to an infectious effluvia proceeding from the first false birth, the ill effects of which is supposed to be in a great measure prevented from spreading, by immediately burying the abortion, burning straw directly over the place, and smearing the hind parts of the cow with tar; but above all, keeping her separate, and as far apart as possible from the other cows, ought never to be neglected; various reasons are assigned as the cause of this accident, but none that appear conclusive, or satisfactorily explained."

P. 68. " The accident of slipping calf, which through this neighbourhood" (Rettendon) " was very prevalent some years ago, is now thought to be very much checked by the practice of bleeding the cows when they are about one-third of their time gone with calf."

P. 127. (Part II.) " The accidents and diseases, to which all cows are liable, are so well known" (?) " that it may not be necessary to state any thing further than a few suggestions, applying to those cases which are but too frequent, and fatally experienced in this county. Bleeding when the cows are from one-third to half gone with calf, is earnestly recommended as a preventive against premature calving, and when the accident does happen, to bury the abortion
immediately

immediately, and to keep the cow as widely apart as possible from the herd. To be particularly careful that she does not receive the bull, which herds with the other cows, at least not till after such a lapse of time, as with good reason she may be thought completely recovered, and free from the possibility of communicating the smallest infection."

I insert those remarks, tho I am not convinced by them that *abortion*, in cows, is *infectious*. Nevertheless, it *may* be so;—and the above notices may serve to agitate the subject, and promote observation; as well as to instruct those who may *believe* in it.

Butter Dairy.—P. 58. (Sandon in the Chelmsford quarter.) " The business of butter-making has been in a great measure relinquished in this parish, from the want of good spring water, and a smoaky taste, which is communicated to the butter, when the cows feed upon some particular pastures, or when foddered with the hay which is mown from them. This has hitherto baffled every means of cure or prevention. When the cows are fed upon tares, other grass, or hay, very good butter is readily obtained; and even when fed upon turnips, cabbages, or that they gather up the fallen leaf; by proper care and attention, the disagreeable flavour in the butter is prevented."

P. 118. (Part II.) " The milk" " after standing twenty-four hours, is fleeted; and the skimmed milk is drawn off from the leads, into vessels (not lined with lead but) of an increased depth; this is called doubling: here it remains for twelve or twenty-four hours, during which time, as the cream rises, it is fleeted two or three times. It is then threbled or put into tubs, or still deeper vessels, where it is occasionally skimmed and kept so long as any appearance of cream or richer milk is found to form upon the surface. The butter which is made from the after-fleetings of the milk, is of a paler colour, and of an inferior quality to that made from the cream, which rises the first twenty-four hours: it is generally churned apart, and sold at a lower price.

" The skimmed milk is usually applied to the purposes of feeding porkers, or small pigs, for the London market; these are always kept very clean, and warmly lodged, particularly in winter, during which season, as well as in the summer months, the milk is always sour before it reaches the troughs, but on that account there does not appear to lie the least possible objection; as the pigs are always found to thrive extremely well, and their fat, from repeated trials of comparison, is firmer, and vastly superior to that of hogs fattened upon peas or meal."—This farther evinces the
similarity

similarity between the Essex and the Buckinghamshire &c. practice.

Suckling Calves.—P. 58. (Sandon.) " These obstacles," (see above) " to the making of good butter have led to the more general practice of suckling, which business seems to be very well understood in this parish. For this purpose the breed of cows from South Wales are most generally preferred; though the calves which they produce are often found weak and unhealthy, and seldom fat so kindly, or pay so well, as those bought in from dairies. To promote the torpor, and quick-feeding of the calf, a ball weighing about two ounces, composed of the powder of fennugreek, wheat-meal, and a small quantity of powdered chalk, blended together with mild ale, is given morning and evening just before sucking; this lulls and disposes the calves to sleep, thereby advancing their fattening, which is generally accomplished in about twelve weeks, paying 4s. 6d. per calf per week, during the whole time: This nutritive opiate is also supposed to have a very good effect in whitening the veal."

SHEEP.—*Breeds.*—P. 128. (Part II.) " As there are but few breeding flocks in this county, the usual mode of stocking with sheep, is to buy ewes in the months of August or September, to entice those that have not already taken the ram, to be so disposed as early as possible, that the lamb may be returned fat in the spring, and the ewe fattened and sold off before the end of summer."

Management of Sheep.—P. 58. (Sandon.) " The grazing of a sheep is generally allowed to the men servants in lieu of washing: This is found to answer a good purpose in calling their attention more frequently to the flock, by which means many of the accidents to which that animal is liable, are often observed in time to remedy, or entirely to prevent."

SWINE.—See Butter Dairy, above; also *Rape Herbage*, aforegoing.

SUMMARY.—Mr. V. at the close of his JOURNAL, inserts a " table of the sum, and of the general average amount of certain facts contained in the preceding Journal;" and moreover recapitulates the " substance" of it as follows:

P. 115. " That the average rent of the enclosed arable land through the county is 14s. 8d. That of the open field 10s. 2d. consequently a difference of 4s. 6d. per acre between the common field land, and that which is held in severalty. That the average rent of the prime pasture ground is 23s. 2d. making a difference of 9s. 1¼d. per acre between the pasture land of the first, and that of the second quality. That the rough and unimproved pastures are

are rented on an average through the county at 6s. 10d.
per acre. That the embanked marsh ground averages
15s. 7¼d. per acre; and that there are 4,600 acres of salt
marsh, which at this time, may be conveniently enclosed
from the sea, and gradually improved to an equal value.
That the meadows in severalty average 22s. 10d and those
that are half yearly 25s. 8d. leaving a difference of 2s 10d.
per acre, which is by no means proportioned to the superior
quality of the latter land. That the arable and grass land
through the county, when let in farms together, and without distinction of price, equals 14s 6½d. per acre. That
        acres of hop land average 31s. per acre. That the un-
dergrowth of the woodlands, cut once in thirteen years,
averages through the county at the stub 5l. 11s. 6¾d. per
acre. That there are 370 acres of thicks or *forest land,*
which, by enclosure, may be improved 12s. 6d. per acre.
That there are, say 10,000 acres of the same description
of land, not producing or being favourable to the growth
of oak or other valuable timber, in the forests of Epping
and Henhault, at present estimated to produce 5s. 8¼d.
per acre, but which, in a state of enclosure for cultivation, might be readily augmented to 20s. per acre:
and finally, that there are 14,237 acres of waste common
land, which being enclosed, would immediately be increased in its annual value 11s. 4¼d. The same table
exhibits the following general average produce through the
county, viz.

Wheat	24 bushels	2 pecks
Rye	20 bushels	
Barley	33 bushels	3 pecks
Oats	36 bushels	2 pecks
Peas	20 bushels	1 peck
Beans	27 bushels	
Mustard	24 bushels	
Coleseed	29 bushels	
Potatoes	335 bushels	

Coriander and Carraway seed 10 cwt. per acre.
" It also shews that the composition at present paid for the
great and small tythes is 3s. 5½d. and that the same has increased through the county 1s. 1½d. per acre within twenty
years. That the poor's rates upon the present rack rents
are 3s. 6½d. and that they have increased through the county
1s. 1½d. in the pound within ten years.
" That the price of provisions and value of labour through
the county, are lastly, as follows :
" Beef 4¾d. per lb.—mutton 5d. per lb.—veal 5½d. per lb.
—fresh pork 5¾d. per lb.—pickled pork 7¼d. per lb.—butter
10¼d. and cheese 6d. per lb.—houshold flour 2s. the peck,
                                                    and

and potatoes 1s. 6¼d. per bushel.   Stated daily labour 9s. 5d.
in the summer, 8s. 10d. per week in the winter.   Task work,
or value of labour in thrashing wheat 30½d.—barley 19¾d.—
oats 14¾d.—peas 27¼d. and beans 14¾d. per quarter.—House
servants: head man's wages 9l. 12s. 2d. Boys 4l. 4s. 8d.
per annum. Womens wages 4l. 4s. 8d. Girls 2l. 5s. per
annum."

SOUTH ESSEX.

BY

THE SECRETARY OF THE BOARD.

1807.

THIS is the seventh occasion on which I have been
unavoidably constrained, in pursuing my present object,
to bring forward the works of this indefatigable Writer.

The following is an extract from his own account of the
two volumes now under consideration; namely a " GENERAL
VIEW of the AGRICULTURE of the COUNTY of ESSEX."

" Introduction" (p. vii.) " The County of Essex was
originally surveyed by Messrs. Greggs. Mr. Vancouver
was next employed to form a new report of it, and his
work was nearly as voluminous as the present one.* Their
two Reports were afterwards put into the hands of the
Rev. Mr. Howlett, to form a new one on the modern
arrangement recommended by the Board. He made very
large additions; but the Committee to whom that work
was referred, having declined to direct the printing, a new
Survey was ordered: this undertaking fell, unsought for,
into my hands. Had any other person offered, I should
most willingly have relinquished it."

With the materials, collected by himself, the Secretary
has incorporated copious extracts from Mr. VANCOUVER'S
Work; and taken, still more largely, it would seem, from
Mr. HOWLETT'S; also a few passages from the original
Report, by Messrs. GREGG.

Whoever is desirous to learn the general bent and
                                                    tendency

* This must allude to the Writer's *own* collection; for Mr. Vancouver's *pamphlet* consists of 213 pages, only: whereas the Secretary's
TWO VOLUMES comprize 855; and are rendered still more " voluminous," by embracing 58 leather-paper engravings!

tendency of those volumes, I refer to the EASTERN DE-
PARTMENT; where the more valuable information, concerning the *Northeast*, or *Suffolk quarter* of the County, as
well as various particulars relating to the County at large,—
may be seen.

The few items that I have deemed it expedient to lay
before my readers, in this place, belong to the SOUTHERN
DEPARTMENT.

SUBJECT THE FIRST.

NATURAL ECONOMY.

WATERS.—V. I. p. 35. " Few counties can be better
surrounded than Essex, in respect of navigation.   The
Thames forms its whole southern boundary; the Stour,
navigable to Shoebury, its northern limit; the Sea to the
east; and to the west, the two navigations of the Stort
and the Lea   The great estuary of the Blackwater penetrates twelve miles into the county, and afterwards is
navigable to Chelmsford.

" The greater part of Essex is well watered, by the many
brooks and rivers which run through its vales.   The hundreds of Rochford, Dengey, and some others, however,
lying near the sea, and the banks of the Thames, called,
in reproach, *the hundreds of Essex*, are rather deficient in
good water; and perhaps their autumnal agues have been
as much owing to this deficiency, as to the noxious vapours
arising from marshes imperfectly drained.   A recent successful experiment, made by the Rev. Mr. Nottidge, at
East Hanningfield, near Danbury, affords the pleasing
hope, that by making wells of considerable depth, water
of the finest quality might often be obtained.   He persevered in the expensive attempt till fine water was found
nearly 500 feet from the surface, which soon arose to
within 120 feet of the top of the well, at which height it
continues to stand, and must be of considerable benefit to
his own family, and many of his neighbours, for whose
use it is always open.

" The parish of Latchingdon dug a well 300 feet deep,
to the very great comfort of the whole.

" The Crouch, a very fine river, and laid down too narrow in all the maps, is from three-fourths of a mile to a
mile wide near Burnham, and has water enough for a 90
gun ship; a 74 might go up almost to Hull-bridge.
Proposals have been, at various periods, made to Government,

ment, for the establishment of a dock-yard here. The
river is a very noble royalty, belonging to Sir Henry
Mildmay, a grant of Edward III."

SOILS.—Under this important head of report, the Secretary is full and intelligent. He divides the County into
eight *Districts;* according to the nature of its soils *. He
thus denominates them:—

1. Crop and fallow clay.	6. Turnep Loam.
2. Fertile Loam.	7. Chalk.
3, 4, 5. Clay.	8 Various loams:—

the last being a *distinction* which covers nearly half the
County.

District 7, "Chalk," is a continuation of the chalk
lands of Hertfordshire. District 1. is likewise situated in
the environ of Hertfordshire; but does not well assimilate
with its lands. These small tracts, however, naturally
belong to the Southern Department; though they do not
come within the outline of South Essex. I will therefore
bring together, here, the several passages relating to the
soils of Essex, which are situated within the SOUTHERN
DEPARTMENT; and place them, progressively, as they stand
in the volume before me.

V. I p. 5. (District 1.) "*Notes on the Soil in the rood-
ing District, No. I.*—This district, marked *crop and fallow*
in the map, and which may also be called the Roodings,*
from similarity of soil and management, is, as appears
by the map, of large extent. What may generally be
called the whole of it (for the exceptions are only of vales
through which brooks run, and the immediate slopes to
them), is a strong, wet, heavy, reddish, or brown loam,
upon a whitish clay marl bottom; poaching with rain;
adhesive: yields very little without hollow-draining; and
good crops, not without manure and careful management."

P. 13. (District 2.) "Directly under the hill on which
Maldon is picturesquely situated, is a tract of marshes of
some extent, but which are not in much estimation for
their quality. They extend on both sides the Blackwater,
from this termination of that estuary to the sea; they are,
however, better than those on the north shore. All the
way hence to Bradwell they are reckoned rather of an
inferior quality, and by no means so good as those on the
eastern shore of Dengey hundred."

P. 15, (the same.) "Foulness Island, I am much inclined
to

* Differing, very materially, from Mr. Vancouver's Districts. See
the last article.

* Query, RED INGS?—Redsoiled hay-grounds of the pastoral tribes.

to think the richest soil in this county. The following is
a note I made on it many years ago:

" The whole island was certainly the bed of the sea;
there are layers of oyster and cockle-shells in it; and every
other appearance confirm the idea: it is therefore thoroughly impregnated with marine salt, not only in its
origin, but from high tides breaking the banks and over-
flowing it. Forty years ago the whole was under water,
and no corn got for two years; but after that much
greater than ever, so as to furnish an effectual proof that
the water did good, after being chastened and corrected
by the atmosphere."

P. 19. (the same.) " Before I quit Dengey hundred, I
should remark, that there is a breadth of fine sound, friable,
rich mould, between the marsh and the heavy land, which
is of superior merit, and ought to be distinguished from
the rest of the country. It is however, too narrow to mark
on the map."—What follows is less intelligible ; being the
produce of abrupt aberrations over Districts 2 and 5.

P. 23. (District 5, chiefly.) " The third strong land
district is that of Dengey, Rochford, &c. from Hanningfield on the western extremity, to Southminster on the
eastern ; and from near Maldon to Pitsey. Of this district,
the eastern part is better than the western. It seems as
if the soil changed gradually as it approaches the rich
selvage that borders on the marshes; yet some of the
hills at St. Lawrence are a strong clay, and others, very
harsh and tenacious, are found at Latchingdon and Snorum.
The western part of the district is not interesting."

P. 26. (District 7.) " In the north-western corner of the
county, there is a small district of chalk ; but small as it
is, with some variations, however, the basis, at certain
depths, all, or nearly all, chalk. At Elmdon, and Strethall,
the surface is heavy; and the point at Heydon Grange,
and Crishal Grange, there is gravel: but the whole must be
considered as a continuation of, and in union with, the
chalk districts of Hertfordshire and Cambridgeshire.

" Within less than a mile of Walden, the chalk is visible,
and the soil changes entirely to a dry turnip soil on a chalk
bottom. Near the town, is a large and deep excavation
for burning lime. This chalk stratum extends by Audley
End to the hills of Littlebury, thence to the Chesterfords,
and so into Cambridgeshire and Hertfordshire.

" About Audley End, the hills are all chalk, and the
vales good loam on gravel, but with variations. On the
hills, the soil is thin, in some places not more than four or
five inches on the chalk, and they *burn* in a hot summer.
Much of the chalk is hard, and bad to plough up; for
which

which reason they are careful not to plough too deep.
Elms thrive in the vales; and they have a proverb—*Good
elm, good barley: good oak, good wheat.*

"Hadstock is dry, with wet hills; Ashdon, quite heavy;
Little Walden, the same; Strethall, cold and heavy;
Elmdon, the same; Chrishal, part heavy, and part on a
basis of gravel.

"Near Hockerill, the soil is turnip land, and the vales
and lower slopes generally dry and good. throughout the
way from Chesterford thither."

P. 27. (District 8.) "Around Chelmsford, very good
turnip land. The southern tract, from Thorndon to the
Thames district, heavy, wet, and poaching, and not much
more in the husbandry than in the soil to excite attention.
The potatoe district near London is, in a measure, artificial.
In the broad space from Hanningfield to Waltham Abbey,
every sort of soil is to be met with. But in all these cases,
the distinctions do not run into such masses as to enable
me to strike off any more districts sufficiently different
from the rest."

To follow the Surveyor, farther, over this wide spreading, heterogeneous district, in which the soil varies at
every step, could not afford any satisfactory information.

SUBJECT THE SECOND.

POLITICAL ECONOMY.

APPROPRIATION.—*Epping Forest* *.—V. II. p. 160.
"This forest was formerly called the Forest of Essex,
being the only forest in that county, and anciently comprehended the whole of it. By a charter of grant of King
John, dated 25th of March, in the 5th year of his reign,
and confirmed in the 8th of Edward the Fourth, all that
part of the forest which lay to the north of the highway
from Stortford to Colchester (very distant from the present boundaries) was disafforested. The forest was farther
reduced by a perambulation made in the 29th of Edward
the First, in pursuance of the *Charta de foresta,* but the
metes and bounds of it were finally, by an inquisition
and perambulation taken on the 8th September 1640, by
virtue of a commission under the Great Seal of England,
in pursuance of the act of the 16th of Charles the First,
for settling the bounds of the forests.

"The

* From the fifteenth Report of the Commissioners of Land Revenue.

" The boundaries fixed by that perambulation, of which comprehend twelve parishes lying wholly within the forest, and parts of nine other parishes, which are situated partly within, and partly without the forest, viz.

" *Parishes wholly within the Forest.*—Wanstead, Layton, Walthamstow, Woodford, Loughton, Chigwell, Lambourn, Stapleford-Abbots, Waltham Holy Cross, Epping, Nasing.

" *Parishes partly within the Forest.*—Chinkford, Stratford, East Ham, West Ham, Little Ilford, Great Ilford, Barking, Dagenham, Navestock, Theydon-Bois.

" We found in the office of the Surveyor-general of the Crown Lands, an ancient plan or draught of the forest, delineating the bounds according to the perambulation in the 17th of Charles the First, and the nine walks into which it was then divided; but not distinguishing the open from the enclosed lands, or the private property from that of the Crown; nor describing the contents of either; we have therefore endeavoured to form an estimate of its general contents, from the map of the county of Essex published in the year 1777, from a survey taken a few years before, in which the bounds of the forest, and the division between the open and enclosed lands, are described. According to a computation made from that survey, the forest contains, in all, about 60,000 statute acres, of which about 48,000 acres are the estimated contents of enclosed private property, and the remaining 12,000 acres the amount of the unenclosed woods and wastes.

" The Crown has in this, as in other forests, an unlimited right to keep deer in all the unenclosed woods and wastes within the perambulation, unless some parts have been disafforested by grants which have not come to our knowledge; and the owners and occupiers of lands within the bounds of the forest have a right of common of pasture for horses and cows, no other cattle being commonable in the forest.—Those within the parishes of Stapleford, Lambourn, Chigwell, Barking, and Dagenham, and at Woodford-bridge, within the parish of Woodford, turn into the part called Hainault forest. The cattle are sent in as early in the spring, and remain as late in the winter, as the owners choose; but the forest is constantly cleared of them during the fence month. The cattle are marked by the reeves of the respective parishes, with a particular forest mark for each parish; and we are informed that the general rule has been, to admit one horse or two cows for every 4*l.* of annual rent; but that, in some instances, the reeves have marked cattle in proportion to the value of newly-erected houses, which we conceive to be an infringement of the rights of common
                                            appertaining

appertaining to ancient messuages and lands, as well as of
the rights of the Crown, by surcharging the forest.

" We have received representations from the owners and
occupiers of lands in twelve parishes within, and adjoining
to the forest, of the injury they sustain from the deer; and
requesting that we would recommend to the Legislature
the disafforestation and enclosure of the forest, or that the
deer may be removed, or confined within a park, or parks.
These representations are signed by more than two hundred persons, among whom are several of great property,
and of the first respectability.

" On a survey of the timber in the King's woods, taken
in the year 1783, it was found that the whole number of
oak trees, from ten feet upwards, was 11,055. Of these,
2760 were reported to be trees of thirty feet and upwards,
and to be fit for the use of the Navy; 7825 were young
trees, from thirty feet down to ten feet each; and the rest
scrubbed and unthrifty. On the whole, the number of oaks
was less than four trees to the acre, and of those thirty feet
and upwards, less than one to an acre.

" The surveyor whom we employed to take a plan of
these lands, represents the greatest part of them to be of
a strong loamy soil, very favourable to the growth of oak
timber; and that even those parts which are of a lighter
soil, are productive of fine oaks. The situation of the
forest, for convenience and cheapness of carriage of timber
to the dock-yards, is the most favourable of all His Majesty's forests, being only three miles distant from Ilford-
bridge, whence the river Rodon is navigable to the
Thames.

" From many circumstances stated in the preceding part
of this Report, it appears obviously to be for the interest
of the public, that the part of this forest called Hainault,
in which the soil, timber, and wood belonging to the Crown,
should be retained and improved as a nursery of timber for
the supply of the Navy.

" That part is situated so near the river Thames, that the
expense of the carriage of the timber to the dock-yards
could not exceed 5s. the load, which is less than the expense of carriage from any other forest to any of the dock-
yards; and it is so near to London, where the office for
the general superintendance of the forests must be kept,
that it may be frequently visited by the principal officers,
without much loss of time or expense.

" The great size of some of the trees now growing upon
it, affords a convincing proof of the peculiar fitness of the
soil for the growth of oak. The money necessary for the
enclosure and improvement, may be raised by the sale of
                                                        part

part of the old trees, which ought to be removed as soon as
enclosures shall be made to protect the future growth.—
There are some thriving trees, which, if preserved from
injury, would, at no great distance of time, become useful
for the Navy ; and the underwood, which must always find
a ready sale in London, would yield a larger fund than
would be required for the payment of the officers necessary
for the care and protection of the property of the Crown."

INLAND NAVIGATION.—For some account of *water carriage* in Essex, see the article *Waters,* p. 168, aforegoing.

SUBJECT THE THIRD.

RURAL ECONOMY.

ESTATES.—*Purchase.*—V. II. p. 417. " At the sale of
the late Mr. Rigby's estate, Walton-hall, of 326 acres, 60
of them marsh, with 750 acres of salting, over which the
tides flow, were sold to Mr. Bernard, the tenant, for 18,000*l.* ;
this is, the 386 being worth 31*s.* per acre at thirty years
purchase, and the 750 acres given in for nothing.

" Hare-hall, near Romford, one hundred and sixty-six
acres, seventy-eight of them grass, the rest arable, for which
3*l.* per acre was offered, sold, with a good stone house, for
14,500*l.* sterling—twenty-eight years purchase.

" To multiply the cases would be needless ; I found
throughout the county, that the value of the soil, fairly
rented, was in 1805 from twenty-eight to thirty years
purchase."—Thus far we are furnished with appropriate report.

P. 418. (in continuation.) " Now it is remarkable, that in
1770 I noted and published the price, which was thirty
years purchase.

" This fact, and the same has been found throughout
the kingdom, appears to me a very extraordinary one,
supposing it to run parallel with a great depreciation in the
value of money."

This is writing as if the author really believed that there
is a radical connexion, between the number of year's purchase of land, and the nominal value of money ;—as he
wanders nearly two pages, further, in pursuit of the idea.—
See my YORKSHIRE V. I. p. 29.

WOODLANDS.

WOODLANDS.

IN a chapter, headed "Woods and Plantations," we find an undigested mass of materials, collected from various sources of information; by which we are led to the general idea that South Essex, apart from its forests, abounds in woodlands. But nothing of consideration, as to the specific nature or management of its *private woods*, nor any estimate of their aggregate extent, appears.

For a valuable document, relative to the *forests* of Essex, see *Appropriation*, p. 171, aforegoing.

AGRICULTURE.

PLAN of MANAGEMENT.—(In the "*Roodings*.")—V. I. p. 5. "The standard husbandry of the whole is crop and fallow; that is, 1. Fallow; 2. Wheat; 3. Fallow; 4. Barley; which singular husbandry is universally contended for as the most profitable; and although every farmer perhaps in the district has what is called *etch* (that is, after) crops, yet the quantity is so restricted by leases and agreements, that the variations make no considerable exceptions. Some clover, pease, tares, and a few beans, are scattered about the country; but the generally prevailing features are white corn and fallow."

Having, in passing through these volumes, met with little to engage my particular attention, I seize with greater avidity the subjoined interesting narrative of facts, found in the Reporter's section, "Wheat."—V. I. p. 267. "*Several years past* I found Mr. Taylor, of Wimbish, *making a very considerable improvement;* he had for some years thought, that the spirit of fallowing was not in this country attended by effects adequate to the exertions made, which induced him to try beans, with particular attention to mark the result; his experiments were so satisfactory, that he every year increased the quantity; from four acres to twelve, to twenty-five, to forty, to sixty acres, as he became gradually convinced that he not only gained a produce of itself very valuable, but at the same time prepared for wheat with a success perfectly to his satisfaction. His crops of beans this year are very good; and I thought his wheat, which succeeded the last year's crop, equal to the best on a fallow preparation. He is of opinion, that the horse-bean much
exceeds

exceeds all other sorts, because, growing vastly higher (even to eight feet), it covers the land more.

"Having applied to Mr. Taylor for his further remarks, I had the following note of his *present* opinion:

"I do still continue the cultivation of beans to a certain degree, but not on so large a scale as formerly; the greater part of my arable lands have been planted with them once, and some parts twice and thrice: the result is, that they do not produce so well the second and third time, (even although the same care and expense is incurred), as on the first time of planting them upon the same land; therefore, I conclude my soil is not altogether adapted to a regular rotation of bean crops, as a substitute for fallow, but will do occasionally very well; and what confirms me in that belief is, the land is left much more foul after the second and third trial on the same land, than it was on the first."

I must not forbear to observe, here, that, had this zealous and ready writer, been in the habit of *referring back* to the practices of his *novitial informants*, after they had acquired *several years of experience*, before he sat down to publish their *improvements*,—he would have saved his readers much unprofitable labor, and time ill spent; and inexperienced students many misleadings from the right road of practice.

WORKING ANIMALS.—*Management* of *Cart Horses.*—V. II. p. 351. "Among the best farmers in Essex, I found them very generally in the system of keeping their horses in warm well littered yards, with sheds for them to retire under. Into these they are turned at night, and kept in them day and night when not worked. Mr. Ketcher, of Burnham, has one for his cart-horses in common, and another for mares and foals.

"Mr. Wright, of Rochford-hall, has a yard into which horses are turned every night; nor is there a shed in it. His teams have not stood in the stable for ten years."

MANURES.—*Chalk.*—The following notices, respecting this prevalent manure in South Essex, are interesting. They appear to have been reported with due consideration.

V. II. p. 203. "This manure has been largely used in Essex for time immemorial; but I found it carried in the Hundreds near forty years ago, in much larger quantities than at present. As the country became chalked, less was of course wanted; and of late years a prevalent idea has spread almost every where, that it answers badly when spread a second and a third time. In many districts, it is now only used in composts."

P. 206. "Considerable quantities of chalk are brought
from

from Kent by sea to Maldon, and the farmers take it some miles by land; but chiefly by the inland navigation: it is brought to Hatfield, but more to Tolesbury: they mix it with earth and dung."

P. 207. " The larger part, perhaps the whole of Mersea Island, has been chalked; at present, what is carried is chiefly on to the heavy land. Mr. Bennet Hawes has clean chalked land a second time, and it answered well.

" There is a circumstance relative to this manure, which should convince us that our fathers had more knowledge in matters of husbandry than we are sometimes ready to admit. It was a very old saying, that *chalk is good for the father but bad for the son*, and that there is some truth in the maxim, is strongly felt in Essex. Mr. Western, in describing the husbandry around Kelvedon, used this expression relative to the opinion of farmers on this manure, *they hate old chalked lands; such are worn out.*

" At St. Lawrence, in Dengey hundred, the fact came still nearer to ascertainment. Mr. Pattison assured me, that the strong soils on a stiff clay upon their hills, would lett readily at 20s. but if old chalked land, at only 15s. nor is there, he said, any question of this fact."

P. 209. " Mr. Beauvoir's father at Downham, who died in 1757, disapproved very much of his tenants chalking their lands; and discouraged it all he could, without an absolute prohibition. He had seen many cases in which the first chalking had great effects for one lease, and after that the land was sure to be considerably the worse for it, and would not at that time of day lett so well as land that had not been chalked, though the liberty to chalk were precluded. When done, and exhausted in consequence, which was the usual event, it required many years to recover."

Gravel, as a Manure.—V. II. p. 221. " Mr. Sperling, of Dynes-hall, in Great Maplestead, has greatly improved some pieces of spungy land, loose hollow sandy loam, by laying from sixty to eighty loads per acre of gravel on it." —The specific quality of the said gravel is not mentioned.

Nightsoil.—V. II. p. 241. " Mr. Newman, of Hornchurch, has found that this manure for pasture is, of all other sorts, the most capital; two waggon loads an acre, at 7s. besides carriage, are beyond every thing, and secure a carpet of herbage. On corn land, he thinks it forces straw too much."

ARABLE CROPS.

BEANS.—V. I. p. 362. " I was assured that there is a large field at Walton, which produced beans and wheat for
thirty-six

thirty-six years; and that another field was known to produce one year thirteen quarters and a half of beans per
acre, by some accounts; by others eleven and a half."

POTATOES.—V. I p. 382. " At Ilford, where I made inquiries concerning the cultivation of potatoes, for which
that neighbourhood is so famous, the favourite potatoe was
formerly the red-nosed kidney, which is now neglected,
because it is almost sure to be curled. The champion is
now very generally preferred, which does not curl. The
preparation is an autumnal ploughing, dunging in the spring,
about fourteen loads an acre, which cost 5s. a load, spread
on the field just before the second ploughing, on which they
plant. Immediately after the plough, a man dibbles across
the land, followed by a woman who drops the sets, for both
which operations they are paid 7s. or 8s. an acre; the rows
twelve inches by fourteen or fifteen, and some twelve
square. Early in the spring, sixteen or eighteen hundred
weight are planted on an acre; they are hand-hoed twice,
each time at the expense of 4s.; they are dug up with
three-pronged forks, and picked carefully clean. The
product is from eight to fifteen tons an acre, when the
crop stands to full perfection; but great quantities are
taken up in summer, when the product is not so considerable."

P. 393. " The hundred weight of potatoes is 126 lbs.;
a ton therefore is 2520 lbs. or 36 bushels, at 70 lbs. per
bushel; eight tons are 288 bushels."

P. 391. " Mr. T. Pittman, of Barking, is one of the
greatest potatoe planters in the kingdom, if not the greatest. Has generally from two to three hundred acres; soil
a shallow loam on a gravelly bottom; burns in a hot
summer. He had 300 acres last year, which, when the
exertions and expenses necessary be considered, must be
admitted as a business of almost unexampled extent and
vigour. What would a Kentish man say to 300 acres of
hops? Yet the expenses of potatoes are fully equal to those
of hops. He never attempts them without dung; that
from his yards, mixed with what is brought from London
(not nightsoil, as it makes them scabby); the state in which
he prefers it is that of heat; to spread it as hot as possible :
the dung now in his yard cannot be used till March; but
hot will then go as far again. This expression plainly im-
plies *long* dung; not, however, fresh, for it has undergone
a mixture in order to get a heat; the heat destroys all
weeds; in two or three months it is fit for use, but the time
depends on the weather. The dung being turned in by one
ploughing, the sets, 16 cwt. per acre, are dibbled in on
every furrow at nine or ten inches apart, and lightly harrowed;

rowed; no rolling, as the looser the surface is left the better; depth five or six inches: many farmers plant every other furrow after the plough, but Mr. Pittman prefers dibbling. The sets should not be small, and with from one to three eyes. Before they come up the ground is shimmed over; this is considered as a new contrivance; some years ago it was done by hand-hoeing. They hand-hoed sufficiently to keep them quite clean, and for mould-ing up enough to prevent any green roots from being exposed to the air: he never ploughs them up, but always digs with three-pronged forks; they are all holed or *pyed*. An article of attention not customary formerly, is that of washing. Mr. Pittman washes his whole crop!! What an undertaking! to wash four and twenty hundred or *three thousand tons* of potatoes! He dug a well that cost 200*l.* for having water in a building convenient for this purpose; they are washed with smooth paddles and very carefully, or the roots are damaged for market. They have two enemies in their growth; the *thousand legs* eats and makes them scabby, and a large grub of a bottle green colour eats out the heart."

P. 394. "Mr. Greenhall, whose father was for many years by far the greatest potatoe-planter in England, is himself a very considerable one. Last year he had 300 acres, and yet his farm is not of the extent which this circumstance might be thought to imply, for he grows them for many years in succession on the same land, for twenty and even thirty years together, dunging for them every year, but not more than eight or ten loads an acre, about half a common manuring for this crop. In this suc-cessive method of culture, the crops are just as large and the potatoes as good as in a varied course; he sees no difference."

But not, *yet*, in any one of the Reports of the four Surveyors of Essex, do we find particular notice of the *Irish practice*, in that County; or of the contracts entered into between the Irish planters and the Essex farmers:— a connexion which, I have always understood, gave rise to the extensive cultivation of potatoes, in that County.

CULTIVATED HERBAGE.—*Clover.*—V. II. p. 12. "This plant has been so long introduced in Essex, that in every part of the County it is very liable to fail: many of the farmers assured me that the land was sick of it; others did not ascribe the loss to any satiety of that sort, but found the necessity of varying their courses, in order that clover might not return so often."

Raygrass.—V. II. p. 26. "Mr. Wakefield, of Burnham, weans many calves, and therefore must have ray-grass, as
it

it agrees extremely well with them; better than tares, which are apt to *run through them.*"

A volume might be written *against* raygrass, without producing sufficient evidence to outweigh the above short paragraph, in its favour.

GRASS LANDS.

UPLAND HERBAGE.—V. II. p. 95. " The part of the county in the vicinity of London which is under grass, wants little discrimination; it is within reach of that capital as a market for hay, and as a supply of manure; the consequences are considerable exertions and high rents; marshes in the hands of butchers rise to 9*l.* and 10*l.* per acre; and hay lands at Woodford, &c. are at 2*l.* and late leases 3*l.* Mr. Hatch, at Claybury-hall, has lately lett 100 acres at 3*l.*

" Around the Ongars, thence to Epping, a large district in that vicinity, and much of the way to Harlow, is covered with very rich grass, kept in good order by the exertions of the occupiers; the rent is from 30*s.* to 50*s.* when valued distinctly from other land. Much is mown for hay, of which large quantities go to London; and much applied to daries of cows, and some to herds of suckled cows."

MARSH LANDS.—*Thames Marshes.*—V. II. p. 123. "The marshes on the banks of the Thames are greatly superior to those on the ocean, or the Blackwater: at Avely they lett for 3*l.* an acre, the tenants doing half the repairs of the wall; they are not allowed to mow them, which is justly thought to be very mischievous to such valuable bullock land: here I was informed, that the best are at Plaistow, and lett at 7*l.* or 8*l.* per acre to London butchers."

Sea Marshes.—P. 124. " A circumstance in the marshes of Dengey hundred occurs, which has not equally struck me on other coasts; and this is, their rising in elevation towards the sea; it does not appear to be regularly thus; but at Southminster, on the marshes of Mr. Bawtree, it is strikingly so. The first line of marsh next the uplands is lowest, and are at the same time the poorest; they gradually rise in advancing towards the sea. It does not at once appear to what cause this is to be attributed, unless the sea has of late ages been much more productive of ouze than in former times."

This is an ordinary circumstance.—Wherever foul waters occasionally overflow the grounds adjacent to their natural or accustomed channels, the deposit is, of course, greatest where the water first begins to stagnate, or lose its current, or other state of agitation. If for the word " poorest," as applied to the marshes bordering on the uplands, we put *least profitable*,—their comparative *wetness*, and consequent *coldness of situation*, would readily account for it.

Management of *Marsh Lands* and other *Grazing Grounds.*—V. II. p. 102. " *Mowing and feeding.*—Lord Petre has at Thorndon one pasture which he values very highly for its quality in feeding; and on inquiry of Mr. Miles, for the circumstances of it, I found that it had never been mown.

" Mr. Coverdale, of Ingatestone, has some rich grazing meadows on a brook, which are never mown; they are noted for their fattening quality: he thinks (erroneously I conceive) that it would be better to mow now and then.

" Mr. Williams, of Ongar, whose experience and abilities merit great attention, never mows his best grazing lands.

" Mr. Hanbury, at Coggeshall, who grazes on a respectable scale, mows and feeds distinctly—he is clear that grazing lands on these cold hills should not be mown."

In a cursory view of a grazing-ground district, no matter whether of water formed marshes, or rich aboriginal upper lands, it is easy to distinguish, perhaps at some miles' distance, the parts that have been recently *mown* from those which have been for ages, invariably kept in a state of *pasturage*,—by the different colors and general appearance of their herbage; and, on closer examination, the difference becomes more obvious.

The herbage of long-pastured fertile lands is composed of the finer, more nutritious grasses;—native raygrass, in the spring and autumn at least, being generally most prevalent. By allowing the stronger grasses, and the coarser deep-rooting herbs, to rise to a state of full growth,—and especially if they be suffered to stand until they reach a degree of maturity,—the more tender delicate grasses, and feebler legumes, become overtopt and deprived, or abridged, of their required air and light. Not only the parts, above-ground, but the roots, are thus enfeebled,—while the roots of the stronger plants gain strength, and possession of the soil; thereby checking the future growth of nutritious pasturage; which, by taking repeated crops of hay, may be so far injured as to require a length of years to restore it to its former state,—as " grazing ground."

On the other hand, by constant mowing, provided the soil be replenished with manure in proportion to the exhaustion, the *bulkiness* of the crop will encrease. I have observed, in different instances, that after grass land has been pastured, during a course of years, the first, and even the second, succeeding crop of *hay* has fallen short of the expected *quantity*. Its *quality*, in this case, however, never fails to be of superior goodness.

Hence

Hence, in situations where hay and pasturage are alike
required, as in dairy districts, and where the grazing or
fatting of cattle is not the leading object, it will generally
be found good management to pasture mowing grounds,
from time to time, to improve the hay.

If any excuse be required for this digression, I have only
to say that the ideas it contains have become familiar to
me; and I have not, before, met with so fair an opportunity to bring them before the public.

Saltings.—V. II. p. 129. " From the southern point
of the marshes against the ocean, between the Blackwater
and the Crouch, there is a breadth of saltings (salt marsh
not embanked, over which the tides flow) which are very
valuable, and in some places of considerable breadth."

Lands washed away by the Sea.—V. II. p. 130. " Notwithstanding the embankments, by which much land has
of late years been gained from the sea, on the coast of
Dengey hundred, yet that element in time past has made
great depredations here. There is a sand called Buxey-
park, and old seamen now living have heard their grand-
fathers say when they were boys, that Buxey-park was
covered with trees; and it is asserted, that foundations of
houses have been seen there. Also at St. Peter's Chapel,
at Bradwell, the sea gained much in former times, as the
remains of buildings are said to be still visible on the sands
at low tides."

LIVESTOCK.

DAIRY.—*Food of Cows.*—V. II. p. 304. " Mr. Hanbury
has another application of oil-cake, which is much more
uncommon; indeed I have met with it but once before—
that of giving it to his milch cows. They have four cakes
a day and the best hay, and the effect on their milk is
extraordinary; cows almost dry have immediately a flow
of milk: they are kept tied up and and warm like the
fatting beasts, being let to water twice a day. Last winter
two thus fed supplied his family of twenty with butter,
milk and cream; and they are with four cakes a day
always in nice sleek order in the coldest weather, far
beyond the state of other cows differently fed: the butter
very good, without any taste, but rather light coloured.
Two cows gave all the winter from 12 to 15 *lb.* per week,
besides the milk and cream used."

Suckling Calves.—V. II. p. 299. " Mr. Sperling, of
Dynes-hall, when he was in the suckling system, made it
a rule to cut his bull calves as soon as he bought them,
which renders the veal much the better: they were stalled,

and kept quite clean and curried as well as his stall-fed bullocks."

Diseases of Cows.—V. II. p. 305. " Mr. Williams, of Ongar, is one of the most successful graziers in Essex. Some years ago he kept 70 to 80 cows for suckling, but had such losses by their slipping calf (even to the amount of 60 out of 80) that he gave up the business, and commenced grazier."

SHEEP.—Of fiftyeight plates that are interspersed in these volumes, I perceive only one which requires especial mention, here. This represents a *moveable bridge,* of a simplex and practical construction, *for passing sheep over the water fences of marsh lands :*—A valuable invention of Mr. WAKEFIELD of Burnham.

The bottom is of plank, twelve feet long and twenty-one inches wide, from out to out. The thickness of the planks is not mentioned. On each side is a slight railing, two feet three inches high ; formed of four standards and three rails. Under it, a pair of wheels two feet high are placed, about four feet from one end ; and, at the other, a draft iron is fixed; doubtlessly to hang a horn to, for the greater facility of moving it, from place to place.

WILTSHIRE.

WILTSHIRE.

THIS COUNTY aptly divides into
The Vale Lands of North Wiltshire;
The Chalk Hills of South Wiltshire; and
The Sandy Lands which separates it into nearly equal parts.

This line of separation, however, though nearly correct, as to the *outlines* of the *County*, is not quite so in regard to its internal distinguishments:—the Marlborough and Albourn Downs—detached *Chalk Hills*—being situated to the northward of it.

In reviewing the Reports from the *Western Department*, I extracted much valuable information from DAVIS'S WILTSHIRE (the only one sent in from this County); concerning its *Vale Lands*, or *Dairy District*.

What I have to consider, in this place, regards the *Chalk Hills* and their *intervening valleys;* and to notice the *Sandy Lands;* which, compared with the other two, are inconsiderable: Thus taking cognisance of the whole County.

" GENERAL VIEW
OF THE
AGRICULTURE
OF THE
COUNTY OF WILTS.
BY THOMAS DAVIS,
OF LONGLEAT, WILTS, STEWARD TO THE MOST NOBLE THE
MARQUESS OF BATH.
1794." *

THE QUALIFICATIONS of this Reporter, as a *practical* man, intimately acquainted with the RURAL ECONOMY of
WILTSHIRE,

---

* When I examined the part of this Report, which relates to the *Western Department*, the quarto edition, now before me, was the only one in being. Since that time, and some years after the death of the author, it was, I understand, reprinted, and *published*. But not finding, on enquiry, that any useful addition, or alteration, had been made in it,—*I prefer the original.*

WILTSHIRE, were such, perhaps, as no other man possessed, for the purpose of giving a masterly account of its best practices.

It is to be observed, however, that his Report is not wholly free from theories which would seem to have been too hastily formed. But the shortness of the time, expended on the performance, gives the less room for censure. Mr. Davis's report was one of the earliest that were sent in to the Board. It was delivered to the members in January 1794.

After speaking of the queries put by the Board, and the answers they required, the Reporter proceeds, in his " Introduction," p. 5, as follows.—" These answers will be deduced not only from the observation of the compiler during the present survey, but also from the practice and opinions of the most experienced farmers in the county of Wilts, collected during a long and extensive intercourse with them; and will, it is hoped, comprize a full and just account of the present state of husbandry in the county, with candid and unbiassed remarks on its merits and demerits.

" The author is well aware, that notwithstanding he has taken the liberty of altering the arrangement of the queries proposed by the Board, so as to suit the particular circumstances of the county, and avoid repetition as much as possible, he has still found it necessary, in some instances, to use the same arguments *more than once*, in order to give full and satisfactory answers to each query; and on that account he hopes he shall stand excused.

" The hasty manner in which this account was necessarily drawn up (which is of less consequence, as the Board purposes to have it well revised and corrected before it is published) must apologize for numberless tautologies, inaccuracies, and omissions, which have unavoidably escaped detection."

Mr. Davis appears to write, throughout the work, from his own knowledge, of the practice of the County:—not, as an *enquiring tourist*, from memorandum-scraps, taken down from the prompt assertions of others.

The MANNER in which this Report is written, is of a superior cast:—a circumstance which appeared to me as a matter of some surprise. It seemed extraordinary that a man, who, I understood, had been introduced into active employment, at a very early age, and who through life had been practically immerged in business, should have acquired a habit of classical composition;—a qualification which evidently shows itself in various parts of the work;—until I was informed—from very good authority I believe—
that,

that, in this part of the business of Report, Mr. D. was assisted by a *friend;* " but in this part, only."

Nevertheless, some of the immature theories, spoken of, betoken them to be the reveries of a scholar, rather than the experiencial conclusions of a landsteward. This by the way.

I dwell not, here, on the frequent want of perspicuity, nor on the total want of appropriate digestion. The latter is with me a minor blemish. The work, viewed in the aggregate, is so abundantly furnished with good sense and useful information, that, had it not at length been *published,* I might have been induced to transcribe a still more ample portion of its contents, than I have, under that circumstance. It is one of the few Reports to the Board of Agriculture whose entirety is worthy of preservation.

The number of pages—one hundred and sixtythree.

A perspicuous map of the County, colored agreeably to its lands, is prefixed to the volume.

THE COUNTY AT LARGE.

EXTENT.—P. 6. " It is about 54 miles in length, and 34 in greatest breadth, and contains about 1,372 square miles, or 878,000 acres."

SURFACE.—P. 6. " There is a very striking difference in the external appearance of the south-east and north-west sides of this county, the former being composed of a broken mass of chalk hills, which enter the county from Berkshire, Hampshire, and Dorsetshire, and terminate in an irregular line of bold breaks and disjointed masses, running from the north-east to the south-west side of the county; and the latter being chiefly composed of a rich tract of vale land, stretching north-east and south-west through the county, under the foot of those hills, but rising gradually north-west till it joins the high lands of Gloucestershire."

DISTRICTS of Wiltshire.—P. 6. " In speaking of this county, it is usual to separate it into two districts, viz. ' South Wiltshire,' and ' North Wiltshire;' and the division is generally made, by supposing an east and west line passing through the county at or near Devizes, thereby leaving *Marlborough Downs* in *North Wiltshire;* but in treating of the county *agriculturally,* it will make a more natural division to draw an irregular line *round the foot of the chalk hills,* from their entrance into the north-east part of the county from Berkshire, to their south-west termination at Maiden Bradley, thereby comprehending *the whole of Wiltshire Downs,* with their intersecting vallies and surrounding

rounding verges, under the name of ' *South Wiltshire,*' or, perhaps, more properly speaking, ' *South-east Wiltshire,*' and calling the residue of the county ' North Wiltshire,' or more properly ' North-west Wiltshire.'

" The natural appearance, as well as the agricultural application of the two parts of the county, well warrant this division into south-east and north-west Wiltshire, the first comprehending the chalk hills, usually called Wiltshire Downs, whose general application is to corn-husbandry and sheep-walks; and the latter being remarkable for its rich pasture land on the banks of the Lower Avon and the Thames, so famous for the feeding of cattle, and still more so, for the production of one of the most excellent kinds of cheese this island can boast.

" As the difference in the soil, situation, and productions of the two districts is so very great, it will be necessary, after premising some general remarks on the whole county with respect to its property, to treat of them as two distinct and separate districts, at least so far as the queries proposed relate more peculiarly to either district separately, and then to subjoin the answers to those questions which relate generally to the whole county.

" The answer to the 1st head, viz. ' The soil and climate,' will fall more properly under enquiry, when the two districts come to be spoken of separately.

" But the answer to the second, viz. ' The property of the land,' wlll be best understood as applied to the county at large, and is therefore given here in a short summary, reserving the detail to be given in the description of each district." This is duly considered, masterly writing.

ESTATES and TENURES.—P. 8. " The greater part of this county was formerly, and at no very remote period, in the hands of great proprietors. Almost every manor had its resident lord, who held part of the lands in demesne, and granted out the rest by copy or lease to under-tenants, usually for three lives renewable. A state of commonage, and particularly of open common fields, was peculiarly favourable to this tenure.

" Inclosures naturally tend to its extinction.

" The north-west part of Wiltshire being much better adapted to inclosures, and to subdivision of property, than the south, was inclosed first; while the south-east or Down district, for many reasons that will hereafter be given, has undergone few inclosures, and still fewer subdivisions; and during the same period that a great deal of the property of the former district has been divided and subdivided, and gone into the hands of the many; property in the latter
district

district has been bought up by the great landholders, and is now in fewer hands than it was in the last century.

" There are undoubtedly many exceptions to this general remark, and there is in both districts a great deal of property in mortmain, belonging to churches, colleges, schools, and other pious and public foundations, which necessarily remains in its original state; but, *generally speaking*, it may be said, that a great part of the north-west district of the county, is possessed by small proprietors, and that by far the greatest part of the south-east district, is the property of great landholders."

OBJECTS of HUSBANDRY, in the County at large.—P. 4. " The principal productions of the county, serving immediately for human food, are,

> Corn—chiefly wheat and barley.
> Cheese and butter.
> Fat calves.
> Fat cattle and sheep.
> Fat pigs.

" The manufacturing towns within the county, and in the eastern part of Somersetshire, and the cities of Bath and Bristol, furnish a constant regular demand for these productions, and London takes no inconsiderable part of them.

" To these articles serving immediately for human sustenance, may be added one that serves eventually for that purpose; viz. Sheep for store; of which great numbers bred in this county, are sold off yearly, to be fatted elsewhere, chiefly in the eastern counties, for the London market.

" And to these productions of human food, may be added a very material article of human necessity, viz.

" Wool, of which the vast quantity that is raised here, finds a never-failing demand in its own manufactories, and those of the adjoining counties."

SOUTH WILTSHIRE.

SUBJECT THE FIRST.

NATURAL ECONOMY.

EXTENT.—P. 9. " The district usually called South Wiltshire, but more properly South-east Wiltshire, comprehending that part of the county called Wiltshire Downs, is divided into two principal subdivisions, called Salisbury
Plain

Plain and Marlborough Downs, and contains in all about 780 square miles, or nearly 500,000 acres."

SURFACE.—P. 9. " The distant appearance of the whole, is that of a large elevated plain, but the surface is broken into numberless inequalities, and intersected by several deep vallies, formed by brooks or rivulets" (no) " chiefly rising within this district, and on which the villages, with very few exceptions, are situated."

CLIMATURE.—P. 10. " The climate of Wiltshire Downs, is so well known for its coldness and keenness, as to be almost proverbial. The height of the hills, and their exposure to the south-west wind, from the Bristol and British Channels ; the want of inclosures in the vallies, and the draught of air that necessarily follows the rivers, undoubtedly contribute to make this district healthy both for men and cattle ; but the length of the winters consequent to such a situation, is certainly unfavourable to many of the purposes of agriculture."

WATERS.—P 9. " The greatest part of the springs which rise in the part called Salisbury Plain, run southward or eastward, and joining at or near Salisbury, near the south-east corner of the county, make the river called the Wiltshire or Upper Avon. Those which rise in the part called *Marlborough Downs*, join near Marlborough, and make the river called the Kennett, which leaves the county at Hungerford, after receiving the streams which rise in the Bedwin Vale."

SOILS.—P. 9. " The soil of this district, though various, is in a certain degree uniform. The hills are chalk, with its usual accompaniment of flint."—What immediately follows is not sufficiently accurate description. The close of the passage, however, is just.—P. 10. " The sides of the hills which have been the most washed, are the thinnest and weakest soil, and the level tops, which have been very little washed, or not washed at all, frequently the deepest and strongest."

Sandy Soils.—" But there are some very singular sand veins, running through a large portion of this district, which deserve particular notice. One very narrow, but very fertile vein enters the county at Mere, on the borders of Dorsetshire, and takes a north and north-east direction round the outside edge of the Downs, keeping nearly close to their foot, by way of Maiden Bradley, Warminster, Westbury, and Lavington, towards Devizes, where it meets and unites with a much wider and still more fertile vein, coming down the Pewsey Vale from Burbage.

" Another vein also enters the county from Dorsetshire, being the continuation of the sand-hill on which Shaftsbury stands,

stands, and passes through Donhead, Ansty, Swallowcliffe, Fovant, &c. under the foot of the Down, till it is stopped by the high ground in Burcomb Field. This vein is also met by another branch, or rather a ridge of sand-hills, coming from West Knoyle by Stop Beacon and Ridge, and joining the last-mentioned branch at or near Fovant."

Clayey Soils.—" There are some instances of strong clays and clayey loams on the skirts of this district, but as they make no part of the corn and sheep division of the county ; and the quantity of this land is small, and its management is the same as that practised in similar soils in North Wilt-shire, it will be needless to say more of it here.

" These soils, with all their consequent mixtures and va-riations, may be said to constitute the far greater part of this district."

SUBJECT THE SECOND.

POLITICAL ECONOMY.

APPROPRIATION.—*Common Pastures.*—P. 77. " The idea that Wiltshire Downs (and particularly Salisbury Plain) are all ' waste land,' is so general, that few who have travelled over them, especially from Devizes to Salisbury, will believe the contrary.

" But in the common accepted sense of the word ' waste lands,' viz. ' land in a state of nature capable of cultivation, but of very little value in its present condition,' Wiltshire downs are undoubtedly ' not waste land ;' and although there are many inconveniences in their present mode of occupation, it will, perhaps, not be very easy to prove, that they do not produce *more food*, in their present hard-stocked state, than they will (or at least than such lands usually do) when in a *state of severalty*, especially as a great proportion of them cannot be improved by tillage.

" There is on Marlborough downs a tract of some hun-dred acres of land, called ' Albourn Chace,' which may truly be called ' waste land,' and, in its present situation, a blot in the county, being merely a cow common all the summer; while the sheep, for which a great part of it is much better calculated, are starving for want of it.

" There are, in every part of this district, common mea-dows, which, though valuable in their present state, might be made much more so, if put in a state of severalty : and there are many common marshes, which might be improved

by

by inclosing; but these are, in general, small; and it may
be said, with truth, that there are no very extensive tracts
of waste land in this district. But in another sense of the
word, ' waste land,' viz. land already cultivated, but in a
defective manner, ' common-fields may be called the worst
of all wastes ' Common-pastures may, in some instances,
be made the most of, by mutual agreement, without a division; but common-fields never can."

Common Fields.—P. 78. " It has been already remarked,
and the assertion is founded on an accurate enquiry and
observation, that at this time the greatest half of the parishes
in this district are wholly, or partly, in a common-field
state. Reasons have also been given, why it has so long
remained in that state, on account of the peculiar shape
and situation of a great number of manors, and the local
difficulties attending a division. And these reasons have
hitherto operated to preserve many of them in that state,
though proposals are daily made for a division.

" Many advantages, it is certain, have been derived from
inclosures already made; and it may be proper now to state,
the probable advantages to be expected from inclosing, or
at least dividing, and putting in severalty, those lands now
in a state of commonage, with the most practical means of
obviating such disadvantages as will necessarily arise from
a new order of things, in a country less favourable than
many others, to improvements of this kind.

" The peculiar disadvantages, attending the common
field state of husbandry in this district, have already been
said to be, the obligation of plowing and cropping *all kinds
of soil* alike; the almost total preclusion that a common
flock makes to any *improvement of sheep stock*, the difficulty, and in some instances, the impossibility of raising
sufficient *hay* or *green winter food* for the stock; and particularly the very great expence and trouble, and the additional number of *horses* necessary, in occupying lands in
detached and dispersed situations.

" The advantages to be necessarily derived from an abolition of these impediments to good husbandry, need not be
enlarged upon; they speak for themselves: but it must be
remarked, that, in many parts of this district, these advantages apply much more forcibly to the case of the great
farmer, than of the small one.

" It has been already remarked, that the commonable
lands of this district consist usually of three or four arable
fields, a common sheep down, sometimes a common cow
down, and, in some instances, a common meadow."

On the *Business* of Appropriation.—P. 79. " The custom of a division has been, to give to every land-owner an
allotment

allotment of arable land, in one or more of the fields; a sheep down as near the arable land as possible, and a portion of the common meadows, if there are any. But of these, it is seldom thought necessary to *inclose* any but the common meadows, and perhaps a small part of the arable near home."

Further on *appropriating* Wiltshire Manors.—P. 83 ." In every division of commonable lands in this district, it should always be kept in view, that a lasting improvement in the *land*, and not merely a temporary one in the *rent*, is the great object of all inclosures. The soil of Wiltshire downs is of that kind, that *it may soon be made worse*, under unskilful hands. A state of ' severalty,' where every farmer can manage his land as he pleases, is certainly infinitely preferable to one of tenantry, where every one is alike obliged to pursue the same husbandry. But it must be remembered, that although a common field system of husbandry does not make the land *better*, it keeps it from growing *worse;* and as all men are not equally good judges of agriculture, there have been instances, without any relaxation in the industry of the tenants, but merely by their proceeding on a bad plan of husbandry, where the produce of a whole parish or manor, has absolutely been less both in corn and stock, after a division of common field lands, than before. A sure sign, that however the rent might be improved, the mode of husbandry was not so. In short, the remark has frequently been made, that ' severalty makes a good farmer better, and a bad one worse.' "

There is novelty, as well as ingenuity, and much truth, in the above remarks.

On *Fencing* appropriated Lands.—P. 83. " In the article of the *expence*, of a general division of commonable lands, (which in some counties is a very serious consideration) South Wiltshire, and the other *sheep folding districts*, have great advantage, as it is seldom necessary to *fence* the new allotments, except, perhaps, a small quantity of land near home.

" In these counties, where sheep are folded every night, and never without a shepherd in the day, hedges are seldom necessary for the distant lands. And, indeed, there are many situations in South Wiltshire, in which hedges would never grow to perfection."—These, let it be said, are just and valuable observations *.

SUBJECT

---

* Those curt remarks are not directed to the notice of men of mature knowledge, either in agriculture or " letters"; but to the attention of less informed *students*,—to induce them to pay the more regard to the passages which dictate them. Let this be received as a notice of general application to the whole of my present Work.

SUBJECT THE THIRD.

RURAL ECONOMY.

TENANTED ESTATES.

Estates.—*History* and *Sizes.*—P. 11. " It has been already remarked, that this district is at present chiefly possessed by great proprietors, and that it was at one time in more hands than it is at present. But it is equally clear, not only from history, but from an examination into the nature of its subdivisions, that it was *originally* in much fewer hands than it is now.

" The regular division of the manors in this district, shews that a great number of them were originally in one hand, and that their disposition was a matter of choice, and not of necessity or accident. The vallies of this district, are (almost without an exception) intersected longitudinally by rivulets. The sides of these rivulets, being the most eligible situation for building, because of course crowded with houses as much as possible. These *vallies, with* their accompanying rivulets, (provincially called bourns) are frequently from three to five miles apart, and hills intervene between bourn and bourn. The shape of manors, therefore, necessarily became a narrow oblong. It was necessary that each manor should have water, should have meadow ground, and should have wood for fuel (pit-coal being very little, if at all in use at that time). The proper situation of the meadow ground, was always near the river; for the wood, usually on the summit of the hills, the greatest part of them being evidently once covered with it, and many of them are still so.

" The natural division of the manors of this district was therefore into long narrow strips from river to wood, with a right of the use of both; and as the disposition of much the greatest part of the district is in this way, it shews, that such disposition, was the work of accommodation, given by the original grantors or superior lords, to the grantees or inferior holders: and as a further proof that it was so, there are numerous instances in this district, where a want of meadow, or of wood, was supplied by a grant of those necessary articles, taken out of other manors, at the distance of several miles from the manor to which they were annexed.

" The influx of trade and commerce, and consequently
of

of money, has tended to the division of property, and to
the increase of the number of small freeholders in many
parts of the kingdom. Lords of manors who were inclined
to dispose of their property, found they could make more
of it by parcelling it out in small lots, than by selling it in
entire manors. But this has been chiefly the case where
land lay in the neighbourhood of great towns, and particularly where it could be applied to pasture.

" In this district it has been otherwise ; the small number
of great towns in the south-east part of *Wilts;* the difficulty of raising quick fences in high and exposed situations;
the inaptitude of the land to turn into pasture ; and, above
all, the indivisibility of the manors occasioned by their
aukward shape, and the detached situation of the several
pieces composing each estate ; the difficulty of getting rid
of the common rights over the lands, and of course the impossibility of making much improvement in their value,
seem to be the principal reasons that very few manors have
been dismembered, and sold off among small freeholders.

" The residence of so many of the principal land owners
in the county, on account of its reputed good air, and its
eligibility for sporting, has also contributed in a great degree to prevent any great dismemberment of property."

IMPROVEMENT of Estates.—*Reclaiming wild Lands.*—
Sodburning.—Mr. Davis is peculiarly *argumentative*, on
this controversial topic. His good sense, however, brings
him, on this occasion, as on most others, to the confine of
truth ;—as the following short extract, taken from near
the close of his remarks, on "Burnbeaking," sufficiently
evince.—P. 94. " But however burnbeaking may be *proper*
in *proper cases*, for breaking up new land, it is a matter of
very serious consideration, how far the system of burnbeaking lately introduced, and which seems to gain ground
as a *general system*, upon *old arable land* on Wiltshire
downs, can be reconciled to the rules of good husbandry."

IRRIGATION.—On this subject, we find Mr. Davis superiorly
intelligent. He has evidently bestowed much thought upon
it,—in an ample and the best field of practice this island
affords.

The *History* of the Wiltshire Water Meadows.—P. 30.
" There is, perhaps, no part of this kingdom, where
the system of watering meadows is so well understood,
and carried to so great perfection, as in this district.—
This, which is so justly called by *Mr. Kent* ' the greatest
and most valuable of all improvements,' was *generally* introduced into this district in the latter end of the last, and
the beginning of this century. Many of the most valuable
and best formed meadows, particularly in the *Wyley Bourn,*
were

were made under the directions of one farmer Baverstock, of Stockton, between the year 1700, and the year 1705. And at present there is scarcely a river or brook in the district, that is not applied in some way or other to this purpose.

"An imperfect scheme of watering, had undoubtedly been practised before that period. Perhaps indeed its introduction into this district, is almost coeval with that of folding sheep, with which it is intimately connected. But the *regular mode*, in which both systems are now conducted, is certainly not very ancient. Many old farmers, who have died within the memory of man, remembered when neither of the systems was conducted on any regular plan.

"*Theory of water-meadows.*—The idea of watering meadows, so far as it relates to bringing the water *upon the land*, was taken from *nature*. It must have been always observed, that winter floods produced fertility, provided the water did *not* remain *too long* on the land. The idea of taking the water *off* the land *at will*, and bringing it *on again at will*, is the effect of *art;* and the knowledge of the proper time to do this, the effect of observation."

P. 31. "*Nature and properties of water-meadows.*—It has been already premised, that the principle of a water-meadow, is the power of bringing on and carrying off the water at pleasure. And provided this great object can be accomplished, it is not material what the shape of a water-meadow is, or that the disposition of the trenches (provincially ' *the works of the meadow,'*) should be uniform. But as very little land can be entirely commanded by water, unless its inequalities are reduced by manual labour,—it has been found convenient to adopt two different kinds of water-meadows, one for land lying on declivities, and which must in general be watered from springs or small brooks, and the other for low land near rivers, to be watered from those rivers.

"The first kind is called in Wiltshire, ' *catch work meadows,*' and the latter '*flowing meadows.*' The latter are by far the most general in this district."

The former of those methods belong to the Devonshire practice, rather then to that of Wiltshire. I therefore pass on to the latter;—which might be emphatically named the *Wiltshire practice.*

P. 33. "*Flowing meadows described.*—The other kind of water-meadows, viz. those usually called ' *Flowing Meadows,*' require much more labour and system in their formation. The land applicable to this purpose being frequently

quently a flat morass, the first object to be considered is, how the water is to be *got off* when once brought on; and in such situations this can seldom be done, without throwing up the land in high ridges, with deep drains between them. A main carriage being then taken out of the river at a higher level, so as to command the tops of these ridges, the water is carried by small trenches or carriages along the top of each ridge, and, by means of moveable stops of earth, is thrown over on *each* side, and received in the drains below, from whence it is collected into a main drain, and carried on to water other meadows, or other parts of the same meadow below. One tier of these ridges being usually watered at once, is usually called ' a Pitch of Work ;' and it is usual to make the ridges thirty or forty feet wide, or, if water is abundant, perhaps sixty feet, and nine or ten poles in length, or longer, according to the strength and plenty of the water.

" It is obvious from this description, that as the water in this kind of meadow is not used again and again, in *one pitch,* as in the catch meadows, that this method is only applicable to large streams, or to valleys subject to floods; and as these ridges must be formed by *manual labour,* the expence of this kind of meadow must necessarily exceed the more simple method first described: and the hatches that are necessary to manage and temper the water on rivers, must be much more expensive than those on small brooks.

" The expence, therefore, of the first making such a meadow as this is, will be from twelve pounds to twenty pounds per acre, according to the difficulty of the ground, and the quantity of hatch-work required : but the improvement in the value of the land by this operation is astonishing. The *abstract value* of a good meadow of this kind, may fairly be called three pounds per acre; but its value, when taken as *part of a farm,* and particularly of a *sheep-breeding farm,* is almost beyond computation; and when such a meadow is once made, it may be said to be made for ever, the whole expence of keeping up the works, and watering it frequently, not exceeding five shillings per acre yearly, and the expence of the hatches, if well done at first, being a mere trifle for a number of years afterwards."

P. 34. " *Supposed quantity of water-meadows in this district.*—The number of acres of land in this district, under this kind of management, has been computed, and with a tolerable degree of accuracy, to be between 15 and 20,000 acres.

" Indeed, it has been found so very beneficial, that very few spots of land capable of being watered, remain otherwise,

wise, unless where some *water mill* stands in the way, or where some person who has the command of the water *above*, refuses to let it be taken out of its natural course to water the lands below.

"" Some new meadows might be made, and very great and beneficial alterations made in the old ones, if some plan could be adopted to get the command of water where necessary for this purpose, and particularly in the case of water mills. A remedy for this will be afterwards proposed."

P. 103. " *Use of water-meadows.*—The water-meadows of Wiltshire, and the neighbouring counties, are a branch of husbandry that can never be too much recommended.

" In speaking of water-meadows, it has been often objected, that they are local; and that there are many parts of the kingdom in which they neither *can be made*, nor are they *necessary if they could be made*.

" There are, undoubtedly, *many parts* of the kingdom in which water-meadows *cannot be made;* but nobody will deny, but there are *thousands of situations* where they could be made, in which they *have never been tried.* And as for their use, it may be strongly suspected, that those who deny it have never been in Wiltshire *in the month of April.* Let those who call it in question, point out a substitute, on which a farmer can, with *equal certainty*, depend for the sustenance of his flock in that *trying month.*

" Whatever may be the earliness of the season, with respect to the springing of either ray grass or meadow grass, water-meadows will be a *month* before either.

" And notwithstanding the great advantages that have been derived from the introduction of green winter crops, such as turnips, rape, cabbages, &c. *(advantages to this kingdom almost beyond estimate)* yet this may be laid down as a certain maxim, that, whether the *winter* be hard or mild—whether the *spring* be late or early—nature will always have, in this climate, an ' *interregnum* ' " (!) " *between the end of one year's food and the beginning of another.* The same temperature of the air in the spring, which brings on the grass, will occasion all the green winter crops to run to seed, and not only to lose their own nourishing quality, but to exhaust the land on which they grow.

" A moment's reflection will convince every man, that nature must unavoidably and constantly leave this *chasm* in the year's food. *Winter*, though driven into a small compass, *is still winter, and art alone can expunge it from the kalendar.*"

P. 37. " *Management of water-meadows.*—The management of water-meadows (as nearly as it can be described in
an

an account necessarily so concise as this), is in the following way :

" As soon as the after-grass is eaten off as bare as can be, the manager of the mead (provincially ' the drowner') begins cleaning out the main drain, then the main carriage, and then proceeds to ' right up the works,' that is, to make good all the water carriages that the cattle have trodden down, and open all the drains they may have trodden in, so as to have one tier or pitch of work ready for ' drowning,' and which is then put under water (if water is plenty enough), during the time the drowners is righting up the next pitch. In the flowing meadows this work is, or ought to be, done early enough in the autumn, to have the whole mead ready to catch, if possible, ' *the first floods after Michaelmas*,' the water being then ' thick and good,' being the *first* washing of the arable land on the sides of the chalk hills, as well as of the dirt from the roads, &c. &c.

" The length of this autumn watering cannot always be determined, as it depends on situations and circumstances; but if water can be commanded in plenty, the rule is to give it a ' thorough good soaking' at first, perhaps, a fortnight or three weeks, with a dry interval of a day or two, and sometimes two fortnights, with a dry interval of a week, and then the works are made as dry as possible, to encourage the growth of the grass. This first soaking is to make the land sink and pitch close together; a circumstance of great consequence, not only to the *quantity* but to the *quality* of the grass, and particularly to encourage the shooting of the new roots which the grass is continually forming, to support the forced growth above.

" While the grass grows freely, a fresh watering is not wanted, but as soon as it flags, the watering may be repeated for a few days at a time, whenever there is an opportunity of getting water, always keeping this fundamental rule in view, ' *to make the meadows as dry as possible between every watering ;*' and to ' *stop the water, the moment the appearance of any scum on the land, shews that it has already had water enough.*'

" Some meadows that will bear the water *three weeks* in October, November, or December, will, perhaps, not bear it *a week* in February or March, and sometimes scarcely *two* days in April or May."

P. 38. " *Custom of feeding meadows with sheep.*—It has already been said, that the great object in this district of an early crop of water-meadow grass, is to enable the farmer to breed early lambs.

" As soon as the lambs are able to travel with the ewes, (perhaps

(perhaps about the middle of March) they begin to feed the water-meadows. Care is, or ought to be, taken, to make the meadows as dry as possible for some days before the sheep are let in.

" The grass is hurdled out *daily* in portions, according to what the number of sheep can eat in a day, to prevent their trampling the rest; at the same time, leaving a few open spaces in the hurdles for the lambs to get through, and feed forward in the fresh grass. One acre of *good grass* will be sufficient for five hundred couples for a day.

" On account of the quickness of this grass, it is not usual to allow the ewes and lambs to go into it with empty bellies, nor before the dew is off in the morning.

" The hours of feeding are usually from ten or eleven o'clock in the morning to about four or five in the evening, when the sheep are driven to fold; the fold being generally at that time of the year on the barley fallow. And the great object is to have water-mead grass, sufficient for the ewes and lambs, till the barley sowing is ending.

" *Meadows laid up for hay.*—As soon as this first crop of grass is eaten off by the ewes and lambs, the water is immediately thrown over the meadows, (at this time of the year two or three days over 'each pitch,' is generally sufficient) and it is then made perfectly dry, and laid up for a hay crop. Six weeks are usually sufficient for the growth of the crop. It seldom requires eight; and there have been instances of great crops being produced in five.

" *Nature of water-meadow hay.*—The hay of water-meadows, being frequently large and coarse in its nature, it is necessary to cut it young; and if made well, it then becomes of a peculiarly nourishing milky quality, either for ewes *or* dairy cows.

" The water-meadows are laid up for a second crop, in *some instances;* but this is only usual when hay is scarce: not that it is supposed to hurt the land, but the hay is of that herbaceous soft nature, and takes so long time in drying, that it is seldom well made. It is usually of much greater value to be fed with dairy cows. And for that purpose a flush of after grass, so early and so rank, will be precisely of the same comparative service to the dairy, as the spring feed has been described to be for ewes and lambs.

" The cows remain in the meadows till the ' drowner' begins to prepare for the winter watering.

" *Water-meadows safe for sheep in spring, but will rot them in autumn.*—Water-meadows are reckoned to be perfectly safe for sheep in the spring, even upon land that would rot sheep, if it was not watered, but in the autumn
the

the best water-meadows are supposed to be dangerous. This is at present an inexplicability in the operations of nature, and a discovery of the reason might perhaps lead, in some measure, to a discovery of the causes of the rot in sheep. But the circumstance itself is rather an advantage, than a disadvantage, to this district, as it obliges the farmers to keep a *few dairy cows*, to feed the water-meadows in autumn, and to provide artificial grasses, or other green crops for their sheep, during that period.

" *Proper soils for water-meadows.*—From what has been so repeatedly urged, on the necessity of making water-meadows *dry*, as well as wet, every reader must have inferred the advantage of having them, if possible, on ' *a warm absorbent bottom**.'

" The bottom or sub-soil of a water-mead, is of much more consequence than the quality or the depth of the top soil.

" Not but that land on peaty or clay bottoms, may be considerably improved by watering; and there are many good water-meadows on such soils, but they are not so desirable on account of the difficulty of draining the water out of them, and making them firm enough to bear treading.

" A loose gravel, or what, perhaps, is still better, a bed of broken flints, with little or no intermixture of earth, wherever it can be obtained, is the most desirable bottom.

" On many of the best water-meadows in this district, where the bottom is a warm, absorbent gravel, or rather a bed of broken flints; the soil is not six inches deep, and that depth is quite sufficient, in those seasons when water is plenty, as the grass will root in the warm gravel" (?) " in preference to the best top-soil whatever, and such meadows always produce the earliest grass in the spring. Nor is it so very material, of what *kinds of grasses* the herbage is composed, when the meadow is made. *That kind* will always predominate, which *agrees best with the soil and the water*, provided the supply of water is regular and constant *every winter*, otherwise *that kind* will predominate which will bear *wet and dry*, and some of the worst grasses, in their native state, will become the best when made succulent by plenty *of water.*

" *Long*

" * There is a striking proof of the truth of this remark, in the water meadows near Hungerford, and particularly at Standen. Although they are laid out in no regular plan, and in many instances there are no drains to empty the water carriages, yet the gravel bottom is so very absorbent, that the water will soak out in a few hours, and the meadows be left as dry as if they were watered on the most systematic plan. And few meads in the county produce better crops either of spring feed or of hay."

" *Long grass meadows.*—Nature has given a striking lesson on this subject in this very district, viz. In the two small meadows at Orcheston (six miles north-west of Amesbury), usually called the ' Wiltshire *Long Grass* Meads.'

" These meadows adjoin together, and contain, in the whole, only two acres and an half, and yet the crop they produce in a favourable year is so immense, and of so good a quality, that the tythe hay of them was once (according to the information of the tenant) sold for five guineas." (?)

Mr. Davis's strictures on those small plots of ground,—this narrow slip of land, the confined bottom of a shallow valley, or dip, in the wavey surface of the chalk hills,—are not quite satisfactory. They proved, however, to be sufficient to cause a great sensation,—in the higher regions of the agricultural world!

In crossing the Wiltshire hills, in 1794, I examined, with some attention, the celebrated " Long-grass Meads" of Orcheston. For the result of my observations, see my SOUTHERN COUNTIES, article *Water Meadows.*

Finally, it is proper in me to mention that, throughout Mr. Davis's masterly Report of the water meadows of Wiltshire, not a word escapes him, concerning the SPECIFIC QUALITY of the WATERS with which they are irrigated !—An unfortunate omission which may leave, on the minds of inexperienced readers, an idea that, by *waters in general,* the same beneficial purpose may be effected ;—than which nothing can be less correct. It is by *calcarious waters* the magical effect is produced.

DRINKING POOLS.—P. 98. " Sheep-wells and sheep-ponds are objects of great necessity to a tenant, though of expence to a landlord. Wherever ponds can be made, they are much more eligible than wells, for watering sheep. It is trouble to draw water, and *few shepherds* like trouble; and in hot weather, it is a very difficult matter for a farmer to prevent his sheep from having too much water at one time, and too little at another, when they can get no water but what is drawn for them from wells.

" The custom of making sheep-ponds with rammed chalk is very expensive ; many sheep-ponds on the downs having cost from 25 to 40*l.* and after all, they are liable to be injured by every frosty winter and every dry summer, and are very difficult to be repaired. A cheaper and more durable mode of making sheep-ponds, is much wanted in this district."—For a description of such a mode, see my YORKSHIRE.

MANAGEMENT OF ESTATES.—*Tenancy.*— P. 99. " The usual terms for which leases are granted in this district are, sometimes *seven* years, oftener *fourteen;* now and then
twenty-one;

twenty-one; but of late years, *twelve* has been thought the most eligible term, as being *more divisible* into a regular course of sowing the arable land, either in three fields or in four, as shall be thought most proper for the land; and, considering the disadvantages under which a Wiltshire down farm is too often entered upon, the term of a lease should never be less than twelve years. He must be a good farmer indeed, or have very good luck, who (on a farm fairly rented) can do more than save his own in the first four years."

For a notice concerning *Life Leases* see *Size of Farms,* ensuing.

Covenants.—P. 99. "Repairs of the buildings are usually done by the landlord, except thatching and glass windows, which are usually repaired by the tenants.

"Repairs of the fences and gates are usually done by the tenants, after being first put in repair by the landlord, the landlord sometimes allowing rough timber for gates; but neither the fences nor gates are as yet a very expensive on a South Wiltshire farm.

"The tenant is bound to sow his lands in the course limited by the lease; to keep up a full flock of sheep, and fold them in due course of husbandry on *some* part of the premises; but in the last year, on such part as the landlord shall direct; to spend all hay, straw, &c. on the premises, (long wheat straw sometimes excepted); to spread all the dung on the premises, except the dung of the last year's crop, and (if a lady-day bargain) the straw of the offgoing crop, which are to be left at the disposal of the landlord."

P. 101. "With respect to the payment of taxes, it was usual, till within these few years, for landlords to pay, not only the land-tax, but *all parochial* taxes; but of late years the poor's rates have increased so very much, that landlords have thought it necessary to subject the tenants to the payment of *all* parochial taxes; not altogether with a view to prevent an unnecessary waste of money, in the temporary relief of the poor, but to prevent new burthens being brought on the parishes, by the hiring of *yearly* instead of *weekly* labourers, and thereby settling them and their future families on the parish."

Removals.—P. 99. "The old custom of South Wilts, was almost invariably a Lady-day's entry. Indeed a Michaelmas one, was not at all adapted to the customs of feeding the commonable lands of this district. Some old ' severalty farms' had a Michaelmas entry; but those instances are few."

Nothing can be more untoward and distressing, both
to

to outgoing and incoming tenants, than the custom of Wiltshire, as described by Mr. Davis, in regard to their removal from farm to farm.

P. 100. "The general custom of a Wiltshire Lady-day's entry, is, that the *rent begins from Lady-day*, at which time the tenant enters on all the *green ground*, and brings on his sheep and cows, and lays up the meadows for mowing; but the offgoing tenant sows and takes *all* the crops of corn, not only the wheat that was sown at the preceding Michaelmas, but also the Lent corn that is sown the spring that he quits.

" The new tenant, who is, perhaps, at that time quitting *another farm in the same way*, brings on his horses and oxen, as soon as he has done sowing *his own offgoing crop*, and begins preparing on his *new farm* for wheat.

" The offgoing tenant takes his horses and oxen away at *the same time*, to make the same preparation on the farm he is then entering upon.

" The usual time fixed for the entry of the new tenant, to carry out dung, and prepare for wheat, is, in some parts of the district, as early as the 14th of May; in others, as late as the 24th of June.

" The old tenant keeps part of the house and stable, to make out his corn.

" The new tenant has the other part to prepare for his next crops, and take charge of his own cattle, and make his hay; and in this intermixed way, the two families are situated for upwards of a year, viz. usually till the Midsummer twelve-month after the new tenant's rent commences.

" The old tenant keeps the barns till that time, to thresh out his corn; the new tenant not wanting them (except for sheep-shearing, which is allowed) till the ensuing harvest.

" So that the new tenant has only *one year's produce* of the arable land, for the first *year and half's rent*, and lays out of that money till he quits the farm, *when he also, in his turn*, takes an offgoing crop."

AGRICULTURE.

FARMS.—Their *History* in Wiltshire.—P. 15. " The ancient distribution of the greatest part of this district was in the following way:

" In general, there was in each manor *one* great farm called the Lord's Farm, which usually had its lands in severalty, and distinct from the tenants.

" The

" The rest of the manor called the **Tenantry Part** was divided into small copyhold tenements or farms, called ' Yard Lands;' each of which was originally *nearly* of *equal value*, and enjoyed *equal rights* of commonage.

" These tenants sent their sheep to one common flock, where they were kept by a common shepherd, and their cows and plough oxen to a common herd, where they were kept by a common herdsman.

" As the necessity of a common sheep-flock still continues for the sake of manuring the common-field lands, a considerable part of these small properties, called Yard-Lands, are still occupied in their original state of commonage, although the tenure of them is in many instances changed from copyhold, some to leases for lives, some fallen into the lord's hands and lett at rack rents, and some sold off in fee, and frequently many of them occupied by one person.

" The value of these yard-lands is different in different parts of this district, as is already stated, and of course the quantity of land in each varies very considerably. There are many instances where a yard-land of about 20*l.* per annum, contains about two acres of meadow land, eighteen acres of arable (frequently in eighteen or twenty pieces), and a right on the common fields, common meadows, and other commonable places, for perhaps forty sheep, and as many cattle as they can winter with the fodder growing on the premisses.

" *Inconveniences attending it.*—Much of the singularity of the occupation of the lands in this district arises from its natural situation. The shape of the manors being, as was formerly explained, generally a narrow oblong, and frequently with the houses and buildings at one end, there are many instances where manors are near three miles long, and little more than half a mile wide.

" The application of the land is almost uniform. The common meadows, *of which the greatest part are watered,* immediately adjoin the river: the houses and small inclosures as near to it as possible. Next follows the arable land, until the land becomes too steep or too thin to plow, and then the sheep and cow downs, and frequently the woods at the extremity of the manor, and adjoining the downs or woods of the manors in the opposite bourn.

" In some instances, particularly where the bourns approach their junctions, and sometimes at the heads of the bourns, the lands belonging to each manor are partly on one side of the village and partly on the other, whereby the occupation is rendered more convenient; but these instances are comparatively few.

" The difficulties attending the inclosing or even laying in severalty,

severalty, the commonable lands so peculiarly situated as great part of the district is, will be afterwards explained.

"*General custom of feeding the commonable lands.*—The custom of feeding the commonable lands varies in different parts of this district, as well as the quantity of stock each commoner (or occupier of a yard-land) has a right to put; but in general it is as follows:

"*Sheep commons.*—The common sheep down is open for the common flock during summer and autumn. The unsown field (or summer field) is open till it is all plowed for wheat. The sheep have then only the down, till the harvest is over, and the other fields are clear. They then have those fields and the down until the winter obliges the owners to give them hay. Until this period they are folded on the arable fields in a common fold: but when they begin to eat hay, every commoner finds his own fold and his own hay; the common shepherd feeding and penning the whole. When the ewes are near yeaning, the owners take them home to their inclosed meadows; and by the time all the ewes have yeaned, the water-meadows are ready to take them to grass.

"In some instances, the water-meadows are common for the sheep stock; in others, they are private property.

"When feeding the water-meadows, the sheep are penned on the barley land; and by the time the water-mead grass is eat, and the barley is sown, the summer field (especially if sown with ray-grass) is ready to receive the sheep, where they generally stay till near shear-time, and then go to the down until the stubble fields are broken, at which time (perhaps about the middle of September) they usually put the rams to the ewes. These rams are provided, and the common shepherd paid, at the joint expence of the commoners.

"As in this state of commonage (where there must necessarily be a great scarcity of winter food) it is necessary to reduce this sheep stock before winter, it is customary to sell off the old ewes and the wether lambs about Michaelmas, and to put out the ewe lambs to winter, either on pasture land, or turnips, in other parts of the county, and frequently in the adjacent counties.

"These lambs, are usually put out from the 10th of October to the 5th of April, and the price is seldom lower than 5s. and in some instances this year has been as high as 8s. for that time. And yet after this reduction of stock, the common-field farmers of this district are frequently obliged to buy hay for the rest, which they are often under the necessity of fetching from ten to fifteen miles.

"*Cow commons.*—Cow commons (called cow downs) are frequent

frequent in the undivided parts of this district, but not general. They were more general formerly than now, many of them having been, at different times, turned into sheep commons by consent of the commoners. These cow downs, are usually the best and most level parts of the down lands, and are sometimes worth from 5s. to near 10s. per acre.

"The common herd of cows, usually begin to feed the cow downs early in May (usually Holy-Rood Day), and finish when the fields are clear of corn. At the beginning and end of the season, they are driven to the down in the morning, and brought back in the evening; but in the heat of summer, they are only kept on the down during the night, and in the morning, they are brought back into the villages, where they feed in the lanes and small marshes by the river side (if such there are) till after the evening milking. When the stubble fields are open, the cows have a right to feed them jointly with the sheep: and if there are common meadows (whether watered meadows or not) they have an exclusive right to feed them, till the end of the commoning season (usually St. Martin's Day, 11th (22nd) November, O. S.) when the owners take them home to the straw yards. After the cows leave the cow down to go into the stubble fields, it becomes common for the sheep flock, during all, or a certain part of the winter, when it is again laid up for the cows."

Present *Sizes* of Farms.—P. 14. "The present distribution of the lands in this district may, in general, be divided into two kinds:

"1st. The farms in *severalty* (or those not subject to rights of common). These are in general from 100l. to 300l. per annum: in some instances lower than 100l. but few so high as 400l.

"2nd. The tenantry yard-lands (or customary tenements) which are still subject to rights of common. These are in general from 18l. to 25l. per annum; some as high as 40l. per annum; great numbers of which are still occupied *singly*, although consolidations of them are every day taking place."

P. 109. "*Proper size of a South Wiltshire farm.*—As the only difference between good husbandry and bad, is, that the former, by enabling a tenant to raise a *greater* comparative produce, at a *less* comparative expence, enables him to acquire more profit to himself, and to give a greater rent to his landlord, than he could do by pursuing the latter, it may not be improper here to enquire, *on what sized farm*, as *well as by what mode of husbandry*, a farmer in this district will be best able to do this; and this enquiry is particularly

ticularly necessary at this time, when so great a part of South Wiltshire is emerging into a new system, by the extinction of lifehold tenures, and the abolition of common-field husbandry.

" At a time when this district was, in general, in a state of lifehold tenure, the size of farms was not always an object of the choice of the landlord, but of necessity ; and while the lands remained in a state of commonage, the occupiers were in an equal state of advantage (or rather of disadvantage). But in those manors, where it is intended that the lifehold tenements shall fall into hand, and that farms shall be made out of them, it becomes an object of consideration, ' what the most proper size of a South Wiltshire farm is ;' so as to ascertain the necessity of taking down unnecessary buildings, and to determine the number and situation of those necessary to be built in their room."

In continuation, we find many ingenious remarks, on this much disputed subject—the proper sizes of farms. But the reasonings, in this instance, are less clear and convincing, than they are on most other subjects brought forward by this writer. The inference drawn from them, however, is more satisfactory.

P. 112. " The size of a Wiltshire farm should be, therefore, such as the master's eye, and one *principal* servant in each department, can manage properly ; and for this, one head carter, with such a number of boys as may occasionally be wanted, and one head shepherd, with assistance at seasons of urgency, will generally be sufficient.

" Perhaps, the lowest size of a Wiltshire down farm, that can be managed to advantage, is a good *six* horse business, and the highest a *nine* horse business, or *ten*, at the utmost. Beyond this extent, *two* men are required in each of these subordinate capacities ; a jealousy is excited between them ; the master's eye is insufficient to manage them, and a bailiff is necessary.

" This business becomes then, to all intents and purposes, *two farms ;* and would certainly be better managed, if in the occupation of two *farmers.*"

How much good sense, thought, and precision, are observable in the above extract. Had the extent of a six-horse and a nine-horse business (expressions, no doubt, that are sufficiently understood in South Wiltshire) been given, the sizes recommended would have been more clearly seen. The principle of admeasurement, however, is evident.

The *Plan* of Farms.—P. 95. " The situation and construction of farm-houses and offices, is less variable in South Wilts, than in many other districts ; and being in general
crowded

crowded together in the villages, for the conveniency of water, they are frequently inconveniently situated for the occupation of the lands.

" While the system of common field husbandry existed in its original state, and every yard land had its farm-house, its yard for cattle, its barns, and its stable, and the owner resided upon it, such a crowded situation had its conveniences, as well as its inconveniences.

" In the present state of that system, wherever the small farms are occupied by the owners, the buildings are usually kept in tolerable repair, but whenever three or four, or more of such estates, as is frequently the case, are rented by one farmer, the consequence is, that all the farm-houses except one, are let to labourers, and great part of the out-buildings are suffered to go to decay. And in this ruinous condition, a great part of these villages in this district, which are not yet put into a state of severalty, are at this time."

P. 97. " On account of the oblong shape of many manors, and the consequent distance of part of the lands from home, it is not uncommon for great farms to have ' field barns,' for the better occupation of their distant land, especially where downs have been broken up; and it is a well-calculated plan, not only to save the carriage of the corn from such distant land to the home barn, but also to insure such land a return of its own dung. For the last reason, it is common and necessary to inclose a yard, and make a pond near such barn, for the conveniency of keeping cattle to eat the barley and oat straw in the winter.

" Wheat is generally carried home; seldom ricked at a field barn, unless there is also a house for a labourer adjoining, to protect it.

" In some instances, where common-fields have been divided, one or two of the large farmers have given up their situation in the villages, and taken their allotments in the distant land, and removed the buildings to it, to make way for smaller proprietors.

" And this must be frequently done, whenever a general division of the common-fields in this district takes place."

PLAN OF MANAGEMENT*.—Of *Common Fields.*—The feudal regulations of former times were mostly the same, I believe, throughout the kingdom; namely, two crops and a fallow. Of later years, a third crop has been added in South Wiltshire,—and some other districts; as clover or
other

* For the OBJECTS of Management, in Wiltshire,—see p. 188, aforegoing.

other cultivated herbage: thus enlarging the round to four years.

For the original regulations, in Wiltshire, see p. 203, above.

Of *appropriated Lands.*—P. 53. " *Rotation of crops on the severalty farms.*—After enumerating the rotation of crops usual in the common field system, and the attempts that have been made to approximate as near to good hus-bandry as can be done, 'till that system is abolished, it re-mains to notice what is the rotation of crops used by the farmers of this district, on the farms that are in severalty, with remarks on the apparent excellences and defects of each.

" The principal soils under tillage in this district, have been already noticed to be the white land soil, the flinty loams, and the sand veins.

" A great part of the farms, in this district, have lands of the two former kinds.—A few (and unfortunately but a few) have a share of the latter.

" These soils being totally different in their nature, require, and when in good hands generally have, a totally different management; but as they usually adjoin to each other, and the transition is seldom sudden but gradual, that manage-ment is frequently, and sometimes, in particular seasons, unavoidably *blended,* and from thence comes an opinion, frequently entertained of the best Wiltshire farmers, ' that they have no regular system of cropping.'" And this would seem to be really the fact.

Mr. D. speaks at some length of the courses of cropping, on the three above-named distinctions of land. But he rather conveys his own sentiments than any established practices of the country.

Under the head, " Improvements suggested," the sub-joined passage appears.—

P. 108. " The great errors in the husbandry of this dis-trict, have been already noticed to be the sowing more land with *corn,* and particularly with *wheat,* than can be properly manured with the stock on the farm; and the not making proper provision either by hay, or green crops, to winter all the sheep stock at home.

" These two errors proceed from one cause, viz. an anxiety in farmers to have a certain number of *acres* of wheat every year; and, frequently, without considering whether they have sufficient manure or not, or even whether the land is at all adapted to wheat."—This great error is not confined to South Wiltshire; but is more or less observable in almost every district of the kingdom.

WORKPEOPLE.—P. 88. " The price of labour varies very much in different parts of the county of Wilts, and is chiefly

chiefly affected by proximity to, or distance from, the manufacturing towns.

" In a great part of the South Wiltshire district, where the inhabitants are very little under the influence of manufacturing prices, the prices of labourers in husbandry are nearly uniform; but these prices have been gradually on the advance.

" Twenty years ago, the common winter price was ten-pence a day, from thence it gradually rose to twelve-pence, which now may be called the general price, though in many instances it is risen to fourteen-pence *."

P. 89. " In the corn districts, the resident labourers are seldom numerous enough to get in the harvest. 'Taskers,' or ' labourers, by compact,' from the more populous parts of the county, or from Somersetshire, or other neighbouring counties, take the wheat by the acre to reap. The price is about six shillings per acre, in good seasons, with an allowance of small beer, and a supper once, twice, or oftener, per week. The wives and children of the resident labourers also assist in this operation, while the resident labourers are fully employed in securing the corn."

P. 90. " Wiltshire labourers, in general, are strong and robust, and not deficient in expertness, in what they undertake: in some branches (hurdle and hedge making for instance) ingenious. But there is a remarkable slowness in the step, not only of the shepherds, whose laziness is proverbial, but also particularly of *the ploughmen*, and which they also teach *their horses*, that is noticed by every person who has seen the labourers of other counties, particularly Norfolk. The common step of a ploughman and his horses, in the last-mentioned county, is often three miles and an half in an hour. In South Wiltshire, frequently little more than two."

WORKING ANIMALS.—P. 73. " *Oxen* are not in general use in this district; and in some parts of it, perhaps, not so much as formerly, when there were more common cow-downs; and it is very probable, that the gradual decrease of cow-downs, which will be the consequence of the lands being put into severalty, will tend gradually to reduce the use of oxen, especially in the hilly parts of this district. And although those downs might, in many cases, be much more profitably applied to the keeping of working oxen than of cows; yet, if the present rage for *fine* sheep continues, every other kind of stock must give way to them, and

" * In many parts of this district, the corn is thrashed by the bushel, and not by the day, but the latter is the more general custom."

and as soon as the cows are driven off the downs, the oxen must immediately follow."

P. 74. " As a shifting stock, where a farmer wants more strength at one time of the year than another, oxen are peculiarly proper, being more easily bought and sold, and that at a less loss or risque than horses. And where a farmer has a quantity of rough down land, I am clearly of opinion, that the treating of a few oxen, will increase the sheep-feed more than their eating will diminish it. I have seen so many instances of downs decreasing in goodness, when changed from cow-downs to sheep-downs, as to con- vince me fully of this fact."

This I can readily credit. To light spungy lands, the treading of cattle is far more efficacious in giving them the required texture than that of sheep. The men of Norfolk are convinced of this by long experience. They speak of " jamming" their land with " bullocks," in a tone of pecu- liar satisfaction.

Working *Horses.*—P. 105. " The pride or vanity of stock, has been almost as hurtful to the farmers of this dis- trict, in the article of horses, as in sheep.

" In both instances, the attention has been much more directed to get *large,* rather than *useful,* animals. Large heavy-heeled black horses have long been the fashion, and have almost driven the smart, active, and *really useful* horses, out of the district. Even the breeders of the north say, they can never breed cart colts big enough to please Wiltshire farmers.

" There are, undoubtedly, some situations where the steepness of the hills, and others where the heaviness of the soil, require more than ordinary strength ; but surely it would be better to add to the *number* of horses upon *particular occasions,* than to increase the size of *the whole,* especially as the roads to the market-towns are in general so very good.

" It has been often asserted, that the benefits the Wiltshire farmers derive from their excellent markets, are more than paid for, by the expence of keeping fine horses to carry their corn to them.

" Great horses not only *cost* proportionably more at first than small ones, but require much more and better food to keep up their flesh; and the pride of a farmer, in buying such horses, is generally followed by the pride of his carter, in keeping them as fat as possible. And as their food (which in general is barley) is taken from the barn unmeasured, the expence of keeping them is seldom exactly known.

" There are many instances, where the expence of keeping up a fine team of horses, amounts to nearly the rent of the
farm

farm on which they are kept; and this expence is very seldom counterbalanced, by any profit arising by buying them in when colts, and selling them at five or six years old, to go in stage waggons or London drays, although this has been the great pretence for keeping this kind of horses. Hundreds of colts have been bought at thirty guineas a-piece, *for the chance of selling one now and then* for forty-five of fifty, two or three years afterwards, under the idea that they *earn their bread* during the time the farmers keep them, and the advance in their price is *all gain.*

" But this is certainly a mistake. A large horse seldom comes to perfection till six years old; and during its progress to perfection, it must be *nursed,* and *treated tenderly,* and *favored in its work,* or it will never attain its full size and beauty.

" This nursing and tender treatment must be at the expence of the farmer; and the favor of work, at the expence of the older horses: so that the young ones, instead of *earning* the bread they eat, are eating that which the *others earn.*

" If the farmers in this district were able to breed their own horses, this argument would have less weight; but the great price at which cart colts have been bought for many years, precludes the possibility of getting much by them afterwards. Besides, this kind of horse is naturally too heavy, and too slow in its step, for the purposes of Wiltshire farming, or perhaps, indeed, for the farm use of any district. In light soils, so much strength is not wanted. In heavy soils, the weight of the animal does injury to the land.

" Large heavy-heeled horses are, undoubtedly, fit for steady, heavy drafts on public roads; but, for a farmer's use, a smaller and more active kind of horses will not only step quicker, but will bear their work more hours in a day; and will keep up their flesh, not only with proportionably less food, but with that of an inferior kind."—This, too, I steadfastly believe.

IMPLEMENTS.—*Plows.*—P. 67. " The ploughs used in this district, are chiefly of two kinds:

" 1. The hill country two-wheel plough, with the point of the beam elevated, and swinging upon a brace between the wheels, and the draft chain fixed almost at the centre of the beam.

" 2. The one-wheel plough, so made as to be used with a foot instead of a wheel, in case the land is so wet that the wheel clogs, and will not run round. These ploughs are about eight feet, or eight and an half long, in the beam, and have a long mould-board set at a very acute angle with the sole of the plough, and bent so as to turn down the furrow, or rather, that the furrow may drop from it, as flat as possible.

" The

" The two-wheel plough is chiefly used on thin, flinty land, where deep ploughing would do mischief, and where, in plowing shallow, the stones are liable to strike the plough out of ground. In such soils, the farmers are very sensible that a much lighter, and more simple plough, would answer as well or better, provided it was always used by careful experienced plowmen ; and the increase of good plowmen has occasioned the two-wheel plough to be thrown by, in many parts of this district, as expensive and cumbersome. The single-wheel and foot plough is the most general plough now in use throughout this district, as being applicable to light or heavy land, deep or shallow."

Drags.—P. 70. " For some years, a very heavy triangular machine was used, called an A. Drag, with its tines so fixed on its three sides, as that, when drawn by one point, it made parallel furrows eight or nine inches apart. On these furrows, they sowed their wheat *broad-cast,* and afterwards, by lightly harrowing the ground in the same direction as the furrows, they got a great part of the seed into the furrows, and the rest took its chance.

" But this machine not going perfectly steady, has been still further improved, by putting the tines on two parallel beams, usually four before, at distances of eighteen inches, and five behind, working between them, so as to make parallel furrows of nine inches apart. This is drawn much like a drill-plough, and held by two handles behind ; and is called a nine-share plough, or, where made with eleven tines, an eleven-share plough.

" The shape of the tines has also been altered ; instead of being strait, they are bent at bottom ; the leg part large and hollow, and the foot solid and pointed. These are made strong enough to root up the ground, if ever so hard, into furrows of a proper depth for sowing. Over these furrows they sow their corn, as above described."

MANURE.—*Sheepfold.*—P. 61. " It has been already remarked, that the general manure of this district is the sheepfold.

" This practice is continued through the whole year ; but the great dependence on it, is for the barley crop.

" In the common fields, sheep which are sent by the occupiers of yard-lands, are kept in one flock, by a common shepherd, and folded regularly over the whole field, shifting the fold every night. The size of the fold is regulated by the size of the field they have to cover, so as to get over the whole in time for sowing : but the usual rule is, to allow one thousand sheep, to fold what they call a tenantry acre (about three-fourths of a statute acre) per night. In dunging for wheat, the land near home, being in general
the

the coldest and stiffest, usually gets most of the yard dung (or as it is here called pot dung); and this is frequently thrown over the land and folded upon (especially if the dung be light and not rotten), and then ploughed or raftered in, otherwise it is ploughed in previous to the folding.— South Wiltshire farmers seldom have dung enough to manure many acres; they depend solely on the sheep-fold for the rest : they fold as close to the sowing as possible, waiting day by day for the fold to keep pace with them, and in very dry weather, sometimes fold again after the wheat is sown. After the wheat is sown, the sheep-fold is sometimes, and very properly, put on the down land, but more usually on the wheat *stubs*, which are then getting in preparation for barley ; but this dung is not reckoned of any great value until the ewes and lambs begin to go to the water-meadows ; it then becomes almost invaluable ; and that of ewes is reckoned much more so than that of wethers, on account of the greater quantity of urine they make.

" Five hundred ewes, with their lambs, will fold a tenantry acre in a night *well*, and none but those who have seen this kind of husbandry, can form a just idea of the value of the fold of a flock of ewes and lambs, coming immediately with bellies full of young quick grass from a good water-meadow, and particularly how much it will increase the quantity and quality of a crop of barley. The value of it may fairly be taken at the value of a quarter of barley.

" The circumstance already mentioned, that the flinty loams (the soils peculiarly adapted to barley) abound most in those parts where the county is flattest, and the rivers are widest, is peculiarly fortunate, because, as the water-meadows are the most numerous in those situations, *barley land and its proper manure lie contiguous*, as is particularly the case in the neighbourhood of Sarum.

" And the circumstance, of the land being deepest and strongest near the heads of the rivers, where the water-meads, however good in quality, must be small in quantity ; and where, of course, few ewes can be kept, is not an unfavourable one, as such land being much more proper for wheat than barley, the *spring sheep-fold* is not so essentially necessary."

Chalk.—P. 63. " There are some spots and veins of land, where chalk and lime are used as permanent manures, and are of very essential service—chalk is well known as a corrector of land that has acidity in it, or such as the Wiltshire farmers express it, ' wants to be *sweetened*' to make it bear barley.

" There are *three* kinds of land, on which chalk is used with success in this district.

" 1st.

" 1st. On the *red strong lands* on the highest part of the downs.

" 2dly. On the *sand veins*, particularly on those which are deep and tough, and are of the nature called in Wilts ' liver sand.'

" 3dly. On the strong, *oak-tree clay*, or rather *loam*, in the valley at Mere, Sedgehill, and Semley.

" The red strong land, on the high level parts of the downs, that has been once wood land, and (sometimes expressly called wood sour land) is improved astonishingly by chalking. The chalk is generally dug under the surface, but too often too near the surface. The upper stratum of the chalk is hard, and not soluble, and will always remain in small broken pieces in the land, making the land loose, or, as it is provincially called, ' rubbly.' It should be dug deeper from one great chalk pit, instead of many little ones, and should be carried in carts instead of wheelbarrows. The expence of chalking such land with wheelbarrows, is seldom more than three pounds per acre— sometimes as low as twenty-five shillings*.

TILLAGE.—*Fallowing.*—P. 57. " The custom of South Wiltshire has been always to give a fallow for one year, and in the down land, frequently of two years, previous to a wheat crop; and formerly, in some of the poorer lands, a fallow year always succeeded *every* crop: but the word ' Fallow' in this district, as well as in most others, has two significations; the one meaning a continued ploughing and pulverization of land, to make it lighter and get it clean from weeds, when made foul by repeated crops; and the other, a *mere rest* of the land when exhausted; but both under an idea of enabling it to bear a fresh succession of crops. But as both these practices, and particularly the latter, have been strongly reprobated by many writers on agriculture, and as strongly defended by Wiltshire farmers, it is necessary to inquire into the reasons given by the latter for a continuance of this mode of husbandry.

" The science of agriculture is nothing more than ' the art of knowing and curing Nature's defects;' and the great outlines of this science, are, the knowledge ' how to make heavy land, lighter,' and ' light land, heavier;' ' cold land,
hotter

" * The usual quantity of chalk, laid on land of this description, is 16 wheelbarrows (or a cart load) on a square perch (viz. 160 cart load on an acre.) Autumn is the best season for laying it on, and it will frequently require to lay 3 years before it is dissolved. The land then requires a thin ploughing, or light rafter about Christmas, and should then lie till about Midsummer, when it may be clean ploughed, and will be fit for sowing to wheat in 7 or 8 weeks afterwards."

hotter,' and 'hot land, colder.'—He that knows these secrets
is a farmer; he that does not, is *no farmer.* But for want
of attending to these general ideas, many absurd doctrines
have been propagated respecting agriculture; and in no
instance more, than in the article of fallowing land, which
it has been very common of late to reprobate in the gross,
as a mere waste of labour and loss of crops."

Mr. Davis elicits some ingenious thoughts, and makes
many sensible remarks, on this polemical topic. His sentiments, however, do not *uniformly* coincide with mine.
But as I have had repeated occasions, in the course of my
present work, to express my own, I forbear to dwell on the
subject, in this place.

Depth of *Plowing.*—P. 72. " As to the proper *depth of
plowing,* Wiltshire farmers are particularly cautious not to
plow *below the top soil.* Wherever there is a vein of rubbly
chalk, or small broken flints, immediately under the top
soil, they look upon them to be literally ' the dross of the
land;' and that, if they are plowed up, they are ' poison.'
Many instances are shewn, where lands of this kind, plowed
too deep (frequently single acres in large tenantry fields)
upwards of *twenty* years ago, has not yet recovered its former goodness. And to preserve this top soil as *deep* as possible, the best farmers will not permit the *surface flints* to be
picked off for the roads, for fear of making the land both
lighter and thinner. But in the *sand* veins, where there is a
great depth of top soil, especially about Lavington, it is not
uncommon to plow very deep; and frequently to have a
second plow following in the furrow of the first, so as to
throw up *new* soil, and bury that which is supposed to be
exhausted."

ARABLE CROPS.

WHEAT.—*Soil* and *Succession.*—P. 45. " As to the *kinds
of grain* at present sown, *Wheat* is seldom omitted to be
sown in every round of the common-field arable land,
whether the land is adapted to it or not. The tenantry
fields having been originally laid out without much regard
to soil, the light thin loose lands on the hills, are frequently
obliged to carry wheat every third or fourth year at farthest,
because the deep strong lands in the valley are able to do
it. Of course, this crop is frequently *dear-bought,* by the
value of the manure used in preparation for it, to the great
detriment of the rest of the farm, and particularly of the
turnip crops, if they have any."

Tillage for Wheat.—Having spoken of the bad effects,
in the common field system, of pulverizing light-soiled, exposed lands, by summer plowings for wheat,—thereby " filling

ing the wheat crop with weeds," (!)—and rendering it liable
to be "knee-sick" in the spring,—Mr. D. reports the
modern methods of preventing those effects.

P. 60. "Many modes have been introduced to prevent
this evil, by giving a sufficient texture and firmness to the
land previous to a wheat crop. The best farmers have made
a point of getting their land clean ploughed by Midsummer,
and treading it as firm as possible with the sheep-fold a
long time before sowing;* while the slovenly farmers have
invented, and generally practise a very short and cheap
way of attaining this firmness in the land. They rafter the
land (as they call it), that is, they plough half of the land,
and turn the grass side of the ploughed furrow on the land
that is left unploughed. They do this as soon as they can
spare the feed of the summer field, and leave it in that
state till near the time of sowing, when they harrow it
down and plough it for sowing. This rafter is usually
ploughed *across* the ridges, or, what is better, *diagonally;*
the latter mode being less subject to drive the land up in
heaps before the plough.

"The land thus raftered is sometimes ploughed twice,
but more frequently only once, previous to sowing, and
after it is sown, they drag it 2, 3, or 4 times, and harrow it
4, 5, or 6 times (viz. provincially speaking, they give it ' so
many *tine* with the *drag*, and so many with the *harrow*).'

"It is wonderful how very general this raftering, or half
ploughing, of land for wheat is in this district; it frequently
produces as good a crop as the best management; but the
foul state the land is left in for the next crop, must explode
it as a system, whenever tenantry fields are put in a state of
severalty."

Nevertheless, this was the prevailing practice of the
Wiltshire Down farmers, not many years ago ; and probably
is so still.

Semination of Wheat.—P. 74. "The usual seed-time for
wheat, necessarily varies in the different soils of this district.

"A certain quantity of rain is necessary to sow the down
land : they generally begin with the first rains in September.
It was customary, formerly, to sow much earlier on this
kind

---

* This it an eligible practice ; *provided* the soil can be *thoroughly
cleaned,* from the roots and seeds of weeds, before Midsummer. But
not otherwise.—No good farmer, as I have elsewhere remarked, mixes
weed seeds with his wheat, before he sows it ; nor ought he to sow clean
wheat seed among the seeds of weeds that are previously lodged in the
soil; which is, precisely, the same error in management. See my
SOUTHERN COUNTY.—District, *Isle of Thanet.*

kind of land; but they now find it better to let the land lie, and get as close as possible, before sowing, which prevents the wheat from being *winter proud*, and sometimes from being eaten up by the grub.

" The white land is next sown, and then the flinty loams; and last of all the sand, which is not uncommon to sow sometimes as late as Christmas ; especially when they sow wheat after turnips; which though, perhaps, not strictly reconcileable to the rules of good husbandry, is not an uncommon thing on the sand lands of this district."

P. 75. " The quantity of seed sown to an acre is different in different parts of the district, and at different seasons; but, in general, Wiltshire farmers ' sow very thick.' In broadcast husbandry four bushels (Winchester) of wheat are frequently sown ; seldom so little as two and a half."

Harvesting Wheat.—P. 75. " The wheat harvest is usually as early on the Wiltshire downs as in most parts of England ; and as their corn is seldom full of weeds, they usually carry in three or four days after the corn is cut; and sometimes immediately from the hook, without putting it in mows, as is customary in Somersetshire and Devon. But of late years, it has not been uncommon to cut the wheat before it is quite ripe, especially if there is any appearance of blight upon the straw. In that case they lay it down in gripe, (as they call it) with the ears hanging into the furrow, so as to receive as much of the dews as possible, and turn it for two or three days together before they bind it in sheaf. This is found to improve the grain (provincially the berry) in quality, as well as to increase the quantity. The general custom of Wiltshire, is, to set up the sheafs in double rows, usually ten sheaves together, (provincially a tything) for the convenience of the tything-man; and the sheaves so set up are called an *aile*. The wheat is usually cut remarkably high in this district; and they prefer ploughing-in the stubs to mowing them for litter, as is the case in counties where straw is more scarce."

Gleaning of Wheat.—P. 89. " The Wiltshire farmers are very generous in the article of ' leazing,' the children of the resident labourers being seldom hindered from gleaning, even before the corn is carried off."

Produce of Wheat.—The medial produce, including the tithe, is estimated at twentytwo Winchester bushels. p. 77.

BARLEY.—*Soil.*—P. 46. " Barley is the favourite crop of great part of this district. The climate, and a great proportion of the soil (the flinty loams), are peculiarly favourable to the growth and quality of this grain ; and the water-meadow

meadow and sheep-fold system are particularly adapted to its cultivation.

" But although the flinty loams, and particularly with the assistance of a sheep-fold, are the only lands in the district peculiarly adapted to barley, yet such is the force of custom and imitation, that it is not an uncommon thing, to see the strongest clayey or chalky loams under the same crop, with the same kind of management, whereby, in case of a wet sowing time, the crop scarcely reproduces the seed sown, and the grass seeds sown with it come to nothing. This is frequently the case; and was so particularly in the year 1792. And for this reason, whatever arable fields have been laid in severalty, the almost exclusion of barley crops on the strong heavy lands has been the consequence, as is the case in several instances, particularly in the Pewsey Vale."

P. 76. " In a wet seed time, the white land runs and bakes like melted lead, and ruins the crops; and in a dry one, the barley sown on the sand land frequently comes up in ' two shares,' and ripens unequally; and on both kinds of soil the barley usually ripens very late, and is seldom of a very good quality. In this present summer (1793), the barley on the flinty loams about Salisbury was harvested a full month earlier than that on the sands about Maiden Bradley, and on the white lands about Broad-Hinton, not-withstanding the weather was particulaly hot and dry the greatest part of the time. Query, if this circumstance does not point out the impropriety of making barley a de-pending crop on either of these kinds of land? The farmers on the sand vein, in the Pewsey Vale, seem to be of this opinion, and generally adopt pease, beans, vetches, &c. as a substitute for a barley crop; and on the white lands in Broad-Hinton Vale, the farmers allow barley to be a losing crop, although they have as yet adopted no substi-tute for it."

Semination of Barley.—P. 75. " Barley is sown later in Wiltshire than in most counties. There is a certain degree of coldness in the land in general, which prevents the fal-lows working so early as they do in Hertfordshire, and many other counties; and as the dependence for a barley crop is so much upon the water-mead fold, the time of sowing is regulated by the growth of the water-mead grass, so as to begin when the time of spring feeding begins, and to end when that ends. Perhaps this may, on an average, be from the fifteenth of March to the twenty-fifth of April. The Wiltshire proverb is, that ' barley will do, if it has a May dew;' and they carry this so far, as frequently to injure their crop much by sowing too late."

P. 75.

P. 75. " Of barley, sometimes six bushels; seldom so little as five." !

Harvesting Barley.—P. 76. " The barley and oat crops, are almost uniformly mowed with a scythe in this district. They are seldom strong enough in the straw to require sheafing. They are forked from the swath into cocks, or pooks, and the ground raked by hand.

" Although wheat ripens well, and comparatively very early, in this district, the case is very different, in many parts of it, with the barley crop. Of the three principal kinds of soil which compose this district, viz. ' flinty loam, white land, and sand,' barley seldom ripens kindly on any but the former."

Produce of Barley.—P. 77. Twentyeight Winchester bushels.

OATS.—*Soil.*—P. 46. " Oats are not much cultivated in this district. Perhaps there is a doubt, whether there are not more consumed in this district than what grow in it.

" Barley being, as is before said, the favourite crop, oats are seldom sown in any great quantities, but in such soils and situations as will not bear barley, particularly in the black light soil of the new-broke downs. Even where they have a regular tenantry oat-field, the farmers look upon the cultivation of them to be bad husbandry; and will frequently forego the crop, to give an additional year's rest to their wheat lays."

Semination.—P. 75. " Of oats, sometimes a quarter; seldom less than six bushels."

Produce of Oats.—P. 77. Thirtysix Winchester bushels.

POTATOES.—The following remarks on the value of potatoes, in agriculture and domestic economy, are sensible and just.—P. 51. " Potatoes have of late been very much cultivated in almost all parts of this district, but particularly on the sand lands. The general introduction of this valuable root, has been exceedingly fortunate for the labouring poor, of whose sustenance they now make a very considerable part, especially in a season when wheat is dear.

" A remark has been often made in this district, as to the peculiar aptitude of potatoes to supply the want of wheat, viz. ' that a bad season for wheat is generally a good one for potatoes.' Although this, like other general remarks, is subject to exceptions, it is nevertheless founded in reason.

" Bad crops of wheat are generally occasioned by extreme hard winters, or wet summers. In the former case, the misfortune is known soon enough to increase the quantity of potatoes planted: in the latter case, the wetness of

a

a summer is peculiarly favourable to a potatoe crop. The
reverse does not always hold good—a favourable rain, immediately after a good wheat harvest (as in 1793) may save
a failing crop of potatoes, and then both crops may be
good."

TURNEPS.—And the subjoined considerations on the turnep crop, on the chalky lands of Wiltshire, are not less
marked by good sense, and mature local knowledge.

P. 48. " A common-field system undoubtedly excludes,
in a great measure, the cultivation of Turnips. But it has
been remarked, that even in the inclosed farms of this district, a turnip crop seldom makes a regular part of the
general system; notwithstanding there are very few parts
of South Wilts where their cultivation is not understood,
and practised *at times*, and that a turnip crop seems rather
a matter of accident than of system. There are, doubtless,
local reasons for this seeming neglect of a crop so valuable
in other countries; and it is more candid to inquire into
those reasons, than to condemn, in *a lump*, the husbandry
of a district; especially of so large a portion of a county,
whose farmers have seldom been charged with ignorance of
their own interest, or want of spirit to pursue it. The principal reason seems to be, a peculiar unfavourableness in
the soil of many parts of the district to the growth of
turnips.

" There is a peculiar churliness (provincially ' clottiness')
and want of mellowness in the soil of many parts of South
Wilts, particularly on the white land soils, (probably arising from the coldness of the *sub*-soil) that in some seasons
prevents the seeds from vegetating; and in others, from
coming to any great maturity. There are also many parts
of the down lands, on which it is reckoned almost impossible to get a good crop. And the stiff white lands are
not only unfavourable to their growth, but (in wet winters
particularly) to feeding them off when grown. Both these
kinds of land have been already mentioned as unkindly for
barley, and they are still more so for turnips. And yet
there are, doubtless, many parts of this district, on which,
under the idea that turnips will not grow, they have never
been tried; or in case of their having once or twice failed,
the experiment has not been repeated. Surely it merits
the attention of every farmer to investigate, whether the
fault is really in the land, or whether a little of it may
not be in the management.

" The flinty loams that have been mentioned as so very
kindly for barley, are by the same rule equally so for turnips;
but it happens, that these soils generally lie near water-
meads, where turnips are not absolutely indispensable for
spring

spring food.   The water-mead grass not only being a good,
but a *certain* substitute.

"And although there are, at least, two months in every
winter before the water-mead grass is fit to be fed off, in
which turnips would be very useful; yet as the crop (or
indeed the chance of a crop) is to be purchased at the certain loss of a crop of barley, (and that manured better from
the water-meadows than from turnips) there is some reason
for the neglect of turnip husbandry, in such soils and situations."

CULTIVATED HERBAGE.

RAPE HERBAGE.—P. 50. "Rape (or Cole seed) is much
cultivated on the downs, particularly on those parts that
are peculiarly unkindly for barley and turnips.   It is
reckoned a very nutritive milky food for ewes that have
lambs; but is supposed to exhaust the land, unless fed off
early, before it has taken too deep root.   It is certainly,
when under proper management, a most valuable green
winter food; and particularly as it will grow in those kinds
of soil in this district where neither turnips, saintfoin,
vetches, clover, and, in some instances, not even ray grass
will grow, viz. ' the strong, cold, wood-sour land, and the
black loose soil of the downs.' "

TARE HERBAGE.—" Vetches do not thrive at all on the
soils of the downs of the two latter descriptions: they are
very apt to suffer by mildew: but their cultivation is very
common on the strong loams, as a preparation for wheat.
They are often sown to cut as green meat for horses; and
still oftener for weaning lambs on.   Both kinds of vetch,
' the winter vetch and spring vetch,' are sown in this district,
so as to have a succession of crops during the summer.

"The winter vetch is usually sown early enough in autumn, to be high enough to cover the ground before winter,
and it is usual to ' muckle them over' with loose strawey
dung, to preserve them from the frost."

RYE HERBAGE.—P. 51. "Rye is frequently sown to be
eat off with sheep, but not often suffered to stand for a
crop.—The usual time of sowing it (August) makes it peculiarly proper to supply the failure of a crop after turnips,
and it is not uncommon to harrow in the seed among a thin
crop of turnips, and let both stand and be fed off together."
—This is new; and, as an expedient, may be found very
valuable.

MIXED HERBAGE.—P. 47. "The kinds of artificial grasses
that are usually sown in this district, are—

"Broad clover in the low lands; and

                                        "Ray

" Ray grass, with usually an intermixture of hop clover
(otherwise called trefoil, or nonsuch), on the high lands.

" But in those fields where clover has been long introduced, and repeatedly sown every third or fourth year, they
begin to complain that the land is tired of broad clover,
and therefore frequently vary the sorts, sowing hop and ray
instead of it, and sometimes adding a mixture of marle
grass, or Dutch clover; which last has been found to answer
very well in lands tired of broad clover."

SAINFOIN.—P. 47. "Many of the high lands are proper
for saintfoin; and though there are some of which the soil
is too light and too loose, there are many others which
might be sown with it to great advantage, and so rested
from corn for some years, as is done in the neighbouring
county of Hants; but as this is not practicable in common-
field husbandry, very little of that valuable grass is sown
in this district.

"Perhaps one reason, why the cultivation of saintfoin has
been so little attended to in this district, is, that it is not so
much wanted for autumn food, as in countries where they
have no sheep downs."

RAY GRASS.—P. 48. " The great object of sowing artificial grass in South Wiltshire, is to have a plenty of spring
feed for the sheep, from the time the water-meadows are
fed off, till the time the sheep go to down; and on this
account ray grass may be called the depending, artificial
grass of this district. This grass is less subject to fail than
clover; and makes an earlier spring feed, especially in
high and exposed situations; and being of an exceeding
nutritive nature, is very proper for ewes and lambs."

GRASS LANDS.

PASTURE GROUNDS.—P. 18. " *Natural herbage of the
downs.*—The natural herbage of a great part of the downs
of Wiltshire, is composed, not only of almost every known
kind of grass, but also of a mixture of various kinds of
plants; and the sweetness of the feed depends much more
on its being kept close, and eaten as fast as it shoots, than
on any particular good quality of the grass itself: for
there are many downs that, when close fed, appear to be
a very sweet pasture; but which, if suffered to run a year
or two without a full stock on them, will become so coarse,
that sheep will almost as soon starve as eat the grass:
and even in those parts of the downs, where the finer and
sweeter grasses abound, the soil is frequently so loose and
porous, that nothing but close and constant treading will
prevent them from dying out, or being choaked by the
larger and coarser grasses."

Those

Those are valuable remarks. But they are most particularly applicable to light spungy-soiled sheep walks, like the high downs of Wiltshire; whose prevalent natural plants are mostly of a coarse unpalatable quality; especially in an advanced stage of growth. In that state, they are not merely rejected as pasturage, but become mischievous encumbrances; by overgrowing, and of course weakening, and rendering less nutritious, the finer grasses and legumes—the favorite food of sheep. On the contrary, sheep—which are naturally mountain animals—will crop almost any highland plant, on its first emersion. Hence, by judicious stocking, early in the spring, the stronger taller-growing plants are kept down, their natural growth checked, and, by perseverance in close pasturing, or mowing them off close to the soil, they may be easily kept under, if not entirely destroyed; the soil and the sward becoming in consequence occupied by the roots and the herbage of palatable and nutritious plants. The treading, even of sheep, is no doubt greatly beneficial in bringing about that valuable effect;—partieularly by promoting the propagation of the annual poe, and the more delicate legumes; by bedding their seeds firmly in the soil.

After the above observations, however, it will be proper to remark, here, that I have known the principle of *hard-stocking* carried to an injurious length, by inexperienced sheep-masters heedlessly *generalizing* the above-recommended accurate practice, to lower better soiled and naturally better herbaged lands;—thereby converting *valuable sheep walks* to bare unprofitable *commons*.

And, after this, another remark is equally proper to be made; namely, that on rich rank-growing marsh lands, *under-stocking* is a great error in practice; as it operates in a manner similar to that of *mowing* those and other rich grazing grounds.—See p. 181, aforegoing.

Mr. Davis was a decided and warm opponent to the practice of *breaking up* the higher, thinner-soiled *sheep downs*, of Wiltshire. It is a subject which he has repeatedly brought forward. In the following strictures, more particularly, we see his sentiments developed.

P. 84. " It is not here meant, that no downs should be permitted to be broken up.—A farm may, in some instances, have too much down land, and some part of it, provided the soil is proper, may be broken up to advantage.—Reasons will afterwards be given, that one sort of down (the strong red land) will pay for breaking, while another (the loose black land) will be ruined by it.—Care should therefore be taken, that on no account land of the latter description should be broke at all; and that even if it
should

should happen, that the whole of the down land be of the former description, it should be always remembered, that a farm of ' mere arable land alone,' is not calculated for Wiltshire downs.

" It may be said, that these arguments are confuted by the plain fact, ' that even the sweetest and best pasture lands on the downs will yield a *greater rent*, provided tenants are allowed to break them up ; and, therefore, that such breaking up must be *an improvement* to an estate.' Long experience has shewn, that though this fact cannot be denied, yet the inference deduced from it is exceedingly fallacious.

" The arable land of a Wiltshire down farm, is maintained by the dung of the sheep fed on the sheep down.—Deprive this farm of its down, and how is the arable land to be maintained ? It may be answered, ' by raising artificial grasses on the down land that is broken up.' But will such a land always bear artificial grasses ? Undoubtedly it will, *for a time*, bear ' good crops;' but downs of that description will soon cease to bear *any at all*. What is then to become of the arable land ? Every unbiassed farmer who has known this district, and observed its husbandry for the last 30 years, can answer this question.

" And in this place it may not be improper to observe, that this error, to which the improper breaking, and the consequent impoverishment of much of the down lands, have been owing, has been a custom of computing the value of them, in their present state, *too low*, and the arable land, *which is supported by them, too high.*

" For example, suppose a farm of 200 acres of arable land, and 200 acres of down, and the rent 150*l.* per annum ; viz. 7*s.* 6*d.* for *each* acre. It is very common, in speaking of such a farm, to say the arable is let at 12*s.* and the down at 3*s.* per acre ; and still more common to say, the arable is let at 15*s.* and the down given into the bargain ; when possibly the truth is, that the down is of more intrinsic value than many parts of the arable land, and only appears poor because all its produce is carried off, and no return of manure made to it.

" An offer of advancing the rent of the down to six shillings per acre, is caught at by the landlord as an improvement, without considering, that his arable land, when deprived of the down, will gradually get worse, and that the farm will, in a few years, be worth much less than it was in its former state *."

MOWING

" * There is one striking instance, that shews the real value of down land in its proper light, in the parish of Monkton Deverill. A large
piece

MOWING GROUNDS.—For Mr. D's account of the WATER
MEADOWS of Wiltshire, see the article, *Irrigation*, p. 194,
aforegoing.

Haymaking.—P. 89. "The hay-making of South Wiltshire, employs (comparatively speaking) but few hands.
It is certainly not thought of so much consequence as it
should be: quantity instead of quality, is too often the
object. If the resident labourers, with their families, are
not sufficient to do it in proper time, it is too often deferred
till they are; *'what is wanting in strength, is too often
made up in time.'* The consequence is, that neither the
quality of the hay, nor the neatness of the ricks, are much
attended to. It is in the management of the corn harvest,
in which the South Wiltshire farmers shine, and not in
hay-making."

LIVESTOCK.

On the general subject of domestic animals, Mr. Davis's
sentiments are well grounded. There is a TRUE MEDIUM
in most things, which some men cannot, and many men will
not, see.

P. 104. "The errors in stock may be reduced to one
general cause, viz. 'the pride or vanity of possessing large,
handsome, animals.'"

P. 107. "In summing up the errors in the stock of this
district, it is worthy of remark, that the attempts to improve
the breed of sheep, horses and cows, have uniformly been,
by enlarging the size of the animal."

CATTLE.—P. 28. "Although milch cows have paid so
well of late years, and milk and butter are so indispensably
necessary, the rage for keeping *fine* sheep has almost
driven cows out of this district; and was there not a
necessity of keeping some cows to feed the water-meadows
in autumn (when they are not safe for sheep), and to eat
the barley straw and make dung in winter, there would
soon be very few cows in South Wiltshire. The profit
and loss, of this change of stock, will be afterwards en-
quired into.

"As

piece of down land called Keesley, has been for time immemorial
kept and let for an agistment *sheep-sleight*. It has no arable land
annexed, and *therefore nothing is carried off it*, the sheep that feed it
being folded on it.

"The country that surrounds it is like Wiltshire downs in general,
'about half arable and half down;' and the sheep fed on the latter are
folded on the former: but so little is the improvement, by keeping
any part of this land arable, that every acre of the sheep-sleight is left
for nearly as much as an adjoining acre of arable land, with an acre
of down annexed to it."

" As they are not a *favorite* stock, the farmers of course are not very particular about kinds in the corn part of this district."

P. 107. " The *cow stock* of this district, is not numerous enough to be a subject of much animadversion, with respect to *its kind*.

" The great error in this stock, is the smallness of the *quantity* kept, the rage *for fine sheep* having almost driven the cow stock out of the district.

" South Wiltshire farms are not calculated to keep *many cows*, but the greater part of them would keep more than they do, especially such as have much down land ; and that, if repeated experience may be relied on, without diminishing the sheep stock.

" Where there are water-meadows, cows are indispensably necessary to eat the after-grass ; and in winter they are always so, to eat the barley straw, and make dung. There is always as much distant land on a South Wiltshire farm as the sheep-fold can manure. The home arable should be manured with pot-dung, and more especially when in preparation for a turnip crop."

DAIRY.—P. 28. " The great farmers frequently let their dairy cows by the year, they finding all the keeping, and supplying fresh cows when necessary. The price is usually from 5*l.* to 6*l.* 10*s.* per cow.—in 1793.

" In a large part of the south-west skirts of this district, adjoining to Dorsetshire, viz. Sedgehill, Semley, &c. great numbers of cows are kept purposely for making butter ; and which, with those parts of Dorsetshire and Somersetshire that lye contiguous, furnish a great part of the butter that is used, not only in Bath and Salisbury, but even in the towns immediately in the neighbourhood of the great cheese dairies, in North Wilts (who seldom make any butter except whey-butter), while this county makes so little cheese, that the towns in its neighbourhood buy the greatest part of their cheese from Somersetshire or North Wiltshire. Whether there is really a particular aptitude in cows of one district to produce more butter, and in the other to produce more cheese ; whether it is the peculiar cleverness of the dairy-women in each county in their respective operations, or whether it is only prejudice sanctified by custom, is an object of curiosity, if not of use. But as butter is an article of more constant, indispensable consumption, than cheese, it is a lucky circumstance for the county of Wilts, that there is a large district of that, and the adjoining counties, who" (whose occupiers) " think that it answers their end to make butter for sale."

SHEEP.—*General Remarks.*—P. 19. " The sheep stock of

of this district, is an object of the greatest importance. Indeed it may be called the basis of Wiltshire down husbandry.

" The peculiar aptitude of the soil and climate to sheep ; the singular use of sheep-folding on arable land naturally light and loose ; the necessity of making sheep the carriers of dung, in situations where the distance and the steepness of the hills almost preclude the carrying of dung in any other mode ; and particularly the advantages that art has given this district, of getting early grass by means of their numerous watered meadows, whereby they are enabled to breed lambs, both for the supply of their stock, and for the market; are the principal reasons that have contributed to give Wiltshire the high rank it has among the sheep-breeding counties.

" The number of sheep kept in this district cannot be exactly ascertained ; but from the best information that can be collected, it appears, that the number of lambs bred yearly is at least one hundred and fifty thousand ; and that the whole summer stock of sheep, including lambs, is little (if any) short of five hundred thousand.

" Notwithstanding the seeming immensity of this number, it is an undoubted fact, that the sheep stock of South Wiltshire, has been, for many years, gradually decreasing, and that it is now lower, by many thousands, than it was fifty years ago. On the sand veins, particularly on the rich parts of them in Pewsey Valley, the introduction of a better husbandry, by the abolition of fallows and the raising green crops, has tended to destroy the *summer* sheep stock; but then, as this husbandry enables them to *winter* sheep for the *down farmers,* and that in a much better way than they were heretofore wintered, it may be said to be a gain rather than a loss to this district.

" But on the down part of this district, where the sheep-fold is indispensably necessary to the production of corn, a diminution of the sheep stock is a serious evil. That this diminution has really taken place, and *that* to a *great extent,* is a fact. But as many of the farmers who see it and feel the effects of it, are puzzled to account for it, the cause is not very obvious; perhaps, indeed, it may be produced by a combination of causes. There are *two* that strike every person very forcibly, who has observed the husbandry of the county for the last thirty years. ' The pride of keeping fine sheep, and the rage there has been of late years for the plowing up of the sheep downs.' The former, by flattering the vanity of a farmer, prevents him from seeing his real interest; and the latter, by putting a temporary supply of money in his pocket, makes it his

interest

interest to conceal the future consequences, particularly
from his landlord.

"*Purposes for which sheep are kept in this district.*—
The best clue to this enquiry is an investigation of the
purposes for which sheep are kept in this district. The
first and principal of these, is undoubtedly the *dung of
the sheep-fold*, and the second is the *wool*. The improvement of the *carcase* was not heretofore thought a primary
object, and perhaps is in some degree incompatible with
the *great object* of this district, *viz.* the hardiness of the
animal necessary to enable it to get its food on a close-
fed pasture; to walk two or three miles for that food, and
to carry its dung the same distance back to fold: and the
breeding lambs out of a flock of sheep of this kind, was
heretofore looked upon as a *necessary consequence*, rather
than as a *primary cause* of keeping such flock. A supply
of ewe lambs, for the keeping up this stock, was necessary.
The wether lambs lived equally hard with the ewes during
the summer, and were sold in the autumn; for the wether
stock of those that had no convenience of breeding, and
such of the ewes as were thought too old to breed, were
sold off for fatting. On this system the carcase either of
the ewe or lamb was very little attended to.

"But the practice of the breeders in this district is now
almost totally altered. The first and great object at this
time, is the improvement of the *carcase*, both of the ewe
and lamb, and particularly of the latter; and the attention
is directed much more to the quality of the lambs they
breed, than to the quantity.

"The pride of having fine lambs, and consequently of
having the name of selling them for the highest prices,
certainly tends to lessen the stock of breeding ewes, and
to the exclusion of *old* ewes from that stock; and as such
a stock will not live hard enough to keep the downs close
fed, farmers have been induced to break those downs up,
under an idea of improving their sheep-feed.

"A great portion of this kind of land (as will be afterwards explained) produces great crops, at first, both of
corn and grasses, but being thin and loose in its staple,
is soon exhausted with a repetition of crops; the grasses
that were sown with the last crop soon wear out, the coarse
natural grasses, particularly the 'black couch or couchy
bent,' ('Agrostis Stolonifera'), and that in a starved reduced state, take possession of, and cover the land, and a
young tender-mouthed flock of sheep, will rather starve
than feed on it.

"This evil has grown so serious, that many farmers who
had the misfortune to find their downs in this state, have
been

been obliged to drop breeding entirely, and as they must have sheep to dung their land, are obliged to keep a flock of *wether sheep*, which they renew from time to time, by buying of their breeding neighbours."

Breed of Sheep.—P. 22. " The kind of sheep which are chiefly kept in South-Wiltshire, is what has been long known in Smithfield-market by the name of the *Wiltshire Horned Sheep*. Their wool is moderately fine, and particularly useful, being the kind of which the *second*, or what is called the super-broad cloth (from 10s. to 12s. 6d. a yard), is generally made. The fleeces of a flock of Wiltshire ewes, usually weigh, from two pounds, to two pounds and an half each—seldom higher than three pounds. The value of the wool has been for a few years past, from ten-pence to thirteen-pence per pound—of course, the average produce of each fleece, has been about two shillings and six-pence. The weight of the carcases of the wethers, when fat, is usually from sixty-five to an hundred pounds."

P. 23. " Till within these few years, the sheep, in general, were certainly smaller than they are now.

" The alterations that have taken place, have been principally by breeding them longer in their legs—higher and heavier in their fore-quarters; perfectly white in their faces and legs; with Roman noses, full eyes, and large open nostrils, wide in their bosoms, and little or no wool on their bellies; in fact, by making them a much larger, handsomer animal.

" The opponents of the present kind of sheep say, that those alterations have made them *less hardy*, and *worse nurses*, and in particular *so very nice in their food*, that they will starve on the same kind of land, on which the *old* sort of sheep lived well; and that they are subject to disorders (particularly to the disorder called the *goggles*) which were not known till this alteration of the stock took place. They also say, that this new kind of sheep, being so much nicer in their food, and rejecting the feed of the downs, on which the chief dependence for sheep food is, have suffered the herbage to grow gradually coarser and coarser; and that the farmers, in attempting to remedy this evil, by shortening their stock of sheep, have made it worse; it being a well-known fact, that the closer the downs are fed, the more stock they will keep.

" Under these ideas, many attempts have been lately made, to introduce *new* kinds of sheep, and particularly the South-Down sheep from *Sussex* "

P. 24. " How far this sort will answer, time and experience must determine. It has already so far gained ground, that although they were only introduced into Wiltshire (by

Mr,

Mr. Mighell, of Kennett) in 1789; the number kept in the county is already increased to *fifteen thousand*, and is daily increasing."

P. 27. " From what has been said respecting the sheep-stock of this district, it is clear, that no fair conclusion can ever be made, as to the relative merits of the different kinds, until the contending parties are agreed on the purposes for which such sheep are kept. Many who have argued very violently on the subject, have never considered, that ' sheep bred for *folding*,' are bred to walk : ' sheep bred for fatting,' are bred to stand still. The first was the great object for which the *old* Wiltshire farmers bred sheep; the latter seems to be, in a great measure, the object of the breeders of the present day."

In what appears, aforegoing, it is seen that Mr. Davis was a strenuous advocate for the SHEEPFOLD ; and, conse-quently, for a suitable FOLDING BREED. It is a point which he has urged, again and again. In a section of his work, entitled " beneficial Practices,"—after mentioning the su-periority of the customs of Wiltshire over those of Hamp-shire &c.,—he has made the following remarks.

P. 102. " This custom appears to be ' the use of the sheep-fold ;' and that *not merely to keep the sheep from running away in the night, but with a view to manure the land.*

" The ' pride of sheep stock,' which must inevitably tend to the subversion of the sheep-fold, infected those counties *first*. It is already gone *too far* in Wiltshire; and those who have attempted to stem the torrent of fashion, by introducing the South-Down sheep, deserve the thanks of the land-owners of the county.

" Overplowing and understocking, in high exposed situa-tions, and particularly where the land is light and loose, must always produce bad effects; and these are the natural consequences of keeping flocks of sheep for *beauty*, in coun-tries where they ought to be kept entirely for *use*."

And under the head, " Improvements suggested," are the subjoined.—P. 104. " As to sheep in particular, this pride of stock, however commendable, and however profitable it may be in countries that are adapted to it, does not seem at all suited to the *bleak hills of Wiltshire*.

" ' Warmth and shelter, are as necessary to produce per-fect symmetry in the parts of an animal, as to unfold the wings of a butterfly, or expand the petals of a carnation.' Where these requisites to animal perfection cannot be had, it is useless to attempt breeding for beauty.

" But it may be asked, whether those requisites cannot be had, and warm sheltered situations be found in Wiltshire?
" Undoubtedly

" Undoubtedly they may ; but *not in a sheep-fold on Wiltshire hills;* and particularly at that time of the year when the fold is almost invaluable—' the fold of ewes and lambs for a barley crop.'

" It can never be too often repeated, that so long as South Wiltshire remains a corn country, the *sheep-fold* must be the *sheet-anchor* of its husbandry ; and until a new method can be found to manure its hill land, equally efficacious with the sheep-fold, breeding sheep, as a science, *solely for the beauty of the shape,* can never be introduced with success into this district."

I agree with Mr. Davis in those sentiments. I will therefore add—it is the strong, hardy, long-established, REAL Sussex Down sheep,—a breed which I have long been of opinion are preferable to the *enormous* " Wiltshires," for high, shelterless, chalk hills;—but certainly not the pampered delicate, beautified, modern variety,—that can answer the purpose of the Wiltshire Down farmers. Valuable and proper as the new sort of sheep, that have of late years been loudly praised, under the name of " South Downs," may be to " stand still"—to lie quietly in a well herbaged, well sheltered pasture,—they are altogether unfit for an alpine climature, to feed on unpalable alpine herbage, " to walk two or three miles for that food, and to carry their dung, the same distance, back to the fold."

SOUTH-EAST

SOUTHEAST SOMERSETSHIRE.

THIS portion of Somersetshire is inseparably united with South Wiltshire and the County of Dorset, with which it forms the western extreme of the SOUTHERN DEPARTMENT.

Its natural and agricultural DISTRICTS are two;—namely, the *Vale of Ilchester*, which for extent and richness, combined, is scarcely to be equalled in the island; and the range of *Limestone Hills*, that form the eastern bank of that vale; terminating with the Sherborne hills in Dorsetshire.

THE REPORTER.

THE only Report to the Board, that was sent in from Somersetshire, was by Mr. BILLINGSLEY of Ashwick Grove, near Shipton Mallet, in that County:—a man of superior mind, and much general information, with some share of experience in agriculture, as an *amateur* of the highest class; but, judging from the evidence which appears in his Report, he was not radically versed in the more *orthodox* points of practice.

For remarks on Mr. B's Report, concerning the other districts of Somersetshire, see the WESTERN or DAIRY DEPARTMENT, article *North Somersetshire;* and the PENINSULAR DEPARTMENT, article *West Somersetshire*, ensuing.

NATURAL ECONOMY.

SOILS.—P. 205. "Between Yeovil and Taunton, including the parishes of Martock, Puckington, Barrington, Kingsbury-Episcopi, Lambrook, South-Petherton, Ilminster, Hinton St. George, and the adjacent places, lies a tract of strong loamy land, from sixteen to thirty inches deep, on a substance of clay: a more pleasant country can rarely be found."

Those places are scattered on the western margin of the VALE of ILCHESTER; and the brief passage, in which they are enumerated, may be said to contain the whole of the information of value, that appears in the Report under review, concerning that extensive, fertile, and truly agricultural district.

RURAL

RURAL ECONOMY.

ESTATES.

TENURES.—Mr. Billingsley is an advocate for *life leases*. He has had recourse to figures to show their advantages,—*to prudent leasees.*

TENANCY.—P. 205. " Great confidence exists in the Eastern part of this district, viz. about Wincanton, Horsington, &c. between the landlords and tenants. Estates are there principally held on mere *verbal* engagements, and scarce an instance can be produced of a breach of faith on part of the landlord, or suspicion on the part of the tenant."

P. 206. " The rack-rent leases* are generally for seven years."

AGRICULTURE.

FARMS.—P. 205. " The farms are from forty to six hundred pounds per annum, and are composed partly of rich grazing and dairy land, worth from thirty to forty shillings per acre; partly orchard, from two pounds to three pounds ten shillings per acre. Sheep-walks, from fifteen shillings to twenty-five per acre; and the arable, from twenty shillings to twenty-five shillings per acre."

WORKPEOPLE.—P. 259. " This county is very populous, and the wages low, notwithstanding there are very considerable manufactures.

" Men's daily labour in winter is 1s. per day, with cider; in summer 1s. 4d. Women's daily labour in winter is 6d. per day, with cider; in summer 8d. Mowing grass 1s. 4d. per acre, and one gallon of cider; barley 1s. Reaping wheat 4s. per acre, two gallons and half of cider. And all other labour proportionably cheap."

WORKING CATTLE.—N. p. 218. " When working oxen are fed with turnips they should not have water. J. B."

TILLAGE.—P. 219. " Fallowing is not practised; the prevailing opinion is, that corn crops, equally good, may be obtained after turnips, clover, potatoes, pease, vetches, beans,

---

* In contradistinction to life leases.

beans, hemp, flax, &c. *(if* well manured and *kept clean)*
with those after a compleat *summer fallow.* ' These are
enlightened farmers!'

" Let any man visit this country, view their crops, and
the condition of the land, and many arguments will not be
necessary to make him an *antifallowist,* at least, on soils
like these."

What well experienced farmer, nowadays, summerfallows
" soils like these,"—*after they have been once thoroly
cleansed, by* UNINTERRUPTED TILLAGE?

ARABLE CROPS.—P. 218. " Wheat, barley, oats, beans,
and pease, are in general culture; but there is nothing in
the mode of management worthy of notice."

In these three lines we see all that is said on the ordinary
crops in English husbandry; excepting a few more on
turneps.

To flax and hemp, materials of *manufacture,* some pages
are appropriated. But they rather convey didactic remarks
of the Reporter, concerning what " should" be done, than a
Report of what *is* done, in the practice of South Somersetshire.

TURNEPS.—P. 218. " In this part of the county turnips
are also grown on a large scale. They are universally sown
broadcast, *once hoed,* ✻ and for the most part fed on the
land as a preparation for barley."

ORCHARDS.—There are in England, speaking emphatically, three fruit-liquor districts; namely, that of Hereford
and Glocester shires, or the *May-hill district;* that of
West Devonshire; and that of *South Somersetshire,* which
is situated about the midway between the other two. The
produce of the *Kentish* orchards tends to the kitchen and
the dining room, rather than to the cellar.

The practices of Glocestershire and Devonshire I have
studied, systematized, and published, with solicitous consideration. To that of Somersetshire I have not had a
similar opportunity of attending. Of the Somersetshire
fruit-liquor *trees,* whether in orchards or in hedgerows
(there being in the district now under consideration more
apple trees, *in and by the sides of hedges,* I believe, than
in the rest of the kingdom) I have, however, had ample
means,—in traversing the cider districts at different seasons,
—of observing them. And I can say, with pleasure, they
are creditable to the practice of Somersetshire.

Mr. Billingsley's strictures, on the orchards and fruit
liquor

✻ By the " enlightened farmers" of Somersetshire !—See the head,
Tillage, above.

liquor of Somersetshire, resemble those which he has offered on flax and hemp. They are *didactic* rather than *descriptive*. This line of proceeding was doubtlessly chosen; either because he did not examine the practice of the district, or deemed his own knowledge of the subject preferable.

I do not, however, perceive any thing new or excellent, in Mr. B's remarks, theoretic or practical, to induce me to assimilate them with the matter of this register. It will, nevertheless, be proper to point out an inadvertancy which they involve.

P. 221. " It is found, that a luxuriant gross-growing graft will *never succeed* on a slow-growing stock, and so *vice versa.*"

It is a well established practice, among superior orchardmen, in the Mayhill district,—when such of their favorite fruits as have been engrafted on *free stocks*, until they have, thereby, lost part of their firmness and flavor,—to graft them upon *crab stocks*,—with the intent of bringing them back to their original state; and this *with success.*

GRASS LANDS.—P. 220. " The natural meadows and pastures of this division are kept in high condition; and their artificial grasses may vie with any in the kingdom."

Those few words fill " Chapter VIII. Grass,"—in a Report of the practice of a rich tract of country, which cannot, I conceive, contain much less than one hundred square miles of *perennial grass lands.*

P. 258. " Passing from Crewkerne to the Southward, you enter one of those excavations, or large vales, for which this county is remarkable; comprising the villages and hamlets of Clapton, Seaborough, Wayford, Woolmingston, Partington, Cricket-Thomas, Winsham, &c.

" Within this vale commences a district of twenty miles square," (?) " one half in Somerset and the other in Dorset."

CATTLE.—*Breed.*—P. 243. " The red breeds of Devon and Somerset have been progressively increasing, and they are now partially dispersed over great part of the kingdom; and in respect to their qualities as a *labouring* animal, I never heard but one opinion, and that opinion I can myself confirm from large and long experience, namely, that they are *the best in the kingdom.* In respect to their qualities as a *fatting* animal, I will not speak so decidedly, for I verily believe they have many rivals."

Rearing Calves.—N. p. 248. " In the South-Eastern part of this district, where the dairy land is chiefly applied to the making of butter, and skimmed milk cheese, the calves are taken from their dams at a fortnight or three weeks old, and suckled with skimmed-milk until the middle of May, when

when they are turned out to grass at home, or sold at some distant market for the same purpose. A few dairy-farmers, in this part of the district, have adopted the practice of making flax-seed and hay-tea, and mix it in the milk, with which the calves are suckled. This practice appears to answer very well, for the last month or six weeks of suckling. A. C."

The subjoined notice relates to the practice of North Somersetshire, or the *Cheese Dairy* district. It stands at the foot of the same page with the above extract; which is the reason of its appearing, here.

Fatting Calves.—N. p. 248. "The number of calves fatted in this district is immense—four hundred fat calves have been sold in Shepton Mallet market in one day. To this market, butchers from the neighbourhood of Bath and Bristol resort, and convey the carcases (whole) to those cities in one-horse carts. The veal is delicately white— small in size, viz. from sixteen to twenty-four pounds per quarter. The best is brought from a small village called Batcomb; and its excellency may, perhaps, be ascribed to their giving the calves small doses of metheglin in the milk, and keeping them in a dark place."

Fatting Cattle.—P. 238. "There are two methods of fatting oxen, the one called summer, the other winter fatting; the first is thought the most profitable, and accompanied with the least risque.

"In the first method, they are purchased in February, and are for the most part of the Devon sort, bred either in the Northern part of that county, or in the lower part of Somersetshire. They are bought in good condition, and cost from eight pounds to fifteen pounds each ; during the interval between February and grass time, they consume each about ten hundred or twelve hundred of *inferior* hay, viz. the skimming of their summer leaze. When at grass, they are allowed from one acre to one acre and a half each ox, and some add one sheep to each ox. Horses, if any, are kept very sparingly, not at any rate to exceed one to twenty acres of grazing ground. These oxen will be fat, some before and some soon after Michaelmas, paying for their keep from three shillings and six-pence to four shillings per week.

"Frequent bleeding, in small quantities, is found to accelerate their fatting.*

"The

---

* In Devonshire, *fat* cattle are repeatedly bled (as calves are in most parts of England), to give "brightness of color" to the beef on the shambles ; as well as to make it keep better, in the summer season.

" The next stock are bought in June, July, and August, and are not of so good a sort, being either home-bred or Welsh, and cost from six to eight pounds. These follow the stock purchased in February, and are sometimes stall-fed in the winter, and sometimes fatted in the field; in either case they have the best hay, and good attendance.

" They are fat in April and May, and sell from twelve pounds to fourteen pounds each."

P. 241. " The oxen, when fat, are driven to the London, the Salisbury, and the Bristol markets, at the following ex-pences, (salesman's commission included:) London, 12s. per head; Sarum, 5s.; Bristol, 3s.

" They are nine days travelling to London, a distance of one hundred and thirty miles. It is difficult to say which may be considered as the best market; but the general opinion seems to be, that the London market is calculated for those only who attend it regularly every week, the price of beef per stone greatly varying according to the plenty or scarcity in the market.

" Some farmers graze heifers in preference to oxen, buy-ing them in about the months of March and April, and selling them in October and November. The profit amounts to forty shillings or fifty shillings each for their summer food; and the land is stocked after the rate of one heifer to each acre, together with a considerable number of sheep both in summer and winter; and it is thought by many, that this method of occupation is more profitable than the former."

P. 242. " It is no unusual thing for some of the graziers to give their prime oxen a *second* summer's grass. In this case they are brought to a high state of perfection, and in all probability they pay more the *second* year than the *first*; for it is well known, that an animal nearly fat will consume much less food than a poor one."

" All the graziers of this county are partial to the red oxen of Somerset and Devon; and you seldom see a North-country ox in their possession."

DAIRY.—P. 205. " Few farmers milk their own cows, but let them out to a class of people, scarcely known in other counties, called *dairy-men*. A herd, of a good breed, will now let for seven or eight pounds per cow; a certain portion of land is devoted to their summer keeping, and a sufficient quantity of hay is provided by the farmer for their winter sustenance.

" This practice of letting dairies must have originated either from *pride* or *indolence* on the part of the farmer's household, and ought, in my opinion, to be checked by the landlord.

" When

" When the female part of a farmer's family is unemployed, (and, without a dairy, that must be the case throughout great part of the year) dissipation, folly, and extravagance, take the lead, and domestic care and industry are entirely forgotten. Gentlemen of fortune should therefore set their faces against the practice, and resolve never to let an estate to a farmer whose family was too proud, or too indolent, to undertake the management of the different departments thereof."

This peculiar trait of practice belongs to the *butter-dairy* of South Somersetshire, West Dorsetshire, and East Devonshire. It will be seen, however, in the further review of the Southern Department, that the practice is not confined to that tripartite district.—See also Wiltshire, p. 227, aforegoing.

SHEEP.—*Breed* and *Breeding.*—P. 254. " In the South-East part of this district, the sheep are an improved" (?) " sort of the Dorset, and many considerable ewe flocks are kept to the amount of four to six hundred each ; they begin lambing about Christmas, and the lambs are weaned in May."

P. 242. (after speaking of fatting sheep.) " Ewes and lambs are also the stock of some farmers; they are purchased partly in the autumn in lamb, and partly in the spring with the lamb by their sides, and are mostly of the Dorsetshire or Mendip breed."

Folding Sheep.—P. 254. " Some farmers buy wedder lambs about Midsummer (shorn) and keep them about twenty-two months, constantly folding them : they are then sold (unshorn) to the graziers occupying the marsh lands."

P. 255. " The number of sheep kept in this district is immense, and folding unremittingly pursued."

Fatting Sheep.—P. 241. (in continuation of the above account of fatting cattle.) " Others fat two-years old wedders of the Dorsetshire and Somersetshire breed. The Dorset sort are purchased about Michaelmas, at Sherborne and Stolford fairs, price from twenty shillings to thirty shillings. No hay is given in the winter, unless the weather be uncommonly severe, or the ground covered with snow. They are sold fat between February and May, and weigh from twenty to thirty pounds per quarter. A few oxen accompany the sheep, which are bought in the spring, and fatted the ensuing winter. It is the universal opinion, that sheep are not so profitable stock as oxen."

RETROSPECT.

There are few circumstances that have occurred to me, in prosecuting my present undertaking, which have given

me

me more concern than that of pointing out,—in conformity
with the principle that I have, throughout, deemed it my
duty to observe,—some of the striking defects of Mr.
Billingsley's Report of South-east Somersetshire.

Those deficiencies, however, may perhaps be thus accounted for.   That part of the County is situated at a distance from the district in which Mr. B. resided ; and where,
I understand, he was, at the period of his survey, actively
employed in an extensive line of business ;—and every man
who has attempted to examine, with due attention, the
various practices of an extent of country, with the view of
bringing before the public eye a Report of the leading facts
and attendant circumstances belonging to them,—must be
very sensible of the length of time, and mature attention,
which such an undertaking imperiously demands.   Should
it be asked why Mr. Billingsley accepted the appointment,
it might be answered, and I believe truly, *Mr. B. was
desirous to do a public good,* without being aware of the
time and attention which the task would require.

DORSETSHIRE.

DORSETSHIRE.

DORSETSHIRE comprizes four descriptions of country; three of them bearing distinct agricultural characters; one of them being, nearly, an entire district;—namely,

"The VALE of BLACKMORE" (as it is uncouthly called); which is situated almost entirely within the County of Dorset;—a narrow part of its northwestern margin, only, extending into Somersetshire.—The towns of Wincanton, Shaftsbury, and Sherborne are seated on its borders, and Sturminster near its center. The waters of the river Stour are principally collected within its vale lands; some of which are of a superior quality.——The VALE or DISTRICT of STURMINSTER, or the GRAZING DISTRICT of DORSETSHIRE, would surely be a more appropriate name for those valuable lands, than that which they now bear.

The CHALK HILLS of Dorsetshire form the western extreme of the extensive range of calcarious heights, which I have, heretofore, named the Western Division of the Chalk Hills of the Southern Counties;—the Wiltshire and Hampshire Downs being a continuation, eastward, of the same range.

The DAIRY QUARTER of Dorsetshire is merely an extension of East Devonshire; of whose singular cast of surface it partakes.

The SANDY LANDS of Dorsetshire,—the DISTRICT of WAREHAM,—constitutes the fourth distinction.

"GENERAL VIEW

OF THE

AGRICULTURE

IN THE

COUNTY OF DORSET,

WITH

OBSERVATIONS ON THE MEANS OF ITS IMPROVEMENT,

By JOHN CLARIDGE,

OF CRAIG'S COURT, LONDON.

1793."

MR. CLARIDGE was, I believe, a partner, if not a pupil, of the late Mr. KENT. He was of course well versed
in

in the business of *Estate Agency*.—His QUALIFICATIONS, as
a Reporter of *agricultural* concerns are less evident. We
meet with very little, in the production under view, which
manifests the author's *experience* in that most difficult art.
His *observations* on the practice of professional men, however, must necessarily have been considerable.

Regarding his method of collecting information, Mr.
Claridge has been almost singularly ingenuous.—P. 48.
" The preceding information respecting the county of
Dorset, has been collected by me, partly from twenty years
experience in the cultivation" (?) " and management of
landed property in that county, as well as in most parts of
England ; and by a tour made through it, on purpose, in
the course of the month of September last, in which I endeavoured to collect all the intelligence I possibly could,
from many gentlemen and farmers, who assisted me with
their best information, and to whom I am obliged for their
service and assistance in this business, and shall not fail to
state their names to the Board of Agriculture whenever
opportunity offers."

The most striking defect, in the Report under consideration, is want of digestion, or methodical arrangement :—a sin, however, which, in my creed, is not dead-
ly.—— Saving a few distinct heads, ill associated, the whole
matter may be said to be thrown together, miscellane-
ously ;—without chapters, sections, or other divisions.

An apology,—perhaps an allowable one—may be made
for that and other defects. The original Report of Dorsetshire was one of the very first that was printed. And
to those who know how the early Reporters were spurred
and goaded, as if the appointment of the Board had been
but for a few months, weeks, or days,—a thousand deficiencies may appear to be excusable.

The number of pages—fortynine.

No engraving.

NATURAL ECONOMY.

EXTENT.—P. 5. " Dorsetshire is a maritime County
of about one hundred and sixty miles in circumference ; in
length, from east to west, about fifty-five, and in breadth
from North to South, about thirty-five, containing about
775,000 acres of land."

That extent Mr. Claridge subdivides according to the
several existing states of its lands, at the time he wrote.
On what ground the estimates were made does not appear.
                                                P. 5.

P. 5. " The greater proportion of the land is in pasturage, *ewe leas*, or downs for sheep, of which the following proportions are estimated in round numbers, (viz.)

250,000	Acres in tillage.
50,000	—— water meadow.
90,000	—— pasture.
9,000	—— woods and plantations.
290,000	—— ewes leas and downs.
86,000	—— uncultivated or waste.

775,000."

SURFACE.—P. 6. " The greater part is uneven ground,
and much of it very hilly; it has chiefly a high clift
towards the coast, and a very small proportion of marshy
or fenn land."

WATERS.—P. 6. " It has three rivers, (viz.) The Stower,
the Piddle, and the Froome; the Stower, which is by much
the most considerable, runs quite across it, from the vale
of Blackmoor to the sea, by Sturminster, Blandford and
Winborn-Minster. The Piddle, from Piddletown and Bere-
Regis, to Wareham: and the Froome from the country
north of Maiden Newton, by Dorchester to Wareham.
The two latter are much divided in many places, into a
variety of small streams, by the branches of which, great
advantage is derived in watering of the meadow land
through which they pass."

SOILS.—P. 6. " The soil is mostly shallow, upon a chalk
bottom, a large proportion of it very poor, but some parts
of it (particularly the *vale of Blackmoor*) extremely rich."

P. 17. " The country north of Sherbone, which adjoins
the vale of Blackmoor, affords some of the best arable land
in the county. The soil is a stone brach, very easy to
work, and about three parts in four, are ploughed."

FOSSILS.—P. 6. " It possesses great quantities of stone,
chalk, lime and pipe-clay."

Portland Stone.—P. 41. " As to quarries, the whole island
of Portland seems to be one intire mass of the most beautiful stone, chiefly used in the metropolis and elsewhere for the
most superb buildings, and is universally admired for its
close texture and durability, surpassing any other. The
raising of it, is a laborious business, sometimes employing
upwards of a hundred men, to break down a large jam of
it, afterwards it is divided into blocks, and then conveyed
in cars by horses to the shore."

" There are many proprietors of quarries in the island,
but those called the King's quarries, which belong to the
crown, are by far the most considerable; from thirty to forty
                                                     thousand

thousand tons of this stone, are annually shipped off from
the island."

Purbeck Stone.—P. 41. " The quarries in the island of
Purbeck, are found in the parishes of Sandwich (called
Swannage) Langston and Worthe, near the sea, where upwards of four hundred people are employed in digging and
tooling the stone which is raised here from pits, some
twenty others forty feet deep; they are not open to the
top, but are undermined and underbuilt; it is excellent
stone for walling, floors, steps, and in particular for foot
pavement for towns, for tomb-stones, troughs, and feet and
caps for rick staddles. Another sort of stone is here found
and used for pitching streets, and some of the thin stones
on the tops of these quarries are used for covering of buildings: about fifty thousand tons are annually shipped at
Swannage."

Pipe Clay.—P. 43. " On Norden and Burshen Heath,
about a mile distant from the borough of Corfe Castle,
is found large quantities of pipe clay, which is in great
estimation, and absolutely necessary for the use of the
potters in Staffordshire and other places. About eleven
thousand tons are annually sent from this place for that
purpose, and about one hundred men are constantly employed in digging it. Some of the pits are not more than
ten or twelve feet deep. The mode of digging it, is to cut
it with a thin spade, whilst in a soft state, in square pieces,
which is forked up by another person, to the conveyance
for carrying it off. It is of a white colour when first dug
out, and dries to a hard substance of rather a blue cast.

" The ground where the pipe-clay is dug, is on the surface extremely poor and barren, and although the clay has
the appearance of being a most excellent manure, I find
that it has been tried without success, as it is supposed to
contain some acid matter, which is highly detrimental to
vegetation."

MINERALS.—P. 40. " There are no ores of any kind found
in this county, nor are there any mines of coal."

POLITICAL ECONOMY.

APPROPRIATION.—*Common Pastures.*—P. 43. " Of
the commons in Dorsetshire, the greater part of them in
the inclosed country are stinted, one horse or two beasts to
a leas; the horse leas, is estimated worth thirty shillings,
and

and half that sum for a beast. The land in general over-run with furze and ant-hills, does not in its present state, return more than seven or eight shillings per acre; but most of them highly proper to cultivate, and if converted would be worth eighteen or twenty shillings an acre, as lime for manure is so easily obtained.

" The greatest proportion and extent of waste lands in the county, is in its south-eastern part, from below Bere-Regis; southwards towards Lulworth and the sea, extending all the way to Corfe Castle, Wareham and Poole, from thence towards Christ-Church, in Hampshire, and within a small distance of Winborn Minster, the greater part of which, except a few cultivated parishes which intersected it, is in its present state a most dreary waste, and almost the only advantage derived from it at this time, is the support in summer of a few ordinary cattle and sheep, and the heath, which is pared up by the surrounding villages for fuel."

Common Fields.—P. 46. " Very few parishes in this county, have of late years been inclosed, there are some however, between Winborn Minster and Blandford, and in the vale of Blackmoor, which are said to answer extremely well, and to have much increased the value of the property therein."

PROVISIONS.—P. 46. " Provisions are plentiful, and besides a great abundance of most excellent fish, the markets are supplied in most parts of the county with beef at four-pence per pound; mutton at four-pence halfpenny; chickens at fifteen pence per couple; geese half a crown each, and turkeys at three shillings and six-pence each."

FUEL.—P. 40. " The supply in this article" (coals) " is either from Newcastle to its ports, where they cost from two pounds fourteen shillings to three pounds per chaldron, of thirty-six bushels; or from Wales, which cost about thirty-two shillings per ton weight. The proportion between the Newcastle and the Welsh coals, is as thirteen and a half bushels of the former, to one ton of the latter."

MANUFACTURE.—P. 37. " Among various others of great import to the community, in the county of Dorset, the principal one, is in the manufactory of flax and hemp, in the neighbourhood of Bridport and Beminster; where all sorts of twine, string, packthread, netting, cordage, and ropes are made, from the finest thread used by saddlers, in lieu of silk, to the cable which holds the first rate man of war. The nets made for the fishery at Newfoundland, as well as for home use; and the sails for shipping of every kind, is manufactured of the best quality, as well as sacking for hammocks, &c. and all kinds of bags and tarpaulin; and in addition to the great quantity of flax and hemp used here,

here, not more than one-third of it is allowed by the manufacturers to be of British growth; the remaining two-
thirds of it, is imported from Russia and America, as raw
materials."

PUBLIC DRAINAGE.—P. 13. " Through this vale" (Blackmoor) " runs the river Stower, which is now undergoing a
great improvement, from the general Act of Sewers, by
cutting down the sides and removing obstructions, which
will tend to the general drainage of the country, and be a
lasting improvement."

RURAL ECONOMY.

TENANTED ESTATES.

TENURES.—P. 22. " There is a considerable part of
the county (though perhaps the fee of the whole parish belongs, at most, to one or two persons) which is leased out
for lives, and generally the land is here intermixed and confused by copyhold and freehold tenures. The customary
terms for renewal of leases for lives, are nearly as follows:
For copyhold, two years purchase is taken for one life;
eight, for two lives; sixteen, for three lives; besides the
widowhood. On leasehold, two years purchase for one life;
seven, for two lives; fourteen, for three lives. Though this
mode of letting land on lease is much less practised now
than formerly."

DRAINING FARM LANDS.—P. 26. " Draining, except in
the water meadows, is very little practised in any part of
the county Some of the tillage-land, which is gravelly
and springy, might be much improved by it."

IRRIGATION.—P. 34. " The flooding of meadow land, is
another business, of great importance, in the agriculture of
Dorsetshire. The proportion of water meadows is no where
so great, or any where better managed; the early vegetation produced by flooding, is of such consequence to the
Dorsetshire farmer, that without it, their present system of
managing sheep, would be almost annihilated."

Seeing what Mr. DAVIS and others have written on this
subject, the slight sketch offered, by Mr. Claridge, requires
not transcription. He properly refers to Mr. BOSWELL's
treatise.

TENANCY.—For remarks on *Life Leases*, see the head
Tenures, above.

WOODLANDS.

WOODLANDS.

P. 32. " Though this county is extremely barren, both in
timber and wood, still there are many local spots, appropriated to the growth of underwood in several parts of it,
such as Duncliff in the vale of Blackmoor, Honeycombe
wood in the neighbourhood of Sherborne, and many others
of a similar nature. The soil is chiefly cold and wet, and
the underwood cut at ten or twelve years growth, and produces about five or six pounds an acre for faggots. As to
timber, I could wish I had it in my power to be able to
describe from my own observation, a greater quantity than
I am able to do."

AGRICULTURE.

FARMS.—*Sizes.*—P. 24. " In many parts of Dorsetshire, one man occupies a whole hamlet, parish, or lordship; perhaps from fifteen hundred to two thousand acres,
which I fear has been too frequently made, by laying five
or six farms together, and thereby striking a fatal blow at
the little farmer, who is one of the most useful members of
society."

Enormous farms, such as are above described, are doubtlessly enormous evils. But a due proportion of *great* farms,
as those from 200 to 500 acres of culturable land, are
assuredly, in the present state of society, of great benefit to
the country. Mr. C. it would seem, is a small-farm man.
A GRADATION OF FARMS, in regard to size, is, in my
judgement, most desirable *.

HOMESTEADS.—P. 31. " The land owner in this county
has an advantage over others elsewhere, in the small proportion of buildings, which seems necessary for the farmer's
convenience, in managing his land. A small low built
house of stone, and covered with slate, situate in a bottom.
A barn for wheat, a small one for Lent grain or one barn
with two floors, a stable, ox-house, cow-house, and cart-
house, constitute every necessary; indeed, in one instance
only, they exceed the wants of other tenants, which is in
a house for the dairy-man, but this is either carried on, in
a part

* In my TREATISE on LANDED PROPERTY, p. 138, 4to edition, I
have fully, and I trust satisfactorily, explained my ideas on this important subject.

a part of the farm-house, or in a cottage set apart for that
purpose, but as it too frequently happens, that the farmer
rents more than one farm, he of course has an eligible accommodation for the dairy-man in his power. The farmer's
usual method, is to stack his hay on the ground, where he
is likely to fodder in the winter, and his corn on stone rick
staddles, in a yard adjoining to the buildings. He is not
extravagant in requiring useless or unnecessary ones, a few
cottages are generally included in his bargain."

WORKING ANIMALS.—P. 12. "The breed of horses in
this county, is not particularly attended to : a slight blood
horse is made use of for the field and road, and a very
ordinary stile of cart horse, used in agriculture ; some cart
colts are bred in the vale of Blackmoor, and many others
are brought in, either as suckers or yearlings from other
counties. Some individuals indeed, have good teams, and
are very careful of their horses ; but from general observation,
I am persuaded, the Dorsetshire farmers, pay but little attention to the shape, size, or symmetry of the cart horse.
The stallions are chiefly working horses of farmers, and
cover mares at half a guinea each for the season, and an
average price for a cart horse at five years old, is sixteen or
seventeen guineas.

" I was glad to find that oxen are often used in agriculture here, and the breed are of two kinds ; those on the
western side of the county are chiefly from the red ox of
Devonshire, an excellent sort ; and the others in the more
eastern and northern parts, are a mixture of the Hampshire
and Wiltshire, with many crosses of the Oxfordshire, Gloucestershire, Shropshire and North Country beasts."

MANURE.—*Lime.*—P. 18. " A great deal of lime is used
as a manure, and twenty hogsheads of four bushels each,
per acre, is esteemed a good dressing, which costs four-
pence halfpenny per bushel ; but those farmers who are
situate near coast, draw a great deal of sea-weed or kelp
from the shore, and sometimes spread it at once on the
ground prepared for wheat, and sometimes mix it with earth
and make it into compost, both of these operations have a
good effect.

" An extraordinary instance is well attested by many
respectable people, that some farmers have on a particular
occasion, when there has been a drug of fish upon the coast,
manured their land with them, which has produced a very
florid crop.

" One in particular, is of Mr. Davies, of Swire, who
about four years since manured a piece of land for wheat,
from a shoal of herrings, which cost him no more than one
shilling per load, besides carriage, he scattered them lightly
                                                            over

over the land, sowed it with wheat and ploughed them in, and the crop produced thereby was so rank as to be intirely laid before harvest."

For *Sheepfold,* see *Sheep,* ensuing.

ARABLE CROPS.—*Produce.*—P. 48. " The produce of the county may be thus estimated: 250,000 acres, supposed to be in tillage are divided annually nearly as follows:

35,000 acres of wheat, at 18 bushels to an acre,   78,750 quarters.
75,000 ditto barley, at 30 ditto   281,250 ditto.
50,000 ditto beans, pease, oats and vetches, at 30 ditto, 187,500 ditto.
36,000 ditto fallow and turnips.
53,000 ditto clover, lay and sainfoin, at 1 ton ditto,   53,000 tons.
 1,000 ditto flax and hemp, producing   35,208 stone wt."

WHEAT.—P. 19. " An average weight for wheat grown here, is twelve score, which is two hundred and forty pounds weight per sack, or sixty pounds per bushel." (8 gallons.) " Some farmers in the more open parts of the county think eleven score and a half is a better average weight per sack."

BARLEY.—P. 19. " The growth of barley affords a large produce. A great deal of malt is made for the internal consumption of the county, particularly in the article of strong beer, which is much used. The malt is generally dried with Welch coals. From ten to fourteen bushels of malt per hogshead of sixty-three gallons, with Farnham hops, makes the beer so much esteemed here, which is kept eighteen months or two years before it is drank; and in some of the towns, ten or twelve thousand bushels of malt are made annually "

FLAX.—P. 26. " The growth of flax and hemp, and particularly the former, is of great importance in the agriculture of Dorsetshire, and in the neighbourhood of Bridport in particular; and about the village of Bradpole and towards Beminster, the greatest proportion of it is grown."

P. 27. " It is frequently let to a middle man, (between the farmer and the manufacturer) called a flax jobber, who pays the farmer a neat sum of four or five pounds an acre; he manages the crop, finds the seed and labour, and expects nothing from the farmer but ploughing, and the discharge of parochial taxes "

ORCHARDS.—P. 25. " There are a considerable quantity of orchards in the vale of Blackmoor, and on the Somersetshire and Devonshire side of the county, and the cyder made, is mostly of the Devonshire sorts. It is chiefly used for home consumption, and I heard of no plantations sufficiently extensive, where the grower could sell to other counties, to make any considerable return."

GRASS LANDS.—*Chalk Downs.*—After discribing the Norfolk husbandry, and recommending something like it,

on

on " some rough pastures of the Downs or Ewe Leas, which are now overrun with bushes and furze,"—Mr. C. observes, with true discrimination, p. 21. " I do not mean, however, to recommend the breaking up of any of the best of the downs, as they are valuable in their present state. The land in Norfolk is of that dry sandy nature, that it will not convert into pasture, and therefore lays down in grass seeds seldom more than two years; but the case is very different in Dorsetshire, where the finest verdure is often found on the tops of the hills, and the land almost every where inclined to become good pasturage."

Vale of Blackmoor.—P. 13. " The vale of Blackmoor extends from north to south about nineteen miles from Gillingham and Silton, to Dantish and May Powder; and from east to west, from Compton and Sutton, about fourteen miles, to North Wotton and Long Burton, and contains upwards of one hundred and seventy thousand acres of very rich land, chiefly grazing, dairying, and about one tenth part in arable, with some plantations of orchards."

P. 13. " Some of the land upon the side of this river," (Stour) " is rich enough for an acre and a quarter to carry a full sized Devonshire ox through the summer. Most of the hay in this vale is of an excellent quality, and beasts thrive well through the winter upon it, without any other food."

CATTLE.—*Breed.*—P. 12. " As the cattle are very much used in dairies in this county, very little attention is paid to the size of the beast, or to shape or colour, but if likely to make a good milker, it seems all that is necessary, and is worth from eight to ten guineas, to come into the dairy at a proper age."

Fatting Cattle.—P. 13. " The oxen chiefly fed in the county, are of the Devonshire breed, and go when fat to Smithfield market, and are said to be the finest grained meat in the kingdom." These " are mostly fed in the vale of Blackmoor."

" The other cattle grazed here, are either *home breds*, or heifers, brought from Ringwood and other Hampshire fairs, and when fat, supply the home market, and sometimes are sent to Salisbury."

" There is a shew of cattle and some sheep at Stalbridge, in this vale, every Monday fortnight, through the year, which is the best market for fat cattle in the county, and about one hundred and twenty in number are bought and sold here, one market day with another."

DAIRY.—*Letting.*—P. 14. " The dairies extend all over the county, cow-calves, in general are reared, and bull-calves afford a supply of veal. The management of the dairy, as every where practised in Dorsetshire, is unknown to many other parts of the kingdom. The cows are all let
out

out by the farmer, to a dairy-man, at a fixed price for each cow, according to the quality of the land and produce of the beast. In some of the poorest parts of the county as low as fifty shillings or three pounds per head, per annum, and in others, as high as six pounds ten shillings, or seven pounds; and in one parish near Beminster, called Broad Windsor, as high as eight pounds; but I believe the general average throughout the county, will be about six pounds for a cow of full growth; four pounds for heifers, and four pounds ten shillings, or five pounds, for three years old.

"The usual plan for letting a dairy is this: the farmer finds the dairy-man a certain number of cows for one year, commencing at Candlemas, at a fixed sum agreed on. He feeds, fodders and supports the specific number throughout the year; he finds a house for the dairy-man and his family to live in, and allows him to keep as many pigs and poultry as he thinks proper, and the keep of a mare to carry out his butter, &c. which by producing a foal yearly, is considered a material advantage to the dairy-man, who perhaps sells it when weaned in November from eight to ten pounds. If the farmer is inclined to let his dairy to another man, he gives the dairy-man notice before All Saint's Day, and by custom the quarter of a year from November to February, is deemed sufficient, and the dairy-man quits the house and gives up his bargain the ensuing Candlemas.

"The dairies in general are managed by making all the cream into butter, and from the skimmed milk, an inferior sort of cheese."

SWINE.—P. 14. "The *breed* of pigs in this county is not so good in shape, as either the Hampshire, Berkshire, or Hertfordshire sort; they are of a light colour, feed to about nine or ten score on an average for bacon, and are worth about six shillings and sixpence, or seven shillings per score. As there are so many dairies, an improvement in the breed of this animal might be made by the introduction of the sorts before described."

SHEEP.—*Number.*—P. 7. "The advantage derived from sheep, in the county of Dorset, is very considerable, and it is undoubtedly its greatest object as an agricultural resource; indeed of so much real importance, as to be productive of great national benefit. The number of sheep kept in the county, from the best enquiry and computation I have been able to make, amount to upwards of 800,000; and the number sold annually and sent out of the county, amount to upwards of 150,000."

P. 11. "The number of wethers sold, 50,000; the number of ewes, 100,000; the number reared, 450,000; and the home consumption, 200,000."

Breed

Breed and Management.—P. 7. " Tho greatest advantages are derived from them, as well from the profit upon
the fleece and carcase, as from the quantity of ground manured by them, which I shall endeavour hereafter more
minutely to point out.

" In one particular instance the sheep owners excel all
other parts of the kingdom, which is in providing ewes to
yean at a remarkably early season, *in the midland counties*," (!) " which supply the metropolis with fat lambs.—
In order to shew the principle on which this mode of
grazing is carried on, I shall venture to give a detail of
their process and management, as far as it has fallen under
my observation.

" To describe the true Dorset sheep may be difficult, as
to its size and shape, but I apprehend, that if the face and
nose are white, and the claws or feet without any mixture
of colour, the forehead woolly, and the face long and broad,
the horn round and bold, and projecting rather forward, a
broad shoulder, straight back, broad loin, deep carcase and
short in the leg, it is the nearest to the true description of a
Dorset sheep. This attention to have the sheep without
colour, is considered of material consequence by the breeders
of early lambs, as they are said to be of more value for the
London market, on account of the extreme delicacy of the
meat.

" The season for putting the most forward ewes to the
ram, is the last week in April, for such as are to be sold
the following Autumn. And for the flock (which are to be
kept) about Midsummer.

" The lambing season therefore for the forward ewes, is
about the middle of September, and they are sold about a
fortnight before this time at the fairs near London, from
twenty-six to thirty-two shillings each. The lambs produced from these ewes are suckled in the house, on many
farms round the metropolis, which makes the house-lamb
fit for the table as early as Christmas. The other part of
the flock less forward, do not yean till the beginning of
December, but those yield a considerable profit, by their
lambs being fattened upon grass, very early in the spring
near London, and produce what is called the earliest grass-
lamb. The lambs kept in the hands of the breeders are
always taken from the ewes in May."

P. 9. " There are no ram fairs, or farmers who let out
rams for hire for the season, in this county. But they are
chiefly bred from the farmer's own stock, are put with the
ewes at about a year and a half old, and the better sort of
them, are not esteemed of a higher value, than three or
four guineas per head."

P. 10.

P. 10. " It is generally understood that the original breed of the Dorset sheep is very scarce to be met with, as most of the farmers have crossed their flocks, with the breed of the Hants, Wilts and Somersetshire sheep, which have certainly improved them as to size."

" The sheep are constantly attended by a shepherd the whole day, whose wages is six shillings per week: a great coat yearly, and a breakfast on a Sunday: A dog is found and maintained by the shepherd, and the master has the skins of the dead sheep."

P. 11. " Besides the sheep peculiar to Dorsetshire, there is another very small breed in the county, in the neighbourhood of Weymouth, in the Isle of Portland, the Isle of Purbeck, and about Wareham and Poole, which are inferior in size to Welch sheep: when fat will weight not more than eight or nine pounds per quarter, and the best of the ewes to yean, not worth more than fifteen or sixteen shillings per head."

Wool.—P. 9. " The wool produced in this county, is short and fine, of a close texture, and the quality of it is highly esteemed in the manufactory of that staple commodity called broad cloth. It is sold here by weys or weights of thirty-one pounds standing, and the average price, is ten-pence or ten-pence halfpenny per pound;" (in 1793.) " lambs wool produces about an halfpenny, or a penny per pound less."

Folding.—P. 9. " The wether sheep are constantly folded all the year round, running over the ewe leas or downs by day, and are penned on the tillage by night; they are penned late in the evening, and let out from the fold before sunrise in the winter, and not later than six o'clock in the summer. The ewes are folded only in summer, that is, when they have no lambs.

" The mode of penning sheep indeed, varies in some parts of the county, as well as the size of the hurdle, but in general the size of the hurdle is about four feet six inches long, and three feet six inches high, made chiefly of hazle, with ten upright sticks; and fifteen dozen of them, with a like number of stakes and wriths, to confine them together, will inclose a statute acre of ground, and will contain twelve or thirteen hundred sheep therein very commodiously.— The hurdles are moved every morning, consequently the same number of sheep will manure an acre of land daily. One penning is never estimated worth less than half a guinea, or twelve shillings per acre, and two at a guinea. The hurdles are worth seven shillings and sixpence per dozen, including stakes."

Diseases of Sheep.—P. 11. " It is incumbent on me to take

take notice of a disorder peculiar to sheep, which is sometimes fatally experienced in this county, called the *Goggles;*
it attacks them at all ages, and no remedy is at present
known for it; the first symptoms is a violent itching, which
is very soon succeeded by a dizziness in the head, staggering of gait, and a weakness in the back, as if the spinal
marrow was affected, under which they sometimes languish
a few weeks, and this disorder has been known to be fatal
to the greatest part of a flock, and is considered as the most
calamitous circumstance the sheep owners have to dread;
it is very difficult to assign the cause of this disorder, but
some of the old fashioned farmers think that as no such
disease existed, prior to the introduction of the breed from
other counties, consequently its origin may be imputed to
this cause; but this is an argument perhaps of prejudice,
grounded merely on conjecture, though I own I am inclined to give it some credit."

"GENERAL VIEW

OF THE

AGRICULTURE

OF THE

COUNTY OF DORSET:

WITH

OBSERVATIONS ON THE MEANS OF ITS IMPROVEMENT.

By WILLIAM STEVENSON,

AUTHOR OF THE AGRICULTURAL REPORT OF SURREY.

1812."

I HAVE the less to say, in this place, regarding the
QUALIFICATIONS of Mr. STEVENSON, as a Reporter of
agricultural information; because I shall have occasion to
advert to them, again, in reviewing his Report from
SURREY; which, tho priorly sent in to the Board, stands
posteriorly, in a geographical arrangement.

In

In the subjoined " Preface," we have Mr. S.'s own account of his undertaking.—P. v. " As there are some circumstances connected with the drawing up of the Agricultural Report of Dorsetshire, different from those which attend the drawing up of the County Reports in general, and which could not well be stated in the title-page to this volume, it may be proper briefly to lay them before the reader in the preface.

" In the year 1810 Mr. Batchelor, author of the Agricultural Report of Bedfordshire, was employed by the Board of Agriculture to survey Dorsetshire, and draw up an account of its agriculture : this he accordingly did, but when his MS. was put into the hands of some Gentlemen connected with the county, it was their opinion that the Report might be rendered more accurate and complete, if another survey were made, and the observations and information collected during that survey, incorporated with Mr. Batchelor's Report. This task was assigned to me ; and I accordingly went over the county in the year 1811.

" The additions and alterations I have made in Mr. Batchelor's Report, have been derived partly from what I collected during my Survey, and partly from a very useful work published by Mr. Boswell of Dorchester, entitled ' The Civil Division of the County of Dorset.' This work, besides other statistical information of great local as well as general importance, contains a complete *Nomina Villarum*. I understand Mr. Boswell has some thoughts of publishing the Ecclesiastical and the Military divisions of the county : if he follow up his design (and no man is better qualified for it) he will render an acceptable service to all connected with Dorsetshire, and set an example to other counties, highly deserving to be followed.

" The reader will perceive, that in the first part of the Report, I am much indebted to Mr. Boswell's book ; in the other parts of the Report, which are, more strictly speaking, agricultural, I have incorporated the information which was so liberally communicated to me by all I applied to during my survey, with the MS. Report of Mr. Batchelor. Such parts of his MS. as I deemed irrelevant, I have omitted, and such as were inaccurate I have altered and corrected ; but it is but just to him to declare, that on comparing the notes I took with his Report, I found they agreed in most particulars, and that there was not much necessity to add too, or to alter, the substance of what he had written : my business was rather to make it fit for publication.

W. STEVENSON."

" *Chelsea, August* 12, 1812."

In

In this ingenuous declaration, as well as in the work itself, we perceive Mr. Stevenson to be its *Editor*, rather than its *Author*. We observe very few passages in it (saving the strings of memorandumbook entries, that almost everywhere meet the eye—after the manner of the Secretary of the Board) which convey the idea of a *Survey*. And whether these, in whole or in part, were the produce of Mr. *Stevenson's* or Mr. *Batchelor's* tour of enquiry, is not evident.

The large portion of irrelevant matter, introduced into the volume, is, to an agricultural reader, disgusting. Nearly two sheets of it are filled with civil and ecclesiastical divisions of the County. In those waste pages, not only the several " divisions, hundreds, boroughs, liberties and tithings" are displayed, but the deaneries and churches of Dorsetshire appear ; and, after those, are seen curt descriptions of its numerous market towns ; such as were wont to be engraved on the corners, margins, and interspaces of old county maps.

In Dorsetshire there are only two streams that can be properly denominated *rivers ;* and even these are of the lowest class. Yet we find, under the head, " Waters," descriptions, and *derivations !* of nearly forty " rivers and brooks"—rivulets and rills ; the feeble narrative lingering on to the length of ten or twelve pages. Into some of those shallow streams deep learning is thrown. Even the Piddle has not eluded etymological research.

The number of pages—four hundred and eightyseven ; with an index.

A map of the County, well divided into districts.

SUBJECT THE FIRST.

NATURAL ECONOMY.

EXTENT.—P. 3. " In point of size, Dorsetshire may be considered as rather a large county, compared with the other counties in England. It is said, from the best information to be procured, that the county may be arranged in the following manner :

	Acres
Of Arable land	153,588
Pasture land	169,031
Meadow	73,628
	396,247

Commons

		Acres.
	Brought forward	396,247
Commons		26,916
Downs		31,272
Heath land		29,979
Woods		12,755
Copse		2,779
Plantations		2,620
Waste		1,586
To which add for rivers, water-courses, and roads, land occupied by towns, farm-buildings, &c.		8,000
	Total	512,154."

We are not informed by whom, or by what means, those *nice* calculations were made.

CLIMATURE.—P. 31. " The air of Dorsetshire is rather dry and salubrious than mild and bland ; and the seasons, except in spots very sheltered, or possessed of a very warm soil, are not nearly so forward as they are in other parts of England not so far to the south.

" The air on the hills and downs is keen, as they are exposed, without enclosures, to the winds from the sea. In the neighbourhood of the coast, it rains more in the winter, and less in summer, than is the case in more inland districts ; and, as a necessary consequence or concomitant of this, there is comparatively little snow or frost during the winter months.   Near the sea, also, it is remarked, that the sea fogs hang on the hills sometimes for a week together."

SOIL.—Even the proportionate quantities of the several varieties of soils of the County are set down to an acre !

P. 35. " Chalk	160,759
Sand	85,157
Loam	37,746
Gravel	59,894
Miscellaneous	13,427
Stone brash	29,700
Clay	117,331
Total (except rivers, towns, &c.)	504,014."

The Reporter, however, makes a suitably modest remark, on *this* bold attempt.

P. 35. " This statement can only be an approximation to the truth, but it may serve to furnish some idea of the relative quantities of each kind of soil ; they are much
                                      intermixed

intermixed together in many places, so as to render it a
task of some difficulty to ascertain by what name they
should be described."

Indeed, the section, " Soil," throughout, above every
other section in the volume, exhibits intelligent, appropriate
Report.

P. 37. " The soil of the most elevated parts of the chalky
district, is a thin loam, incumbent on what are called
rubbly chalk stones, below which the chalk becomes more
compact."

P. 39. " The elevated range of hills which runs through
the Isle of Purbeck, from Studland to Chilcombe, consists
of a harder kind of chalk, approaching almost to the
nature of stone, and the surface soil in many places contains a larger proportion of clay than the downs in the rest
of the chalky district."

" The heaths, which together with the fir plantations,
probably occupy 50,000 acres of this district, are in general
barren and unimprovable; the surface soil is in many
places a gravelly sand, occasionally interspersed with flints;
some of the sand is of a black colour, and small portions
of a thin peaty soil appear in several places round the ridge
of hills, which is included between the Frome and the
Piddle, extending from Piddletown many miles toward
Wareham."

P. 40. " The district of clay soils, interspersed with
various loams, gravel, and stone brash, occupies a very large
proportion of the county."

P. 41. " The soil on the coast between Purbeck and
Weymouth is mostly a clay loam, on a calcareous basis, and
of no very fertile quality.

" The coast lands from Weymouth to Burton are, in
general, cold tough clays of a very inferior kind, but intermixed with stone brash, and a few spots of a very fertile
description. Instances of this sort have been mentioned at
Wyke, Abbotsbury, and Bexington."

P. 42. " The Isle of Porland consists (according to Mr.
Parkinson,) of 933 acres of clay, and 1867 acres of stone
brash; it is in general a poor soil, but some of it is fertile."

" The western district is distinguished by the growth of
flax and hemp in the vicinity of Bridport and Beaminster,
and the intervening parishes to the west of Eggerdon Hill.

" The soil of this district is a very rich loam, some of
which is of a brown colour, and is called fox-mould.

" Westward of Symondsbury is Marshwood Vale," (Valley) " which is chiefly in pasturage, and some of it is a
cole clay."

P. 43. " The soil of the Vale of Blackmoor is very rich
in

in general; the ground on the banks of the Stour is a very deep loam, forming some of the most fertile meadows in the kingdom. The rest of the Vale is generally good, consisting of a large proportion of clay. There is also loam upon limestone, rich sand, and a very hard gravel."

FOSSILS.—This is another valuable section of the book under view.—P. 44. " *Slaty Coal*—Is found in great abundance in the hamlet of Ansty, in the parish of Hilton; it burns with a bright and lively flame, but yields, in its combustion, an exceeding disagreeable smell; so that it is not made use of for fuel. It is not unlikely, that good coal might be found beneath, as slaty coal, in some coal counties, lies over the good coal."

P. 45. " *Petrified Fish-Shells*—Are found in the parish of Hilton and its neighbourhood, imbedded in sand-stone, in immense numbers. They are both of the bivalve and univalve kinds; but you can seldom find both of the bivalve shells together. Petrified tortoises, in considerable numbers, have also been dug up in Ansty vale: it is disputed by some, whether they were ever real tortoise or not; but they are of various sizes, and very much resemble the shape of a tortoise. At Lower Melbury, near the seat of the Earl of Ilchester, the tortoise stones are so highly petrified, that they are sawn into slabs, and form beautiful chimney-pieces."

Kimmeridge Coal.—P. 46. " The most singular fossil production that is found in Dorsetshire, is Kimmeridge coal. Kimmeridge is a very small and poor village in the Isle of Purbeck, about one mile from the sea: it is situated near an abrupt termination of a ridge of hills;—these hills, for the most part, are composed of limestone, very compact and white, and, towards the base of the hills, very narrow veins of chert, or petrosilex, appear."

" The fossil called Kimmeridge coal, is found on the cliffs which border on Kimmeridge bay, about sixteen feet below the summit. it consists of an argillaceous slate, impregnated with bitumen to a great degree: the colour blackish brown. It is found in large lumps, lying in a stratum about three feet deep, but disappears at a small distance from the shore. When burning it gives out a sulphureous smell, and a strong bright light. If it is exposed to the atmosphere, it falls to pieces; but when kept under water, and before it is dry out of the cliffs, it is very hard. It is chiefly used in ovens, and by the poor people."

Portland Stone.—P. 47. " The Isle, or rather the peninsula of Portland, is about four miles and a half in length, and two in breadth. It has been long famous for its freestone,

stone, and is indeed one continued bed of it. It is said that
Portland stone was first brought into use and reputation
in the time of James I. who, by the advice of his architects,
employed it in the erection of the Banquetting-house at
Whitehall. After the fire of London, it was much used by
Sir Christopher Wren, in constructing the different public
edifices."

Here, the compiler inserts two extracts of some length,
from Dr. MATON's Observations on the Western Counties;
and Mr. SMEATON's History of the Eddistone Lighthouse;
concerning the " wonderful Chesil bank," and the " famous
quarries" of the Isle of Portland.

Purbeck Stone.—For Mr. Claridge's account of the Purbeck quarries, see p. 244, aforegoing.

Mr. Stevenson says, p. 59. " Mr. Chinchen, of Swannage,
estimates the exports of Purbeck stone, in the five years
succeeding 1801, at 38,750 tons per annum, supposing the
vessels to carry 50 tons on the average; the quantity carried inland may be about 150 tons a year.

" The sort is mostly flag stones for paving, and the
greater part are sent to London."

Potter's Clay.—P. 60. " A considerable stratum of this
valuable substance is found at various depths, in several
parts of the sandy district, in the vicinity of Wareham,
Poole, and Corfe Castle, but the principal part of it is dug
at Norden, near Corfe Castle; and by means of an iron-
rail-way is conveyed to Poole Harbour for exportion."

P. 61. " From 16 to 20,000 tons of potter's clay are
annually exported from Purbeck, and sent to Liverpool,
mostly for the supply of the potteries in Staffordshire, &c.

" About 3 or 4000 tons of an inferior kind of clay are
annually exported from Poole to London and Bristol,
where it is employed in making brown stone-ware, such
as pickling-jars, &c. The bad clay will not burn white, and
the particles of iron cause blisters."

P. 62. " This information was given by Mr. Willis of
Norden, who has the management of the principal clay-pits.

" There is very little potters' ware made in this
county."

SUBSTRUCTURE.—P. 42. " There is a well in the Isle,"
(of Portland) " 100 feet deep; and after passing the rubbish and the strata of freestone, the substratum was found
to be a bed of flints, of the depth of 20 feet."

GEOLOGY.—P. 39. " The heaths near Piddletown, and
six or seven miles farther to the south-east, are remarkable
for the many round deep pits which they contain; they
diminish almost to a point at the bottom, and are not unlike
inverted cones. There is one which appears to be 20 yards
wide,

wide, and 10 yards deep. They are said to become deeper, and an idea is entertained, that they are undermined by concealed streams of water."

For similar appearances, see the *seacoast* of *Sussex*, ensuing.

SUBJECT THE SECOND.

POLITICAL ECONOMY.

APPROPRIATION.—P. 332. "The south-east part of the county, extending from Piddletown, Bere Regis, and Wimborne Minister, to the Purbeck Hills, is a most dreary tract of heath land, and is scarcely capable of any improvement in the hands of the agriculturist."

Cranborne Chase.—P. 334. "This chase is a free warren, and was a gift of the Crown to Lord Rivers, who has a right to keep deer all over it.

"It consists principally of hazel wood, with some black thorns, and a few timber trees: the wood is cut at 12, or 13 years' growth, and the deer are fenced out of these parts for three years, by very high strong hedges, after which time they run all over it, and it is supposed that they do some good by keeping down the blackthorns. The Chase is pernicious to the farmers in the neighbourhood, and is the occasion that few turnips are sown, as the depredations of the deer on this crop are great, and cannot be prevented."

Halfyear Meads.—P. 307. "Or those in which one person has the hay, and another person claims a right to the *aftershear*, are to be met with at Abbotsbury, Swyre, &c.

"It is not remarkable that such customs should exist in or near open fields, where all the farmers have a right of common; but the meadows abovementioned are not near common fields, and no more than two or three persons are concerned in these mixed rights, which are apparently considerable checks to every kind of improvement."

FUEL.—P 438. "In the neighbourhood of Shaftsbury, and generally in the northern and north-western parts of the county, coals are brought from the Mendip pits in Somersetshire, and were sold in 1811 from 2s. to 2s. 6d. per cwt. In the south-eastern parts of the county, the vicinity of Poole enables the inhabitants to be supplied with Newcastle coals, which, in the same year, were sold at 2l. 5s. per chaldron.

"Furze is seldom burnt for common use, being generally

rally bought and consumed by the bakers and brick-makers."

MANUFACTURES.—*Sailcloth.*—P. 447. " The various branches of the hemp and flax manufactories are carried on in many parishes in the west of the county, where those plants are cultivated. At Loders, and other places, young girls are often employed in weaving of sail-cloth; and along the western coast, toward Weymouth, many of the women braid nets for the Newfoundland fishery."

Shirt Buttons.—P. 448. " The manufacture of shirt-buttons is extensively carried on at Shaftesbury, and Bland-ford, and the surrounding villages on all sides, to seven or eight miles distance. Many women and children are employed in this manufacture in most parts of the Vale of Blackmoor, and in several parishes in the Isle of Pur-beck."

TITHES.—P. 96. " The average amount of tithes, on the arable pasture and meadow land, may be estimated at 3s. 6d. an acre; that of commons at 8d.; open downs at 4d.; and heaths at one penny per acre."

" The county of Dorset is remarkable for the great num-bers of parishes in which a very low modus has been long established, in lieu of the vicarial tithes.

" The great tithes of many parishes are in lay hands, and the composition is frequently 5s. or 6s. in the pound rent."

SEA EMBANKMENT.—P. 373. " There are no embank-ments for the purpose of gaining land from the sea; neither is there any land capable of this kind of improvement."

RAILWAYS.—P. 440. " A road of this kind three miles and a half in length, was made in 1806. It extends from the pits of potters-clay at Norden, near Corfe Castle, to a place opposite Poole, where the clay is shipped for Liver-pool."

" The declivity of the road is in some places four inches, and in others five inches for every 20 yards, and the ex-pense attending this work, is stated by Mr. Willis of Nor-den, at about 2000l. a mile for new work. The clay is conveyed on small carriages with four iron wheels, carrying two tons each. Three horses draw 10 tons to the sea-side three times a-day, at the expense of about six-pence a ton weight."

ROADS.—P. 439. " The turnpike roads in the chalky district, are repaired with flints; but limestone broken to pieces with hammers, is the principal material of which the public and private roads are composed in all the rest of the county.

" The turnpikes, and other roads on the dry soils, ap-pear

pear to be in a good state, and have a sufficient convexity to cast off the water, which in sudden showers runs into small shallow pools that are made by the sides of the roads to receive it, and is soon absorbed in the chalky substratum.

"The bye-roads in some parts of the Vale of Blackmoor, and the western division of the county, are miry, and scarcely passable in winter, and the large rough loose stones with which they abound, render them very unpleasant in summer."

LAND MEASURE.—P. 445. "Land is measured by the goad or lug of 15 feet and an inch. A customary acre is therefore equal to about 134 square poles, statute measure."

SUBJECT THE THIRD.

RURAL ECONOMY.

TENANTED ESTATES.

ESTATES.—P. 73. "Estates in this county are in general large, and consequently the owners are few, in comparison with those of most other counties."

TENURES.—P. 74. "The copyhold tenures in this county are now become very few, owing, it is presumed, in a great measure to the frauds practised on the respective lords of manors, by the customary tenants marrying in the last stage of decrepid old age to very young girls, by which, according to the custom of copyhold tenures in this county, the widow is entitled to her free bench on the husband's copyhold.* The few copyholds now existing, consist chiefly of a mere cottage and garden, without any other lands being attached to them.

"There are other lifehold tenures of far greater extent, which are held by lease for one, two, or three lives, or for ninety-nine years; for these a suitable fine is paid by the lessee, at the time the grant is made, and a yearly rent, in general not exceeding one-twentieth part of the yearly value, as the fine is the principal consideration.—These leases contain covenants to secure the buildings from being permitted to fall into ruins, for the payment of rent,

---

* This extraordinary tenure is now, it is probable, nearly extinct. See my WEST of ENGLAND.

rent, and performing the offices, &c. to which the estate is liable.

" The proportion of freehold in this county, compared with what is held by other tenures, is in favor of freehold in the proportion of four to one."

P. 75. " On the whole, it may be said, that in Dorsetshire, life-tenure is wearing out, and fee-simple, more and more prevailing."

P. 76. " ' The inhabitants of Portland are almost all Freeholders; their tenure is gavelkind, whereby the lands of the father are equally divided at his death among all his sons: or the land of a brother or sister among all their brethren, if they have no issue of their own.'—*Hutchins.*"

MANAGERS.—P. 73. " Some of the principal estates are under the care of land surveyors; others are managed by practical farmers; and several large properties are superintended by gentlemen of the law."

IRRIGATION.—P. 360. " The principal farmers are almost unanimous in praise of irrigation, particularly on the chalky district, where the watered meadows are mostly situated, and where the want of them is considered by the sheep farmer as a most serious inconvenience."

Nearly a sheet of letter-press is bestowed on this subject, by Mr. Stevenson. But seeing the mass of information concerning it, which is already before the public, I perceive nothing, in the volume under review, that could beneficially add to it. The only useful purpose to which I can turn it is to extract a few items relating to the *quality of water*, for the use of irrigation. They powerfully tend to corroborate the fundamental principles on which its utility principally rests; and which I have been endeavouring to inculcate, in the mind of the agricultural public, during one quarter of a century, or more.

P. 364. " Mr. Garland of Wareham, is of opinion that the water-meadows nearest that town, owe their indifferent quality to the water which springs out of the immense heaths."

" Mr. Groves thinks bog-waters are of no value, unless when mixed with floods, but the water which descends from hills that have been well supplied with lime and other manures, improves the meadows in a striking manner."

P. 365. " Mr. Bryant thinks the water which is used immediately as it springs out of beds of chalk or limestone, is as useful as the water of floods, and perhaps more useful, as it proves beneficial even on clay soils."

P. 366. " Ridge-work is deemed the best where the water is plentiful, and the water is constantly found to have the most

most fertilizing effect, the nearer it is taken towards the spring head; but Mr. Goodenough believes, there is little utility in snow-water."

P. 368. " The River Stour is not applied to the purposes of irrigation after it enters the chalky district, but it frequently overflows a considerable quantity of meadow land, and its winter-floods are very advantageous.* A gentleman at Canford tried the effects of a stream from the heaths in that vicinity, but it produced rushes, and injured good land.†

" William Salkeld, Esq. is of opinion, that irrigation could not produce any beneficial consequences, if applied to the meadows of the Stour in the Vale of Blackmoor.

" These meadows are in general excellent land, and the river for the most part lies so low, that they suffer scarcely any injury from stagnant water, and need very little draining.

" The occasional overflows of the river are beneficial, but a superabundance of water entirely alters the nature of the vegetation for the worse."

It is unaccountably strange, that, from among those *known facts*, the calcareous principle should not have discovered itself!

P 370. " The streams in Dorset are in general shallow, and have a considerable fall; the meadows are narrow, and the water is supplied with comparative regularity, in consequence of its having to filter through immense masses of chalk previous to its exit at the springs: and hence the process of irrigation is much facilitated."

Yet the idea of rain water taking up (chemically, not in substance) calcareous matter, as it filters through chalk, issuing from the base of the rock, loaded with limy particles, conveying them in streams to the land, and there depositing them, in the state of *effete lime*,—does not appear to have struck the occupiers of CHALK HILLS and WATER MEADOWS!

SODBURNING.—P. 341. " This practice, which is termed *burn-baking*, has made but little progress in Dorsetshire; some of the principal land-agents, &c. are so inimical to it, that it is difficult to suppose their opinion is unmixed with prejudice."

A

* The Stour, as has been observed, rises, principally, out of the vale lands of Blackmoor; and its waters, probably, are nearly void of calcareous particles; saving what the broken line of limestone heights, between Sherborne and Wincaunton, may afford.

† This, I doubt not, is a fact. The astringent waters of heathlands I have ever found to be injurious to nutritious herbage.

A string of opinions and incidents in practice are, never-theless, reported. They are, however, frequently contra-dictory, and, on the whole, of little or no value.

TENANCY.—P. 104 " Leases of twenty-one years dura-tion were common in this county, till near the end of the last century ; but proprietors in general think it now im-proper to put the management of their estates out of their own power for so long a period; and though at present it is supposed, that about one half of the county is under lease, yet its duration is mostly for the term of only seven years, and in many very recent cases, the leases have been limited, even to three years."

Another and longer chain of inconsiderate opinions, prompt sayings, and futile remarks, (of informants) relating to *this* disputed point, is drawn out for the amusement of the readers of the Dorsetshire Report. I do not mean thus to convey, to mine, that every link is faulty, and unfit for inspection ; but to acquaint them that I cannot find one which I think would add to the value of the work I am preparing for them.

WOODLANDS.

WOODS.—P. 325. " Timber is scarce in this county, and the quantity is continually diminishing. The Vale of Blackmoor is said to have been very woody in former times, but at present the greater part of it grows no other timber than what is interspersed in the hedge-rows; which is, however, a considerable quantity of elm, ash, &c.

" There are few parishes that have woods which con-tain timber exclusive of parks, where they are mostly pre-served for ornament, and consequently are of little use to the public.

" There are, it is believed, only 17 parishes in the coun-ty, that have timber woods, and many of them are thinly stored."

A list of those woods being given, the Reporter adds,— p. 326, " This enumeration does not amount to 1500 acres, but there are several other woods in the county which con-tain some portion of timber, beside a number of copses, consisting almost entirely of hazel on the chalky soils."

COPICES.—P. 326. " Mr. Best of Dewlish, says the copses are cut at about six or seven years old, for the purpose of making hurdles, without splitting the hazel.

" When hurdles are made of older wood, the largest branches are split. Ash in copses often stands 20 years or more for poles, hoops, &c."

AGRICULTURE.

AGRICULTURE.

FARMS.—On the *Sizes* of Farms, in Dorsetshire,—see Mr. Claridge's account p. 247, aforegoing.

HOMESTEADS.—P. 83. "Many of the farm-houses, particularly those belonging to the large farms on the chalky district, are very ancient buildings, and have all the appearance of having been the seats of the proprietors in former times.

"They are mostly built with stone; and many of the ancient family mansions are covered with stone tiles, with window-frames likewise of stone, and turrets, battlements, and pointed arches, and carved work, in the Gothic style. Buildings of this kind may be seen, at Athelhampston, Waterson, &c.

"The more ordinary farm-houses, though generally built of stone, are frequently covered with reed thatch."*

P. 85. "In the chalky division of the county, many walls of cottages, barns, &c. are built partly of large flints, and partly of hard chalk, the flints being laid, of course, at the outside of the wall, and with the fractured or black part of the surface in view. The wall round a great part of the park of the late Lord Dorchester, at Milton Abbey, is built entirely with flints.

"There are many mud-walled cottages, barns, &c. in the county, but principally in the district to the east of Dorchester. They are composed of road-scrapings, or other kinds of earth which are a little cohesive, and well mixed with a large quantity of chalk and straw.

"In building walls of this kind, it is necessary to lay a foundation of stone, or such hard materials as will resist the injurious effects of wet, as well as the intrusions of vermin. The implement which is principally used is no other than a dung-fork, and the walls are generally made two feet thick. The first layer, or strata, is built about two and an half feet high all round the foundation of the building, or as far as is convenient; and, after the interval of about a week, which is allowed for the first layer to harden and consolidate, another is added, and the work proceeds

---

* Mr. Stevenson observes, p. 87, "Reed-thatching is very little in use to the east of Blandford." Hence we may say the practice of preserving wheat straw from the flail, for the purpose of thatch, prevails from the middle of Dorsetshire, to the Landsend.

proceeds in a regular manner, till the whole is completed.
Garden walls, &c. are often built in this manner, but have
always a coping of thatch to secure them from the rain."

PLAN OF MANAGEMENT.—P. 189. "The county of
Dorset has been remarkable, in former times, on account
of the very large proportion of its arable land, which was
devoted to the production of culmiferous or white-strawed
corn crops. At present, the successive cultivation of wheat,
barley, and oats, without the intervention of pulse, or
cattle crops, is a practice that is not encouraged by any
of the proprietors of the soil, nor defended by the most
intelligent farmers ; yet it is occasionally adopted by many
who, nevertheless, freely acknowledge its impropriety."

After that unpromising exordium to the section, "Course
of Crops," succeeds a sub-infinity of miscellaneous items,—
a la Secretaire. Out of the mass I have extracted the two
which follow.

P. 194. "In the Vale of Blackmoor, there is but little
arable land, perhaps not more than one-eighth or one-ninth
of the whole; and as the land, for the most part, is not
adapted to the culture of turnips, there is scarcely any
thing like a regular course of cropping, unless in those places
where it is regulated by ancient customs, in uninclosed
fields; and there are but few of these now remaining."

P. 201. "There is a singular custom in the Isle of
Portland, which consists in fallowing half the arable land
every year, and sowing the other half with wheat, barley,
oats, and a few pease and tares."

OCCUPIERS.—P. 75. "It has been remarked, that there
are a greater number of Yeomanry in the western part of
Dorsetshire,—especially in that part which lies detached,
surrounded by Devonshire, than in any other part of the
county."

WORKPEOPLE.—P. 428. "The price of labour, in many
parts of this county, appears to have undergone little
variation for some years; yet, as it is paid partly in kind,
by the allowance of wheat and barley at a low and fixed
price, it has, of course, advanced in some measure according to the increased price of provisions."

"The ale which is given to labourers in hay-time and
harvest, is brewed with four bushels of malt to the
hogshead."—Of this ale, we are told, even women are
allowed "three pints a day or more;" and men "seven
pints."

P. 430. "At Stinsford, labour is 6s. or 7s. a week, with
wheat at 5s., and barley at 3s. per bushel."—This custom
prevails in different parts of the West of England. I have
repeatedly, I trust, shown its impropriety.

P. 453.

P. 453. " The best servants, it is acknowledged, are taken from the families of those who occupy small dairy farms, &c. in the Vale of Blackmoor, and other parts of the county; and who bring up their children in habits of sobriety, honesty, and industry, and give them that small portion of education which is suited to their condition."

P. 454. " There are no statute fairs kept in this county for hiring servants, and indeed very few men-servants are taken into the farmers' houses. It is said to be a prevalent custom to hire servants for only eleven months, for the purpose of avoiding additional incumbrances on the parishes. Hence a deficiency of labourers may be expected as a necessary consequence."

" The custom of allowing the labourers to grow potatoes on the fallows otherwise intended for turnips, appears to be a distinguishing merit in the upland farmers of this county."

P. 455. " The growth of potatoes, as observed by a farmer on the chalky district, affords a means of keeping the labourers more under subjection, and prevents their leaving their master at least during the summer; as in that case the crop would be forfeited."

In a district where hands are scarce, and apt to stray in the summer months, the above is a well judged point of practice.

WORKING ANIMALS.—P. 378. " The parishes where oxen are worked are mostly in the west, and north-west parts of the county, where the Devonshire cattle are kept for general purposes."

P. 418. " There appears but little emulation among the farmers in the breed of their horses, which, though not ill shaped for the purpose of labour, have rather a mean appearance, and are of all colours that are common to horses. They are from 15 hands to 15¼, and but few reach the height of 16 hands. They are short-legged, and have good hoofs, and good bony legs; rather lengthy in the carcass, but not in the extreme; strong in the hind-quarters, and broad in the breast; their shoulders do not fall backward, but stand upright, and a cart-horse is better to be so made.—The collar fits in a more proper manner for work, and is not so liable to choak in going up the steep hills of this country. Their neck is rather short and low, the head rather large; they have not a smart look, but their eyes are rather dull. Now this is the description of a mean unsaleable horse, but which is nevertheless not ill adapted for labour; many experienced waggoners, and drivers of teams observe, that a smart quick look in a horse denotes a hasty passionate temper, while there is a degree

degree of coolness required in cart-horses."—This is well considered, valuable Report.

IMPLEMENTS.—To this favorite object of amateurs,—as if the whole art of farming grew out of it,—the Reporter has appropriated no inconsiderable part of his volume. In his "lengthy" chapter, however, I have been able to discover very little that could add to the value of my present Work. The subjoined historic notice, 1 find, is the only passage I have marked, on *studying* it.

P. 140. " The *nine-share plough* is said to have been originally derived from Wiltshire; it has, however, been used in this county for twenty years, and is now in general estimation on the whole of the chalky district."—See WILTSHIRE, p. 213, aforegoing.

MANURE.— *Yard Dung.*—P. 347. " The principal manure which is used in this county, as well as in all other places, consists of yard-dung, of course, and is here called *pot-dung.*"

For *Sheep's Dung* as a manure,—see *Sheep*, ensuing.

Chalk.—P. 350. " Chalk is in great estimation, and has been found a very useful manure in this county."—A page of contradictory opinions, about the quantity to be set on, follows.

P. 351. " The chalk which is used as a manure is sufficiently soft to be broken, and in some measure pulverised, by the wet and frost; and this kind is seldom found very near the surface of the ground."

Lime.—P. 351. " Lime is much used in the Vale of Blackmoor, in the neighbourhood of Sherborne, Cheddington, Beaminster, Bridport, and along the coast from Burton to Abbotsbury, Fleet, and Weymouth."

P. 352. " The most common quantity of lime is 20 hogsheads, or 80 single bushels, per acre."

" Lime was not used at all in the vicinity of Cheddington, till within the last five or six years, but is now in general use."

Sea Weed.—P. 355. " Sea weed has been advantageously used in composts at Swannage, and is sometimes ploughed into the land in a wet state. The sort that is called *kelp* is known to be the most useful, but opinions are extremely at variance on the merits of *sea-weed* as a manure; from which, perhaps, it may be concluded, that its merits are of a very moderate kind. It is certainly not much in use; part of which neglect may arise from its being difficult to get at in many places.

" At Poole, it is used for making a sort of walls, in several places near the beach."

Sea Water.—P. 356. " Sea-water was distributed in
plentiful

plentiful quantities on a part of Charborough-park, many
years ago; but Mr. Wickins of Mapperton, under whose
direction it was performed, thought its effects were rather
injurious than otherwise."

Herbage and Roots, applied as Manures.—P. 357. " *Green
vegetables.*—Mr. Stent observes, that several small farmers
at East Morden sow buck-wheat for the purpose of ploughing it in; and when this is the case, one bushel and a half
are sown per acre at the end of June or beginning of July,
and ploughed in while in full blossom at the end of August;
it having been previously rolled down in the same direction
as the land is to be ploughed."

P. 358. " Whatever may be the ultimate utility of this
kind of manure, it is much in use on the chalky district,
in the vicinity of Blandford, Wimborne, &c.

" At Sturminster Marshal, and other unenclosed parishes
where the mode of cropping is fixed, it is not uncommon
to sow turnips, for the express purpose of ploughing them
in as a manure for wheat.

" J. Wood, Esq. of Osmington, consumes a part of his
broad clover with sheep, but ploughs much of it in, and
is by this means enabled to get good crops of wheat,
without much manure."

P. 263. " In the open fields, turnips are often sown in
the fallow season, merely for the purpose of ploughing them
in, before wheat is sown on the same land."

TILLAGE.—*Fallowing.*—P. 187. " The system of summer-
fallowing, is very generally pursued in the Isle of Purbeck,
and all along the coast to the borders of Devonshire: yet
what is here termed a summer-fallow, is, in most cases,
no other than a preparation of *ley ground* for a crop of
wheat, by ploughing it three or four times, the first
ploughing being given in June, or July, and sometimes as
late as August."

P. 188. " In the Vale of Blackmoor, the summer-
fallows are sometimes of the same description as those
which are used in Purbeck, &c., but they appear to be
undertaken for the most part, with the view of cleaning
the land." (!) " They are ploughed three or four times
before the wheat is sown, and such as follow *corn crops*,
are broken up immediately after the lent corn is put
into the ground, as is the usual practice on clay soils
in other counties."

ARABLE CROPS.

WHEAT.—*Semination.*—P. 204. " The nine-share plough
is very much used on the whole of the chalky district,
for

for the purpose of making hollows or drills on land
which has been long ploughed and baked down by the
fold. After this operation is performed, the seed is sown
and covered by harrowing in the usual way. On the
lighter soils, of a sandy nature, or on such chalky loams
as have not been long ploughed, the seed is often harrowed in without the previous use of the nine-share
plough. In the Isle of Purbeck, and other districts where
the land is summer-fallowed, the seed is frequently ploughed in."

P. 212. " Mr. Richards of Fleet, dresses his seed wheat,
by dipping it two or three times in a mixture of hot water,
and quick-lime. The operation is performed by means
of a common wicker basket, and is said to be very effectual in preventing of smut."

Harvesting Wheat.—P. 218. " The practice of making
the wheat crop into field stacks, or conical heaps of half
a waggon load in each, and letting it remain in the field
three or four weeks to dry, is very fashionable in the
western part of Dorset, and the Vale of Blackmoor."—
This practice is common to the West of England, and, in
many cases, is valuable.

Produce of Wheat.—P. 221. " The produce of wheat is
said to be no more on the average than 17 bushels 1½ peck
per acre. In several parishes it is stated at 20 bushels
per acre, and even as high as 30, but in many instances
as low as 12 or 10 bushels, and in two parishes the
average produce is not allowed to be more than eight
bushels per acre."

OATS.—P. 234. " A considerable quantity of oats are
grown in this county. In those parts of the chalky district
where the subsoil is of a clayey cold quality, they are
often sown after turnips, and are deemed more profitable
than barley ; but where the soil is lighter, and particularly
in the unenclosed parishes, they frequently succeed wheat."

HEMP.—P. 287. " The culture of hemp in this county
is very much increased of late years, as might be expected
from the high price it has borne in consequence of the
shutting the ports of the North of Europe."

Quantity grown.—P. 287. " At the present time, in the
opinion of Mr. Roberts of Burton, and some others, there
are from 4 to 500 acres of hemp grown in the county
on the average, and about ten times as many acres of
flax. According to Mr. Conway of Netherbury, hemp is
only cultivated in 13 parishes in the county, viz. Bridport,
Loders, Bradpole, Powerstock, Symondsbury, Chidiock,
Bothenhampton, West Milton, Walditch, Stoke Abbas,
Beaminster, Netherbury, and Abbotsbury."

Soil

Soil employed for Hemp.—P. 288. "The soil most adapted to the growth of hemp, is a rich dark-coloured warm and deep loam. The soils where hemp is grown in this county are deep loams of a reddish colour, and termed fox-mould. They consist of a large proportion of very fine-grained sand, and are of great natural fertility; but scarcely tenacious enough in general to produce good crops of beans."

"The hemp-growers seem to be unanimously of opinion, that hemp cannot be advantageously grown on soils that are not naturally almost rich enough to make good gardens; and that the notion entertained a few years ago, that it would succeed on any kind of soils newly broken up, is entirely erroneous."

Manure in use for Hemp.—P. 289. "Manure should be very liberally supplied; an acre should be dressed with 20 pot-loads of yard dung, 20 hogshead of lime, and have a good folding besides, though the latter may be omitted."

Those ideas, respecting the soils and manures that are requisite to the profitable culture of hemp, oppose the wild notion about its being *a great meliorator of land!*— See EASTERN DEPARTMENT.

Major Travers, I apprehend, views the *effect of hemp on land*, in its true light.

P. 289. "Major Travers thinks it absurd to prohibit the growth of hemp, for he says it is well known that much manure must be purchased, or the crop will not prove a profitable one. Under these circumstances several hemp growers concur in the opinion that hemp cannot injure the ground, yet their sentiments on this subject seem to furnish no foundation for that whimsical theory, that hemp does not exhaust the soil, because its thick shade keeps the sun from it. The ample manuring which hemp requires, furnishes a most undeniable proof of its exhausting nature, yet it does not follow from this, that very good crops of wheat cannot be grown after it, or that its growth should be prohibited on rich soils."

FLAX.--*Quantity grown.*—P. 294. "From 1782 to 1792 inclusive, the average amount of the bounty of 4*d.* per stone, paid to the flax growers was 457*l.* 3*s.* 2*d.* per annum, the annual quantity being 27,338 stone weight, and which is supposed to have been the produce of 1700 acres of land.

"Since that period, the growth of this crop has extended over all the western parts of the county, in some measure along the coast towards Weymouth, and rather generally in all that part of it bordering on the county of Somerset.

"At this time, it is supposed that from 4 to 5000 acres

acres are annually applied to the culture of this necessary article.

"The soils proper for the growth of flax are such as possess a considerable share of natural fertility, yet are inferior to those on which hemp is grown."

Management of the Flax Crop.—P. 299. "The management of flax is not thoroughly understood by any, except professed flax-jobbers; and after the land is got ready, it is often let to these people at about 10 pounds or 10 guineas per acre, to sow and manage it at their own expense and discretion. At other times the farmers sow the land, and sell the crop to the flax-jobbers according to its goodness, as the time of pulling approaches."

State of growth in which Flax is *harvested.*—P. 297. "The crop is seldom pulled up before it is ripe in this county, unless it appears to be in danger of rotting from its large growth. The seed ripens, and the crop is drawn up by the roots about the beginning of August."—The produce is of course of inferior quality, in this case, to that which is gathered before the seeds be matured.

" *Ripening*" the *Stalks* of Flax.—P. 300. " *Dew-ripening* is a term applied to the exposure of flax for three or four weeks, on stubbles or meadow land, to the action of the dews and rains; by which means the flax is made to separate easily from the stalk. This is a process which cannot be thoroughly understood without the aid of practice. It requires turning several times, and seems to enrich the ground where it is laid, though this effect does not appear in the grass *more than one season.*

"Neither hemp nor flax are here watered in pits or brooks, as in some other parts of England."

POTATOES.—P. 267. "About thirty or forty years ago, this valuable root was only introduced in a very partial degree into the gardens of Dorsetshire; but of late years its cultivation has extended very rapidly, and appears likely to be still further increased. Potatoes are grown on every kind of soil, but the greater part of those which are intended for sale, are cultivated, as a fallow crop, on the the rich loams in the vicinity of Bridport, Beaminster, Abbotsbury, &c."

TURNEPS.—P. 251. "This kind of crop, which is of the very first importance in the cultivation of light soils, is comparatively of late introduction in the county of Dorset.

"Mr. Park of St. Giles's, who has been many years land steward to the Earl of Shaftesbury, says, that thirty years ago it was common for the farmers to say *they could not live by turnips.* At this time a gentleman, whose name Mr. Park did not recollect, cultivated some turnips, and gave

gave them to some farmers, free of expense, that they might thus ascertain their value. Mr. Park adds, that late as they were in beginning to sow turnips, the improvement of the county, by these means, has been very rapid of late years. There is, however, much still remaining to be done."—It was therefore improvident to bestow twelve pages of paper and printing, on their cultivation, in that County.

BULBOUS RAPE.—P. 251. "Swedish turnips have been introduced into perhaps all parts of the county, but the quantity of them which is cultivated, is very trivial."

RETROSPECTIVE REMARK, on this Reporter's Account of the ARABLE CROPS of Dorsetshire.—By the paucity of information which I have gathered from one hundred and twentyeight pages of matter (more than one fourth of the volume) concerning this important subject in agriculture, it may be conceived that I have treated the book and its author with neglect or disrespect. To frustrate such a false conception, I think it right to say, that I have paid the same deliberate attention to the Dorsetshire Reports, in this and every other particular, as I have to the numerous other Reports to the Board of Agriculture, the merits and demerits of which I have had occasion to estimate.

ORCHARDS.—P. 321. "It is supposed that there are upwards of 10,000 acres of orchard ground in this county."

Raising Orchards.—P. 322. "Mr. Groves of Bettiscombe, has a nursery of apple-trees, and sells a great many at 3s. 6d. each. They are grafted on crab-stocks nine or ten inches from the ground, and clay wrapped round them in the usual way. The top leader or middle branch is cut off for the purpose of making the other branches spread, and none of the side-shoots permitted to grow within six feet of the ground."

"Mr. Groves of Abbotsbury, thinks it improper to support apple-trees with props, after they have become firmly rooted, and has convincing proofs that they thrive the best when the roots are moderately shaken and loosened by the wind."

P. 323. "Mr. Roberts of Burton Bradstock, has planted a small orchard on what he considers to be a very improved plan. Large holes, I believe as much as three feet deep, were dug, and half filled with furze and rubbish, previous to the good mould being put in which surrounds the roots of the apple-trees.

"The trees planted in this manner appear to have grown very rapidly, as is also the case with the quick hedge which surrounds this garden and orchard, the subsoil of which was
also

also mixed with furze and rubbish, previous to the planting of the quicksets."

Cider.—P. 322. " In the neighbourhood of Sherborne, it is common to mix six bushels of sweet apples with three of the sharp or bitter sorts, in making cyder; and in some places a few crabs are substituted for the rough or bitter apples.

" At Bradford Abbas, and some other places, it is asserted that the best cyder is made, by filling the casks with the juice as soon as it is pressed out, bunging them down close, and depending on the strength of the casks to check the fermentation. It seems to be pretty generally understood, that 20 bushels of apples will make a hogshead of cyder; and Mr. Strong of Powerstock observes, that an apple-tree in that neighbourhood has been known to produce seven hogsheads in a season." (?)

GRASS LAND.

The AGGREGATE QUANTITY, in Dorsetshire.—P. 304. " The quantity of grass land in this county is very considerable, especially in the Vale of Blackmoor, which contains very little arable land; not more, as it is supposed, than one-tenth of the whole.

" Perhaps about two-thirds of the chalky district consist of meadows, cow and sheep pastures, and downs.

" The whole quantity of pasture, meadow, common, and down land, is supposed to be 300,000 acres, or about three-fifths of the county."

The QUALITIES of Grass Lands.—P. 307. " The rent of dry meadows appears to vary from 20s. to 30s. an acre, in the upland parts of the county; but the meadows of the Stour, in the vale of Blackmoor, are worth from 2l. to 4l. per acre. In Purbeck, according to the Rev. Mr. Dampier, the rent of meadows varies from 20s. to 40s. per acre."

MOWING GROUNDS.—P. 304. " About 6000 acres of the meadow land in the chalky and sandy districts are regularly irrigated; and such as are not subjected to this process, are either mown or fed with sheep or dairy cows. In the Vale of Blackmoor, the meadow land, on the banks of the river Stour, and the other rivulets which fall into that stream, is in general very rich, and is applied, in a great measure, to the production of hay for the wintering of dairy cows or fat beasts."

P. 309. " The abundant produce of the water-meadows, together with the custom of keeping the cows almost entirely on straw, during a considerable part of the winter, render it unnecessary to mow any very large portion of upland pasture."

GRAZING

GRAZING GROUNDS.—P. 308. " The rich feeding land of this county extends through all the lowest parts of the Vale of Blackmoor, and detached spots of fertile pastures may be seen in other parts of the clay and stone-brash districts; but the upland chalky part of the county contains very little pasture-land that is ever applied to the purpose of fattening sheep or cattle.

" Many wether sheep and beasts are fattened in the Vale, perhaps one-third of that fertile part of the county is applied to this purpose."

DAIRY GROUNDS.—P. 309. " *Dairy-Grounds* are common in every part of the county.

" The low pastures of the chalky district, as well as those of a similar discription in Purbeck, and along the coast to the borders of Devonshire, are not, in general, adapted to the purpose of the grazier, and are therefore applied to the support of dairy-cows, which furnish the Portsmouth and London markets with potted, or firkin butter.''

DOWN LANDS.—P. 335. " The downs occupy a large portion of the county, and are in general destitute of shelter, either from trees or hedges."

" The down grasses are mostly of a slender and diminutive kind, yet the herbage is said to become hard and unpalatable, if it is not fed down very close. In some parts of the downs there is an intermixture of a kind of hard *carnation*, or sedge-grass, of a blue or a yellow colour; and in other places the herbage consists almost entirely of wild burnet, mouse-ear, moss, &c. In general, the downs appear smooth and agreeable to the eye, but there are occasional patches of ling, or heath, and furze."

P. 336. " The upland part of the county contains a very great extent of down-land, as well as some rough and coarse pastures, which in their present state are but of little value. A great part of this land might be converted to tillage, to the profit of both landlord and tenant. It would keep more and better stock than it does now in its natural state, and would produce large crops of corn under good management, and a proper rotation of crops."—This is assertion, only.

" Mr. Wickins would never suffer maiden downs to be broken up, as he believes a turf of equal value could never be restored. Such as have been broken up near Blandford, and elsewhere, he observes, have been reduced to a *caput mortuum* by burning, and will never recover their fertility; many of them are not worth 5s. per acre, while others are worth 8s. or 10s. an acre."

LIVESTOCK.

CATTLE.—P. 374. " There is no select breed of cattle in this

this county; the dairy cows of the chalky district, and the south-eastern parts of the county, are a long horned kind, rather short in the leg, with white backs and bellies, and dark spotted or brindled sides.

" They are a mixture of various breeds from Hampshire, and other neighbouring counties, and more regard is paid to the quantity of milk they are likely to produce, than to any other quality. The coast of Dorset being directly opposite to the Isles of Alderney, Jersey, and Gurnsey, it it may be expected that a few of those kinds of cows are kept, as well as others that are called Norman or French cows; but no attempt has been made to ascertain their relative merits. In the western part of the county, as well as in the Vale of Blackmoor, the cows are mostly of the Devonshire kind. This circumstance may be admitted as furnishing a strong argument in favour of that kind of cattle; but perhaps, at the same time, it may render it probable that they are best adapted to low and sheltered pastures, and have more merit as feeding, than as dairy beasts."—This is considerate, intelligent Report.

DAIRY.—Mr. Stevenson adopts Mr. Claridge's leading remarks on this subject. See p. 250, aforegoing.

The extractable matters, in the volume now before me, on this object of husbandry, are as follow:

P. 387. " Whatever may be the utility of letting cows to dairymen, it will be admitted as a proof that the farmers have more business than they have leisure or inclination to attend to; and therefore, that it would be much better for the country, and not much worse for themselves, if the size of their farms were diminished. The dairy and cheese-making processes are too servile employments for the wives of the large farmers, and indeed it would be absurd to suppose the wife or daughters of a man possessed of property to the amount of 10 or 15,000*l.* would engage in the drudgery of the dairy. Some of the farmers let as many as a hundred dairy cows to three or four dairy-men; and in the last century it is probable that the labour of such a dairy was performed by half a dozen farmers' wives, who deemed it no drudgery, while they were permitted to consume a part of the produce."

P. 388. " In the Vale of Blackmoor, the farms are not so large as in the upland part of the county; and many of the leaseholders and others in that district, manage their own dairies in the same manner as is common in other parts of the kingdom."

The subjoined touches on a minutia of practice which is new to me; but not of high import.

P. 384. " Some of the skim-milk-cheese, which is called by

by way of ridicule, *double Dorset*, is streaked with a kind of blue mould, and Mr. Ottan says, this blue cheese is made by breaking and sprinkling the curds with flour after they have been pressed.

" Others ascribe the blueness of this cheese to the soil, but it does not appear to be known whether it is ascribable to the soil or the management; at any rate, it is deemed an excellent quality, and renders the cheese which possesses it far more valuable."

SHEEP. — *Breeds.* — The present Dorsetshire Breed. — P. 393. " The county of Dorset seems to have been long in possession of the breed of sheep, which is remarkable for supplying the metropolis with house-lamb at a very early season "

The Portland Breed.—P. 394. " In the Isle of Portland, there is a very small breed of sheep, and there are a few of the same kind at Studland, but they are not kept generally, as might be inferred from Mr. Claridge's account, ' in the neighbourhood of Weymouth, the Isle of Purbeck, and about Wareham and Poole.'

" They are said by many to be the true Dorsetshire breed; the farmers, and breeders of sheep in that island, contend that there is none of the true breed in the rest of the county, all the others having been crossed by the Somersets and other kinds of horned sheep; but be this as it may, they are very much improved either by keeping or breeding. The Dorset sheep, when compared with such as are kept at present in the Isle of Portland, will weigh three times as much; and it is not to be wondered at, as it may be observed that there are 3000 sheep kept on the Island, which contains but 2800 acres, of which 800 are waste, 400 arable, 250 meadow, which leaves but 1350 acres of pasture for sheep, and this is very poor land, rented at 7s. an acre. Thus it appears the land is stocked at the rate of two sheep and a quarter per acre, much of which has scarcely a blade of grass upon it. The Isle of Portland sheep are horned, remarkably small, and rather short in the carcass, when fat not weighing more than 10lbs. a quarter; their wool weighs from one pound and a half to two pounds a fleece, and the price of the wool in 1806 was 50s. per wey of 30lbs., but this year (1807) only 46s. a wey. Several of these sheep have black noses, and are rather black intermixed with white near the hoof, in which case they are said to be *brooked*. The Somerset sheep are remarkably white in the face and the legs, and it is very seldom that a Dorset sheep is to be seen with the least inclination to any black hair on their face and legs, from which it seems probable they have been mixed.

mixed. It is very well authenticated, that the Portland sheep have had no cross of blood, and it is said to be as fine flavoured mutton as any in the kingdom."

P. 396. " The Portland mutton is sold by the quarter at 10s. 6d. in general. It is never weighed, but would come to 1s. a pound when common mutton is only 7d.; it seldom weighs more than 10 lbs. a quarter."

The *Management* of Sheep.—P. 411. " *The general Management of Sheep* in this county is very uniform. The lambs which are bred for the regular supply of the flock, are dropped at Christmas, or soon afterwards, and the couples are kept in the best ewe-leazes, &c. on grass, hay, and turnips if necessary, and such as have watered meadows, depasture their sheep there, on the early grass, till Old May-day, when the lambs are weaned, and the sheep go to fold; but sometimes the two latter circumstances take place as early as Lady-day. The ewes are folded constantly, and kept on the downs, on artificial grasses, and other pastures, till near the ensuing Christmas, at which time they have another crop of lambs, the rams having been put to the flock about the end of July.

" The lambs are generally shorn about Midsummer, at the same time as the rest of the flock, and between this time and Michaelmas the *pur lambs* are sold to dealers, &c. from Somersetshire, and other districts, where breeding flocks are not so generally kept as in the upland parts of Dorset. In the summer and autumn, the *chilver lambs* are frequently folded, being fed on grass, rape, turnips, and hay, from the latter end of summer till the following spring. They take the name of ewe-hogs sometime in the autumn, at which time many of them are sent to the Vale of Blackmoor to be wintered, and the rest of them consume the greater part of the turnips in the county, with a portion of hay, made from artificial grasses, and stacked in the middle of the turnip fallows for that purpose.

" In the next summer they are put to the ram, and they produce a crop of lambs at the age of two, three, and four years successively, under a similar system of management as before described, and are called by the name of two-toothed, four-toothed, and six-toothed ewes.

" When they enter on their fifth year, the lambs are weaned by the end of April, and the ewes are depastured on water-meadows and the best ewe-leazes, and folding is omitted, to induce them to take the ram in May and June, and get them in condition for sale at the ensuing Michaelmas; at which time they are almost invariably sold at Weyhill in Hampshire. It is a general custom in this county,

county, to colour the old ewes all over with reddle, which is mixed with water in a tub and put on with a mop; and no other reason is assigned for this custom, than to distinguish them from the Somerset sheep, which are brought to the same fair. It is a general plan, to endeavour to procure the lambs to fall as soon as is convenient after the dealers and graziers who purchased them at Weyhill have disposed of them in the neighbourhood of the metropolis, which they supply with the early house-lamb,—a luxury, which sometimes produces in a few weeks more money to the grazier than the ewe cost, in repayment for a considerable quantity of care and expense."——This is circumstantial, praiseworthy report.

Washing Sheep.—P. 418. " This necessary operation is performed in some parts of the county by *women,* who stand in the water, and hold the sheep under *spouts* that convey the stream upon them, in the same manner as is generally done by men in other parts of the kingdom" (?); " but of late years a new and easy method has been adopted at Frampton, Abbotsbury, and many other places. A pit is made in any convenient part of a stream of water, capable of containing about a score of sheep, the sides of the pit are walled, and there are proper conveniences for letting in fresh water, and the sheep are merely put into the pit, and pushed about from side to side, with crooks, poles, &c. for two or three minutes. Mr. Goodenough, Mr. Groves, and other respectable farmers who have tried this plan, have no hesitation in saying, that the sheep are thus made as clean" (?) " as by the old tedious and disagreeable method, and with a great deal more expedition."

Folding Sheep.—P. 348. " *The Sheep-fold* is probably held in as high estimation in this county as in any part of the world. It is considered by most of the farmers not only as a manure of a very useful kind (which no person will dispute), but as an indispensable requisite in the cultivation of the arable land, and without which the produce would decline very considerably."

P. 349. " It is remarked by Mr. Bridge of Winford, as a common opinion, that the *gund, shab,* or *scab,* in sheep, is caused by folding too thickly, and consequently that many prefer folding thinly, and go twice, or even three times over the ground. This gentleman is of opinion, that 1000 sheep should manure an acre in a night, which may be called halffolding, and is worth about 20s. This is very near the opinion entertained by some farmers in Bedfordshire, that the manure of sheep is worth a farthing each per sheep per night."

P. 409. " There is probably no part of England where
the

the practice of sheep-folding is more admired, or more earnestly pursued, than in the county of Dorset. There are but few farmers in the upland districts who keep wethers, but such as do, fold them continually either on the arable or green land, from one end of the year to the other. The ewes are mostly folded from Lady-day till they are ready to drop their lambs, which is about Christmas, after which time they are thought to deserve a more tender and careful treatment."

Yet, after reciting the pratices and decided opinions of the first occupiers, and after the above general remarks, the Reporter has had the temerity to set up the following groundless notions, against the long-established practice of a County.

P. 410. " The custom of putting the sheep into a fold, where the land is tolerably level, and where the manure is wanted on the very spot that produces the grass on which the sheep are depastured, appears to be a very useless practice, calculated to destroy a great many hurdles, and sometimes much grass, to make additional labour for the shepherd, to harass the sheep, and cause distempers amongst them, to hinder their feeding when their appetite incites them to it, to prevent their food from being converted to nutriment, and to expose them in winter to all the severities of the season."

HAMPSHIRE.

HAMPSHIRE.

THERE are very few separable and entire DITRICTS, either natural or agricultural, in Hampshire. Its Chalk Hills form but a link of a long chain of similar calcarious heights. The lower lands, on the northern margin of the County, unite with the southern bank of the vale of Newbury, and the forest lands of Berkshire. And the Heathlands, on the eastern border, are the outskirts of those of Surrey and Sussex. *The New Forest,* and the *southern foot* of the *Chalk Hills* (northeastward of the estuary of Southhampton) are tolerably well defined districts.

The Isle of Wight is itself a *country;*—abounding with natural and agricultural districts ; bearing, as I have elsewhere intimated, a striking resemblance of the ISLE OF ISLES.—For a *prose* description of that lovely Islet, see my SOUTHERN COUNTIES.

The COUNTY of SOUTHAMPTON has had no less than four pens employed, by the Board of Agriculture, to give a view of its Natural, Political, and Rural Economics.

Messrs. DRIVER'S Report made its appearance, in July, 1794.—The Rev. —— WARNER's Isle of Wight, and the " Postscript" of the SECRETARY of the BOARD, would seem to have come out, *about* the same time, as the three, in the copy which lies before me, are paged in continuation, and stitched up together ; the whole making seventyeight octavo pages, on quarto paper, only.

The last, but not the least, either in size or quality, is the " reprinted," otherwise *published* Report, on octavo paper, by Mr. VANCOUVER,—the Reporter of *Cambridgeshire* and *Essex.*—See the EASTERN and the MIDLAND DEPARTMENTS.

" GENERAL

"GENERAL VIEW

OF THE

AGRICULTURE

OF THE

COUNTY OF HANTS,

WITH

OBSERVATIONS ON THE MEANS OF ITS IMPROVEMENT.

By ABRAHAM and WILLIAM DRIVER,

OF KENT ROAD, SURREY.

1794."

HOW far those gentlemen were qualified for the task they undertook, we can but surmise from what their slight sketch affords us. From their being superiorly intelligent, concerning forests and woodlands,—from their having been employed to survey the New Forest, in 1787,—and from their urging the public, as well as individuals, to propagate timber,—one is led to the idea that they were professional men, in the line of *planting* and *wood surveying*.

The following extract is a sufficient apology, for the deficiency in useful information, concerning the *agriculture* of Hampshire.

P. 7. " When we first undertook to report the state of the Agriculture of the County of Hants, we were not altogether aware of the time and attention it would require, to make a complete and particular statement of the whole county ; and we find from experience, the more we investigated the subject, the wider the field expanded to our view. Nevertheless, had our other avocations permitted it, we would with pleasure have entered into the minutiæ of every parish in the district, and have made a detailed, and not a general report, on the state of its Agriculture, and the means of its Improvement. But as that was impossible, we must request the Board to accept the following sketch, which is considerably shortened, in consequence of our having been robbed of our portmanteau, &c. containing a considerable number of papers, by some footpads, on our return from the survey. If there should,

should, however, be found any information in the following sheets, that may tend to the improvement of this county, or of the kingdom at large, it will afford us ample compensation for the trouble and expence we have sustained in the course of making this survey, of which we hope the Board will accept ; and if at any future period the Board should have occasion for a further investigation of the subject, we shall be extremely happy to render them all the assistance in our power."

The number of pages fortyfour.

NATURAL ECONOMY.

EXTENT.—P. 9. " It is sixty miles long, thirty miles broad, and 150 miles in circumference ; containing 1481 square miles, or 1,212,000 acres." (?)

SOILS.—Messrs. Driver appear to have paid especial attention to this material object of Report.—P. 10. " In the course of our survey, we found a great variety of soils, but by far the greatest proportion tending to a chalk, particularly upon the uplands ; nevertheless, there is a considerable proportion of rich land, and water meadows, which are very productive. On the north side towards Berkshire, the land is in general deep and a good staple, produces great crops of corn, and considerable quantities of oak and elm."

" Towards Basingstoke, the land upon the top of the hills is in general very deep, strong land, with chalk underneath, which produces large crops, particularly in dry seasons, as it never burns."

P. 11. " The land towards Whitchurch is generally chalky, with a thin staple, but produces good crops of corn and saintfoine."

P. 12. " Towards the New Forest the land changes from a chalk, to a loam and gravel."

" In the neighbourhood of Lymington, the land is very irregular, the hills in general poor, and the meadows rich."

P. 13. " About Redbridge" (at the head of the estuary of Southampton) " there are some valuable salt marshes."

" Towards Winchester and Alresford, the land is high and chalky, with a thin staple, and continues much the same till you approach Alton, where are some considerable beech woods, which run very high and straight."

P. 15. " There is a considerable quantity of salt marshes towards the sea," (near Portsmouth) " of a fertile quality, which let from 30s. to 50s. per acre.

" Toward

" Towards Petersfield the land is more open, with a considerable quantity of down, some of which is very good."

P. 14. " Towards Fareham and Warnford the land continues much the same, the hills are chalky and pretty much covered with beech woods."

" Towards Portsmouth, the county is more inclosed, and interspersed with timber and underwood; the land in general being stronger and deeper."

I do not mean to intimate that the above remarks, on soils, are particularly luminous. But they serve to show, that the Board's Surveyors were not altogether inattentive to the *cultivated lands* of the county.

POLITICAL ECONOMY.

APPROPRIATION.—P. 29. " *Waste Lands.*—We cannot take this subject into consideration, without expressing our astonishment, that century after century should be suffered to elapse, without some efficient measures being taken to cultivate the waste lands of this kingdom, particularly those belonging to the Crown, when it is a very clear case, that if they were properly managed, they would produce sufficient to pay a very considerable part of the interest of the national debt. In treating upon this subject, we do not mean to confine ourselves to this county, as the same argument will hold good in every part of the kingdom, and although there is a vast quantity in Hampshire, yet we apprehend more will be found in other counties, particularly in the adjoining county of Dorset."

After proposing the improvement of those *public* waste lands; by applying " the richest to agriculture, and the rest for planting;"—the Reporters proceed to speak of the *private* wastes of Hampshire.

P. 30. " What we have hitherto said upon this subject, relates to the waste lands belonging to Government. We shall now briefly state our opinion on that which is private property, of which there is an immense quantity throughout this kingdom. The same argument will nearly apply to this as to the other, excepting that it is, in general, poor land; in which case, the general observation is, that it produces nothing when inclosed. This argument may hold good when applied to agriculture, but cannot with respect to planting, as we can easily prove, that each acre, at the end of twenty-five years, will yield at least 100*l.* worth of timber and fire-wood, supposing the whole cut down at that period;

period; or if properly thinned, the remainder with continue to improve in the same proportion. We should therefore hope, the great advantages arising therefrom, would be
a sufficient inducement to gentlemen possessing that species
of property, to pursue it upon an extensive scale ; indeed,
we cannot conceive that any gentleman can sit down
easy, and say he has discharged his duty to his family,
when he is conscious he has neglected to pursue those
measures, which, in a few years, would increase his property so amazingly."

The next touch on *parochial* wastes ;—and, having recommended a " general inclosure bill," they enumerate
" the principal waste lands in the County of Hants, exclusive of the forests."

P. 31. " East Woodhay, near Newbury, contains about
1200 acres ; it is principally fed with young cattle, and some
few horses are bred there, but the horses are of little value;
a few good cows, however, are bred.

" This would make good arable land, and some part good
meadow ; if inclosed would be worth about 7s. 6d. per ann.
At present it is of very little value, as there is no timber.
The Bishop of Winchester is lord of the manor.

" King's Clear contains about 1000 acres, upon which
young cattle of a good sort are now bred. If this were inclosed it would make good convertible land either for the
plough or for feeding, but principally for feeding, and would
be worth about 15s. per acre.

" There is a considerable quantity of waste lands adjoining the above commons, which continue through the county
towards Berkshire.

" Froxfield Barnet Common, containing near 1000 acres,
at present produces very little, but if inclosed would be
worth 8s. or 10s. per acre. The parishioners have wished
to have it inclosed, but upon application to the lord of the
manor, who has the great tythes, he refuses to have an
allotment of land in lieu of these tythes, for which reason
the inclosure, at present, we understand, is dropt.

" At Botley, near Southampton, is a considerable tract of
land, about 7000, or 8000 acres, of which a great part is
very useful land for cultivation, and some parts very fit for
plantations of firs, timber, and underwood. It now produces
very little, but if inclosed would be worth about 10s. per
acre.

" Waltham Chase contains about 2000 acres, belonging to
the Bishop of Winchester, which, if properly attended to,
would produce a great quantity of fine timber ; and a considerable proportion would make fine pasture and meadow
land, which would be worth at least 20s. per acre. There

is

is also a considerable quantity of good corn land, which would be worth from 10s. to 12s. per acre.

"Bagshot Heath contains a very considerable tract of land, the greater part of which is in Surry: upon a rough calculation, between 2 and 3000 acres may be in this county. It is principally of a very light sandy soil, and produces very little. If plantations of firs were made, they would thrive well, and become profitable.

"The total quantity of waste lands in Hants, exclusive of the forests, but including 5,675 acres in the Isle of Wight, is *supposed* to be 104,845 acres."

Forests.—It is among forests, woodlands, and wastes, we find Messrs. Driver feelingly alive to their mission.

P. 34. "There are several considerable forests in this county, viz. the New Forest, Alice Holt, Woolmer, and Bere, which we shall describe separately, beginning first with the New Forest, which is by far the most extensive.

"The New Forest is situated on the south side of Hampshire; it was formerly bounded on the east by Southampton river, and on the south by the British Channel, being near thirty miles in length, and ninety in circumference; but since the disafforestations by Henry the Third and Edward the First, its boundaries are much reduced, and now only extends from Godshill, on the north-west, to the sea, on the south-east, about twenty miles; and from Hardley, on the east, to King-wood, on the west, about fifteen miles; containing within those limits about 92,365 acres, the whole of which does not now belong to the Crown: as several manors and freehold estates, to the amount of 24,797 acres, are private property; about 625 acres are copyhold, belonging to his Majesty's manor of Lyndhurst; 1004 acres are leasehold, held under the Crown; 902 acres are encroachments; 1193 acres are held by the master-keepers and groom-keepers, attached to their respective lodges; and the remaining 63,844 acres are the woods and waste lands of the forest.

"In all the freeholds subject to the regard of the forest, which are of the nature of purlieus, the Crown reserves certain rights.

"The copyholds within the manor of Lyndhurst entirely belong to the Crown, and are granted to tenants by copy of Court Roll, according to the custom of the manor. The timber on this manor is also the property of the Crown. The leasehold estates in this forest are entirely the property of the crown.

"There are a considerable number of encroachments, chiefly made by poor people, excepting those which the proprietors of neighbouring estates have added to their
own

own, all of which the Crown has a full power to lay open again.

" The New Forest is divided into nine bailiwicks, which are subdivided into fifteen walks, viz.

" BAILIWICKS.	WALKS.
Burley Bailiwick	Burley Walk, Holmsley Walk.
Fritham ditto	Bolderwood Walk, Eyeworth ditto.
Godshill ditto	Ashley ditto.
Lynwood ditto	Broomy ditto.
Battramsley ditto	Rhinefield ditto. Welverly ditto.
South ditto	Whitley Ridge ditto. Lady Cross ditto.
East ditto and the Nodes	Denny Walk, and the Nodes. Ashurst Walk.
Inn Bailiwick	Ironshill ditto.
North ditto	Castle Malwood ditto, Bramblehill ditto.

" The officers of the Forest are, a Lord Warden, Lieutenant, Riding Forester, Bowbearer, two Rangers, Wood-Ward, under Wood-Ward, four Verdurers, High Steward, Under Steward, twelve Regarders, Nine Foresters or Master Keepers, and thirteen Under Foresters or Groom Keepers. Besides the above officers, there is a Surveyor-General of the Woods and Forests, who appoints a Deputy, and a Purveyor of the Navy; but these are not properly officers appointed solely for the New Forest; the Surveyor General being superintendant over other forests; and the Purveyor of the Navy is paid by the Navy Board as an officer of Portsmouth Dock-yard.

" It does not appear to us necessary to mention here, the duties of each officer, but we are warranted in saying this much, that if each officer were to do his duty, without considering his private emolument, it would tend much to the increase and preservation of the timber in this forest; whereas on the contrary, it is certain, that the interests of all the inferior officers so clash with that of the forest, that it is in vain to expect either a preservation of the timber now growing in the forest, or an increase from new plantations, while the present system remains, as it clearly appeared to us from the survey we made of the New Forest in 1787, by order of the Commissioners of the land revenue, that the principal care of the timber, and inclosures for its preservation, depended chiefly upon the Under-Keepers, whose emoluments are mostly derived from deer, sale of browsewood, rabbits, and swine, all of which are inimical to the preservation

preservation and increase of timber; and the evil consequences of these emoluments, being allowed instead of an
adequate salary, are very conspicuous.

" In the first place, the forest is so so overstocked with deer,
that upwards of three hundred died in one walk in 1787.
With respect to the cutting of browse-wood, it admits of
many depredations, such as cutting away the holly and
thorn, the great preservation of the young oak, and too
often the oak itself is included in the fall.

" With respect to rabbits, they are encouraged in almost
every walk, but particularly in those of Welverly and
Rhinefield, where three inclosures, made for the preservation of timber, have been converted into warrens, to the
amount of 835 acres; and with respect to swine, some of
the keepers are considerable dealers in them, which are suffered to continue in the forest during the whole year. One
of the keepers only, had between seventy and eighty swine
at one time.

" All these circumstances concur in the destruction of
young timber, and unless some means are taken to prevent
these and other abuses, in a few years there will be no
timber worth mentioning left upon the forest. As it appears from actual surveys made of the timber at different
periods, how much the timber has decreased, and what
the forest was formerly capable of producing, which account we shall take the liberty of subjoining.

"Date of survey.		Number of trees.	Number of loads.	Total loads.
1608	Timber fit for the navy	123,927	197,405	315,477
	Dotard and decayed trees	number not mentioned.	118,072	
1707	Timber fit for the navy	12,476	19,873	19,873
	Dotard trees not stated			
1764	Timber fit for the navy	19,836	36,662	40,497
	Defective oaks	1,743	3,835	
1783	Timber fit for the navy	12,447	19,827	20,830
	Defective oaks	596	1,003	

" From other accounts, it appears that the Navy have
been supplied with about 885 loads of oak timber per
annum, on an average, from this forest, for the last twenty
years, which is the only produce to the public. The annual expenditure of the forest appears to be about 3400l.
per annum, and the annual clear profit, about 1,015l. on an
average; therefore it appears that all the timber in the
New Forest growing upon 63,844 acres of land, has produced a profit only of 1,015l. per annum, on an average,
for the last twenty years, without making any allowance for
the

the deficiency in the present stock, compared with the stock twenty years ago, or rent for the land.

" Having thus pointed out the improper management of this forest, it may be expected we should endeavour to form some plan for its improvement; we shall therefore take the liberty to suggest our general ideas upon that head."

Among those suggestions are the following hints to Government.—P. 39. " To give up certain privileges, and to destroy or park the whole of the deer, which are now extremely numerous, and injurious in a great degree to the adjoining lands."

P. 41. " With respect to the number of officers necessary to superintend the forest, after it is properly regulated, it may not be necessary to particularize here; but we may just mention that a very few, under a competent Board, would be fully sufficient for the whole management, and those should be paid a salary adequate to their employ, and on no account suffered to receive any emolument or fee whatever from the forest."

These are, in truth, valuable suggestions. But had it struck Messrs. D. that their plans would interfere with the SACRED RIGHTS of PATRONAGE and PLUNDER, they would scarcely have given themselves the trouble to propose them.

Some account is offered, concerning the other forests of Hampshire. But it is not of sufficient interest to require particular notice.

MANUFACTURES.—P. 15. " There are but few manufactories of any extent in this county, and those are chiefly of cloth, shalloons, and coarse woollens."

TITHES.—Having lamented the evils which attend the present method of tithing, the Reporters relate, apparently from their own knowledge, the following ludicrous transaction; which, in itself, is sufficient to show the impropriety, regarding the existing mode of remunerating the labours of those whose duties are to disseminate the principles of peace and harmony among mankind.

P 33. " We will mention one instance in a parish in this county, which happened last autumn, where tythes were taken in kind. The clergyman and the farmer were at variance, and the farmer, determined to be even with the clergyman, gave him notice that he was going to draw a field of turnips on a certain day. The clergyman accordingly sent his team and servant at the time appointed, when the farmer drew ten turnips, and desired the other to take one of them, saying he should not draw any more that day, but would let him know when he did."

SOCIETIES.—P. 11. " At Odiham a society has been established for the improvement of agriculture."

This

This, if I rightly recollect, was one of the very first of the establishments that are now common in most parts of the kingdom. Where men of experience take the lead, they are well calculated to promote the true principles of practice, and to give a right bias to agricultural conversation.

RURAL ECONOMY.

TENURES.—P. 21. " In this county a considerable quantity of land is held under the Bishop of Winchester, as well as under the Dean and Chapter, upon lease for twenty-one years, renewable every seven, which is a very great bar to improvements in agriculture, as the fines upon renewal are always increased, in proportion to what improvements have been made.

" A considerable quantity of land is also held upon three lives, and though it is now the custom in many places, for the lords to let the lives run out, yet it is much against their interest so to do, upon a fair calculation; as, when the lives all drop, the land is generally in very bad condition, and the buildings very much out of repair."

There is some truth, in the last remark; but by no means to the amount intended to be conveyed by it. All life-lease holders are liable to pay to the full amount of dilapidations; and I have rarely known an instance, out of many, of its not being settled to the satisfaction of the proprietor of the estate. The great and almost only difficulty, in allowing lifeleasehold tenements to revert to the " lord," lies with the *stoppage of income*. A man who has no other income than what arises from the *fines* of leasehold tenements, *cannot*, unless his estate is large, and his expenditure comparatively small, suffer his farms " to fall into hand." For, at the demise of the last life, instead of receiving, immediately, an ample portion of the fee-simple value of the land, he is bereft even of its rental value, for six or twelve months to come.

IRRIGATION.—P. 19. " This county is particularly famous for water-meadows, which are extremely productive, and in general very well attended to. The farmers seem aware of the great advantages arising from them, as in many instances they are at considerable expence in purchasing a supply of water, besides the first expence, which is from five to six pounds per acre, exclusive of the continual repair of the sluices, &c."

P. 11. " From Overton towards Stockbridge, and from thence

thence to Redbridge, there is a beautiful vale, well covered with water-meadows."

P. 12. " Towards Fordingbridge and Downton, there are some good water-meadows."

P. 14. " Near Warnford there are some good water-meadows on the banks of the river Itching."

REMOVALS.—P. 21. " They are principally Michaelmas farms, and the new tenant enters upon part of the land the first of January, and the first of May, preceding the end of the lease, in order to prepare for wheat and turnips; in a farm of 500 acres about thirty acres the first of January, and about seventy acres the first of May; a certain quantity of saintfoine is also to be left, and paid for by the new tenant."

WOODLANDS.—See *Appropriation*, aforegoing.

AGRICULTURE.

FARMS.—P. 17. " The size of the farms in this county vary much, the most predominant are from 200*l.* to 300*l.* per annum."

WORKPEOPLE.—P. 27. " The servants of farmers are generally fed with pork and pudding the greatest part of the year, except on Sundays, when a joint of meat is sometimes allowed."

IMPLEMENTS.—P. 18. " A nine-share plough is frequently used for the opening of land, in order to make furrows for wheat before sowing, with four horses double; this is also found very useful for backing in barley which was ploughed after wheat, in the autumn, and then only with this nine-share."

MANURE.—P. 12. " Here" (New Forest) " we find chalk a principal manure, which is brought ten or twelve miles; of which they generally allow ten or twelve load per acre."

P. 19. " There is on the sea coast, near Emsworth and Havant, a fine marle, that is found to improve the deep land very much."

HOPS.—P. 13. " The planting of hops has of late years increased in the following parishes, viz. Bentley, Froyl, Binstead, Hollybourn, Alton, Chawton, Farrington, Silbourn, Kingsley, Great and Little Worldham, Hartley, Maudit, and Shoulden, South Warnborough, Neatham, and Long Sutton; all of which are upon the borders of Surry, and the great repute of the Farnham hops has been the principal cause of the planting in these parishes. Upon the best information we have been able to procure, the whole

whole may be estimated at about 800 acres. Notwithstanding they are in the adjoining parishes to Farnham, yet they have never been able to procure so much at market by 40s. or 50s. per cwt. as those with the Farnham mark, though they are equally good; and the farther from Farnham, the greater the difference in value."

HORSES.—P. 26. "This county is not remarkable for the breed of good horses. The farmers in general breed their own horses for teams, but not for the saddle. A great number of small horses are bred upon the forests, where but little attention is paid to their shape or size, as they run promiscuously together; and from the barrenness of the soil, for want of cultivation, they are extremely small, having scarcely any thing to feed on but heath, from which they have very properly derived the appellation of *heath croppers.*"

DAIRY.—P. 27. "The breed of cows, in Hants, is in general very indifferent. The Welch breed has been introduced of late, and found to answer very well; but as there are few dairies in this county, very little attention is paid to the breed."

SWINE.—P. 27. "This county is particularly famous for hogs. The farmers encourage the largest sort, as most profitable for large families. The hogs in the neighbourhood of the forests, feed principally upon acorns and beech mast."

SHEEP.—*Breed.*—P. 23. "The original Hampshire sheep is horned, and for the most part with a white face, though some few have speckled faces; they were formerly long-legged and narrow, but are now much improved, and are short legged and well carcassed; they are an excellent kind for fatting; their wool is also much improved."

The *Number* in Hants.—P. 23. "Hampshire is considered as a great breeding county, and the stocks in most parishes are very large, although they are supposed to be reduced one-third, on account of the downs having been broken up, and the inclosures which have lately taken place. The following is a particular account of the stock in the following parishes in this county, which may afford some information to the Board upon that interesting subject."

P. 25. "From the best accounts we have been able to get, we conceive the number in the whole county to be about 350,000."

Market for Sheep.—P. 11. "A very considerable fair is held at Weyhill once a year, which is particularly famous for sheep, and it is supposed that upwards of 140,000 are sold there in one day."

" GENERAL VIEW

OF THE

AGRICULTURE

OF THE

ISLE OF WIGHT,

(Forming a Part of Hampshire.)

WITH

OBSERVATIONS ON THE MEANS OF ITS IMPROVEMENT.

BY THE REV. MR. WARNER.

1794."

REGARDING the qualifications of the writer of this Report, I say nothing. It is a mere sketch,—a slight topographical account of the islet. The twenty pages are suitably written.

EXTENT.—P. 47. " Its superficial contents are reckoned at 100,000 acres."

SURFACE.—P. 48. " The face of the country is various, beautiful, and picturesque; consisting of gently swelling hills, diversified with intermediate vallies, verdant well watered meads and rich corn fields. A chain of hills stretches from east to west through the heart of the island."

CLIMATURE.—P. 47. " The air, particularly in the higher southern parts, is extremely wholesome; frequent instances of longevity occurring, and a general appearance of health and vigour prevailing among the lower ranks of people."

SOIL and FOSSILS.—P. 47. " The soil is extremely different in different parts of the island; and sometimes exhibits a remarkable variety, even in the same parish—Thus for instance, in Brading, the most eastern parish, the following varieties occur: the south part consists of a free, kind-working earth, mixt with a small proportion of sand; the west, of a light loam, mixed with chalk; and the north and east parts of a stiff clay, scarcely yielding to the operations of the husbandman. In many parts of the island, the soil is gravelly; in others flinty; but its general character is a strong and loamy earth, well calculated for agricultural purposes.

purposes. It abounds with marle, both shell and stone ; chalk, fuller's and brick earth ; tobacco pipe clay ; stone of different qualities; and various kinds of sands; of the last, a fine white sort is found in the parish of Fresh- water, on a manor belonging to John Urry, Esq. of Yar- mouth, esteemed far superior to any other in the kingdom, and used in great quantities for the glass and porcelaine manufactories."

" Its fertility is almost proverbial, having long since been said to produce more in one year, than could be consumed by its inhabitants in eight ; an improved husbandry in- troduced of late years has increased this fertility, and from what I have been able to collect, we may now estimate its annual production to be at least ten times as much as its consumption."—But see *Workpeople*, ensuing.

APPROPRIATION.—P. 57. " There is but little waste land in the island ; and this chiefly exhibits a sandy soil, which would not probably pay the expences of its cultivation.

" Perhaps, indeed, Parkhurst or Carisbrook Forest, lying in the centre of the island, may at present be properly deno- minated waste land, as it remains in an inactive useless state, without affording any advantages to the Crown, whose property it is ; and very trifling ones to the inhabitants who reside in its neighbourhood. This tract of land, which contains 3000 acres, is situated to the north of Newport and Carisbrook ; and though called a forest, has long been without a tree of any value ; there is, however, a lodge still kept up, and a keeper appointed, whose office it is to pre- serve the deer and the wood, of which scarce a vestige re- mains. Notwithstanding the inattention paid hitherto by Government to Parkhurst Forest, the soil is, in many places, extremely good ; and capable of being applied to the most valuable purposes."

POOR RATES.—P. 63. " A few years back, great abuses having been experienced in the management of the poor, in the different parishes of the island, the gentlemen deter- mined to adopt some mode of remedying the evil ; and ac- cordingly, in 1770, a general meeting of the respectable in- habitants was held, in which it was proposed that an Act of Parliament should be procured, to consolidate the poor rates of the several parishes, and to erect a House of Industry for the general reception of the paupers.

" The proposal being agreed to, a Bill was accordingly obtained, and a large building erected on part of the Forest of Packhurst, eighty acres of which were granted by Par- liament for this purpose."

WOODLANDS.—P. 55. " Timber was formerly extremely plenty in the island, but the inhabitants have had so good a

market

market for it at Portsmouth, and the other dock-yards in and near this district, that little now remains; of this little, the oak and elm appear to be most flourishing."

FARMS.—P. 52. " The farms in the Isle of Wight are of a moderate size; from 100*l.* to 400*l.* per annum, with a few at 500*l.*"

WORKPEOPLE.—P. 64. " It is a source of great pleasure to the feeling and reflecting mind, to observe a general appearance of content and decency among the labouring poor of the island, a discription of people, who, in other parts, are too often overwhelmed with want and wretchedness."

P. 65. " The rates of wages, as well as hours of work, vary in different parts of the island. In Brading parish, labourers have two guineas for the harvest months, and their board; eighteen pence per day for grass mowing, and their beer; and one shilling per day during the rest of the year, when employed. There hours of work are, in winter, from seven to four; and in summer, from six to five. In the southern and western parts, they get fourteen pence per day, but give an additional hour of labour, viz. from five to five in summer, and from seven to five in winter.

" The crops, however, of the island are so large, (most of the land being in tillage) that the resident labourers are by no means sufficient for the cutting down and harvesting of them. This dearth of hands is supplied from the western counties, and between six and seven hundred labourers annually pass into the island, a little before harvest, and hire themselves to the different farmers for the month. The usual wages for this period are, two guineas if it be peace, and about forty-five or fifty shillings if it be war. They have their board also. For the time they are employed before and after the month, they have two shillings per day, food and liquor.

" During the last harvest, there were near seven hundred Dorsetshire and Somersetshire men employed; and as a warm press was at that time on foot, each of them was allowed a protection from government, during his passage from his own habitation to the island and back again.

" The character of the labouring poor in the isle of Wight, is that of an honest, industrious, and sober people."—Hence, much of the work of husbandry is performed by strangers; who consume the produce of other districts, during eleven months of the year.

WORKING ANIMALS.—P. 54. " The horses are of different breeds, but in general large, and *I think* black. As there is some emulation among the farmers with regard to the beauty and strength of their teams, the draught horses are fine animals, and kept in good order."

DAIRY.

DAIRY.—P. 54. " The cows are mostly of the Alderney breed, though mixed with English sorts; which the farmers think renders the butter better than it would otherwise be."

P. 55. " The dairies produce, in considerable quantities, two sorts of skim milk cheese; the Dorsetshire, and what is emphatically called Isle of Wight Rock; they are extremely hard, can scarcely be cut by a hatchet or saw, are to be masticated only by the firmest teeth, and digested but by the strongest stomachs."

SWINE.—P. 55. " The hogs are of a breed, I believe, peculiar to the island, at least I do not recollect seeing any of the same in other places; they are large and tall, marked with black spots, and have very deep sides. The bacon is excellent."

SHEEP.—P. 53. " The numbers of sheep annually shorn are computed to amount to 40,000. Last year upwards of 5,000 lambs were sold to the London butchers alone; and in August, when I happened to be at Newport, one of these dealers bought 1,500 at a single purchase. The breed, in general use, is the Dorsetshire."

" POSTSCRIPT

" POSTSCRIPT

TO THE

SURVEY OF HAMPSHIRE.

IN A LETTER TO SIR JOHN SINCLAIR, BART. M. P. PRESIDENT OF THE BOARD OF AGRICULTURE,

FROM THE

SECRETARY TO THE BOARD.

1794."

THE SECRETARY's ostensible motive, for writing twelve pages on the rural affairs of Hampshire, was a dutiful return for a favor granted by the Board—" to apply a portion of the absence from town with which the Board has indulged me, in procuring such information as I could best rely on, in some county *not yet reported.*"—So that, in this instance, the *Postscript* was written before the *letter!*—But no matter as to the *misnomer.* When a man *frames* a motive for his actions, he is apt to commit blunders.

It so happened that, at the time this *Postscript* was written, Mr. DAVIS's WILTSHIRE had recently been distributed, among the members of the Board. In Mr. D.'s Report, it was found, that he had entered a *masterly protest against breaking up the sheep downs of the Chalk Hills.* And, if one may venture to judge, from the otherwise unaccountable circumstances attending *the Postscript,* it was deemed prudent to dispatch the Secretary down into Hampshire, to endeavour to collect materials, the better to enable him to bring out a *counter protest.*

P. 67. (in continuation.) " And having an opportunity, through the attentions of W. P. Powlett, Esq. M. P. an Honorary Member of the Board, to examine a very interesting district in Hampshire; I have viewed with care, and collected by means of that gentleman's friendly and patriotic exertions, some practices, that will, I trust, be thought interesting to the prosperity of that county.

" For some miles, in various directions, around Sombourne, in the vicinity of Stockbridge, the district, in past times, has been chiefly a *down country;* but, now mostly broken up and converted to tillage. This change has been effected in a manner, and with effects, that will throw
some

some light on two very material inquiries: 1st. Paring and
Burning; and 2d. Courses of Crops; and the result will
shew, in what respects, breaking up of sheep downs, may
or may not be advisable."

With astonishment, let it be asked, what has the vicinity
or district of Stockport to do, in the case at issue! The district of Stockport,—a dilation of the valley of the Teste,—
is a deeply soiled fertile plot of country; wearing no resemblance of the thin-skinned high land sheep walks that are
restricted by Mr. Davis. The marshlands, and the meager
thin soiled sandy lands, of Norfolk, are scarcely less alike.

In ancient time, it is more than probable, all the valley
lands and lower grounds, situated between the Chalk Hills
of the southern counties, lay in a state of pasturage; tho
they are, now, and many of them have evidently long been,
subjected to the purposes of aration : some of them having
had extraordinary labor bestowed upon them, apparently
to that intent. Yet it does not appear that, in any age
before the present, the HIGH DOWNS have been violated by
tillage.

In all human affairs, there is a line which separates right
and wrong. Heretofore, the true lines of division, between
the arable, and the pasturable, lands of the wide range of
the calcareous heights, under notice, appear to have been
pretty accurately drawn, by men of practice and long experience in their right management. And it is to be lamented (seeing as will be shown in the course of this volume,
that all men of superior knowledge in their management
are of one opinion) that, during the late thoughtless rage
for " improvements"—true or false—among men, without
experience,—and who of course knew not where the true
lines lay,—they have, in many instances, been obliterated
with the plow.

Let men who have *permanent interests*, in the lands on
which the right lines are still legible, look to them, before
it be too late.

I say nothing, here, of " Paring-and-Burning,"—the other
object of the Secretary's mission,—as it will come under
notice, in the course of the volume.

                                        " GENERAL

"GENERAL VIEW

OF THE

AGRICULTURE

OF

HAMPSHIRE,

INCLUDING THE

ISLE OF WIGHT.

DRAWN UP FOR THE CONSIDERATION OF

The Board of Agriculture and Internal Improvement.

By CHARLES VANCOUVER.

1813."*

THIS is the third work of Mr. VANCOUVER which I have had to examine; and the fifth time I have found it requisite to bring his literary labors before my readers,—in pursuing my present undertaking.—See *South Essex*, p. 151, aforegoing;—where Mr. V.'s qualifications, as a Reporter of rural affairs, are noticed, and his mode of survey, for his earlier Reports, explained.

In the present instance, his general plan of Survey and Report has been differently conducted. In his former Surveys, the several parishes of the County to be reported were gone over; and examined with attention. An appropriate, but elaborate, mode of proceeding.

In this volume, the method of collecting the materials of which it is formed, does not so clearly appear. No parochial journals are here found, nor do any tables of facts, concerning " agriculture and internal improvements" present themselves. But, in their stead, many ill drawn, or ill executed, *plates* (most of them of trifling import) are placed; as it were to encrease the bulk and expence of the volume; and, *thereby*, to promote its sale!—such being the taste and fashion of the times!!

What

* The Reporter's introduction is dated, March 1808; the engravings, with which the volume abounds, the 1st January, 1810; the title-page, 1813. Thus the manuscript of the Report of Hampshire, *would seem* to have lain *five years* in the literary cabinet of the Board. But see the *Secretary's Hertfordshire*, aforegoing.

What render the book still more bulky and expensive, are ten large folding tables, regarding the *political character* of the *principal towns*, &c.

Mr. Vancouver, however, has not been an idle spectator, in Hampshire. There are many subjects on which he treats with commendable intelligence. What serve to interrupt, and tend to annoy, the agricultural reader, are the irrelevant matters which the volume contains ;—the unnecessary attention that is bestowed on points of practice which, *now*, are well understood ;—and an unfortunate display of theoretic arguments, that are urged on unsound bases.

The calculations of profit, on various productions of husbandry, and on different plans of management, are, from the insuperable difficulties attending them, nugatory ; and can only disgust experienced cultivators, and lead the inexperienced astray.

The arrangement of the materials is very defective ; and the editorship unpardonable ; in some instances, perfectly ridiculous ; as will appear in the ensuing abstract. Some of the subjects are reported, conjointly, by carrying them on, in concert, through several of the Reporter's districts (eight in number) ; while others are spoken of distinctly, and some of them, again and again, under different heads. This renders the task of reference and re-examination perplexing ;—there being no index to direct the enquirer to the object of search.

The number of pages—five hundred and twenty.

A map of the County, colored, or purported to be colored, according to its surface soils.

The subjoined is an extract from the Reporter's " Introduction," which is dated—" Brokenhurst, New Forest, Hants, March, 1808."

" The Survey of the County of Devon being completed, and the Report on the Agriculture, Manufactures, and Commerce of that District delivere over to the Honourable Board of Agriculture ; at the desire of the President, Sir John Sinclair, the Surveyor in May last entered upon a similar examination of the County of Hants, in which pursuit he has been closely engaged to the present time."

SUBJECT THE FIRST.

NATURAL ECONOMY.

EXTENT,—*of the Isle of Wight.*—P. 3. " Its superficial contents are calculated by the Author from Faden's large map of the county, at 94,000 acres."

Of

Of the rest of the County.—P. 3. " The area of the other part of the county, deduced from the same authority, is found to contain 1,512$\frac{4}{6}\frac{6}{4}\frac{4}{0}$ square miles, or 968,149$\frac{3}{10}$ statute acres."

CLIMATURE.—This is one of the items of information that are spoken of, *by districts ;* and is seven times brought forward, within the limits of a few pages. I will transcribe what is said of it under the three principal divisions of the county.

Chalk Hills.—P. 8. " The air, through the whole of this district, is dry, thin, and healthy. The westerly gales are by far the most common and violent; but those from the opposite quarter are found most injurious to fruit, and repressive to vegetation, in the spring and early part of summer."

New Forest.—P. 9. " A great mildness of climate distinguishes the whole of this district. The westerly winds are found to be by far the most common and violent. Along the borders of the Southampton water, agues and fevers still prevail, although by no means so general as they were experienced about twenty years ago."

Isle of Wight.—P. 10. " If we except those places where agues and fevers prevail, and the objections already urged against the climate of the woodlands, these districts exhibit all the variety of climate any where to be experienced in other parts of the county : there being a difference of at least a fortnight in the seasons of the Seventh District, between the red sandy loams on the south side of the Downs, and the light rubbly character of soil which is found high upon the Downs on their north side. The air, through the whole of this island, is favourable to the human constitution : much advantage is annually derived from it to its unhealthy visitors, particularly those afflicted with pulmonary complaints, upon retiring for a short time to its southern borders.

" The Surveyor has much to regret, that, during his whole progress through the county, he was not so fortunate as to meet with, or hear of, a single individual who kept any register of the weather, of the quantity of rain that falls, or any other meteorological tables "

WATERS.—*Rivers and Brooks.*—P. 7. " The principal rivers which water this couty are the following : The Avon rises in Wiltshire, and enters this county near Fordingbridge, whence it passes through Ringwood, after which it unites with the river Stour in the harbour of Christchurch. The Teste rises in the north part of the county, and running southwards, forms several islands at Stockbridge ; thence it passes through Rumsey, and enters the Southampton

ampton inlet at Redbridge. The Itchen, also called the Abre, has its source at Chilton Candover, near Alresford, whence it pursues a southwardly course through the city of Winchester, thence again southwardly, to its junction with the Southampton water."

Wells and Drinking Pools.—P. 47. " The want of a regular supply of water during the continuance of dry weather, in the chalk districts, is an inconvenience generally experienced, although the little which may be occasionally procured is of the best and most reviving quality. To remedy this evil, ponds are constructed at great labour and expense, for the purpose of retaining the downfall waters, as a supply for both sheep and cattle. These are bedded with the most retentive clay or loam that can be conveniently procured, and paved within and above their upper sides with large smooth flints, as well to prevent poaching in wet weather, as to secure it as much as possible from the action of the frost, which once penetrating the made ground, it becomes porous, and incapable of retaining water until it is again renewed.

" In such situations as are out of the reach of a constant supply of water from brooks, rivulets, or streams, tanks and reservoirs are also constructed to receive the rain water from the dwelling-house and buildings; and here wells are sunk from one to three and four hundred feet in depth, through the solid chalk rock, and which in a dry season affords a supply for domestic use, as well as for the sheep and all the farming stock of the occupation. Whole villages are thus frequently supplied with water, drawn up in large buckets by a tread wheel; but even this supply in the month of October will sometimes fail, when all the inconvenience and distress of such a situation may very easily be imagined. In some instances it has been known, that a continuation of dry weather during the autumnal months, and even after the great demand of harvest, will have left *more strong beer than water within the boundaries of a parish :* in such situations, the labour and expense reqnired to supply the family and a part of the stock with water-carts, is absolutely incalculable; every endeavour, however, is constantly employed to mitigate the evil attendant on the failure of so important a necessary of life; but which all the high downy parts of the chalk district are to a greater or less extent subjected, that are not visited by water-courses, or lie within the reach of permanently living streams."

SOILS.—This, too, is a conjoint subject of districts. It is, first, passed through seven, with climate; and is, then, travelled over the whole eight, alone :—thus becoming the occupant of more than two sheets of paper.

It

It is, however, too valuable a part of the volume, to be passed by, without due consideration.—I will first copy the whole of the brief sketches which accompany " Climate," and then extract, from the detailed account, in the section, " Soil," some interesting particulars, relating to the two principal divisions of the County.

" District 1. " (namely, the northern margin of the County, bordering on and uniting with, the lands of Berkshire and Surrey.)—P. 8. " Woodlands and the wastes of Bagshot, clay, sand, gravel, and peat ; the last found upon the wastes and in some of the enclosed low grounds."

" District 2."—(the Chalk Hills.) P. 8. " Strong flinty loams and hazel-coloured mould on chalk, occasionally veined with gravel : more or less peat in most of the vallies."

" District 3."—(the eastern margin of the Chalk Hills, uniting with the light barren lands of Surrey and Sussex.)— P. 9. " Malm, sand, and gravelly loam, clay and peat : the latter found chiefly upon the wastes ; also in Woolmer and in Alice Holt forests."

" District 4."—(the New Forests and its environs.) P. 9. " Light sand and gravelly loams, intermixed with clay and brick-earth on substrata of argillaceous and calcareous marl. Much peat and turf moor prevailing on the heath and low grounds, particularly in the forest of Bere, Waltham Chase, and New Forest."

" District 5."—(the Portsmouth quarter of the County.) —P. 9. " Chalk of Portsdown, and the islands of Portsea and Haling, a strong flinty, and a tender hazel-coloured loam, prevailing in the islands and low grounds."

" District 6."—(certain marginal lands of the Isle of Wight, lying principally on its northern shores, but partly along its southern coast.)—P. 10. " North and south borders of the Isle of Wight, rough strong clay, argillaceous and calcareous marl."

" Districts 7 and 8."—(the interior or main area of the Isle of Wight, which comprizes soils of almost every description.)—P. 10. " Tender, red sand, and gravelly loam, with argillaceous and calcareous marl, chalk, and its usual accompaniments, red loam and flints."—We now enter upon the Soils of the *Chalk Hills* of Hampshire.—P. 15. " Notwithstanding the uniformity prevailing in the internal composition or structure of this district, which chiefly consists of a firm unbroken bed of rock chalk, its soil or surface covering is so much varied and blended with each other, as to require much attention to the describing of it in such a manner as to make all its varieties clearly and distinctly understood.

" The

" The first of these soils, covering some of the highest
parts of the district, is provincially called hazel mould, a
light, dry, friable, sandy soil, of a moderate staple, and
resting upon a chalk rubble (that is, partially dissolved
chalk mixed with small broken flints), and which in its
native state, affords a short but very good sheep pasture ;
and which, from its superior elevation, is not early affected
by a spell of warm dry weather ; but when reduced to a
state of tillage, becomes of very little value indeed. This
land, after being opened to aration is very liable to wash :
upon many of the brows and side hills of the principal
eminences, the light materials have been carried off by the
heavy rains, when the remaining surface exhibits a collection of what its subsoil was originally composed of, and
which altogether appears unfit for any other purpose than
of conversion to a rabbit-warren.

" The second description of down soil which we shall
here have occasion to notice, consists of a black vegetable
mould, generally of a moderate depth, and lying directly
on a bed of flints and rubble, and by which it seems interrupted at some distance from the chalk rock below. This
soil is evidently produced from an ancient vegetation produced at such times as this species of down was in a forest
state : a conjecture much strengthened by the number of
thorn bushes, ewe, furze, and juniper which are still found
scattered upon it. This sort of down, when properly (that
is, hard) stocked with sheep, produces a remarkably sweet
herbage, and is still less liable to be affected with a continuance of drought than the soil above described. When
appropriated as cow common, or not stocked sufficiently
close with sheep, it is apt to produce a dwarf species of
ling and furze, but which may always be kept down and in
an improving state, by stocking with that sort of sheep
which are best calculated to browse in such situations and
upon such an herbage.

" The third class of down land we find occupying a large
portion of this district. It consists of a thin grey loam,
lying almost immediately on a firm bed of chalk. Here the
sheep pasture is generally short, but of a most excellent
quality : it is, however, more suddenly affected in a dry
season than the preceding classes, but, in like manner, requires to be kept pared close down, to preserve the natural
sweetness of its herbage.

" A fourth class of land at present occurring upon the
Down, and also forming a large portion of the tillage land
in the country, consists of a deep, strong, red, flinty loam,
lying at various depths, of from one to eight or ten feet,
upon, and partially dipping into the rock chalk below.
                                                        This

This character is usually found to occur on the flat tops of all the lesser eminences in the District, and derives very great and important benefits from chalking, the preceding classes not being in the slightest degree benefited by that material. The depth of this red loamy stratum, above the chalk, sometimes subjects it in the winter season to an excess of moisture; but which is generally much relieved by a due attention being paid to gripping and water-furrowing. This circumstance, however, appears in many places to have given rise to a coarse, tough, and wiry herbage. It abounds with large ragged flints, and though naturally of an arid quality, is capable after chalking of producing excellent wheat, and a prime sample of barley.

"A fifth description of land is found to occupy the brows and side hills of this last class, but which has been much lessened of its loamy proportion by the winter rains and melting snows: here is generally but a thin staple of soil, and that chiefly composed of dissolved chalk,—tough and clingy when wet, harsh and chisselly, but when worked at a proper crisis, is found loose and friable; and not unfrequently applied to the culture of turnips, and a convertible system, as well as for the culture of sainfoin, for which it seems most particularly adapted.

"Below the hang of the hills, a deep, strong, grey loam very frequently occurs, intercepted at some distance from the chalk rock by chalk rubble, but not containing so many of the coarse ragged flints, as may be noticed in the red tough loams of class No. 4. This land when wet, rises in a tough livery slice, and when dry, becomes extremely hard and chisselly. The tillage of this class, as well as that of No. 4, is extremely arduous, expensive, and heavy; but when the proper season is obtained for conducting its operations, the labour and difficulty of its husbandry is much lessened. The crops of wheat produced on this latter soil are very considerable, though in general it is not held in very high esteem for the culture of barley.

"Another description of strong land is found in divers parts of this district, assuming a much darker colour than either the grey chisselly or red flinty loams. It is generally found of a good staple, and lying on a similar subsoil at a considerable distance from the chalk below. This land was observed to wear the marks of being too frequently overcharged with moisture; but in favourable seasons it yields excellent beans, as a precursor to, or after wheat, in the place of a fallow.

"The surface of most of the hollows, and lower sides of the hollows, with which the whole of this district is intersected (and exclusive of the vallies which afford the
rivers

rivers and other living streams), is formed of an assemblage of small flat flints, combined with an extremely tough, but proportionably small quantity of loam; and which continues at various and indefinite depths to the chalk below. This is provincially termed shrave, of which there are two sorts, the one just mentioned, which gives the idea of a bank of shingle upon the sea-shore; the other, a red coarse pebbly gravel, mixed with a small portion of tough red loam, or more commonly with a dry, harsh sand, or small gravel, affording a warm subsoil, producing an early vegetation, and is generally applied to the culture of wheat, turnips, barley, and the artificial grasses.

" It must follow, from what has been already stated, that the higher parts of this district have much the appearance of an elevated plain, broken into many irregular parts, and intersected by several deep hollows, in which the brooks and rivulets, rising chiefly within the district, descend on a southern course towards the sea. Along these vallies considerable tracts of meadow and pasture ground are found. On the margin of these water-courses, or rather the vallies through which they pass, for obvious reasons, are seated the greater part of the inhabitants.

" The soil of these low grounds partake very much of a black vegetable mould or moor, on a strong calcareous loam, sometimes superinduced with an adventitious sand, or stratum of fine gravel, or apparently broken into chasms, occupied with large bodies of peat, and which is occasionally dug for fuel, or burnt in the manner practised in Berkshire for manuring ashes."

Soils of the *New Forest*, and its environs ; or the *Southern Vale Lands* of Hampshire.—P. 22. " The soil of the cultivated lands bordering upon the forest of Bere, and Waltham Chase, including the crown demesnes, and other enclosed parts of those forests, consist partly of a thin vegetable mould upon strata of deep sand, coarse gravel, and a moist grey loam upon a woodland clay. A gravelly loam of a more uniform texture, assuming a light brown or rather hazel colour, seems partially to occur in this variety, and particularly to distinguish the neighbourhood of Southwick, Wickham, Bishop's Waltham, and Botley. The cultivated parts of the parishes of Titchfield, Crofton, Rowner, and Alverstoke, consist of a thin light friable mould upon a gravel, a rich hazel-coloured loam upon a brick-earth, and a moist grey loam upon a strong, blue, white, and yellow clay. The same variety extends through all the cultivated lands from Gosport to the Itchen river.

" The

" The soil of the heaths and commons which occur in this part of the county, and which are generally found to compose the higher lands between Gosport and Titchfield, between Titchfield, Bursledon, and Botley, and between the two latter places and the Itchen river, is not materially different from the same variety of soil and substrata which form the character of the new enclosures at Fareham, and which are found composed of a thin black gravelly mould, and a moist grey loam, on substrata of sand and gravel, strong white and yellowish clay, potters' clay, and brick-earth. Intervening between these latter and the top-mould, is often found a thin subsoil of gravel, but which may be rendered useful, if due advantage is taken of it, for conducting the sub-waters into drains properly constructed to receive it.

" The late enclosures of South Stoneham, consist chiefly of a thin, black, gravelly mould, upon a bed of harsh gravel, a peaty mould upon a blue and yellow clay ; and, upon the whole, differing but little from the varieties above noticed in the parish of Fareham.

" The frequent intersections of clay and gravel occasion many wet and boggy places, round which, peat is dug, or rather turf is pared, to a depth of four or six inches, by the inhabitants for fuel.

" A country veined with clay, sand, and gravel, continues through the parishes of North Stoneham, Townhill, Swathing, Bishopstoke, and Otterbourne ; ascending northwardly from the latter village, the miscellaneous soil and substrata suddenly terminates in the great body of chalk forming the character of District No. II.

" The cultivated lands north of Southampton, Millbrook, and Redbridge, are much contracted by the extensive commons of Nutshaling and Southampton, but their soil generally consists of a mild gravelly loam and a tender loamy clay. This valuable character pervades to a considerable extent, the commons of these places; but as we approach Chilworth and Badsley, it is found to abate somewhat of its natural superiority.

" Considerable enclosures have lately taken place in these latter parishes, from which, by the aid of draining and the application of chalk, great advantages may be expected to be derived in future. The same variety of soil and substrata prevails through the southern parts of Timsbury; but northwardly it enters the chalk district. A substance called malm, of which there are two sorts, black and white, is found on the borders of Timsbury and Rumsey, and much used as an alterative manure on the sour clays and gravelly heaths composing the enclosures

closures recently made in those parishes: it is applied in
quantities of about eight waggon-loads of 66 bushels each
per acre.

" The country south of the Buckholt and Houghton
hills, including the parishes of East and West Tytherly,
consist of a strong flinty loam upon a chalk, and which
is found to extend southwardly as far as the parish of East
Dean, and the northern parts of the parish of Lockerly.
The southern parts of which, East Dean, Shirfield English,
and East Willow, consist of a thin gravelly loam on a
subsoil of close retentive clay; below which, very often
occurs deep beds of sand and gravel. This land is very
subject to springs, which in their present neglected state,
prove very injurious to the country. As the land rises
eastwardly from the river Teste, a more uniform substratum,
and a stronger staple of land, occurs, and in which there
was observed a very thriving growth of oak timber.

" In the lower part of the country the oak tree clay
disappears, and elm generally, with some ash, are found
to flourish on a more genial surface and open subsoil.
The low grounds bordering upon the river Teste, possess
a general character of loose moor or vegetable mould,
beneath which is a calcareous substance also called malm
(i. e. marl or chalky clay), and much valued as a manure,
either upon the light or stronger loams which occur in
the parish of Rumsey Extra; the quantity applied agrees
with that before-mentioned.

" Descending southwardly from the heaths towards
Paulton's-park, we find that noble demesne to possess a
soil and substrata not only highly favourable to the growth
of oak, but to forest trees in general. The park and surrounding country preserves a smooth and uniform appearance, till broken south-eastwardly by Hill Common and
Tachbury Mount. A considerable extent of flat low ground
then occurs in the same direction, including Netley Marsh;
thence towards Eling, and for some distance westwardly
into the New Forest. The soil of this plain is generally
a moist grey loam of a thin staple, on a woodland clay and
brick-earth. That of the adjacent enclosures, of a freer
and more open quality.

" The country along the confines of the New Forest,
and the western side of the Southampton water, is much
broken, exhibiting along the river hills a considerable
variety of top and under soil, and consequently affording
several wet and spongy places, many of which have been
much relieved, and some completely cured, by judicious
draining. On the demesne of Cadland, these improvements, under the direction of Mr. Elkington, have been
carried to a considerable extent, which has not only
contributed

contributed to adorn this otherwise interesting country, but at the same time to render its climate more salubrious to the inhabitants.

" Leap Pond is an extensive, though highly improvable morass; and as the property in the waste appears to be vested in two gentlemen only, and each possessing highly interesting demesnes in its neighbourhood, it was not without some surprise that it was observed to have lain so long in its present condition.

" The soil in the manor of Beauley may be taken generally as a specimen of that which occurs in the country round Lymington, and thence westwardly along the sea-coast for three or four miles. This consists of two leading characters: the one a mild gravelly loam, approaching a hazel colour, lying on an open subsoil sometimes terminating in sand or gravel, but more frequently intercepted at various depths from a deep bed of red, blue, and white marl below; the other a thin light black gravelly mould, generally of a moderate depth, and lying on a close stratum of clay and brick-earth of various colours, and under which at a still greater depth, is occasionally found the same field of marl first noticed."

Mr. Vancouver's account of *the Isle of Wight*, in regard to its soils, is, I will venture to say, superior to that which would have been given of them, by any other of the Board's Surveyors; yet, owing to the variety and intermixture of lands which that islet comprizes, and which would require a small volume, to describe them with valuable effect, I do not feel myself warranted to transcribe, into this register, his detailed account of them.

I must not, however, deprive myself of the pleasure of saying, here, that Mr. Vancouver has my best thanks, and ought to have the thanks of every well wisher to the accumulation of facts in the rural science ; for his luminous report of the soils of the most interesting parts of Hampshire. He has a happy turn of mind toward the observance, as well as the verbal delineation, of the lands of a country.

FOSSILS.—*Limestones.*—P. 41. " The only difference that appeared to exist in the great body of *rock chalk*," (?) " is that of the white and the grey *stone:* the first when burnt into lime, falls into clear white powder ; the second into a cream-coloured powder, and is particularly applicable for a cement in water-works. The *grey chalk*" (?)* " is raised in large quantities near Petersfield, and is

* This is doubtlessly " the Claystone" or " Blue Lias," of various districts.—See *Homesteads,* ensuing.

is transported from the Burriton hills, a distance of fifteen miles, to Portsmouth, and where it is burnt into lime for the use of the Royal Dock-yard."

Potter's Clay.—P. 42. "A great variety of potters' clay occurs in different parts of the county. At Cowes it is worked to a considerable extent; and under Pool-heath it is found of various depths of from ten to twenty feet."

Glass Sand.—P. 42. "A vein of white sand is found in Alum Bay, at the north-west end of the island, (Isle of Wight) and is much in demand for the glass-works of Bristol, Liverpool, along the west coast of England, Scotland, and throughout Ireland."

MINERALS.—P. 40. "The mineral substances found within this county are but few. A quantity of what is called copperas stone, was formerly collected on the southern shores of the Isle of Wight, and sent to the copper works to be smalted. Alum has also been made in some of the western coves of the island, but neither the gathering of the copper-stone, or carrying on the alum-works, appear to be all attended to at the present time. No other description of minerals were heard of or noticed in the county, save in a few instances the casual occurrence of ironstone, which in the woodland district sometimes appeared, but no where of sufficient value to render it an object for the purpose of manufacture."

SUBJECT THE SECOND.

POLITICAL ECONOMY.

STATE OF APPROPRIATION.

THE APPROPRIATED LANDS, of Hampshire.—The following brief accounts of the states in which those lands lay, in 1808, in different parts of the County,—are well entitled, I conceive, to a place in this register.

Northern Vale Lands.—P. 77. "The proportion of productive country within this District, and excluding the heaths and commons (which are very considerable), are estimated as follows: of arable there is about one half; grass, three-twentieths; and of timber and coppice woodlands, the remainder, or seven-twentieths."

Chalk Hills.—P. 80. "The proportion of productive country (excepting the old pared and burnt downs, and which are

only

only applicable for rabbit-warrens) may be thus estimated: six-twentieths down sheep-walk; five-twentieths light,
thin-stapled, sainfoin land; four-twentieths red, flinty-grey,
chisselly, and shravy loam; two-twentieths pasture and
meadow ground on the permanent greenside; and three-
twentieths coppice-wood, oak, and beach woodlands."

New Forest.—P. 85. "An almost insurmountable difficulty appears to occur, on a Survey of this nature, in stating in all cases the relative proportions of a country thus
occupied; but where public and private property, individual, church, and crown lands, are so blended and mixed
together, as in the district now before us, it is in a manner
impossible, on so cursory a view, to form any thing of an
estimate upon which the slightest reliance should be placed.
Difficulties, however, have seldom repressed the efforts of
the Surveyor, in attempting to accomplish whatever he
conceived to be right; and therefore, to the best of his
judgment, and excluding the forests, chases, heaths, and
common lands from the estimate, he will venture to state
the following proportions, as applicable to the enclosed and
productive property only. Arable or tillage lands, twelve-
twentieths; upland-meadows, embanked marshes, and other
feeding grounds, three-twentieths; water-meadow and osier-
beds, one-twentieth; coppice and timber woodlands, four-
twentieths."

Interior of the Isle of Wight.—P. 89. "This District is
generally well wooded, and the proportion of land under a
convertible system of up and down husbandry, to that
lying permanently on its green side, may be stated at about
five of ploughed land to one under grass."

The UNAPPROPRIATED LANDS.—*Forest Lands.*—P. 5.
"The *New Forest* occupies a large extent of the south-
western division of the county; and on its south-east and
eastern quarters are the chase and forests of Bere and
Bishop's Waltham, and of Woolmer and Alice Holt. Parkhurst or Carisbrook forest, lying north-westwardly of, and
at a short distance from Newport, in the Isle of Wight,
afford, with other extensive and highly improvable wastes
in the county, objects of great national concern."

P. 496. "The appropriation of the forests, somewhat in
the manner here suggested,* would not only tend to a considerable increase in the national population, but at the
same time be the means of producing a number of additional useful hands for agricultural employment, by gradually

---

* That of "consigning them to the care and direction of the honourable Board of Agriculture"! p. 495.

ally cutting up and annihilating that nest and conservatory
of sloth, idleness and misery, which is uniformly to be witnessed in the vicinity of all commons, waste lands, and
forests, throughout the kingdom. Was the condition of
these people in the smallest degree ameliorated by the little
property in a horse or cow which they may eventually become the owners of, far, very far indeed, would it be from
the intention of the Surveyor to recommend any measure,
that in its consequence might tend to abridge them of such
prospective advantages; but in viewing their habitations,
the appearance of themselves and families, to say nothing
of their morals, in comparison with what is daily to be
witnessed in the family and appearance of the steady day-
labourer in other parts of the country (that afford none of
the advantages ascribed to the situation of the forester, or
the equally wretched inhabitant of an extensive common),
is quite sufficient to justify the Surveyor in an earnest wish,
that old as he now is, he yet may live to see the day when
every species of inter-commonable and forest rights may
either be extinguished, or in a progressive state of forwardness to be abolished and utterly done away.

" The incalculable mischief at present done by the trespass of the deer in the cultivated enclosures binding upon
and near the forests, is an evil that ought not to be sanction-
ed by any authority whatsoever."

For Messrs. Driver's circumstantial and valuable observations, on the Forests of Hampshire, see p. 288, aforegoing.

Common Pastures.—For the extent and general remarks
concerning the " Waste Lands" of Hampshire; see, also,
Messrs. D.'s account, aforegoing. The following observations I extract from Mr. V.'s Report.

P. 318. " It may be remarked through the whole extent
of this country, that there are none, or at least very little,
of that description of wastes which in Devonshire are called
moors, all of which, in a greater or less degree, bear evident marks of a former cultivation, and which are appurtenant to particular estates, many having the sites of their
former meets and bounds still traceable, and (for which
though rent is paid) are pastured in common, and according
to the usage of such places, by the occupiers of such estates,
and in a sort of joint tenancy: of this description of waste
or intercommonable land, there did not appear to be any
deserving of particular notice in this county.

" The wastes in general through the county, whether
forest, or heath and commons belonging to particular
parishes, present generally two distinct rights to the inhabitants of their vicinage; one, the right of common of pasture, which is the right of taking the verdure or herbage of
                                                        such

such wastes by the mouths of cattle; the other, common of turbary, which is the right to pare turf from the surface of those lands, or dig in or upon them peat for fuel.

" In regard to the royal forests, neither of these rights are exercised, without some trifling consideration being paid by the persons claiming, both as to the right of turbary and pasturage for cattle.

" The parochial commons lie open, in general, to an unrestrained exercise of these rights by all who reside within their respective perambulations; but this, from the great overstock by which the commons are generally crowded during the summer season, produces little or no substantial benefit to those who claim and exercise it. The right of turbary in many cases has led to so shameful a deterioration of the surface of some of the more valuable wastes in the county, as seems loudly to call for its being in future regulated by some restraining authority; an evil which in no way can be so wisely and effectually cured, as by placing such intercommonable lands in a state of severalty, and consequently commuting such rights by apportioning land in lieu of them."

P. 320. " There being neither mountains, bogs, or fens, properly so called, in this county, the object for farther examination in this chapter, is the present state and extent of salt marshes, or rather large tracts of sea mud. These occur upon the inlets, and along the southern shores of the county, and in the Isle of Wight; and although they are not generally raised to the highest level of the common spring tides, and consequently not covered with the herbage peculiar to salt marshes which may have attained that height of perfection (from the deposition of silt and sediment made upon them by the land and tidal waters, and in the manner formerly explained by the Surveyor on this subject), yet in many places the surface of these banks of mud assume a sufficient degree of richness, from the mild hazel-coloured loam of which they are composed, to justify trials on a small scale to embank and improve them.

" A long range of mud or salt marsh, on the west side of the Southampton river, extends through the parish of Fawley: this is subject to be slightly covered during the top of the ordinary neap tides; but from its superior height above the level of the present embanked marshes, and the annual growth of long marsh grass and samphire it affords, seems likely to answer a valuable purpose, if embanked from the sea; by which means a double purpose would be answered—a considerable tract of valuable land would be obtained, and the descent of the tidal and land waters, being confined to the navigable channel of the Southampton river,

river, would produce a more effectual scour in the bed of
that river, than can possibly be expected from the loose
and circuitous course they now take in wandering through
the sands; and a straighter channel, with deeper water,
would be brought nearer to the town and harbour of that
port."—The extent of those literally waste lands, is laid at
2,000 acres.

P. 321. " About 4000 acres of this description of mud are
found along shore between Hurst Castle and the mouth of
Beauley river. In the inlet or harbour of Portsmouth there
are about 3000 acres, and the harbour of Langston and
Emsworth, taking only so much of the latter as lies within
the county of Hants, will amount to 5500 acres, all of
which are nearly dry by the first quarter's ebb, and consequently the tidal waters can produce no scouring effect
whatever, or contribute in the smallest degree towards
keeping open the mouths of such harbours as admit so
much of the last part of the flood-tides to enter, and spread
over these extensive mud banks, and which appear in many
places to be nearly raised to their highest level.

" Some valuable tracts of marsh might be obtained by constructing a bank a little above the town of Yarmouth, across
the mouth of that river, in the Isle of Wight; thus cutting
off the ascent of the tide-waters, and which upon a small
unimportant stream of that magnitude, can have no possible ill effect whatever. The gradual silting or growing
up of this harbour, is a sufficient demonstration of this
truth; and the value of the land which would be thus obtained to the estates lying on each side of the river, would
also be considerable.

" The inlets of Shalfleet and Newton afford also some small
pieces of salt marsh ready for embanking; but the object
which engaged the attention of the Surveyor most particularly on this subject, is the bason on the eastern side
of the island, called Brading harbour."—The embankable
lands of Brading haven are estimated, by Mr. V., at 500
acres.

Mr. Vancouver, while speaking, at some length, on the *improvement* of those uncultivated lands,—in terms similar to
those that have been offered, again and again, to the attention of Government,—elicits the subjoined happy thought.—
P. 474. " If we consider the aggregate extent and quality
of the forests and waste lands of this kingdom as lying in
the English channel, or any where in an equally favoured
climate on the coast of the island, would not the most un-
sparing efforts be made by Government to conquer and
secure them, not less for the addition which such possessions
would make to the national stock, than for the advantage
they

they might afford in a commercial or hostile point of view, against the efforts of our enemies. Will the Government then continue less attentive to the realizing of such important advantages, and those in the very heart of the empire, at the very threshold of the throne? Surely it ought not."

FUEL.—P. 389. " Through all the woodland parts of this county, the peasantry are tolerably well supplied with fuel, and which is obtained by a claim they exercise pretty freely, of taking what is called *snapwood*, that is, all the fallen branches, and such as they can snap off by hand, or break down with a hook fixed in the end of a long pole: for this purpose they have been observed to visit most of the demesnes, and private as well as other woodlands through the county.

" When this resource fails, turf pared from off the heaths and commons is easily obtained, as it may generally be purchased dry for about 6s. per thousand. These, in some parts of the county, the farmers bring home to the labourers, for so much of the ashes as the labourer may be able to afford, after manuring his garden, potatoe, or cabbage patch.

" Peat cut and dried, affords another resource for fuel to the peasantry of the country."

MANUFACTURES.—P. 6. " Its *manufactures* consist of woollens, leather, silk, bed-tickings, and the coarser kind of earthen-ware; and in the naval arsenal at Portsmouth, may be seen one of the most important magazines in the united kingdom."

For a note concerning the *seacoast Salt Works* of Hampshire, see *Embankments*, ensuing. See also the article *Markets*, ensuing.

POOR TAX.—In an extract, from Mr. Warner's Isle of Wight, may be seen (p. 296, aforegoing) a plan for *consolidating the Poor Rates of parishes*, and *building " a house of industry."*

Of this establishment Mr. Vancouver speaks favorably. Such a plan is by no means peculiar to the Isle of Wight. But an establishment of that sort, unless it be put, *and kept*, under the wisest and most strict regulations, will ever become, like *other* houses of industry and *manufacture*, a nursery of vice; especially to the young; and, in many cases, a heart-rending prison to the aged. I was willingly led to hope that the measure had been altogether abandoned, rather than to hear it recommended by a man of mind and observation *.

Mr.

* More will appear on this topic, in *Young's Sussex*, ensuing.

Mr. Vancouver's political tables have been mentioned, (p. 302, aforegoing). In an abstract of those tables, the " total of the money raised by poor and other rates," in the County at large, at the time of writing, is made out to be £153,427; the average " rate in the pound rent" (rack rent) 4s. 5½d.; and the " total expenditure, on account of the *poor*," £130,983.

If that table be nearly correct, it is a valuable document, in the topography and polity of the County ; and proves Mr. Vancouver's indefatigable exertions, in forming instruments of that nature.

TITHES.—This is one subject of five, which pass, in company, through the Reporter's Districts. The other companions are *Farms,—Occupiers,—Rent,—*and *Objects of Husbandry,*—in Hampshire.

District 1*. P. 77. " The rectorial tithe is too frequently taken in kind; but when agreement takes place between the occupier and person interested in the corn tithe, the commutation is usually from 4s. to 5s. in the pound on the rack-rent value of the occupation. The vicarial tithe is mostly compounded to the satisfaction of both parties."

District 2. P. 80. " The great tithe through this district is but too frequently taken in kind ; but when commuted, the great and small tithes together generally pay about 5s. in the pound upon the full rent of the farm present value. The vicarial tithe was observed in too many cases to be drawn ; and when it is commuted upon the woodlands, it is generally paid by the owner or occupier, 2s. in the pound on the amount of sales in the wood."

District 3. P. 82. " The great and small tithes are commonly commuted in this District for about 4s. 6d. in the pound, on the rack-rent value of the occupation."

District 4. P. 84. " From a number of instances collected on the Survey of this District, the commutation paid for the great and small tithes is found to amount to about 27½ per cent. upon the present rack-rent, or value of the farms; but it is deeply to be regretted, that so many instances occurred, particularly on the western side of the county, of the tenth meal of milk being demanded, and paid with every other species of tithe, great and small, in kind."

District 5. P. 86. " Great and small, are generally commuted for 5s. in the pound on the rack-rent value."

District 6. P. 87. " This is by far too frequently taken in kind, but when commutation takes place, the great and small tithes are generally valued at about 4s. 6d. in the pound upon the rack-rents."

District

District 7. P. 89. " Tithes either belonging to the church, or in the hands of lay improprietors, are but too frequently drawn or taken in kind. When a commutation takes place for rectorial and vicarial tithes, it is seldom less than 6s. 6d. and 7s. in the pound, upon the full improved rent or present value."

PUBLIC EMBANKMENTS.—I insert, here, the subjoined remarks, on this subject (which fill the chapter " Embankments"); although they are neither so intelligent, nor intelligible, as the same writer's valuable paper, on the embankment and drainage of the *Waterlands of Cambridgeshire.*—See EASTERN DEPARTMENT.

P. 351. " If we except the embankments of Brading and Yaverland, in the Isle of Wight, some of which in their present improved state, exhibit specimen of the best feeding land in the county, the appropriation of almost all the other embankments on the coasts of the islands, as well as of the main land, has been that of saltings, for the manufacture of sea and medicinal salts.

" Many of these salt-works are now abandoned, but the brine and bitumen with which the former saltpans are saturated, preclude all expectation for a great length of time of these levels being convertible to agricultural purposes.— The sea-weed or sea ore, of which most of the mounds or sea walls are formed, is found to last a prodigious length of time, and to sustain the constant lashing of the tidal waters with extraordinary firmness. There is no other point in the formation of these banks that can afford the humblest hint towards permanency or imitation, even to one who has never before seen works of such a nature ; for in their construction against a long and heavy fetch or swell of the sea, it is utterly impossible for any form to be less efficacious, or worse contrived."

INLAND NAVIGATION.—*Rivers.*—P. 7. " This river" (the Itchen) " was made navigable from Southampton to Winchester as early as the reign of William the Conqueror."

Canals.—P. 393. " Out of the three distinct lines of canal which originate in this county, there are two that terminate in the Southampton river. Besides the objects of improvement connected with these canals, the Kennet navigation, leading from Newbury to Reading, is thought to have produced considerable advantages to the north-western side of this county.

" The Basingstoke Canal, however injurious to many estates through which it passes, and fraught as it may have been with disappointment to many of the first adventurers, is yet regarded as a valuable acquisition to the northern parts of the county.

" The

" The Redbridge and Andover Canal affords considerable advantage to the interior country, by bringing to it the foreign supplies of the most heavy and bulky nature it may require, and facilitating the surplus of its agricultural produce to market; yet along the valley of the Teste many inconveniencies were witnessed by the penning of the water, to the injury of the low grounds through which the canal passes. From Redbridge there is a branch of this canal which connects immediately with Southampton; a collateral branch also proceeds up the valley between East Dean, Leskerley, and East Tytherley, which is navigable to Alderbury Common, and within two miles of Salisbury.

" The Winchester and Southampton Canal is perhaps one of the most ancient in the kingdom. The act for constructing this canal was obtained in the reign of Charles the First, but from the want of a suitable trade upon it, however advantageous to the city of Winchester and the surrounding country, it does not seem to have answered the expectations of the first adventurers; the same, indeed, may be stated of the Andover Canal, which is not supposed to have paid one shilling to the proprietors since its first establishment, now about nine years ago."

ROADS.—*Parish* Roads.—P. 391. " In general, good; some, the very best in the kingdom. To this general statement some exception must be made to parish roads, whether in the woodlands or the more open parts of the county. In the former situation their indifferent state may be more justly ascribed to their narrowness, and being overshaded with trees, than to any want of good and sufficient materials to make and repair them.

" In the chalk district, the quarters of the parish roads are found so very high, and the ruts so deep, as to render it no less difficult than dangerous for loaded carriages to turn out of them."

P. 392. " Nothing can possibly exceed the goodness of the roads through the New Forest, and the southern parts of the county. It is no less true than strange, to say that the traveller may pass from Lymington to Christchurch, and thence to Salisbury, without a turnpike, and all the way upon parochial roads, which may vie for goodness with the best turnpikes in the kingdom. Neither are there turnpikes in the Isle of Wight."

Toll Roads.—P. 392. " The public or turnpike roads are, however, no where better than what may generally be met with in Hampshire: materials of an excellent quality are to be had in most situations."

Wheel Carriages.—While the Reporter is suggesting " Improvements"

"Improvements" (in a chapter appropriated to that purpose) he proposes the following regulation.—P. 504. "One thing seems indispensably required for the public accommodation, but this is only to be obtained by legislative authority; it is that of fixing upon one standard width for the track of all waggons, carts, and pleasurable carriages; and to ordain, that all wheel carriages, wheresoever made in the island of Great Britain, whether designed for business or pleasure, after a certain time should be made and constructed agreeably thereto."

In *by* roads, already *deeply rutted*, such a regulation would be greatly advantageous; especially to gentlemen who travel, with sober pace, over the island at large, in their own carriages; no matter whether they move on four wheels or only two. But on *wide barrel roads*, such a restriction would be mischievous; inasmuch as it could not fail to *form ruts*,—which are the greatest evil of roads of that description. "Turnpike Roads" require a *diversity*, rather than a *unity* of *span;*—in order to *prevent ruts*, as much as may be, and thereby to render their entire surfaces equally travelable*.

MARKETS.—P. 395. "Within the county, and at no great distance from its eastern and western borders, there are some of the best corn and cattle markets in the kingdom. These places generally afford opportunities for obtaining the best times price for all sort of agricultural produce, and at the same time exhibit assortments of manufactured goods, in all the variety of home or foreign taste, for domestic consumption."

The Reporter next proceeds to open his *topographico-political chapter;*—which is thus entitled:—p. 396. "Political character of the principal towns in this district, seat, and circumstances of manufactures and commerce, fisheries, agricultural societies, &c. :"—with such irrelevant materials (*chiefly†*) filling fifty pages!

Those miscellaneous matters, with many others, are treated of, *districtwise;*—the several market towns of the County being separately brought forward, according to their situations within the outlines of the Reporter's Districts. The following are among the favorite topics of attention.

The locality of the town under consideration.

Its

* And the four-in-hand man,—the fast-driving Jehu,—would have an insuperable objection to the Reporter's plan. He delights in a narrow span, and a high seat, to give *life* to his vehicle—to give it action and lightness of motion—thereby to avoid, or easily to overcome, many obstructions, which a wide-span carriage, for the want of lateral motion, has to surmount.

† See Poor Rates, p. 318, aforegoing.

Its ancient name or names.

The etymon of its modern appellation.

Its ancient history; if any belong to it.

The remains of ancient buildings, &c.

The battles fought in its neighbourhood.

Its modern *picture.*

Its public buildings and other works.

Its manufactures and traffic.

Any thing curious or surprising, which it can claim as its own.

Its municipal relations; if it has any.

Its body corporate.

The members it sends to Parliament.

The returning officer; and

The qualification of the voters.

Now, to many or most men of leisure and general enquiry, those topics, when duly handled, are capable of affording much entertainment; and I have the pleasure of informing that class of readers, that the work I am now speaking of is *respectably done.*—But it really is neither decorous, nor *fair*, for a professed writer on *agriculture* to trespass, thus openly, on the neighbouring field of *topography;* seeing how many industrious men there are who, at present, are working, hard perhaps, in that their own field of literature.

I trust, however, the author, notwithstanding the above *mitigated* remarks, will accept my thanks for one portion of his ample and mostly *interesting* information: namely, that which describes the *Seawater Saltworks* of Lymington: a subject that was entirely new to me. Formerly, it appears "saltings" were prevalent on the southern shores of this island*.   SOCIETIES

*Those works, being appendant to *landed property*, I here insert a short extract, from Mr V.'s lengthened account, to convey a general idea of the process.

P. 420. "The manufactures for which Lymington is most noted, are those of culinary and medicinal salts from sea water. This business is pursued much less now than formerly, but still carried on to some considerable extent, particularly by one gentleman, Mr. St. Barbe, who very obligingly favoured the Surveyor with the following, as well as much other useful information.

"The salt works at Lymington, formerly very extensive, are perhaps equal to any *marine* manufactory of that kind in the kingdom. The sea water is first admitted into feeding ponds, from whence it flows into levels, in which there are partitions, forming pans, as they are called, of from twenty to thirty square perches each: these receive the sea water from the feeding ponds to the depth of about three inches, and from which it passes from the higher to the lower pans, exposed to the action of the sun and wind, until the brine becomes of a sufficient strength to be pumped up by small wind engines into a cistern, whence it is conveyed by troughs into the respective iron

pans

SOCIETIES of Agriculture.—P. 398. " An Agricultural Society was established at *Odiham* in the year 1783; but of late years the objects of this institution appear to have been little attended to." See p. 291, aforegoing.

SUBJECT THE THIRD.

RURAL ECONOMY.

TENANTED ESTATES.

ESTATES.—P. 51. " The largest estates, as well as the most extensive occupations, are found in the chalky parts of this county. The highest individual rental of lands lying within the county, was not understood to exceed 8000*l*. per annum. Much of the land in the county has undergone a transfer of late years from its former owners, and in which have been included some very large and valuable estates. A considerable subdivision of property has also taken place."

TENURES.—P. 53. " Tenures are various. Those estates which are supposed to have formerly composed a part of the demesne lands of the see of Winchester, are granted by the Bishop as freeholds, for, or upon three lives, and generally renewed to the families in possession for many successive generations. The fine or renewal varies, from one and a half to one and three quarters, and two years improved rent, valued by competent persons in the vicinity. These estates chiefly consist of ancient manor farms and houses, and to which certain feudal rights still appertain. In some cases, the timber on these estates has been reserved to the use of the see, allowing only a sufficiency for repairs, with the bark, top, and lop, of the same; in others, the whole was originally relinquished

pans for boiling. The ordinary size of these boiling pans is about 8 feet 6 inches square, and about 11 inches deep, but of which depth about 8 inches only is filled with brine, which is kept gently simmering until the last hour, when the heat is much augmented, for the purpose of drying the salt, which has been all along forming on the surface of the brine, and falling through it to the bottom of the pan, thus gradually diminishing the brine in the pan at the rate of about half an inch per hour.

" The extent of ground required for evaporation, exclusive of the feeding ponds and cistern, is about three roods, or 120 perches to each pan."

quished to the tenant family, who consider these estates
as tenancies for life, renewable for ever on the terms
above stated.

" *Copyhold* tenures, or lands held by copy of court roll,
are granted from manors vested in the church, other pious
foundations held in mortmain, and the nobility, gentry,
and lay proprietors of the county. They are of several
kinds, such as copyholds of inheritance, with a fine small
and certain on alienation or death, customary, which refers
to the usage of the manor, whether the fine on such occasions is paid by heriots, or commuted for a former specific
sum, or arbitrary, and which latter often involves the
tenant in a situation he by no means approves of : these
tenures are granted by the Bishop of Winchester, the Dean
and Chapter, the Warden of Winchester College, the colleges of the respective universities, other public and private
bodies, and nearly in the following manner :

" A valuation of the net annual rent of the estate is
made, and upon that data, two years' purchase is demanded
for one life, with the benefit of widowhood ; eight years
for two lives, with the benefit of widowhood ; sixteen years
for three lives, with the benefit of widowhood.

" Leaseholds, or lands held on lives by lease or indenture, also derived from the preceding sources, and which
upon renewal, the net annual value being previously ascertained, pay two years purchase for one life, seven years
for two lives, fourteen years for three lives, with a small
annual reserved rent, which varies according to circumstances, but is generally considered to apply a just equivalent to both parties.

" Leases for terms of years are also granted by the afore-
said authorities ; these are generally for 21 years, renewable every seven, with a fine of from one and a quarter
to one and a half yearly value."

P. 61. " In the Isle of Wight the great bulk of the land
is freehold. The copyholds chiefly consist of small tenements ; and although the College of Winchester, and New
College, Oxford, have some property near the middle of
the island, it does not appear that there are any church
demesnes upon it. The largest individual income accruing
from lands in the island, is not supposed to exceed 5000*l.*
per acre. Leases for 14 and 21 years absolute, have been
very judiciously granted of some of the principal occupations in the island ; and with regard to other species
of tenure, they may be generally referred to what has been
already stated on those subjects with regard to the county
at large."

DRAINING Estates.—A good deal is said on this subject ;
but

but little of interest made out. The art would seem to have been, at the time Mr. V. took his survey, still in its novitiate; notwithstanding *Mr. Elkington* formerly made his appearance in the County; and performed in it, with success.

SODBURNING.—This argumentative subject has engaged much of Mr. Vancouver's attention. It is twice brought forward; and in both cases joined with *Manures!* I perceive nothing however, in Mr. V.'s arguments, though often very ingenious, but not always conclusive, that is sufficiently scientific or *new* (some *chemical tenets* excepted) to be admitted, *as they stand*, into this register. I therefore leave them untouched. His practical ideas, concerning the operation, are, I think, nearly just. He is an enemy to it, *as a practice*, but its friend, *as an expedient*. What appears to have urged the Reporter to speak so largely, and so *warmly*, on the operation and its effects, was the Postscript (as it has been misnamed) to Messrs. Driver's Report, by the Secretary to the Board. See p. 299, aforegoing. At the head of the Chapter entitled " Means of Improvement," Mr. Vancouver suggests some valuable *principles of improvement* (that will be found at the close of this article) to which, it is possible, the said Postscript gave birth; as they are *pointed* with the following passage.—P. 451. " As these observations necessarily involve a question of the highest importance in the agricultural concerns of this county, and as a Postscript to the former Agricultural Survey of Hampshire by the Secretary of the Board, seems strongly to inculcate the practice of paring and burning, and of resorting to it as a means of improvement *in all cases whatsoever*, and as this point will be best considered under the head of Manures (that being the sole renovating principle upon which all agricultural produce can be expected to be procured), we shall assign to that subject the first place in our present enquiry."

IRRIGATION.—Nor do I find any thing, on this operation, which requires particular notice; excepting what will appear under the head, *Grass Land*, ensuing.

TENANCY.—In continuation of what is said on *Tenures*, see p. 323, aforegoing, is the following notice on tenancy.— P. 54. " Leases also for 21 years, determinable every seven, by a twelvemonth's notice from either party: here the annual reserved rent is supposed to be a full equivalent for the occupation.

" Leases of 14 years (absolute), sometimes occur; but here it is much to be regretted that these, as well as leases for 21 years, are getting much into disuse, there being

being several estates in the county held at will, and thus
constituting an evil which the Surveyor is concerned to
remark as very much increasing."

The event, which I have long foreseen, has at length
come to pass, (October 1815). Leases for twentyone
years, that have been entered into within the last seven,
are no longer blessings to leasees. On the contrary, should
leasors persist in the fulfilment of them, and the present
times continue, they must, in many cases, prove their ruin.

COVENANTS.— P. 55. " Upon occupations held at will,
or for terms of seven, twelve, fourteen, or twenty-
one years, the repairs of buildings, cartage of materials,
thatching and glazing excepted, are sometimes, though
rarely, done by the landlord, the more general usage being
for all the old established and new necessary buildings
to be put in good repair for the incoming tenant, who
being afterwards supplied with rough timber, including
weather-boards and flooring plank, bricks and tiles at the
kilns, stones at the quarry, and lime at the kiln, is bound
to keep them in the same condition during the continuance of his occupation."

P. 57. " The crop is generally provided to be expended
on the premises, but when hay or straw is sold, a proportionate quantity of stable dung is required to replace such
draughts of the essential means of preserving the occupation in heart and good condition. Three waggon loads
of dung are not considered as more than equivalent for
each load of hay or wheat straw" (!) " sold from off
the farm."

REMOVALS.—P. 56. " The tenant generally enters at
Old Michaelmas."

P. 60. " The old tenants commonly retain possession of
the barns for the convenience of thrashing out their crops,
and are usually indulged with a homestead, as an outlet
for their cattle whilst feeding upon the straw; but the
premises are always cleared from the whole of the former
establishment by the beginning of the ensuing May."

" In other cases, it has been customary for the incoming tenant to enter upon a part of the occupation in the
month of January (preceding the termination of the lease
that is to expire the ensuing Michaelmas), for the purpose
of preparing turnip fallows."

RENT.—This is reported by *districts*, with farms, occupiers, tithes, &c.

District 1.—P. 77. " The highest average than can possibly be stated of land in this district, cultivated solely
for the purposes of farming, is 16s. for arable and 30s. for
the grass, including meadow and prime pasture land."

District

District 2.—P. 80. "The average rent of the strong tillage land through this District, may be stated at 17s.; the higher and thinner-stapled land at 12s.; and the old downs or sheep-walks, from 5s. to 7s. 6d. and 10s. per acre. Many of the old pared and burnt downs are of so little value, as to bear no price whatever in this estimate. Upland meadows and good pasture land, 32s.; water-meadow, from 40s. to 60s. per acre."

District 3.—P. 82. "The dry meadows and best feeding ground, are usually rated at about 35s. per acre; the land subject to a course of tillage, about 15s.; and the water-meadows, including osier-beds, about 50s. per acre."

District 4.—P. 84. "The mild, gravelly, and sandy loams, are rated from 20s. to 28s. per acre; some instances occur, particularly in the parish of Titchfield, of arable land being valued as high as 35s. per acre. The dry, stony, or light sandy loams, from 16s. to 21s. per acre; the strong sour loams, or clay, from 14s. to 18s. per acre; water-meadow, from 40s. to 4l.

District 5.—P. 86. "That of the arable in the open common-fields fluctuates from 18s. to 24s. per acre; the enclosed land of a similar quality, but in higher condition, and rendered much more productive by skilful, appropriate, and independent management, from 25s. to 32s. per acre; pastures and rich feeding grounds, including the embanked marshes not employed as saltings, from 25s. to 35s. per acre."

District 6.—P. 87. "The strong loamy clay, which gives a character to this District through its several divisions, essentially reduces the current value of its arable proportion to about 14s. per acre. The meadow, pasture, and marsh lands, lying generally on the same close, wet, and cold subsoil, are not rated higher than from 15s. to 25s. per acre."

District 7.—P. 88. "The prevailing character of soil in this District, generally allowing for its being constantly employed in the growth of green legumens, or white straw crops, gives to it a most decided superiority over any other District in the island, and affords the rent of its arable to be taken at an average of 25s. per acre; not but that there are some farms in this District with no extraordinary portion of feeding land, which rent tithe-free at 40s. per acre. Embanked marshes, dry and wet meadows, and rich feeding grounds, run from 30s. to 45s. per acre."

District 8.—P. 89. "The rent, or value of the tillage land, may be rated from 12s. to 18s. per acre; the sheep-downs,

downs, from 5s. to 7s. 6d.; and the marsh and rich feeding grounds from one guinea to 35s. and 40s. per acre."

WOODLANDS.

MR. VANCOURER speaks on this subject, at considerable length. The following are the more valuable facts brought forward, relating to the produce and general practice of the County.

WOODS.—*Oak.*—P. 307. " In that part of the county which, in this Report, is called the Woodlands, a very fine growth of oak may generally be observed. The chalk district also is by no means destitute in many places of a highly ornamental and valuable proportion of oak woods. The most southern parts of the county, and the forests in particular, have formerly yielded an abundance of this valuable timber, but which of late years have suffered a great diminution in their annual produce."

Ash.—P. 299. " The finest *ash* noticed any where upon the Survey, was in Hackwood-park. The late noble, and justly lamented owner of this demesne, informed the Surveyor, that he had recently sold some of the prime shafts of the Hackwood ash for 4s. 6d. per foot. This was understood to have been purchased by the London coach-makers."

Beech.—P. 298. " In almost every part of the chalk district, beech woods, and groves of this timber, seem to grow and flourish with peculiar vigour. The forests and other woodlands are also found to contain large proportions of this species, and which when standing single, grow to a considerable size. Though the beech woods are very promising in every part of the chalk district, those at Ditcham Grove appear to be the best, and by far the most extensive. This timber is chiefly of the white sort, and which from being regularly thinned from the first planting (and which never ought to exceed a a yard square) have now arrived to a very towering, clean, and regular growth. When this timber averages about 25 feet meetings, or half a load per tree, it makes good plank timber, and will then be worth in the woods from 18d. to 20d. per foot. The forest beech however seldom exceeds in value 15d. per foot; 10d. may be taken more generally as its average, where felled."

COPPICES.—P. 292. " *Coppice Woods.*—A species of produce that is found much to vary in its quality and value, as the predominance of timber may have affected its
growth

growth, or the ground producing it may be of a warm and dry, or of a cold and springy nature.

" Birch, withy, alder, hazel, wild cherry, ash, and sometimes oak, are found the most prevailing and most profitable coppice-woods, and whether strictly in that sense, as undergrowth in the timber woodlands, or forming the broad irregular hedge-rows so frequently occurring in many parts of the county.

" The age of cutting coppice, or rather undergrowth, in the woodland district, whether in hand, or in the occupation of the tenant to the adjacent farm, varies from eight to ten years growth, and which may be stated to yield, standing at those respective ages, a net profit equal to an annual rent of from 10s. to 25s. per acre."

P. 295. " In the chalk district the coppice-wood consists chiefly of hazel, withy, oak, ash, maple, white-thorn, some little beech, and wild cherry. This is seldom cut earlier than at fourteen years growth, and commonly sells, standing at that age, for nine guineas or 10l. per acre. A number of *oak heirs* and *ash tillows* are left at each cutting; the latter are either continued through a third period, or cut down the subsequent fall for the demand then for them. The wattled hurdles made in these woods, are found to be far more durable than those made of the same materials in the woodland district, where the coppices are generally converted much in the manner just noticed."

P. 296. " The coppice in the southern parts of the county growing upon a clay or marl bottom, is usually cut down at nine years growth: it consists chiefly of hazel, withy, alder, birch, and some ash. Much of this wood is used as small hoops for the four gallon tubs, formerly, and at present not wholly out of demand, along the coasts of this and the adjacent counties, and still sent in large quantities to the islands of Jersey and Guernsey. A number of straight hoops are also exported in bundles to the West Indies."

OZIER BEDS.—P. 301. " There are but few of the vallies and low grounds in this country that do not afford a greater or less quantity of peat moss. In the valley between Stockbridge and Rumsey, and in other places where the peat is cut with the short spade, the land is made good again for water or for dry meads, or for the more common puspose of planting oziers."

P. 302. " The manner of reclaiming the peat lands excavated with the short spade, is to cast them into beds six or eight feet wide, with a trench or interval of 18 inches, and as occasion may require, from one to three feet

feet deep. Oziers are then planted on those beds, at the average distance of about 18 inches square. When the old stools are exhausted, but which with occasional renewing will commonly last about 20 years, the stubs are grubbed up, and after the ground has been well cleansed and dressed with road-scrapings, or such earths as may be most conveniently at hand for giving compactness to such loose and moory soil, the whole is formed into ridgework for irrigation, or that improvement not attainable (its future drainage being previously secured), is laid down with hay-seeds, cow-grass, white clover, &c. without a crop, and with a view to dry meadow or permanent pasture."

AGRICULTURE.

FARMS.—District 1.—P. 76. " Notwithstanding that, within a few late years, a number of small farms have been united into one occupation; their average size at this time, through the whole of this district, does not exceed 80*l*. per annum."

District 2.—P. 79. " The down farms, or those generally situated in the down districts, are from 200*l*. to 800*l*. per annum."

District 3.—P. 81. " In this District they vary very much, from 20*l*. to 300*l*. per annum."

District 4.—P. 83. " In a District which lies so very wide and scattering, and consequently contains so great a variety of soil and substrata, it is reasonable to suppose that much diversity will occur, as well in the extent of the farming occupations, as in the character of the occupiers. The *size of the Farms* are therefore rendered so very unequal, as to reach from 30*l*. to 400*l*. per annum. The recent consolidation of farms in the different parts of this District were much complained of, as a circumstance unfavourable to the regular supply of poultry and other small articles of country produce, and which are generally yielded from the lesser occupations of the country. These complaints, however, are by no means of such a nature as to merit serious consideration."

District 5.—P. 85. " There are many farms of considerable extent and value in this District, and which may be generally stated as running from 250*l*. to 300*l*. per annum."

District 6.—P. 87. " In this divided District, the occupations in their consolidated state may be said to vary from 100*l*. to 300*l*. per annum."

District

District 7.—P. 88. " The occupations in this District are stated to run from 50*l.* to 500*l.* per annum."

District 8.—P. 89. " The farms in this, as in every other chalk and consequently sheep District, run very large, extending from 200*l.* to 800*l.* per annum."

HOMESTEADS.—P. 63. " Farm-houses did not challenge any particular attention as to the excellence or defects of their conveniences. They are mostly of great antiquity, and those in the occupation of the larger farmers were formerly grange or manor houses ; in the construction of which there appears to have been originally but little design, and in the appropriation of their present apartments, no farther order than that which seems to accord the best with the comfort and convenience of the family."

P. 64. " A very excellent practice seems to be fast gaining ground in many parts of the county, of building wheat barns, as well as corn stacks in general, upon stone stands or staddles. The barns thus constructed are usually of beech, elm, and fir-boards, with oak, beech, or elm plank, for thrashing-floors ; the other part of the bottom of the barn or mows may be formed of any other old and useless plank or boards."

P. 65. " The building materials in general use through this county are, stone, flint, brick, cob or mud, oak, elm, beech, and fir, or home deal."

P. 70. " A *cement,* which seems to acquire additional hardness by continuance under water, has been composed by Mr. Roberts, of Abbotstone, and is much used in the neighbourhood of Alresford, and other parts of the county, where its excellence is known. It is prepared, one-eighth wood-ashes, one-eighth coal-ashes, one-eighth dry sand, and one-eighth the white, chalky, clay malm, or marl, found uniformly under the peat-moors in the vallies of that country" (shell marl) " and four-eighths lime, procured from the grey chalk-rock in the neighbourhood of Petersfield : the whole put together and tempered a few hours only before it is used. This cement is admirably calculated for waterworks, and appears to possess a strong attractive power upon the earthy parts of the water with which it may come in contact ; a circumstance evinced by the incrustations left by the water in its passage through tunnels, mills, &c. built with a cement prepared in this manner."

The blue limestone encrusted with white, and burning to a sulphur-colored lime, which is found in various parts of England,—and is raised near Petersfield—see *Fossils,* aforegoing,—is commonly applied to the purpose of forming waterwork cement. The ingredients, abovementioned, may, or may not, be preferable, to clean-washed fine gravel.

COTTAGES.

COTTAGES.—P. 70. " This county seems generally to be
much better supplied with comfortable dwellings for the
peasantry, than many others in the kingdom, much attention being paid by most country gentlemen to this important point of accommodation and improvement on their
respective estates."

P. 73. " Colonel Mitford, of Exbury, has erected several
new and convenient cottages. In placing these buildings,
the Colonel has had it no less in view to prevent the appearance of any nuisance from the street, than to supply
each tenement with a sufficiency of garden ground ; he has
therefore turned the rear of these cottages upon the street,
and their front upon the gardens."

" There are but few farms in the Isle of Wight that have
not cottages attached to them. This affords considerable
advantage to the farmers (particularly in a country where
objects for the employment of the peasantry are so much
multiplied as in this island), by giving them a greater controul over the labourers, and in a greater measure commanding their services, when the labours of the country
require to be most promptly executed."

In the Isle of Wight, where there are not resident workpeople sufficient, to gather in the harvest, such a controul
may be warrantable.

OCCUPIERS.—District 1.—P. 76. " The occupiers may be
divided into two classes : those of the higher order are represented as a sober industrious sort of men, seldom leaving
home, but when their business calls them to fairs or markets. Attentive, and sparing no labour or expense in the
improvement of their occupations, particularly in the article
of chalk ; in the purchase of Berkshire peat-ashes, and
woollen rags, procured from London and Portsmouth.
Their dwellings usually afford most of the comforts and
conveniences of life, and in this manner they are supposed
to be getting forward in the world.

" The holdings of many of the smaller farmers not
affording constant employment for themselves and teams,
they are found much engaged at wood cart, in conveying
timber to the Basingstoke Canal, and in carting materials
for the repair of the public roads : with these exertions,
and by wintering a few sheep belonging to their southern
neighbours, they contrive to rub on tolerably well ; and if
lucky with their little stock and horses, by frugality and
good management, do rather more at the end of the year
than make ends meet."

District 2.—P. 79. " *The farmers* are generally a smart,
active, intelligent set of men, well educated, liberal, and
inspired with a general emulation for the improvement of
                                                        their

their stock, particularly their flocks, on the success of which their very all depends. From the capital necessarily connected with such an extent of occupation, they seem with their industrious habits as much entitled to, as they really do enjoy, most of the comforts of life, and that in an ample and very liberal degree. They are, withal, many of them possessors of small estates, which their thrifty management keeps upon the increase; and hence they happily combine the opulence and respectability of both tenant and yeoman."

District 3.—P. 81. "The different gradations in society which are thought to rise above the *mere peasant* level in this District, are, first, the forester; who, from time to time, has encroached a few perches from the forest, and which at length amounting to two or three acres, constitutes what he conceives a sort of independence to himself and family. Upon this he pretends to grow as much grass and hay as will suffice to bait his working horse, or horses, night and morning; a few potatoes; and some bread-corn for his family. His principal exertions are directed to the cutting, rearing, and carting of peat-fuel, and of procuring or removing any other combustible matter to the neighbouring towns and villages. In winter, he jobs at wood-cart and in carrying stones or gravel for the highways; and thus, with raising a forest colt or two, provincially called *heath-croppers*, and one or two, of an equally inferior species of neat cattle, is found to get on easily, and in some respects independently, through life."

The other gradations of occupiers are the *little* and the *great* farmers; or, as it would seem, the underling and the overbearing farmers.

District 4.—P. 83. "The most extensive occupations are in the hands of *farmers* of considerable intelligence, they are not generally, in point of capital, found to hold as high a station as the principal occupiers in the chalk districts. Many of them, however, in addition to the land they rent, are occupiers of their own estates; and thus, as before noticed, contribute to give additional weight and consideration to the tenantry of the country. They are in general active and industrious, and spare neither pains nor expense in improving the sheep stock and husbandry of the country. The improvement of the native horse and neat cattle in the country must for ever remain stationary, so long as the wastes and forests remain open, and that such an indiscriminate mixture of worthless males of both kinds have free and unlimited access to them.

"The condition of the lesser farmers may be very well referred to what has been just stated in the preceding District." P. 84.

P. 84. " Very few, indeed, are seen to rise gradually above that condition of life in which they first started."

District 5.—P. 85. " *The farmers, graziers, butchers, and gardeners* occupying this District, seem justly to appreciate the value of their respective situations."

District 6.—P. 87. " *Farmers* may generally be considered as a sober, careful, industrious, and well-informed set of men, often occupying their own small freeholds in addition to what they hire, and upon which, as well as upon their rented land (where protection and encouragement are afforded under a reasonable term of years), no labour or expense is spared in improving their occupations, by chalk, marl, and mixing the different earths together."

District 7.—P. 88. " Many of the larger *farmers* occupy, in addition to the land they hire, their own small estates, and from the pains and expense they bestow in improving their stock and husbandry (which, though evidently a few years behind their neighbours on the mainland), are entitled to much praise for the readiness with which they strive to adopt and emulate superior management."

District 8.—P. 89. " *Farmers* are in nowise inferior to the larger occupiers in District No. II."

Capital of Occupiers.—(Chapter " Obstacles to Improvements.") P. 445. " Circumstances of this nature among some of the woodland and forest farmers, may be regarded as obstacles to improvement, but generally throughout the county there does not appear a want of talent, industry, or capital, among the farming community."

WORKPEOPLE.—Mr. Vancouver has given a circumstantial and readable Report of the farm servants and laborers of Hampshire. It it too diffusely written for insertion, here, at full length. Some particulars of it, however, are entitled to extraction ; as it is of modern date, compared with most others of the Board's reprinted Reports. The time of collecting the information was probably in 1807.

House Servants.—Wages.—P. 381. "The wages of the head carter are about eleven guineas; that of the head carter's mate, about nine guineas. When a boy supplies this place, in driving plough, and assisting to take care of the horses, his wages may be placed at 4*l.* or guineas. Second carter's wages about the same with first carter's mate ; his boy or assistant, the same as the other man's boy. The teams generally consist of five horses, and when the head carter's mate is not employed in helping to feed and take care of the horses, or accompanying the team on journeys upon the road, he is usually employed in thrashing or helping to dress corn, gripping, fencing, or other jobs, about the farm. The thrasher receives about ten guineas per annum, and when

when more plough-teams are kept, the wages of the plough-men and boys are generally regulated by their strength and qualifications, varying from 20s. to 50s. below the wages of the second carter and his boy. The day's work is usually performed in one journey of eight and an half or nine hours. The servants in these cases are all considered as boarding and lodging in the house."

In *this* quarter of the island, (northeast Yorkshire) the wages given to farm servants, of the same degree, were, about the same time, nearly twice as much.

P. 385. " The dairy-maid and cook's wages are about five guineas each; girls from two and an half to three guineas, with board, washing, and lodging; cow, crow, pig, and milk-boys, procured from the adjacent villages, and generally receive from 4d. to 6d. per day. The shepherd is generally a villager, who has 12s. per week the year round, besides perquisites, which usually attend his situation as butcher."

The *Food* of Farmhouse Servants.—P. 383. " The ordinary breakfast of farm-servants is bread and skimmed-milk, with the remainder of what bacon was left the day before: their lunch or noonchine, consists of bread and cheese, with the small beer they take in their kegs to the field. Their dinner is usually prepared between three and four o'clock, and consists of pickled pork or bacon, with potatoes, cabbages, turnips, greens, and broths, seasoned to the palate with a variety of garden-stuff and pot-herbs, thickened with wheat flour. The general bread corn is wheat; the remainder of the dinner, with bread and cheese, is given to them, with a pint of ale for supper, and the remnants, as before-mentioned, are eaten the next morning: this is their weekly diet, Sundays excepted, when they usually partake of whatever fresh meat may be prepared for the heads of the family."

P. 388. " The animal food chiefly consumed in farm-houses is pickled pork, and some cured bacon; with both a considerable portion of vegetables are dressed and served up. The universal bread corn is wheat, which is used as well among the *peasantry* as in farm-houses, and in the latter with the broad bran and coarse pollard only taken out."

Farm Laborers.—Wages.—P. 385. " The stated daily labour through the county may be taken in the winter at 9s., in the summer at 12s. per week."—P. 386. " In hay time, the wages of 2s. per day are continued, with drink and occasional eating. In harvest the same wages, with drink, board certain, and sometimes lodging at the farm-house."

Mr.

Mr. V. repeatedly mentions the indolence of farm laborers in Hampshire.—P. 381. " Labour, in general, is very loosely performed; the regulations badly, or rather not at all enforced, as to the stated hours of work, or the proportion of labour required to be performed for making out day-work, and when not employed by contract."

P. 385. " It was a matter of no small surprise, to notice in Devonshire, the labourer on his way home in the summer season at five o'clock in the afternoon. In this county the same thing may often be witnessed, from one to one and a half hour earlier in the day : in the winter season there are but few labourers that reach their work sooner than eight, or about an half hour after that time in the morning, and commonly quit work at three."

He thus endeavors to account for those dilatory habits.— P. 384. " There is scarcely any part of this county that does not afford a temptation at no great distance, for withdrawing from the common labours of the field, the resident *peasantry* of its neighbourhood, and rendering a supply of labourers as uncertain, as on the most pressing occasions, they are difficult to obtain.

" The peat meadows in Berkshire draw numbers from the north western parts of the county. The forests, wastes, and woodlands, allure many to task-work in such places, cutting wood and raising fuel. The saltings and fisheries on the coast offer employment for a number of hands during summer; a number are continually employed in the transport of timber from the woods to the canals, and other boatable waters; and to crown the whole, Portsmouth, and the other ship yards on the coast, afford a constant market for all the prime and picked labourers in the country, leaving little behind but feebleness and debility, to carry forward the common labours of the county.

" This evil does not appear to rest here, for from the very high wages these people are capable of making at the task-work they are chiefly engaged in, they are able to dispense with the ordinary hours of attendance; and thus an example of idleness is set to the more supine and inactive labourer at home, and who without corresponding exertions, thinks himself as fairly entitled to such indulgence as the younger, stronger, and more vigilant man."—These are sensible, well considered observations.

WORKING ANIMALS.—In the established practice of professional occupiers, the slow-paced breeds of heavy *horses* appear to be prevalent, or universal.—P. 376. " Although it is necessary in most parts of this county to have strong teams for carrying out the crop, performing long and heavy journeys upon the road, and for hauling chalk, marl, clay,
&c.

&c. nearer home, yet among the larger sort of horses generally through the county, there is by far too much bone,
and being often in low condition, they have too frequently
a coarse, heavy, and uncomfortable appearance."

Nevertheless, among proprietors, who occupy for amusement or conveniency, a spirit for working *oxen* is evidently
shown, by several circumstantial notices.

IMPLEMENTS.—The Reporter has furnished matter enough
to fill more than forty pages of print, on this *popular* subject; and has thought it fitting to embellish his chapter
with ten engravings. I am, however, so dull of apprehension, or so intimately acquainted with the merits and demerits of implements of husbandry, that I cannot perceive,
in those lengthened details, even one item of information,
that would materially add to the value of my Work.

MANURE.—This is a subject on which Mr. Vancouver has
bestowed especial attention. Remarks, on various species,
are found in three distinct parts of his work.   In his
section, " Soil," fossil manures are incidentally noticed.
In another, headed " Paring and Burning," the several
species and varieties of manures, in use, in the county of
Southampton, are brought forward in detail. And, in the
final chapter of the book, entitled " Means of Improvement," the subject is entered upon in a theoretic way ; the
writer descending to first principles ; reasoning on abstract
premises ; and indulging in speculative opinions.

Regarding the latter portion of the author's labor, it
would be very improper not to allow that his arguments are
often ingenious; some of his positions well founded; and
his dictates frequently entitled to consideration. But they
are injudiciously placed in a report of provincial practices.
I therefore consign the Reporter's *philosophy* of Manures,
to the critical examinations of others; and confine myself to the *substance* of those which are in use, in Hampshire.

We search in vain, however, both in the table of contents and the body of the book, for a chapter or section,
entitled MANURE.—Turn we, therefore, to " Sect. II. PARING
and BURNING," for the following detail.

Marl.—Different varieties of fossil substances, to which
this name is attached, are raised, in the new-forest district,
for the purpose of meliorating its surface soils. The specific
qualities of those fossils, any further than their colors convey, do not appear. Neither the nature of their grosser
parts (unless in a few instances) nor the proportion of calcarious matter they contain, is mentioned. Of course, the
report, as to the quantity set on, is vague ; and the calculations, on the expence of marling, can convey no practical
                                        instructions

instructions to the cultivators of lands lying out of the district. This want of *analysis* is the more observable, as in the author's theoretic disquisitions, he is not sparing of *chemical language.*

The use of marl, on the vale lands of South Hampshire, as in various other vale-land districts in the kingdom, appears to be on the decline.

P. 339. " In the cultivated parts of the country, and on some of the wastes between the Southampton and Beauley rivers, argillaceous and calcareous marl prevails (the former being often converted into a most beautiful white brick), yet there are many farmers in this quarter who seem much disposed to relinquish the advantages to be derived from this valuable manure, and in its place apply dressings of chalk."

Chalk.—P. 340. " The use of marl has, however, been generally superseded by that of chalk, particularly on all the stronger lands within a convenient distance of the Southampton river, and applied at the rate of 35 and 40 tons per acre, brought round from Fareham, Portsdown Hill, and even from the coasts of Kent and Essex in the river Thames; and usually costs in the vessel, about 4*s.* per ton."

P. 342. " There is a very common opinion amongst most improvers with chalk, that the deeper the chalk is procured, the better it answers the purpose for manure, from its falling more readily to powder by exposure to the air; and it is on that ground that so great a preference is given to the chalk which is obtained from the tunnel of the Basingstoke Canal, which is carried through Grewel-hill. This chalk has obtained so great and just a reputation, that vast quantities of it are transported along the canal; and the chalk-pits at Odiham and Kingsclere, are not unfrequently deserted by the neighbouring farmers, for the sake of procuring a superior chalk, though at a much greater expense, from the tunnel under Grewel-hill."

Lime.—This the Reporter classes among " stimulant" manures:—whereas, the two former—Marl and Chalk— appear (p. 344) as " alteratives."—P. 344. " In the Vale of Petersfield lime is getting much into use as a manure: it is generally made of the common white chalk of that country, and burnt in kilns with culm or small coal."

Ashes.—P. 346. " Turf, beat, peat, and coal-ashes, are all much used, and whenever they can be reasonably procured, in this county."

" When the Berkshire peat-ashes are used, they are applied most commonly for sainfoin or young seeds in the month of February, seldom exceeding 20 bushels per acre,
                                                                    and

and costs at the wharfs 7*d*. per heaped Winchester bushel.
The common peat or turf-ashes will usually cost about 4*d*.
per bushel."

Sea Weed.—The occupiers, along the coast of Hampshire,
appear, by this report, to be unmindful of this species of
manure.

Marsh Mould.—P. 344. " Very great improvements have
been made on the light sandy lands in the neighbourhood
of Christ-church, by ouze procured from the low grounds,
and which in times of old were apparently accessible to
the sea water. In places where no material injury is likely
to result from lowering the surface ; the green sward is
carefully pared off, and a spit or more of the rich tender
loam (formerly deposited by the land and sea waters) is
taken out, when the green sward is again carefully replaced,
and no injury is supposed to accrue to the grass land,
provided the work is properly done, and during the winter
season."

Sheepfold.—P. 349. " Whenever the tillage land and
winter-fallows are so wet as not to admit penning with the
sheep, the upland meadows are sometimes folded in an enlarged space, giving such land about a two-third dressing.
This succeeded by an ensuing moist season, will much improve and augment the ensuing crop of grass ; but whenever the dry March winds dispose the folded surface to
crust or bake, and which will sometimes happen, harrowing, or lightly scarifying, affords immediate relief ; besides
its tending to the more complete destruction of the moss,
and consequently encouraging a closer and sweeter pile of
herbage. When the average produce of hay for some years
has been about 30 cwt. per acre, by this treatment it has
been frequently improved to two tons and upwards, of a
superior quality, and with a proportionate increase in the
value of the aftermath, or second growth."

SEMINATION.—In a section, or division, of the work
under examination,—entitled " Miscellaneous: chiefly in
comparison with the drill and broadcast husbandry,"—is the
following passage.—P. 217. " However well informed, experienced, and candid men, may have been led to differ in
opinion on this subject, such difference is presumed to have
arisen from no other cause than the peculiarity of the soil
to which either the broad-cast or drill husbandry may have
been applied, leading to conclusions on both sides equally
vague and erroneous, but from which it can only be inferred upon this, as well as upon most other occasions,
where truth and utility are the sole and only objects in
view, that opinions both for and against either practice have
been well and correctly founded ; and that in equally eligible

ble situations both practices are proper and advisable to be pursued. This truth can no where be more fully shewn than from what has taken place on the experimental farm in the parish of Clanfield, lately belonging to, and under the direction of the South Hants Agricultural Society.

" Mr. Jolliffe, the present very respectable occupier of that farm at Clanfield, relates, that after a trial of about five years upon two hundred acres of arable land, one moiety of which was exclusively employed in the drill, the other in the broad-cast husbandry, the Society thought proper to decline any farther trials in illustration of their respective excellence, and the stock, crop, and lease of the farm, were sold. This farm is now cultivated on the most improved system of broad-cast management, by the gentleman just mentioned : his green crops are good, and the white straw crops vastly superior to the generality in that neighbourhood. It is here to be observed, that the soil of this farm varies from a tough red loam abounding with flints, to a dry chalk rubble, a strong grey chisselly loam."

I do not mean, by bringing this fact forward, to impress on the minds of my readers that Mr. Vancouver is, or was at the time of writing, an *antidrillist;* as that would be unfair. He has, in the course of his work, repeatedly spoken favorably of the " drill system." And has, moreover, bestowed a sheet and a half of paper and printing, with of course much time and hard labor, on vague *calculations* of *comparison,* between the two operations.

ARABLE CROPS.

To this important subject, the Reporter has appropriated one fourth of his volume. With what profit, in the estimation of its Reviewer, will presently be seen.

WHEAT.—This princely crop is treated of, *districtwise;* in a section entitled " *Tillage;*" not only at the commencement of the section and along the heads of the pages throughout, but in the table of contents. No such section, head, or other division, as *Wheat* is to be found in the book, tho the subject of it fills more than two sheets; through which I have patiently pursued it—district after district—without, I can almost say, instruction, or even interest. The few extracts, subjoined, are all that I feel myself warranted to incorporate with this Work.

P. 134. (District, Chalk Hills.) " Whether the soil consists of a dry chalky rubble, or approaches a bright hazel mould, the open field, or tenantry lands, as well as those that are in severalty, are generally first opened about Midsummer, by half-ploughing or raftering, and which with one, or at most

most two succeeding earths, with proportionate dragging, barrowings, and rolling, the toughest and most matted green sward is readily subdued. This being effected, dung, or sheep-fold, or when the late fallow did not take place, but that some prior green crop has been penned off upon the land, forms the usual manure for procuring crops of wheat on such land. The seed required is about three bushels and a half per acre, sown broast-cast, and let in with the nine or eleven-share plough; harrowed twice in a place lengthwise, and then across the ridges, until the seed is as completely covered as may be deemed necessary, or that such a mode of proceeding will admit of; but when the necessary dressing has not been completed before the wheat is sown, folding in dry weather upon the sown wheat, and even upon the green wheat between Christmas and the middle of April (the ewes and lambs feeding in the day-time upon turnips or in the water-meadows); is found to produce a very great advantage to the ensuing crop. By this practice one instance occurred upon the survey upon lands of this description, where the improvement made was such as to yield a produce of 46 bushels to the acre; it is always found most abundantly to answer, by giving that consistence to the surface of these soils, so favourable to the future growth of wheat, affording a more uniform plant, with much longer and better set ears at harvest."

P. 154. (Isle of Wight.) " Spring wheat has been sown in the island, but when put in *so late* as Candlemas,* is always liable to mildew; an effect seldom experienced in the wheat crop under any other circumstances, and when the crop is sown in due season. A lamentable example of this practice occurred not many years since, of an ingenuous and speculative farmer sowing, *under the recommendation of high authority, about 60 acres of spring wheat,* the average produce of which was scarcely a sack of merchantable wheat per acre ; and the man was consequently ruined."

" Throughout the whole of this county, the wheat is commonly rolled with a heavy roller in the spring of the year; it is also occasionally harrowed, particularly on the chalk rubbly and strong grey loams, both of which are extremely liable to bake and encrust upon the surface, in such a manner as to set the plant fast after heavy rains and a sudden drying wind in the spring of the year.

" There are but few parts of the county where the early wheats

* The *true spring wheat* (triticum œstivum) should not be sown until two months *after* Candlemas.

wheats are not fed by sheep, cows, or young cattle, in the month of March, and sometimes as late as new Lady-day."

BARLEY.—P. 158. " The common modes of cultivating barley in this county are two, one after turnips, the other upon a wheat stubble, which has been winter-fallowed."

OATS.—Tartarian or *Reed* Oats.—P. 163. " This grain, however justly it was condemned on our first knowledge of it, has from early and thick sowing been found most wonderfully to improve within a period of twenty-five or thirty years : by these means it has in a few instances been brought to a superior quality of the average above stated," (36 lb., the Winchester bushel,) " and with an excess in quantity to the amount of six or eight bushels per acre."

PEAS.—P. 167. " A considerable mystery still seems to hang over certain properties of pease, with regard to their boiling well for soup or porridge; good boilers being sometimes sown upon fields which have never been known to refuse yielding a produce possessing a similar quality, but that effect afterwards ceasing, and a hard indissoluble pea has been produced, that continued for several successive periods; whilst on the other hand, land that had never been known, or even suspected of being able to communicate a boiling quality to its pease, would unexpectedly give to the produce of an hard, and almost impenetrable pea, all the properties of being excellent boilers."

This, as well as the above, is an item of information which is new to me.—No authority is named.

POTATOES.—P. 184. " This important root is judiciously attended to in a greater or less degree throughout the county, and for human food almost exclusively.   The general practice is to cultivate them in rows from eighteen to twenty-seven inches a-part.   Grass potatoes, or those cultivated upon old lay ground in beds, and in the manner practised in Ireland, are by no means uncommon."

TURNEPS.—P. 175. " This valuable plant seems to be daily gaining ground among the most respectable farmers and best agricultural characters in the county."

This crop appearing, in the above notice, to be still in its nonage, in Hampshire, it would be unreasonable to expect much practical information of value, concerning its culture, there.   The following information, however, is worth registering.   It would have been a satisfaction to have been informed in which of the Reporter's districts the practice prevails.

P. 177. " In preparing for the tankard, and other common turnips, the usual practice is, to give the first earth about Candlemas; upon this earth muckle and sheep fold,
that

that is, littering the sheep-fold with long dung from the straw-yard, and penning upon it about half the usual quantity of sheep per acre until Midsummer, or dung, or mixing, previous to the last earth, and sow the manured land thus fresh ploughed in every day, between the 10th and 25th of June. The same management is pursued in the culture of turnips designed for late or winter use, with this difference only in point of season, that the later turnips may be kept sowing through all July."

In his section, "Turneps," this Reporter speaks not only of BULBOUS RAPE, but of KOHL RABI—or "Hungarian turneps;" and, on the latter, in such terms as SIR THOMAS TYRWHITT must be well pleased with.—P. 180. "So extremely sanguine (and perhaps with good reason) are some gentlemen, on the superior excellence of this plant, that there is scarcely a circumstance unfavourable in the culture of turnips in general, that this plant is not stated to be provided with the means of controuling."

CULTIVATED HERBAGE.—*Rape* and *Raygrass.*—P. 214. "Mr. Richards, of North-house, sows rape about the 1st of July, about 6 lb. per acre, with three bushels of ray-grass for spring food. The rape will generally be ready for the first feeding by the beginning of October, when a small bite also of the ray-grass will appear. The feeding it thus early, and occasionally with the coleseed to Christmas, has not been found in the slightest manner to injure it. The ray-grass with the coleseed in the spring of the year, affords an admirable pasturage for the ewes and lambs, and about Midsummer (by which time the prime and best virtues of the ray-grass is expended), the field receives a short summer fallow for wheat, and frequently with no other dressing than what is thus procured. The autumnal and spring food thus produced, is considerable, and equally acceptable at both seasons."

SAINFOIN.—P. 191. "This very excellent *grass* is cultivated with universal success on all soils having an understratum of chalk; it is sometimes sown upon land of a thin gravelly texture, and lying upon a deep bed of dry pebbly gravel; but here it does not seem to flourish as well as upon the thin dry chalky downs, for which it seems more particularly adapted, and where it is generally found to continue a fair mowing plant for 12 or 15 years."

Sainfoin *Hay.*—The subjoined remarks, on making it, are worthy of the consideration of its growers.—P. 192. "This hay should never be so far dried as to become exhausted of its sap before it is put together: its undergoing a good full heat in the stack, seems particularly necessary for the purpose of maturing its juices into that saccharine
principle

principle which gives to it its best and most nutritious
quality. This point attained, sainfoin will preserve nearly
as good a keeping quality as that of any other hay, but
otherwise it will become harsh and sticky, when such parts
will be refused, even by hungry store cattle, for the softer
and more inviting qualities possessed by well got barley
straw."—This being as it may, horses will not be found to
be quite so fastidious.

Breaking up Sainfoin Leys.—P. 193. " The most common mode of breaking up the old sainfoin-lays is to half
plough or rafter them as shallow as possible about Candlemas: in this state the ground lies for about a month,
when taking the advantage of a dry spell, the rafters are
dragged and cross-harrowed, when the balks of whole
ground left by raftering are taken up by the breast-plough.
These, after laying for some time, are tortured with the
drags and harrows, and afterwards collected into heaps, and
burnt. The breast-ploughing, collecting, and burning the
green sward, will cost from 15s. to 25s. per acre. The
former surface thus destroyed, and the ashes spread, the
field is readily reduced to any state of subsequent tillage
for turnips or for wheat ; and when sufficiently in time, the
early tankard-turnip is first cultivated, fed off, and the
ground sown with wheat as early as possible."

GRASS LANDS.

WATERED MEADOWS.—We have no estimate of the *ex-
tent* of this variety of grass lands, within the limits of Hampshire. A pretty accurate account, I believe, of their *localities* may be seen in p. 292, aforegoing.

On the *Management* of " Water Meads," the following
passages, which appear in the Reporter's chapter " Grass
Land," are entitled to transcription.

P. 269. " These meadows, when lying on a sound dry
bottom, are regularly hurdled off, leaving open hurdles for
the lambs to pass through and feed on a-head. The couples
are seldom suffered to remain on the water-meadows all
night; but as the weather, or other circumstances may
point out, are folded upon the winter fallows, lay, or stubble
grounds. The usual hours of keeping them on the meadows, are from eight o'clock in the morning till six in the
evening, and this generally continues from the last week in
March till the first week in May, both inclusive.

" As soon as the first shoot of the water-meadows is thus
taken off by the ewes and lambs, the carriages and lateral
conductors of the water are examined and righted, and the
watering is renewed each section of the meadow in the
manner

manner before noticed, but not requiring more than two, or at farthest three days at a time, and in about seven or eight weeks from the time the couples were removed, the hay crop is grown, and becomes fit for mowing; the watering being frequently repeated during the greater part of this period, and till within eight or ten days of the mowers going into the meadow.

" The cutting of the grass young, and in full sap, is indispensable for preserving its nourishing qualities."

P. 272. " These water-meadows are sometimes, but rarely, laid up for a second crop. They are more frequently fed, after the second summer-watering, with grazing or store cattle; but when depastured by milch-cows, the increase of the dairy produce from such a fresh and succulent herbage, is represented to be very considerable, and that without abating in any respect of its high land pasture quality. The meadows are commonly thus fed till preparation is making or nearly completed for the winter flowing."

P. 277. " An opinion is strongly cherished, that the hay and after-grass of the water-meadows (let the meadows be ever so well managed, and their produce equally well saved) do not contain that feeding or fattening quality which is known to appertain to grass voluntarily produced upon an equally well drained, and in other respects similarly circumstanced soil, but without the aid or stimulus brought on by irrigation. Cattle or horses, they contend, feeding upon the hay, or pastured upon the after-grass of watered ground, will generally hold their own, or, in other words, keep to the condition they were in when put to such food: they will grow or increase in size, but not in condition, from such fodder or pasturage."

This opinion, I believe, is general among occupiers of watered meadows. The nutritious quality of the early spring shoots is very probably given by raygrass, which forms a principal part of the herbage, at that season:—a fact, this, which I speak of from my own examinations.

",DRY MEADOWS," and LOWLAND PASTURE GROUNDS.— P. 262. " *Meadows.*—Those of the greatest extent and value are found along the respective water-courses in the county.

" In the woodland part of the county, the proportion between the enclosed, cultivated, arable, and grass land, is stated about one-seventh of the latter to six-sevenths of the former."

P. 264. " The herbage, on the general run of these low grounds and pastures, is not thought equal to the feeding of a cow or steer exceeding 7½, or at the utmost eight
score

score per quarter. The better, and indeed prime pastures
(of which the District before us affords but a small proportion), will nearly finish an ox of 10½ or 11 score per
quarter, in the same time, that is, between the middle of
May and that of November; but in either case, the extent
of ground over which the feeding cattle would be admitted
to range, was not satisfactorily ascertained.

" No manuring or compost was particularly understood
as being applied, either as to time or expense, in the renovating of these grass lands. The produce of hay from
those of the first quality, was estimated at 36 cwt. per acre,
and of the inferior 22 cwt. The after-grass not consumed
by the dairy cows or store cattle, is usually applied for the
agistment of sheep taken in during the winter months, at 7s.
or 8s. per head, and in the manner before noticed.

" The rent or value of this land, whether meadow or
pasture, is found, from various statements, to fluctuate
between 15s. and 50s., and which, on a general average,
is thought to equal about 28s. per acre.

" In the chalk district, the proportion of permanent grass
land (excepting the sheep downs) is small in comparison to
the extent of land subject to a system of up and down husbandry. It consists of some upland meadow or pasture
ground, and which seemed to occur in the greatest quantity
south of Overton, and extending towards Popham and the
Strattons. The low grounds and vallies of the Teste, the
Auton, the Itchen, and the river that passes through Titchfield, and obtains its exit into the sea at Hilt-head, exhibit
many laudable exertions which have hitherto been made,
and are still making, in converting the eligible parts of such
vallies into water-meadow."

For a method of *forming* " dry meadows," see ozier
beds, p. 329, aforegoing.

HIGH-LAND PASTURES, or " MAIDEN DOWNS."—Mr. Vancouver properly advocates the cause of this species of
permanent herbage; showing, in different parts of his
work, the propriety, or necessity, of preserving them in
their natural state; and arraigning the *officious* meddlings
of theory, with well grounded practice; in terms not un-
similar, in tendency, to those expressed, p. 300, aforegoing,
on the same topic.

The subjoined extract sufficiently declares Mr.V.'s opinion
on this subject.—P. 266. " The most striking shades of
difference in the soil of the sheep downs, have already
been noticed under three distinct heads, in the Chapter
which treats of soil generally. It will therefore be only
necessary in this place to say a few words on their herbage,
and what appears to the Surveyor as being the best
                                                          mode

mode of managing and preserving it in its purest excellence.

"It is found to consist of a prodigious variety of plants and grasses, as well upon the black mould as upon the soils possessing a grey and a hazel colour, and whether of an equally loose, or of a more close and compact nature: the value of all, but particularly of the former, will very much depend upon the close treading and paring (by the sheep) which it constantly undergoes. This done, the pasturage will preserve its value; and hence it follows, *that sheep of a peculiar size and hardiness are alone proper for such sheep-walks, and no others;* for whenever the down sheep-walk rises above the height of good store sheep range, the coarser grasses get a-head, and the flocks will suffer considerably before they will feed upon it.

"The large tracts of maiden down which within a few years have been reduced to the lowest stage of exhaustion and sterility, from the short-sighted policy and ever-to-be-lamented practice of paring, burning, and destroying, their native green sward, have contributed in a most alarming degree to the diminution of sheep in such parts of this district. Were it possible to cultivate rape, or any species of green crop upon these exhausted lands, and upon which the stock might depasture without appropriating the ordinary resources of in-field manure for raising such crops, the evil would in some degree admit of mitigation, and a larger proportion of the former sheep stock of the occupation would not only yield a correspondent profit as stock, but by their folding, contribute in a more extensive degree to the renovation and improvement of the ancient tillage lands. These advantages, however, are greatly abridged in the cases here alluded to, and the evils attendant upon them not only operates in a two-fold degree, but at the same time without the least shadow of relief or remedy.

"A very general opinion prevails throughout the chalk district, that unless the larger farms can have water-meadow at one end, and a maiden down at the other, or at least some sort of permanent grass land, it is utterly impossible for such farms to be conducted to advantage, and as they should be: hence the incalculable injury resulting to estates, not only from the breaking up of old down land, but by paring and burning, utterly despoiling it of all its fruitful energies."

ORCHARDS.—P. 289. "In the woodland, chalk, or malmy districts, very few apples are attempted to be raised beyond what is necessary for kitchen use. The chalky character composing so large a proportion of these districts,

tricts, seems by no means adapted for orchard ground
on a large scale. Upon the marl or clay bottom lands
in the south and south-western parts of the county, orchards
were more generally observed, and from which a few families were in the practice of making two or three hogsheads of cider annually; but this appeared no where to
be an object of much concern among the rural inhabitants.
In the Isle of Wight it is somewhat different; for although
the orchard ground even there is of no considerable extent,
there are but few farmers who do not make from two to
six hogsheads of cider annually. It is made chiefly for
home use; but its excellent quality (principally derived
from the strong brown loams upon which the greater part
of the orchards are cultivated) often carries it to so high
a price, as to form a powerful temptation with many of
the farmers for selling certain parts of their annual produce to their northern neighbours, by whom it is in much
demand and held in high estimation."

VINEYARD.—Mr. Warner, in his sketch Report of the
Isle of Wight, mentions, at some length, an experiment
which Sir Richard Worsley was prosecuting at the time
Mr. W. wrote, (in 1793 or 4) with a view to produce *Wine*,
in the Isle of Wight! The subjoined is Mr. Vancouver's
account of the result.

P. 259. "On a subject so new and interesting, the
Surveyor could not fail of being sensibly disappointed,
when, upon his approaching Undercliff, he was not only
refused admittance to that charming little spot, but from
the cliffs above, the whole of the late vineyard was shown
to him in the condition of a verdant lawn, and, with the
only visible remains of the works of the vineyard, a stone
wall about five feet high ranging through the middle
of it."

Either the climature of this island has changed, or certain classical writers must have mistaken *apple* for *grape*
wine; or have fastidiously refused to write *cider*.

LIVESTOCK.

HORSES.—*Forest Ponies;*—provincially "Heath Croppers."—P. 376. "The ordinary height of the heath or
forest horse of this country is about twelve hands. They
propagate indiscriminately upon these wastes, where they
seek their living throughout the year, and at four years
old may generally be purchased for about 5*l.*"

CATTLE.—*Breed.*—P. 352. "Hampshire does not appear to possess, as exclusively belonging to the county,
any specific breed of *cow* cattle. The Sussex, Suffolk,
Leicester, Hereford, Glamorgan, North and South Devon,
and

and Norman breed, are indiscriminately met with, and
have their respective advocates, in every part of the county.
The Sussex, Suffolk, Hereford, Glamorgan, North and
South Devon, command however as general a preference
for draught, as does the Norman for the bucket, or the
use of the dairy."

For a notice concerning the *native* or *forest* breed of
cattle, see the head Occupiers, p. 333, aforegoing.

DAIRY.—*Butter*.—P. 359. " What has already been observed with regard to the indiscriminate mixture in the
breeds of cattle employed for draught in this county, will
equally apply as to the different breeds of cows in use
for the dairy, where, although the genuine Norman and
crosses from that breed, are universally preferred, yet necessity seems to command in the present day, that a considerable mixture of different breeds should be admitted
in composing a dairy of any extent in this county."

No reason is offered for this puzzling assertion. The
subjoined account of the merits of the Norman cows,
which is almost wonderful, considering their inferior size,
has a tendency to weaken it.—P. 362. " A cow of the
Norman breed, belonging to Mr. Anthony Groves, of Lymington, produced in 1797, in ten months and twenty days,
1336 gallons, two quarts, and half a pint of milk, beer
measure, which at 2*d*. per quart, sold for 44*l*. 11*s*. 0½*d*.
Another cow also, of the Norman breed, but of less size,
which belonged to Mr. Richard Jennings, of Milford,
yielded, from 15 to 16 lb. of butter for several weeks
after calving. This cow was fed on hay in the winter,
and had a range over three paddocks with an old horse.
Mr. Groves's cow was fed in the house during winter, with
grains and hay."

Letting Butter Dairies.—P. 364. " There are many cows
kept for the use of the dairy, that are rented out to dairy-
men and their families at from 7*l*. to 9*l*. per cow."

" This practice obtains very generally throughout most
parts of the county, including the Isle of Wight."

Suckling.—P. 362. " *Suckling*.—For this purpose, a number of cows are kept in different parts of the county, and
many calves are suckled for supplying with veal the markets of London, Portsmouth, Chichester, Winchester, Newbury, Reading, Salisbury, &c."

SHEEP.—Hampshire, it would seem from Mr. V.'s Report,
has no established breed,—no one that it can call its own.—
P. 365. " In the woodland district of this county," (the
Northern Vale Lands,) " the heath sheep and Old Hampshire, or the native Wilts breed, were those formerly the
most prevalent, but which in many places are now found

to

to have given way to a cross of the New Leicester upon the native speckled-face Berkshire and Old Wiltshire breeds."

P. 366. " It is however contended by many discerning and experienced men, that the breed best suited to the woodland district, is the old round-nosed, close-horned Wiltshire, which, from their superior height, are stated to stand better out of the dirt, and to bear with seemingly less suffering, the wet cold layer of the woodland clays, than the New Leicester, or any crosses of that breed upon the native Wilts or Berkshire."

" The native breed of the South Downs in Sussex, are spreading to a very wide extent throughout this county."

P. 368. " Upon the chalk downs in the Isle of Wight, the Sussex breed are becoming equally general, and so far as they are known, are as justly appreciated in such situations as on the more extended downs in other parts of the county."

The *Spanish* Breed.—P. 371. " The gentlemen" (whom) " the Surveyor had an opportunity of seeing, and who appear to have paid most attention to the improvement of wool by a cross with the Spanish Merina, are as follow."—Those gentlemen were Mr. Richards of Northhouse, Col. Cunningham of Malshanger, and Col. Mitford of Exbury.

Wool,—which Mr. Vancouver styles " one of the most important articles in the whole catalogue of rural economics,"—(p. 497.) has principally engaged his attention, while speaking of sheep; whether in the section bearing that name, or in proposing " Means of Improvement."

As a material of manufacture (native or foreign) wool is of the highest consideration, in this country; and, as such, forms a prominent object in English husbandry.—But seeing how much has been written of late years on the subject, and the small compass which every thing that *can* be said of it lies,—I perceive nothing in Mr. V.'s sentiments, concerning it, that would materially add to the useful information of my readers.

SWINE.—P. 378. " The native hog of this county is a coarse, raw boned, flat-sided animal, agreeing in no respect with the idea entertained of it in other parts of the kingdom: the great number fed for a few weeks in the close of autumn, upon the mast which the forest and other woodlands produce, in the county, and the excellent mode of curing hog-meat practised by the house-keepers, have contributed in a far greater degree to establish that superiority ascribed to Hampshire bacon, than any inherent excellence in its native breed of hogs. Very few, however,

of

of the genuine native hog are to be met with, the common stock being either the native Berkshire breed, or a considerable predominance of that blood in the native swine of the country."

FISHERIES.—*Salmon.*—P. 49. " In all the rivers and inlets discharging into the sea, salmon are caught in their season: this fishery, however, is by no means so productive as formerly, particularly in the great supply that was drawn from the Southampton Water : this must be ascribed to the caprice of the animal in quitting its former haunts, and *certainly not* to the destruction of the young fish on their return to seaward in the winter season." (?)

Carp and *Tench.*—Market fish ponds, similar to those of *Surry* and *Sussex,* are found on the margin of Hampshire, bordering on those Counties.

PRINCIPLES OF IMPROVEMENT.

Mr. VANCOUVER, in conformity with the plan of the Board, has collected, at the close of his Report, his ideas concerning what he conceived to be the subjects of improvement, of the established practices of the County. In this, as in other instances of the same kind, I have, on the principle of simplexity, incorporated such particulars, as I have deemed to be entitled to notice, with those which I have found in the body of the Work, on the same subjects.

What I think it right to lay before my readers, in this place, are some well conceived, GENERAL PRINCIPLES, concerning the IMPROVEMENT of the " NATIONAL TERRITORY."— P. 450. " The objects which at all times, but which at this momentous crisis seem to press with the greatest force on the attention of Government, and upon the thinking part of the community of these kingdoms, are manifold and various, but which may generally be conceived under one or other of the following heads.

" First, the means of procuring from the national territory, and with the least possible expenditure of human labour, an ample and never-failing supply of animal and vegetable food.

" Secondly, in providing raw materials for manufacture, to the full extent the soil and climate of these islands will admit of ; and,

" Thirdly, The raising of naval stores, as far as possible, within ourselves, for the purpose of preserving our present maritime superiority."

After assuming another position,—concerning *population,—*

tion,—which I do not conceive to be altogether tenable,— Mr. V. draws this spirited inference.—P. 451. "Any practice therefore that does not ultimately tend to preserve the natural fertility of the national territory, is politically and morally wrong; and the advocates for such practices, be they who they may, are acting under a blind invincible prejudice, and to all intents and purposes becoming the most dangerous of all enemies to the permanent improvement, internal strength, and external importance of the country." *Hear ! hear !*

SURREY.

SURREY.

SURREY has not an entire *District* within its outlines. Its *Northern Vale Lands* form part of the VALE of
LONDON. Its *Heathlands*, on its western confine, unite
with those of Berkshire, Hampshire, and Sussex. Its
Chalk Hills are a portion of the EASTERN CHALK HILLS
of the SOUTHERN COUNTIES. And its *Southern Vale Lands*
were evidently cast, by Nature, in the same mold with similar
lands in Sussex;—together forming one of the most extensive vales in the kingdom; bearing the popular name of the
WEALD or " WILD" of SUSSEX.

For details, concerning those several component parts of
the County of Surrey, see my SOUTHERN COUNTIES.

" GENERAL VIEW

OF THE

AGRICULTURE

OF THE

COUNTY OF SURREY,

WITH

OBSERVATIONS ON THE MEANS OF ITS IMPROVEMENT.

BY MR. WILLIAM JAMES, AND MR. JACOB MALCOLM,

OF STOCKWELL, NEAR CLAPHAM.

1794."

THE QUALIFICATIONS of those Gentlemen, for the task
of reporting the rural practices of a County, are not difficult
to appreciate; tho they are not, by themselves, immediately expressed; otherwise than by the title page.—They
were, I believe, at the time they wrote, nurserymen, on an
extensive scale, and of good repute.

Their

Their performance evinces them to be, or to have been (for I know not which, at this time is strictly proper) men of mind, and not wanting in exertion. On the few subjects which they may be said to have handled, they are satisfactorily intelligent.—These subjects are *Woodlands* and *Planting*; the *Appropriation* of uncivilized Lands; and the forming and keeping of *Roads*. On most other branches and subdivisions of natural, political, and rural economy, as they are connected with *Agriculture*, their work is very defective.

Insufficient, however, as this Report certainly is, as a *picture* of the rural practices of Surrey, it would betray a want of knowledge of the human mind to image that men (or a man, for the pronoun singular is once at least used) of business, and good natural abilities, should sit down to write a book, without eliciting some useful or interesting ideas; and it will be seen that, in the work now under consideration, I have been able to select a few passages that may be acceptable to my readers.

The number of pages—ninetyfive.

Two sketch engravings:—one of them of a horse hoe, the other of the form of a road.

No map.

NATURAL ECONOMY.

EXTENT.—P. 8. " The county is computed to be thirty-nine miles in length, from east to west; and twenty-five miles in breadth, from north to south; and 146 miles in circumference; and, taken as a plane, contains about 481,947 statute acres."

WATERS.—The " rivers" of Surrey are the *Wandle* (a calcareous " bourn," or brooklet) which rises out of the northern margin of the Chalk Hills. The *Mole*, a larger stream, a brook, which originates in the Weald, or Southern Vale Lands, and passes, a short distance, partially beneath a skirt of the Chalk Hills, in its course to the Thames. And the *Wey*, which has its rise in the Heathlands; and which, by a circuitous course, descends leisurely into the same capacious receptacle. This is a minor river; and is navigable for some miles from the Thames.

SOILS.—P. 8. " The upper soil is very various, consisting of black mould, clay, sand, chalk, and loams, of different depths. The under soil is of different strata, but principally composed of chalk and gravel, thereby rendering it dry, healthy, and pleasant."

This

This does not well apply to the southern vale lands—
the Weald or "Wild"—of Surrey; which is a clay-
bottomed, wet, unpleasant passage of country.

POLITICAL ECONOMY.

APPROPRIATION. — *Common Pastures.* — Much of
the Reporters' time has been occupied, in surveying, and
estimating the extents, of the unappropriated lands of
Surrey; descending to small commons and greens, down
to fifty or even twenty acres in extent ;—noting the soil or
soils and circumstances of each ; with a view toward their
inclosure and cultivation,—*or planting.* They have set
down the whole quantity at 96,000 acres ; and, on that
quantity, have made some political calculations.—For instance :—p. 24,—" Waste, $\frac{1}{4}$ of 96,000 acres = 24,000 acres
at 3 qrs." (of grain, as wheat, barley, oats, &c.) " per acre
= 72,000 qrs. at 27s. = £97,200."

On counting the several estimated quantities, I find that
instead of 96,000, there are not 75,000 acres of unappropriated pasture grounds :—namely, of *heathland* 50,720
acres (of the very worst lands in the island), and of grassy
commons, 23,750 acres; comprizing much very bad land.
Nevertheless, in the first page of the body of the Report is
the following passage.

After mentioning the favourable locality of the County,
with respect to the metropolis, and water carriage, the
Reporters say (p. 7.)—" Will it not then be matter of
surprise, that at the close of the *seventeenth* century, there
shall be found, in a county like this, commons and wastes
of the magnitude of 96,000 acres ; *the much greater part of
which, if not the whole*, capable of being made subservient
to the purposes of *agriculture*," (!) " and thereby enabling
us to supply those foreign markets, which stand in need of it,
with that superabundance which, to our shame be it spoken,
we draw at this time from Flanders, Holland, and America?"

I have thought it right to mention those mis-statements,
lest POLITICAL ARITHMATICIANS, who, I fear, are not always scrupulously inquisitive about their *data*, should
quote them, implicitly, as coming from the " high authority" of a Report to the Board of Agriculture.

Common Meadows.—This partially appropriated species
of " property" is still prevalent in the County of Surrey.
Messrs. James and Malcolm enumerate sundry instances,
and, among the rest, the celebrated RUNNEY MEAD ; which,

I

I believe, may be taken as a tolerably fair specimen of this inconvenient kind of " Landed Property."

P. 49. " Runneymead contains one hundred and sixty acres of good soil, and at present lets for twenty shillings per acre, tythe free. It is the property of ten persons, and in small parcels. After the 12th of August it is common to all the parish, who turn on an indefinite number of cattle, until March, when it is shut up again; but being subject to be flooded in the winter, it becomes poached by the number of cattle that are on at that time, to the destruction of the herbage, and consequent loss to the proprietors. This would be remedied by an inclosure, and would be worth from forty to sixty shillings per acre."

Common Fields.—The Reporters have also enumerated, and noticed the extents, the soils, and other circumstances, of the several open arable fields of the County. The subjoined list, with the extent of each field, is placed at the close of the detail.

P. 53. " Common fields.   No. of acres.

1.	Croydon,	1500
2.	Cheam,	3000
3.	Ewell,	650
4.	Epsom,	800
5.	Leatherhead,	2000
6.	Ashted,	700
7.	Fetcham,	150
8.	Bookham, .	450
9.	Clandon, East and West,	300
10.	Merve,	510
11.	Egham,	300
12.	Hythefield,	250
13.	Thorpe,	350
14.	Mortlake,	
—	Putney,	
—	Wandsworth,	1340
—	Battersea,	
15.	Sundry small common fields not worth particularizing,	135

12435"

INLAND NAVIGATION.—The *Thames* navigation bounds the northern margin of the County, for more than twenty miles. And the *Wey* " becomes navigable to the Thames at Weybridge, being of infinite benefit to the county, which it supplies with all sorts of necessaries, particularly coals from London. It is here worthy of remark, that the first locks that were constructed were erected upon this river by a gentleman of the name of Weston." p. 9.

ROADS.

ROADS.—This subject, and that of planting, are the only ones, which the Reporters speak of, as *practical* men. Their remarks and recommendations, tho of some length, are mostly proper. Few of them, however, are *new*. They are similar to those which I have long been inculcating. They contain some passages, which, as *corroborants*, are entitled to a place, here.

On the *Width* of Turnpike Roads.—P. 65. " The width of a road should be just as much as the extensiveness of the thoroughfare requires; that is to say, every approach to the metropolis, and for a distance not exceeding six miles, should have a road of forty feet wide, with a foot-way on each side of ten feet: beyond that distance the road may with great propriety be reduced to thirty-four feet wide, which is sufficient for four carriages to pass abreast, and which is more than perhaps may ever meet at one time in one spot. Exceeding this width all is useless, and adds greatly to the expence of keeping in repair. The foot-way here should be eight feet wide; beyond the distance of twelve miles, and to the land's end, the road should be thirty feet, and the foot-way six feet."

Their *Convexity.*—P. 65. " The convexity of every road should be just so much as, according to its width, no water shall lodge on the center or on its sides, but pass quickly to the edge, which should be higher than the ditch on the other side of the foot-way."

The Reporters have given an engraved diagram of what they conceive to be the proper dimensions, and form, of public roads. The width of the carriage road, in their sketch, is twenty feet, and the rise or convexity, at the crown, two feet; with a footpath, on each side, ten feet wide :—thus filling up the whole width of a *Parliamentary road!*

Messrs. James and Malcolm, however, have sufficient good sense to see the *extravagance* of such a width;—unless in the immediate environs of the metropolis; and, it may be added, in the immediate neighbourhoods of a few other large trading towns. My principal objection to their scale of roads lies in the width of cross-country roads, between town and town. Thirty feet of *hard road*, I conceive, is *much* too great. And more than one footpath, by the side of such a road, is quite unnecessary.

See my Treaties on Landed Property; or the abstract of it; for general observations on this important subject, in a civilized country.

On *Watering* Roads.—P. 67. " We cannot close this account without noticing the impolicy of watering the roads in the summer; for however pleasant and convenient it may be to be free from dust, yet the watering of such roads

proves

proves by their uniform badness, at almost all seasons, how
much it *wears* them; and the inevitable bad effect it has
upon them; and therefore wherever that is practised, and
pipes for the conveyance of river water are laid, it is in
vain for the public to expect or to look for good roads
there."

There is some truth in this statement; and the arguments
upon it are not groundless. But the mischief ensuing, from
the watering of roads, principally arises, I believe, not from
its *wearing* them; but from another cause: namely that of
its preventing the wind from operating in the manner it
otherwise would, in the valuable work of freeing the surface
from pulverized materials; and thus performing, in the
least expensive and most compleat way, the requisite business of *cleaning them*.

The surface of unwatered roads, unless in very close
situations, seldom fail, in the summer season, of being un-
burdened of their more finely pulverized, and no longer
useful, materials,—*by the wind;*—leaving the partially reduced matter on the surface. This desirable circumstance
not only renders a road pleasant to be travelled upon, but
tends to prevent the wear of the unground materials.
Whereas, by the operation of artificial *scraping*, this valuable matter is removed with the mud or wet dust; and is
thereby more than wasted; as it requires to be farther removed as a nuisance.

On the contrary, in the neighbourhood of London, and
wherever the operation of *watering* is practised,—by way
of " laying the dust,"—it is not merely laid for the day;
but, if the watering be continued, is effectually *arrested;*—
its thickness, in dry weather, daily increasing; until a fall
of rain turn the accumulated mass into a *bed of mud;* which
is become too soft to sustain, any longer, the tread of animals, and much less the wheels of carriages; yet is too
consistent to form a *current*. Whereas, had the same rain
fallen on a surface, free or nearly free from dust, or other
encumberance, it would have tended to *cleanse it*, rather
than have been the mean of *fouling it:*—the rain water
would have flowed off a well-formed road, and thereby
have *washed it;* and would not have been *arrested*, in its
turn, by the dust, which the waterings had collected.

I have seen the Kensington road covered, footlock or
midleg deep, with *puddle*;* and the road itself,—the *inundated* hard materials,—(gravel) kept in a soft " rotten"
state,

* And see Mr. Middleton's account of other roads in Middlesex;
p. 119, aforegoing.

state, week after week perhaps, during the summer months:—a circumstance which would, I think, be difficult to explain in any other way, than that which is here suggested.

Far be it from my intention to convey, in those remarks, any desire to suppress, altogether, the watering of roads. My aim has been merely that of endeavoring to trace its effect.

On *Turnpike Trusts.*—P. 62. " For several years past, the turnpike roads of this county have been under the direction of treasurers, who are trustees of the roads, and are appointed by the trust at large, at a meeting held for that purpose. A knowledge of the fundamental prinples of making roads is not deemed at all necessary to the election of such treasurers, but they are generally some respectable gentlemen in business, (if near town) and whither perhaps they go every day. Each appoints some inferior tradesman of the district in which he lives to be the surveyor, and who may be a carpenter, a bricklayer, or any other profession as it may happen ; so that without a particle of knowledge in the maintenance and principles of roads on either side, is the expenditure of hundreds of pounds committed to the day labourers, who are for the most part old and decrepid, and who being generally left to themselves, take every advantage : and as the surveyor does not know how much should be done, he is easily imposed upon by the men ; and as the money does not come out of his pocket, it is not very material for him to give himself much trouble about it."

Parochial Surveyors of Roads.—P. 67. " With regard to the parish roads, a mixture of good and bad, as is generally the case, is every where found ; as the office is elective, and passes from the one to the other every year, and among a certain class of the inhabitants, it too frequently happens, that as the ideas of the successor do not correspond with those of his predecessor, so, instead of following up what he had judiciously begun, a fresh system is pursued ; and thus is the money squandered away in idle and futile pursuits, instead of lowering the rates, by following wise measures. The money that is thus sunk, would generally more than pay an able surveyor, and one surveyor might superintend several parishes."—For a variety of similar remarks, see different volumes of this Abstract.

RURAL

RURAL ECONOMY.

ESTATES.—P. 26. "It does not appear, that in this district the land is generally possessed by large proprietors; and its contiguity to the metropolis, as well as the salubrity of its air, may contribute in some degree to produce this effect: it will not, however, admit of a question, but that there are some very large proprietors. However, as that is no criterion, it may be taken for granted, that there are perhaps few counties where the land is possessed in a fairer proportion."

IRRIGATION.—P. 37. "It does not appear, that watering of meadows is any where practised in this county, of sufficient extent to deserve particular notice; and indeed such is the nature of the county, that very few parts of it are capable of so desirable a practice at all; that which is watered does not appear to be done according to any *new system,* but simply conformable to the ideas of the possessor."

The fact is—Surrey has very litttle calcareous water, that can be used for this purpose. The Wey collects its waters from heathlands; and the Mole from noncalcareous vale lands.—The Wandle, it is true, is calcareous—almost purely so. Its head, the "Bourn," above Croydon, rises abruptly, and periodically, in a chalk hill valley; and the rest of its waters constantly boil up, at the feet of those hills. But its course is short, and its waters are, or have been, too profitably employed in the works of *manufacture* to be applied, in quantity, to the purpose of *agriculture.*

The MANAGEMENT of ESTATES.—The following truisms are so tersely put, and tell so well, *almost* throughout, that I must not refrain,—though they are not especially applicable to the management of landed property in " the County of Surrey,"—to give them a place, in this register.

P. 58. "To ascertain the fair proportion of rent between landlord and tenant is no very easy task; it requires a person possessed with a thorough knowledge of soils, a perfect acquaintance with the qualities of stock, and with the best systems of agriculture in use, and a character that will not be warped from his duty either by the opinion of the landlord, or by the artful insinuations of the tenant. Such a man is best qualified to do justice to both; and well would it be indeed, if gentlemen setting aside their prejudices and conceits, would make that the rule of their conduct."

WOODLANDS

WOODLANDS AND PLANTING.

These relative subjects, as I have before observed, are two of the few topics of enquiry to which the Reporters have paid particular attention. And their third—the State of Appropriation—appears to have been attended to, the more closely, with the view of collecting information that might forward the business of the second.

P. 67. " In the first part of the survey of this county, a full and particular account was given of every common, and piece of waste land, or barren heath, that is to be found in the whole district, marking distinctly, as we proceeded, the quality of the soil, and its aptitude to the growth of oak and other timber; from whence it will be deduced, that there does exist in this county a large tract of land, uncultivated and unemployed, and which, without injury to any person, might, under a proper system, be in part appropriated to the growth of timber, and ultimately tend to a lasting benefit to this kingdom."

Their opinion regarding " the prospect of a deficiency," is briefly this.—P. 68. " It appears but too visibly manifest, that the prospect of a deficiency does not so much arise from the want of a progressive state of timber, but from the present unfortunate system of cutting it down, as soon as it attains that age and size which would make it so desirable for this country that it should remain, as it is then past all danger; (the size we mean is about eighteen inches diameter.)"

The subjoined is their *liberal* scheme for preventing such a *licentious* proceeding.—P. 68. " Might it not be worth while for Government to purchase such timber standing at a fair valuation; and by an agreement with the proprietor to suffer it there to remain until wanted, paying a certain annual rent as might be deemed adequate for the use of the ground they occupy? Every person having oak to sell, in a situation to be conveyed to any of the dockyards, to be obliged to make a tender of it to Government first, and upon their refusal, to be at liberty to dispose of it as he pleased; and no man should be at liberty to cut down one tree without directly planting three in its stead, and which he should engage to protect effectually :"—whether, of course, the land may or may not be proper for that purpose!

The one thing most needful, under the present circumstances of the island, regarding this matter, is to *unburden* well soiled *culturable* lands (such as oaks of the sizes mentioned are found upon) from the *encumbrance* of large spreading timber trees (such as the dock yards of Government

ment require) rather than to *triple the load!* The Reporters of Surry, however, are not the only *planters* that
have recommended, aye and practised, so *improvident* a
plan.—For more general remarks on this subject, see
NORTHERN DEPARTMENT;—County of *Westmoreland.*

The Reporter's article, headed "Woods and Woodlands," is of considerable length; being a sort of *treatise*
on planting. If therefore it had possessed much merit
as such, it would have been improper for a place, here.
The subjoined remarks on *nursery grounds*, may however
be admitted;—as they convey the mature counsel of professional men.

P. 40. " And here we beg leave to say a word or two
further, that however necessary dung may be to the gar-
dener, to give that stamina to the ground, which such
repeated croppings may require, yet no such dressing is
at all necessary for the nursery. On the contrary, dung
is found to be in some cases injurious to forest trees,
and in all superfluous; and the only practice which forty
years experience enables us to say is necessary, is to fresh
trench the ground as soon as the preceding crop is off;
and plant it with some other sort of tree, which, from
being different in nature and quality, will thrive as well
as if the ground was but just broke up; and it is nothing
more than the frequent removals, and careful prunings,
that give to the trees raised in the nurseries, that decisive
superiority which they are distinguished for, and not by
being forced with dung, as has for a long time been er
roneously supposed."

AGRICULTURE.

FARMS and OCCUPIERS.—P. 26. " Neither are the
farms occupied in an extreme, as to extent. Perhaps
it may be said, that a great many are too small, being
from thirty to forty pounds a year, and very few exceed
from 3 to 400 pounds, probably 130 pounds a year may
average the county. It is generally observable, that upon
these very small farms, every species of bad husbandry
is practised; foulness of the land, the want of ability to
manure the soil, a poverty of produce, and the occupation
in a state little better than that of wretchedness and
misery, too strongly evinced by their more wretched
habitation."

HOMESTEADS.—P. 60. "Perhaps in no part of the kingdom is the construction and situation of farm houses, and
their

their respective buildings, less variable than in those of
the county under consideration. They are for the most
part very ancient, and therefore little in point of superior
construction can be expected from them. If they still
answer the purposes for which they were intended, it is
all that can be required of them."

ARABLE MANAGEMENT.—Under a head, named "District
Practices," the subjoined line stands first.—P. 31. "The
practices of this district* are in no way noticeable."
And this is the only line, in the chapter or section, bearing
that title, which relates to the established practice of
aration, in Surrey!

GRASS LANDS.—P. 26. "From the natural *formation* of
the county of Surry, as well from the information which
this Survey has furnished us with, it clearly appears,
that the arable greatly exceeds the pasture land; and
considered in that light, it is not to be expected, that
men will pay so much attention to the quality of their
pastures, as to be at all curious about the introduction of
new grasses, however strongly recommended by their peculiar good properties; and which in their opinion may not
be considered as even secondary. The only pastures of
any extent, are those which are to be found in the
neighbourhood of the Thames, and these not in the best
state of improvement; indeed very little fine hay is to
met with in any part of the county."

LIVESTOCK.—On this, the remaining subject of rural
economy, we find very little more, concerning the best
established practices in the County of Report, than on the
two preceding divisions of it.

CATTLE.—Neither the milking of *cows*, nor the suckling
of *calves*—popular topics, in the neighbourhood of the
metropolis,—is noticed in this Report of Surrey.

On the *fatting* of cattle and SWINE, by the DISTILLERS
and STARCHMAKERS, in and round London, some interesting
details appear. But these are branches of business which
belong to *manufactures*, rather than to *agriculture* †.

Nor on SHEEP,—even the fatting of *house lamb*—a considerable article of farm produce, in Surrey,—do we find
any thing to instruct or interest; saving the subjoined
passage.—P. 29. "That very able agriculturist, Mr. Ducket
of

* That is to say, the *County*; which is not, in the Report under
notice, divided into *districts*.

† The numbers of cattle and swine, fatted in that way, are extraordinary. There are bullock sheds, we are told, that will hold 600
head, at once; and that one distiller fats three thousand, and a starch-
maker nearly the same number, of large bacon hogs, annually.

of Esher, ranks foremost in his management of this very
delicate and useful article: he rears upon an average 500 a
year; and for this purpose the Dorsetshire ewes are the
only sort he keeps, as he considers them the best nurses,
and producing lambs all the year."

" GENERAL VIEW

OF THE

AGRICULTURE

OF THE

COUNTY OF SURREY.

DRAWN UP FOR THE CONSIDERATION OF

The Board of Agriculture and Internal Improvement.

BY WILLIAM STEVENSON.

1813."*

IN reviewing Mr. STEVENSON'S DORSETSHIRE (aforegoing) I was induced by the variety of sources from which
he collected his materials, to consider him in the capacity
of an editor, rather than in that of an author. In the
volume which is now before me, he appears in a more dis-
tinguishable character:—not as an author, merely, but as a
well qualified Reporter of rural affairs. To the performance of *that*, he was probably pressed—dragged—goaded—
into the service. In executing *this* he evidently felt his
subject, and wrote as an admirer of it.

It is to be observed, however, that much of it reads as
an *extemporary*, rather than as a *studied* work. But
altho it is not uniformly instructive, it rarely offends. To
general readers, and especially to *amateurs* in *agriculture*,
it cannot fail to be interesting; and will be found, in the
abstract of it, to convey much useful information.

Of the MODE of SURVEY pursued in collecting materials
for this Report, I find no account; nor any notice, by the
author, concerning the rise or progress of his work.

Such valuable facts, as arise out of the practice of Surrey,
and such instructive remarks as the writer not unfrequently
                                                    elicits,

---

* Another new title page ! The *Survey* for this Report appears, in
different parts of the work, to have been made in 1806, or 7.

elicits, will be incorporated with the other valuable materials that I have been able to extract from the Board's
Reports.

The number of pages—six hundred and seven; with an
intelligent index.

A colored map of soils.   No other engraving.

SUBJECT THE FIRST.

NATURAL ECONOMY.

EXTENT.—P. 3. " Its area contains 811 square miles,
or about 519,040 acres."

SURFACE.—P. 42. " The surface of almost the whole of
Surrey, except the Weald, is gentle hill and dale. In some
parts of it, the hills rise to a considerable height, and present very commanding and bold views."

Mr. S. has extended this article to several pages; partly
from his own observations, and in part with quotations.

CLIMATURE.—P. 19. "The climate of Surrey is deemed
very healthy in most parts of it between the Weald and the
Thames, particularly near the northern foot of the chalk-
hills : the dryness of the soil and climate in this part of it,
and the entire freedom from the smoke of the metropolis,
by the prevalence of the westerly winds, have deservedly
given it this character."

P. 18. " The spring in this county is early, and is not so
often checked and thrown back by frosty mornings, or cold
raw easterly winds, as in some other counties more to the
south, but at the same time more exposed. The summers
are generally very dry and warm—to such a degree, indeed,
that even those soils which are not easily baked by the
heat, the friable and sound loams, are sometimes rendered
as hard as clays are in a less sultry climate. The harvest is
early, generally commencing within the first ten days of
August; and from the steadiness of the weather at that
important time, there is seldom any corn out in the fields
after the first week of September. Of course, in a county
where the soils and elevations are so various as they are in
Surrey, the climate must vary in some degree, not only
with respect to moisture, but also with respect to warmth,
and the state of forwardness. On the high cold lands about
Effingham-hall, the snow often lies a fortnight longer than
it does on the adjacent lower-lying grounds; and on the
chalk-hills, where they are not broken in their surface, and
sheltered, the snow lies longer, and the harvest is later, than

on

on the adjoining vale lands. Perhaps the earliest part of the county is near Godalming, on the rich, dry, well-sheltered sandy loams."

WATERS.—The rivers, or brooks, of Surrey are enumerated in p. 354, aforegoing. In the report now before me, I perceive little on this head to interest the reader who is in search of useful information, concerning rural affairs. The subjoined passage, relating to the calcareous Wandle, shows, within a small compass, how much the operations of agriculture are liable to be thwarted by those of manufacture. The waters of the Wandle, as to quality, might well be classed with those of the southern Avon ; with which the inestimable meadows of Wiltshire are irrigated.

P. 68. " This river takes its rise a little to the south of Croydon, and flowing by Waddon and Beddington, is greatly increased by some very powerful and constant springs which rise at Carshalton ; from this place the Wandle runs by Wallington, Mitcham, Morden, Merton, Tooting, and Wandsworth, at which last place it enters the Thames. In this course of rather more than ten miles, it turns nearly forty mills of different kinds."

SOILS.—Mr. Stevenson has extended this article to a considerable length; and has rendered it an important section of his work. It opens with a laudable attempt to define the different varieties of soils ; but not, I think, with scientific decision ; which, I conceive, is a *desideration* that nothing but ANALYSIS can effect,—with sufficient precision.

Mr. S.'s classification of soils stands thus :—1. " Clay."— 2. Loam ;—which he subdivides into " strong loam,"—" less adhesive loam, or hazle loam"—" calcareous loam" and " sandy loam."—3. " Chalk"—" bare chalk, very slightly covered or mixed with earth."—4. " Heathy, or moorish soils."

Those varieties are separately traced over the face of the County ; their several situations or localities being noted, and some of them described with much intelligence, and with sufficient interest to entitle them to admission into this abstract.

Clays.—In comparing the clays that are found on the north-side of the Chalk Hills, with those which lie at their feet on the south, Mr. S. mentions, among others of more ordinary distinction, the following.—P. 22. " The clay of the Weald is not affected by dry weather to such a degree as the northern clays: in the latter may be seen cracks, or rather rents, nearly a yard in depth, and several inches broad, in long-continued dry and sultry weather ; but in the Weald, the ground does not contract nearly so much.

I had

I had a good opportunity this very dry summer (1807), of observing the different degrees in which the two kinds of clay were affected by the heat: while the northern clays were rent in all directions, there were to be seen but very few and very trifling cracks in the Weald of Surrey. This circumstance, however, may perhaps be more justly accounted for, from the situation of the Weald than from the nature of the soil: from the low situation of that part of Surrey, and the difficulty and slowness with which the ground there is dried, from the flatness of the surface, and the want of ventilation and sun (compared with the more open, elevated, and sloping ground in the north-east of the county), the moisture will be longer retained, and, of course, the contraction of the soil will be less—not because it is less pure clay, but because it is not nearly so dry."— These remarks appear to my mind, highly creditable to Mr. Stevenson, as a man of observation.

P. 24. " The pale and less fertile clay occupies nearly the whole of the Weald of Surrey. This district, which joins the Weald of Sussex and Kent, extends in its most southern part the whole breadth of Surrey, from Wilderwick to Haslemere, a distance of more than 30 miles. It contracts on the western side, as we proceed from Haslemere to Godalming; and about half way between these towns, it is deeply indented by the sandy loams. From near Hascomb to the northern boundary of the Weald, the breadth is not much more than 20 miles. The medial distance between the borders of Sussex and the northern limit of the Weald, is about four miles.

" This is by far the most extensive tract of uniform soil in the county of Surrey: except on the northern side, where it rises towards the sandy loams, there is no difference to be perceived in the whole compass of it, except what evidently proceeds from peculiar situation. Its elevation in general is very trifling—less, it is said, than that of any other vale district in the island. Its surface, also, is very uniform: there are, indeed, a few spots raised above the general level of the Weald; and it is the soil of these rising grounds, which forms the only exception to the general soil of the district. The colour of the soil on the eminences is darker, and the quality more fertile; arising, in all probability, from the more dry and better ventilated state of the ground, and from the greater quantity of vegetable matter, which would be produced and decay in such a situation, than in those which were more cold and less kindly."

P. 26. " Proceeding northwards, and omitting for the present the loamy soils, which are formed by the junction of
the

the clay of the Weald and the sandy loams, and also the valley and hills of sand and sandy loams, which stretch nearly the whole breadth of the county between the chalk and the Weald—we come to a very narrow stripe of singular land. This is called in Surrey the ' black-land,' and is the same with what in Sussex and Kent is called ' maam' soil. It is a very strong tenacious clay, of a blueish black colour, and a waxy nature : when it is completely dry, the blueish tinge increases ; and in proportion as it becomes more wet, the black colour appears stronger, and less mixed. The line of this soil is not to be found to the west of Betchworth : none of it appears at the bottom of Box-hill ; but as you proceed along the foot of the chalk-hills from this place towards Riegate, you find a regular and continued line of it, lying between the very foot of the chalk and the beginning of the sandy loams. It goes thus entirely through the county, and enters Kent, where it is said to terminate at Rochester. It follows every winding of the chalk-hills, and runs close up to them on the north side, and to the sandy loams on the south. The black-land seldom exceeds 300 yards in breadth, but in some places it is contained within a much narrower compass."

P. 27. " The next kind of clay that appears in a northerly direction, lies on some parts of the flat surface of the Surrey Downs, towards the south side of them, and generally between the extensive heaths, and the bare chalk of the rugged and steep precipice. In crossing from Ewel to Riegate, the nature of this soil is completely seen. On the flat of this broad part of the Downs, lies Walton-heath, a ferruginous unfertile sand, entirely free from chalk. After we cross the southern limit of this heath, and just before we come to the white cliffs which overlook the town of Riegate, the clay appears mixed with flints : its extent is not great, nor does it appear where the surface is sloping. The colour of it is dark red ; and in tenacity, it does not seem to yield much to the black-land. It is probable, that there is chalk both under the heath and under this clay ; as where the Downs are not so broad, more to the west, the chalk continues, without interruption or mixture, from the northern to the southern extremity. The flints that are found on the red clay just described, add to the probability that it at least lies on chalk."*

This specimen of the noncalcareous lands that are scattered

* Those flints may be the effect of chalk having been set on the land, as a manure. I have observed flints on clayey lands, that had been known to be chalked ; tho situated at a considerable distance from any bed of chalk.

scattered on the chalk hills of the southern counties,—in Wiltshire, in Surrey, and in Kent,—is well described. Those clay lands on chalk, however, are not uniform in quality ; but vary, considerably, in different situations.

The *Depths* of Clays, in Surrey.—P. 31. " The depth of the different clays in Surrey varies much : in the Weald, it is seldom possible to plough deeper than five or six inches without bringing up the *till*, or ferruginous subsoil : the clays about Malden, Chessington, &c. are considerably deeper—some of them, indeed, are several feet deep."

Loams.—Calcareous Loam.—P. 34. " Along the northern skirts of the chalk-hills, there is a great quantity of this soil, extending from Croydon, with little interruption, very near to Guildford : as we approach this town, the soil becomes rather more light and sandy. Perhaps the richest tract of this soil lies between Croydon and Epsom, which may safely be reckoned among the best in the county of Surrey : it is, indeed, the purest hazle loam, with the advantage of lying on a bed of chalk. The depth varies according to the elevation : near the limit of the chalk, it is very deep ; as we ascend towards the Downs, the depth declines, till little more than three or four inches are left between the soil and the chalk rubble "

Sandy Loams.—P. 36. " The best defined, and perhaps the most extensive tract of this description of soil, lies between the Weald and the Downs. It stretches across the county from the borders of Kent, near Limpsfield, by Godstone, Blechingley, Riegate, Dorking, Shire, and Albury, with a breadth seldom exceeding half a mile ; till at Albury it expands, and stretching to the south, comes round by Wornersh, Bramley, Godalming, Mousel, Elsted, Pepperharrow, and Seale. This extent of Sandy loam varies in colour and in fertility : perhaps the richest part of it lies round Godalming. It is every where of great depth, and rests on a sandstone base, which hardens as it deepens."

Fossils.—*Ironstone.*—P. 49. " Considerable quantities of iron-ore are found in the south-west part of the county, about Haslemere, Dunsfold, and Cranley ; and in the south-east part, about Lingfield and Horne. It is probable that this ore exists in considerable abundance in most parts of the Weald ; but from the decline of the iron-works in Surrey, in consequence of the high price of fuel, it is not now an object to search for it."

Fuller's Earth.—P. 50. " There are great quantities of this useful earth found in Surrey, about Nutfield, Riegate, and Blechingley, to the south of the Downs ; and some, but of inferior quality, near Sutton and Croydon, to the north of them. The most considerable pits are near Nutfield

field, between which place and Riegate, particularly on
Red-hill, about a mile to the east of Riegate, it lies so near
the surface, as frequently to be turned up by the wheels of
the waggons."

" It is not known how long this earth has been dug in
Surrey: the oldest pit now wrought is said to have lasted
between 50 and 60 years; but it is fast wearing out. The
seam of fullers'-earth dips in different directions: in the
pit I particularly examined, it inclined to the west with a
considerable angle. There are two kinds of it—the blue
and the yellow; the former, on the eastern side of the pit,
lay within a yard of the surface, being covered merely with
the soil, a tough, wet, clayey loam: a few yards to the
west, the blue kind appeared, with an irony sandstone of
nearly two yards in thickness, between it and the soil.
The blue earth in this pit is nearly 16 feet deep. In some
places the yellow kind is found lying upon the blue. There
seems, indeed, to be no regularity either in the position or
inclination of the strata, where the fullers'-earth is found;
nor, as far as I could learn, any mark by which its presence
can be detected. It seems rather thrown in patches, than
laid in any continued or regular vein."

P. 51. " The yellow and the blue earths are of different
qualities, and are used for different purposes: the former,
which is deemed the best, is employed in fulling the kersey-
meres and finer cloths of Wiltshire and Gloucestershire; the
blue is principally sent into Yorkshire, for the coarser cloths."

Firestone.—P. 53. " In the neighbourhood of Godstone,
Gatton, Mestham, Riegate, and Blechingley, are large
and extensive quarries of stone, of a peculiar quality. This
stone, especially that which is dug out of the quarry near
Mestham, at first is soft, and unable to bear the action of
a damp atmosphere; after, however, being kept under
cover for a few months, its texture becomes so compact,
that it can resist the common heat of a house-fire: and in
consequence of this property, it is in very general demand,
in London and the neighbourhood, for fire-places."

" On the White-hills, near Blechingly, the stone is
rather of a different quality, and considerably more valuable. It is said to have been formerly much used by the
chemists, bakers, and glass-houses; but is now principally
employed by the last. It is much softer than the stone
from the other quarries, but requires more skill and caution in working it. ' It is of such a peculiarly fine quality
for sustaining the utmost heat, that it is sought after by all
the principal glass manufacturers in every part of the kingdom; large quantities being now shipped for Liverpool, and
the North.' "

Limestone.

Limestone.—P. 55. " Large quarries of limestone, affording lime equal in purity and strength, for building, to any
in the kingdom, lie a little to the north-west of the town
of Dorking. The stone is of a blueish grey colour, and
contains a very small proportion of flint. The lime from
this part of Surrey is in great demand in London, and the
neighbourhood ; and is particularly serviceable for the parts
of such buildings as are to lie under water. The West
India Docks, and those at Wapping, are built with it."—
Doubtlessly, argillaceous:—the " blue lias," or "claystone."

Brick Earth.—P. 58. " At Nonsuch, in the parish of
Cheam, is a very singular and valuable bed of brick-earth,
from which bricks capable of resisting an intense heat, or
fire-bricks, as they are called, are made. This kind of
brick-earth is found close adjoining to the common
brick-earth, from which it differs in being of a yellowish
colour, and in evidently containing a greater proportion of
sand. This kind of brick-earth has been long known and
wrought : from an account of Leland, it appears to have
been used to make crucibles in his time."

SUBJECT THE SECOND.

POLITICAL ECONOMY.

APPROPRIATION.—This Reporter has opened two
chapters for the reception of information concerning this
important subject. One of them is entitled " Enclosing,"—
the other " Heaths, Commons, and Common Fields." Into
the latter, he has transcribed the details that appear in the
original Report ;—see p. 355, aforegoing. What are seen,
as new, in the reprinted Report, are general reflections on
the subject, rather than provincial information.

The following account of the extent of appropriation,
that has recently taken place, has its value.—P. 480.
" Within these twelve or fourteen years, there have been
enclosed and improved, of

	Acres.
Heaths, about	4500
Commons, about	4900
Common-fields,	2700
Total enclosed,	12,100

" So that about one-seventh part of all the waste lands
have been enclosed within the above period; viz. rather
less

less than one-eleventh part of the heaths, rather more than one quarter of the commons, and about one-fifth part of the common-fields."

MANUFACTURES.—P. 563. " Although Surrey can by no means be called a manufacturing county, yet from its vicinity to the metropolis, and from the convenience of its streams for water-mills, there are several manufactures of importance established in it.

" The river Wandle, the course of which from Croydon to the Thames is not more than ten miles, supplies a great number of flour, paper, snuff, and oil mills, and mills for preparing leather and parchment, and for grinding logwood; and affords excellent water, and convenient grounds on its banks, for very large calico and printing works: the latter are principally in the parishes of Croydon and Mitcham. The flour-mills of Mr. Perry, of Merton, are supposed to be amongst the largest and most complete in England, and have been erected and supplied with water at a great expense and labour.

" The river Mole, besides several flour-mills, turns the iron-mills near Cobham, and the flatting-mills at Ember Court. Very extensive and valuable powder-mills lie on the banks of the small stream that rises in Ewel, a little below that place, near Malden.

" Paper-mills appear to have been more numerous formerly in this county; but there are still several on the different branches of the Wey.

" A very extensive iron-work is carried on at Garratlane, in the immediate vicinity of the Wandle, and the rail way, by Mr. Henckell.

" At Godalming are very considerable manufactories for weaving all kinds of stockings; and latterly, the manufactory of the patent fleecy hoisery has been established here: there are also manufactories for combing wools, and making worsteds, blankets, tilts, and collar-cloths."

P. 565. " There were formerly very extensive iron works in the Weald, but there are now none left. A good deal of charcoal is manufactured there."

P. 566. " Most, if not all of these manufactures, being in a great measure independent of the fluctuations of trade, partly from the nature of the articles manufactured, and partly from the constant and regular demand created in London, are free from one of the most serious and increasing evils attendant on the manufacturing system in many other parts of the kingdom. The workmen are not only seldom out of employ, but their wages and employment are regular and constant, so that poverty and idleness, which result from the stoppage of vent, or from great extremes in
the

the price of wages, are not nearly so frequent here as in other manufacturing districts."

For an injury of manufactures to agriculture, see p. 360, aforegoing.

POOR RATES.—P. 96. " The poor-rates in this county vary very much in the different parts of it. From the ' Abstract of the Returns made in the House of Commons, of the Expense of the Maintenance of the Poor in the year 1803,' it appears that the average of the different hundreds was as follows:

Average rate per Pound.

The hundred of Blackheath,	£.0	7	4½
———— Brixton,	0	4	2
———— Copthorne,	0	5	3¾
———— Effingham,	0	6	8
———— Elmbridge,	0	4	1½
———— Farnham,	0	8	0½
———— Godalming,	0	9	11
———— Godby,	0	3	9½
———— Kingston,	0	3	6½
———— Riegate,	0	5	7¼
———— Tanridge,	0	5	2¼
———— Wallington,	0	5	8¼
———— Woking,	0	5	11
———— Wotton,	0	8	4
Guildford town,	0	7	1¼
Southwark borough,	0	5	3½

" The general average of the county in that year, was 5s. 8d. : the lowest rate was 8d. and the highest was 18s. in the pound."

TITHE.—P. 92. " The complaints of the farmers in this county, are as general as in the other parts of England, on the subject of tithes ; not that there is more litigation or dispute between them and the tithe-holders than are to be found elsewhere. The objection to them is grounded on the rigid exaction in kind, or upon the instances that occur where they produce ill-will and expensive lawsuits.

" It is the common opinion in Surrey, that a farm tithe-free, is better worth 20s. per acre, than another farm, equally favoured in soil and situation, but which is tithed, is worth 13s. This at first sight appears a disproportioned difference ; but something more than the mere loss to the farmer, by his being obliged to pay tithe, must be taken into the account. He feels himself cramped in his exertions and improvements."

Mr. S. enters on a discussion of this bare-worn subject. But not, I think, successfully.

CANALS.—P. 557. " There is good reason to believe that the

the first locks erected in this kingdom were those on the Wey. Sir Richard Weston, of Sutton, near Guildford, brought this contrivance over with him from the Netherlands, between 1645 and 1650. Under his direction the plan for rendering the Wey navigable from Guildford to Weybridge was formed; a bill for that purpose was brought into Parliament in 1650, and passed in 1651; but the navigation was not carried into execution till towards the end of that century. In 1760 the navigation was extended to Godalming."

P. 559. " The Croydon Canal was first projected in 1800, and the Act obtained for it in 1801. According to the preamble of the Act, the reason for making this canal is, to open a communication for the cheap and ready conveyance of all kinds of commodities from the counties of Sussex, Surrey, and Kent, to the metropolis; and of coals, manure, and other articles, from thence into the country; and to supply the towns of Croydon, Streatham, Dulwich, Norwood, and Sydenham, with water. The canal is to run from near the town of Croydon, through the parishes of Croydon, Battersea, Camberwell, Deptford, and Rotherhithe, and of Beckenham and Lewisham, and the township of Sydenham, into the Grand Surrey Canal in Deptford parish. Mr. Rennie gave in two estimates: one on the plan of a canal, and boats carrying 25 tons burthen, which amounted to 64,100l.; the other on the plan of the boats being conveyed from one level to another by inclined planes, amounting to 46,516l. The former plan, though much more expensive, was preferred, and the canal is now completed as far as Norwood."

Public Railways.—P. 553. " The iron rail-way that has lately been made between Wandsworth and Mestham, is the first instance of the application of this mode of forming roads for general use; the other rail-ways in the kingdom being confined to the carriage of goods belonging to individuals, and not open in the same manner as canals are. The Surrey rail-way was first projected and begun in 1802 and 1803: the part that runs from Wandsworth to Croydon was soon completed, and the success of the undertaking induced the proprietors to carry it on to Mestham."

The subjoined remarks bear the semblance of good sense; and, when applied in a general way, may be just. If it should turn out that the railway, from Wandsworth to Mestham, will not *pay*, there can be few lines of communication, in this island, on which it would be prudent to construct public railways,—on the *extravagant* plan and scale, on which that of Croydon appears to have been formed. For, if various fossil productions, manures, corn,

manufactures,

manufactures, and fuel, are not able to support them, what else can there be to induce speculators to plan and execute them?

P. 556. "Notwithstanding the advantages of iron railways with respect to facility and motion, this road does not appear to be much used, nor is it probable that railways will ever come into general use. The expense attending the formation of them, except where the ground is naturally level, is enormous; and it is evident that the advantages, and consequently the gain, are confined to carriage in one direction. The iron rail-way from Croydon to Wandsworth, lies in the neighbourhood of so many extensive manufactures, that it may possibly answer; but the division from Mestham to Croydon, running through a tract of country destitute of manufactures, and having only the lime, fullers'-earth, stone, and corn to depend upon at the further extremity, can never pay very well."

SUBJECT THE THIRD.

RURAL ECONOMY.

TENANTED ESTATES.

ESTATES.—P. 73. "There are no very large estates in Surrey: it is supposed, that the largest does not much exceed 10,000*l*. per annum; and there are but few which reach near to that annual rent. The yeomanry in Surrey are by no means so numerous as they are in the adjoining county of Kent; though in the western part of the county, round Guildford, and in some parts of the Weald, there are several gentlemen who farm their own estates, of from 200*l*. to 400*l*. per annum."

TENURES.—P. 76. "The tenures in this county are principally freehold; there is not much copyhold. In the Weald of Surrey, Christ's church Hospital possesses a considerable estate. There is also, in different parts of the county, a good deal of land held under church leases."

IRRIGATION.—Nature, as has been intimated, has forbade an extensive use of this practice, in the County of Surrey. The chalk hills are mostly narrow, and throw out but a small, portion of calcareous water,—compared with those of Hampshire, Dorsetshire, and Wiltshire. Nor are there flat moory bottoms to receive it; as in those Counties; down which the copious streams flow leisurely, yet with sufficient descent to keep their currents alive.

The

The waters of the Wey and the Mole are noncalcareous, excepting so much as the latter may imbibe in its conflict with the chalk, at the foot of Box Hill. The Wandle is the only *collected stream*, which flows in the County, that is specifically adapted to the purpose of irrigation; and this, as has been shown above, is rendered in a manner useless, by mills of manufacture.

By the subjoined notice, however, it appears that, in the Godstone quarter of the County—the southeastern corner of it—where the principal branch of the Medway has its rise, some *slender branchlets* that are fed by the filtered water of the chalk hills, are, or were, applied to that purpose.—P. 516 "In the south-eastern corner of the county, in the parishes of Godstone, Oxted, Tanridge, Lingfield, and Crowhurst, irrigation appears formerly to have prevailed more, and to have had more attention paid to it than at present."

DRINKING POOLS.—P. 82. "Chalk is also used, especially on the hills, to line the drinking pools; great care is taken to render the bottoms of these water-tight, in the following manner: after a lining of chalk, half a foot thick, has been laid and rendered even and firm by being well beaten down, a mixture of pounded chalk and hot lime is spread over it, and this is repeated, till all the crevices or holes are filled up; thus, not only is the water prevented from oozing out, but the attacks of worms are prevented."

MANAGEMENT of Landed Estates.—*Managers.*—P. 74. "The management of most of the estates in this county is in the hands of attorneys; that is, the drawing up of the leases, the insertion of the terms and covenants, and the superintendance of their execution during the currency of the lease, are committed to their care. This has been long the subject of much and general complaint—in some respects, justly; but certainly in other respects, without the least foundation."

P. 75. "It is as absurd to employ an attorney to frame the agricultural covenants of a lease, or to constitute him the sole judge of their observance or breach, as it would be to give into the hands of a farmer, the charge of putting the covenants into the technical language of the law."

TENANCY.—P. 98. "Most farms in Surrey are lett on leases: the duration is generally for twenty one years, though some are only for seven or fourteen years. A few farms are lett for three lives; the lease being renewable, generally on the payment of one year and a half's rent; sometimes two years' rents are paid, besides the usual fee to the steward of the manor. Church lands are commonly lett for twenty-
ne

one years, renewable every seven.   There are, however, some
extensive farms in this county, which are held without a
lease, from year to year, entirely at the will of the landlord;
and this custom is rather upon the increase in Surrey."

RENT.—P. 91.   "If we except that part of Surrey which
lies within the influence of the London markets, the rents
of this county may be consi.ered as low.   The best lands,
that is, the hazel loam, on a subsoil of chalk, and the
rich sandy loams near Godalming, run from 25s. to 30s.
per acre, where the leases have been granted within these
last ten years.   The clays of the Weald are in general
very low rented; many farms there being lett for 10s.
per acre, and few of them reaching 20s.   The clay land
in the other parts of the county is lett from 15s. to 20s.
per acre.   On the chalks, above the hazle loam, where
the soil is thinner, the rents run from 16s. to 20s. per acre.
When we come within seven or eight miles of London,
the rent rises considerably, running from 40s. to 3l.   Still
nearer the metropolis, the ground that is possessed in
small quantities by cow-keepers, nurserymen, &c. letts
for 6l., 8l., and sometimes 10l. per acre."

REMOVALS.—P. 107.   "The usual term of entry to the
arable farms in Surrey, is at Michaelmas; the outgoing
tenant keeping possession of the barns till the May following."

WOODLANDS.

THE Reporter has furnished a long chapter on the Woodlands of Surrey; more particularly concerning those of
the Weald or Southern Vale Lands of the County.   In
registering the rural economy of the Southern Counties,
I paid what I considered to be due attention to their
woodlands, in various situations; most especially to those
of the "Weald of Sussex;" which is intimately united
with that of Surrey; they being similar parts of one and
the same widely extended vale.

Such passages of the Report now before me, as I may
judge will throw additional light on the general subject,
I will transcribe into my present Work.   The matter at
large is much too diffuse for insertion, here.

P. 424.   "There are many reasons for the belief, that
the *Weald of Surrey* was formerly an entire wood, and
that it was cleared and cultivated at a much later period
than the other parts of the county."

This suggestion, I think, is highly probable.   I will
extend it a step farther, and say,—from what arose to me,
in examining the Vale of Horsham, in 1791, it struck me
that

that the wide-spread woodlands, which it evidently once contained, formed the *last*, of the forests of England, which reached the agricultural state.

In traversing its site, I saw the remains of some of its *posts;* which, tradition said, formerly stood across it, " as *guides* to *letter carriers*," and doubtlessly to other travellers. Other wide forests, it is probable were supplied with similar helps. And hence, *possibly* the expression of sending letters by the *post* (a contraction of posts) at this day.

COPPICE WOODS.—*Species.*—P. 426. "These consist principally of the oak, birch, ash, chesnut, sallow, hazel, and alder."

Filling up Coppice Grounds.—P. 427. " This is done by cutting the shoot about half through with a bill : the shoot thus cut is laid along the ground; at each of the joints a cut in the direction of the bough is made, over which a little fine mould and turf are laid; the shoot is kept close to the ground by means of pegs. At each point, the shoot that is plashed will take root, and throw out several saplings. As soon as the shoot that has been plashed appears to have taken sufficient root in each of its points (which generally happens in two or three years), it is entirely separated from the parent stool."

This valuable practice I have observed. For filling up small vacancies, with the native woods that happen to grow on their immediate margins, the practice is highly eligible. But where the vacant plots are large, and especially when more valuable woods are desired, the Kentish practice—of sodburning the surface, and digging the ground as for a *plantation*,—is required.

The *wares* of coppice woods, in Surrey, are the same as in Sussex.—P. 429. " The following are the principal purposes to which copse-wood is applied, arranged according to the comparative profit they bring :—Hoops; gunpowder charcoal; charcoal for other purposes; poles of the largest size, for hop-plantations; hurdles; faggots; kiln-faggots."

P. 435. " The woodlands in the other parts of Surrey contain, in general, a greater proportion of coppice, and fewer timber trees, than those we have been considering in the Weald: this is more particularly the case on the chalk-hills of the county. The kinds of wood in the coppices are much the same as in the Weald: the uses to which they are applied are also similar, except that charcoal is much more frequently made from the underwoods of the Weald, than from those of the other parts of the county. Stakes, edders, hurdles, hoops, and faggots, are the principal products of the copse-woods now under
                                                      consideration.

consideration. As we approach the metropolis, the under-woods are cut at much shorter periods than at a greater distance: from seven to ten years is the usual age of felling, at the distance of 15 or 20 miles from London.

" Besides the coppice that grows along with the timber, there are in most parts of the chalk-hills what are deno-minated ' shaws:' these are small spots of copse-wood, unmixed with timber. They are found to be very advan-tageous while growing, as shelter for the sheep; and are used, when cut down, for hurdles, &c."

WOODS.—*Draining.*—P. 437. " The most commendable part of the management of the woodmen in the Weald of Surrey, is that which respects the draining their woods: the soil is so retentive, and the surface so inadequate to carry the water off, that this practice seems to have forced itself in a manner, upon their notice and adoption, as the only method of preserving their woods from destruction: and from the great and evident good effects produced by keeping the surface dry, under-draining has been em-ployed, with results equally beneficial, in many parts of the Weald."

Raising Woods.—P. 438. " By some of the most ex-perienced and successful woodmen of the Weald, the following method is pursued. The field in which it is intended to sow the acorns, is completely summer-fallowed; and during this operation it is thoroughly cleaned of all root-weeds, and has a good dressing of manure and some-times of lime given it. At the last ploughing it is ridged up so as to keep it as dry as possible during the winter. Wheat is then sown in it at the usual season; and after the wheat is well harrowed in, acorns are put in with a dibble, at about one foot distant from each other. When the wheat is reaped the ensuing autumn, the seedling oaks are not sufficiently high to be cut or injured by the sickle; the stubble serves as a kind of protection to them during the winter."

Sowing the acorns at the same time the wheat is sown, and harrowing them in, together, is much preferable to *dibbling* them in; especially on a tough retentive soil, such as the oak delights in. The holes formed by the dibbles are liable to hold water, and thereby to rot the acorns; which can scarcely be deposited too loosely and shallow in the ground.

Mr. S. touches on the disputed subject of whether oaks should be raised from the *seed,* or be *transplanted;* and quotes (p. 439.) what he considers as a case in point,— in favour of *planting.* But the case quoted proves nothing. The *seedlings,* that sprang up in the wood, among the
interwoven

interwoven roots of timber trees and underwoods, had almost insuperable difficulties to struggle with; while those which were planted, " by a man who took great delight in planting," had, from their infancy, the entire ground to themselves. The quoter should have recollected, before he wrote, that the quotee was a *planter*.

Box of Boxhill.—P. 445. "*Box*.—This is known only as a dwarf, or garden shrub, in most parts of England: in Surrey, and the adjoining county of Kent, however, it flourishes as a tree of considerable size. The hill in Surrey on which it is found, was originally called the White-hill" (?); " but from the great number of box-trees with which it has long been covered, it is now much better known by the name of Box-hill.

" The common report, probably handed down by tradition, is, that the Earl of Arundel, in the reign of Charles I. brought the box-tree from Kent, and planted it on the White-hill*.

" The soil of Box-hill is a thin pale-coloured loam, lying very near the chalk: the elevation of the hill is considerable, and the greatest quantity of box is found on the south or precipitous side.

" The period of time required by the box-tree to arrive at a proper size and quality of timber for cutting, is not exactly known; but it is supposed, that more than half a century is necessary for this purpose. The succession of the crop is kept up, partly by the seeds which are annually scattered, and partly by the shoots from the stools, after the timber is cut.

" The price of this wood was formerly much higher than it is now: this is owing, in some measure, to the diminished demand, and the importation from Holland and other parts of the Continent; but principally, to the greater quantity which has latterly been cut on Box-hill. The former proprietor of the estate sold the box for 15,000*l*.: the purchaser was to be allowed 14 years to cut it down: hence the supply has been much greater than formerly; and as, while it was scarce and dear, substitutes had been found for it in many manufactures, the price has necessarily declined very considerably. In the 1802, 40 tons were cut on Box-hill; and when the limited use to which this

" * Mr. Manning, author of the History of Surrey, is of opinion, that the box on Box-hill is coeval with the soil;" (?) " it can actually be traced back to the beginning of the seventeenth century: in a lease dated 1602, the tenant covenants to use his best endeavours to preserve the yew, box, &c. In an account taken in 1712, it is supposed as much had been cut a few years before, as amounted to 3000*l*."

this wood can be applied, is considered, it is by no means surprising that the price should have fallen more than 50 per cent. It will not now bring more than 5*l.* or 6*l.* per ton."

AGRICULTURE.

FARMS.—*Sizes.*—P. 84. " The Weald of Surrey offers less variety in the size of its farms than any other part of the county; and the further we advance into the Weald, and recede from good roads and a dry soil, the smaller the farms in general become. There are scarcely any farms in this part of the county which reach 300 acres; most of them run from 100 to 150, and the smallest do not contain more than 40 or 50 acres.

" The size of the farms on the sandy loams is also small in general, running from 100 to 300 acres: a few falling below the first number, and perhaps a very few rising above 300 acres.

" In the western parts of the county, about Bagshot and Cobham, there are scarcely any farms above 200 acres; and in general they run from 150 to 200 acres.

" On the borders of the Downs there are a few very large farms, *i. e.* farms from 600 to 1200 acres. Within seven or eight miles of London also, especially about Streatham and Norwood, there are some farms of from 500 to 700 acres and upwards. But the usual size, both in the Downs and within seven or eight miles of London, is from 250 to 300 acres. Nearer London, the ground is in the hands of market-gardens and nurserymen, and of course is held in small quantities.

" The largest farm in the county is at Wanborough, between Guildford and Farnham: it contains 1600 acres, comprising a considerable quantity of chalky soil, on that part of the ridge, which from its appearance, is called " The Hog's Back." It is in the possession of Mr. Morris Birkbeck, whose activity and intelligence are fully equal to the proper management of this large concern."

HOMESTEADS.—P. 79. " In passing into the Vale or Weald of Surrey, the eye is not more struck with the appearance of inferiority in the management of the lands, the badness of the crops, the uncouthness and want of intelligence among the farmers, and the general circumstances attending inadequate skill and capital—than it is with the ruinous and mean appearance of the farm-houses and offices. In the other parts of the county, the farm-houses are generally sufficiently large

large and convenient, in good repair, and kept neat and clean: their size, and the mode and materials of their construction, vary with their age. The oldest are built entirely of brick, and their covering is generally of large heavy slatestone; others are of brick-nogging, covered with tiles; and many are built of a framing of wood, lathed and plastered, or rough-cast."

OBJECTS of HUSBANDRY.—P. 146. " In the neighbourhood of large towns, little arable land, in general, is to be seen; and this is the case on the Middlesex side of London: but in Surrey, on the contrary, the proportion of arable land is very great, all over the county; and this proportion hardly seems to diminish as we approach the metropolis."

PLAN of MANAGEMENT.—The Reporter has extended his section " Course of Crops" to an unwarrantable length; seeing how little it contains, respecting the established practice of the County under Report. It commences with a discourse concerning the author's own ideas of the subject; a dissertation, by the way, which does him credit as a *writer*. He next enumerates, *a la Secretaire*, strings of courses, on the several varieties of lands in the County, as they were found on the farms of *individuals;* in all or most cases putting down what may be well termed, in ordinary situations, the *impracticable course.*

Having past over nearly twenty pages of the section, we come to the following ingenuous notice.—P. 196. " Before proceeding to state the rotations pursued in the different parts of Surrey, that go against the fundamental maxim of agriculture, by bringing two white or corn crops immediately together, it is proper to premise, that the rotations already mentioned, are by no means the most common in the several districts where they are said to be followed. There is perhaps, a greater variety of rules and practices, even within the compass of a single parish in Surrey (if the Weald be excepted), than in most of the other counties in England: so that the practices adopted by one farmer are frequently very different from those of his nearest neighbour. The judicious and commendable rotations already noticed, are to be found in a more or less extensive degree, in the several districts specified along with them, and there is good reason to believe they are becoming more prevalent; but whoever from this account should expect to find that practices directly opposite were banished from these districts, would be much disappointed."

The fact is, the County of Surrey has—had some years ago—NO REGULAR COURSE OF CROPS; every occupier appropriated his fields and parcels of lands to the purposes to which he knew they were best adapted. And, by the
above

above notice, it pretty evidently appears that the same principle of management was pursued in 1807, by professional occupiers.—Even on the chalk hills where regular flocks of sheep were kept, and where regular supplies of food, in summer and winter, were of course to be provided, every man, speaking generally, provided them in his own way;—according to the existing circumstances of the lands in his occupation, and the principles of management which long experience had led him to adopt.—It only remains to be added, that, under a plan of management, so pursued, there were, then, many " good farmers"—" knowing men" —" capital agriculturists"—on those hills.

OCCUPIERS.—P. 88. " The character of the farmers, like the size of farms, is very various in Surrey: there are still to be found, especially in the Weald, and the more remote parts of the county, many of the old class of farmers; men who are shy and jealous in their communications; unwilling to adopt any new mode of husbandry; in short, with much of the ignorance and prejudice of former times, and with all its rigid and inflexible honesty—on whose bare word the utmost reliance may be placed, and who have so little of the *impartial* spirit of commerce, that they prefer selling their grain to an old customer at a lower price, to deserting him and accepting a higher offer from one with whom they have not been in the habit of dealing. The ' round-frocked farmers' (for they pride themselves on frequenting the markets in the dress of their forefathers) are equal enemies to improvements in agriculture and relaxations in morals."

P. 89. " In other parts of the county, less remote and distant from the metropolis, the farmers are more on a level with the age; they understand their own business, according to the new and more improved methods of conducting it, extremely well; but they are either unable or unwilling to communicate the knowledge they possess. To this general character there are, however, many exceptions: there are among the Surrey farmers, men who would lose nothing in point of liberal and useful knowledge, if they were placed by the side of the most intelligent agriculturists in the island."—And so there were, half a century ago; as will appear under the head, *Turneps*, ensuing.

WORKPEOPLE.—P. 540. " It is a very general and well-founded complaint in Surrey, that it is extremely difficult to get a sufficient number of hands to work the land properly; and that the servants are extremely unsettled, continually wandering from one master to another."

A remedy for this evil is suggested by the Reporter:— first, in the legitimate section, " *Labour ;*" and, afterwards,

in

in his chapter entitled " Means of Improvement ;" as will
presently be noticed.

The *Wages* of Workpeople.—P. 542. " When servants
are hired by the year and boarded, the wages are" (were in
1807?) " from 11*l.* to 15*l.*: by the week, without board,
the wages are from 13*s.* to 15*s.* A ploughboy gets nearly
the half of a ploughman. A shepherd is allowed from 12*s.*
to 15*s.* a week, with one bushel of oats per month for his
dog : and in some places, the keep of three or four sheep
besides."

The *Food* of Farm *Laborers.*—P. 544. " The principal
animal food used by the farm servants," (laborers) " is pork
or bacon broiled over the fire. It may be thought, that
where a man has a large family to support, it would be
much more economical to buy" (boil) " such kind of meat,
as, with the assistance of pease or barley, might go a long
way in supplying nourishing food, by being made into soup
or broth. This was suggested to his servants by a very intelligent farmer in Surrey, but the reply was a satisfactory
answer, that the price of fuel was so enormously high, that
the additional quantity requisite to boil their meat, would
cost more money than would be saved by the different mode
of cookery."

The Reporter's plan for *improving* farm workpeople, in
England, may be thus briefly given.—To prevent their
" wandering from one master to another,"—" encourage
married servants, in preference to unmarried, and employ
their wives and children in hoing turneps, &c.";—and
thereby " induce the farmer's servants to marry;" and,
moreover, to " substitute a certain quantity of corn, or the
price of a certain quantity of corn, for part of their money
wages";—p. 540:—and—" if a free cottage were allotted
to each; and if, moreover, their interest in the farm were
increased, by being allowed to keep a cow—they would
not only have little temptation to remove, but they would
even be deterred, by the difficulty and trouble to which
unmarried men are not exposed;—p. 589.

The above may be termed the Tweedside practice; as it
is established on both sides of that river. And fortunately
will it be for the occupiers of Tweedside farms, if they can
preserve it in perpetuity. It is a desirable plan *for farmers,*
who thereby become powerful sovereigns in their several
domains.

Whether this plan is a relick of feudal baronage, or has
risen out of the border warfare of former times ; when every
laird, or considerable proprietor, had his bastile, tower, or
keep (the ruins of some of them not long ago remaining) in
which he placed himself, his family and his domestic animals,

in

in a degree of security, during the night time (the former in the upper stories, the latter at the base); or whether the arrangement grew out of the dissolation which those warfares produced; or out of more ordinary circumstances; * is a point which requires not to be settled, here.

Let the rise of the Tweedside organization of farm workpeople have been what it may, it will, I conceive, be wise, in the Tweedside occupiers, to endeavour to preserve so convenient, so moral, and, of course, so valuable a system ;—so far, I mean, as it goes to employ married laborers, living in " free cottages," placed under the eye, or ready observance of their employer †. But it were as easy to remove the Cheviot Hills, as such a system, into the environs of London:—even if Tweedside parents, Tweedside schools, and Tweedside morals were to be sent forward to prepare the way. The spirit of " independence," otherwise *licentiousness*, which prevails among farm workpeople, in the interior of England, would operate as a bar against any thing resembling circumscribed " liberty."

I am well aware that something might be done, in England, toward improving the present plan of managing farm servants, by encoraging and preferring married men, to a certain extent, and under certain circumstances‡. But, while the dwellings of farm laborers continue to be fixtures, scattered over the face of the country, as they now are, and as they necessarily will be for a length of time to come;—owing to the intermixture of properties, and the varied sizes of farms;—the Tweedside plan, at large, must remain impracticable. Under existing circumstance, a certain number of single men, as domestic servants, to be ready at a call, are, in most cases, indispensably necessary.

WORKING ANIMALS.—P. 536. " Large, heavy, black horses are usually employed by the farmer. Their winter keep is two bushels of oats per week, and straw (usually cut), each horse: their spring food, tares, and two bushels of

* See NORTHERN DEPARTMENT, p. 371.

† In England, it would be nearly as eligible to suffer farm laborers to occupy a few acres of land to grow bread corn, as to keep a cow. Surely, it would be an improvement, in the Tweedside practice, to furnish workpeople with MILK, in fixed quantity, as with OATMEAL.

‡ In a super-populous parish or township, it may be the interest of landed occupiers to prevent, rather than to encorage matrimony, among its *settled* inhabitants. If Tweedside, or any other district, is so thinly inhabited, that its occupiers find it difficult to procure farm workpeople, it may, I think, be eligible, *in that case*, (notwithstanding what I have ventured to suggest above) to *settle* a married couple with a cow, and induce single men to marry ;—to multiply population.

of oats. Hay is given them after harvest, and during seed-time: they are turned out after the clover is cut. Chaff is generally given, mixed with their corn. The black oats are by many preferred for the purpose of feeding horses."

"The keep of horses has greatly risen in expense within these few years: this proceeds partly from the actual increase in the price of food, harness, &c.; and in some degree from the greater pride which the farmer takes, in seeing his horses in good condition. The Surrey farmers reckon, that when every thing is taken into the account, each farm-horse stands them in nearly 50*l.* per annum." (?)

IMPLEMENTS.—The Reporter extends his chapter, bearing this title, to twenty or thirty pages: not one line of which, I conceive, would add to the value of this register. Numerous species and varieties, especially of plows, which happened to be *visitant* in Surrey, at the time of the survey, are not only enumerated but described; very prudently, however, without the encumbrance of plates.

TILLAGE.—*Plowing.*—P. 147. "Surrey may be considered as a county which in general is well tilled; that is, the several operations of ploughing, harrowing, rolling, &c. are performed with more care and skill than in many other counties in England. In the Weald, especially, the ploughing is done with great neatness and care."

Fallowing.—Nearly a sheet's length of paper is "stained" with argumentative matter, concerning this *selfevident* subject.

MANURES.—*Marl.*—P. 496. "Towards the east and south-east parts of Surrey, there is a traditionary belief, that marl was formerly much used; and the pits and ponds found in those parts, are supposed to be evidences that such was really the case."

Clay.—P. 503. "The only instance of the application of clay that I met with, was at Oatlands. Mr. Kendal, steward to the Duke of York, found the poor and lifeless soil on the new inclosures there, much benefited by spreading clay, or more properly brick-earth, over it: he had been able to procure but a very small quantity, but its good effect on the crop growing when I saw the field (turnips) was very evident and striking."

Chalk.—P. 496. "Chalk-pits or quarries are very abundant in Surrey; and as they are generally wrought without much expense or difficulty, the application of chalk is very general in all parts of the county, except the more immediate neighbourhood of London and the Weald. In the latter, lime is considered as more proper for the tough and cold clays of that district; and in those parts where the

the different manures supplied by London, can be procured at an easy and short carriage, the chalk is at a considerable distance.

" Besides other chalk-pits of less extent and note, there are pits at Croydon, Sutton, Epsom, Leatherhead, Bookham, Effingham, Horsley, Clandon, Stoke, Guildford, and Puttenham, on the north side of the Downs; and at Godstone, Caterham, Riegate, Mestham, Buckland, and Betchworth, on the south side.

" There is some, though no very considerable difference, found in the effects produced by the chalk of several of these pits: this arises, upon examination, from the greater facility with which some kinds of chalk *fall* or *run*, compared with the degree of the same quality in others. At the same time there can be no doubt, that nearly in the proportion in which this quality exists, is the impurity of the chalk, as it evidently proceeds from the mixture of clay: but as the great object is, to get the chalk mixed intimately with the soil as speedily as possible, impure chalk which falls down readily, is properly preferred to chalk more pure, which lying in lumps unmixed with the soil for many years, is not only useless, but actually in the way of the plough.

" Formerly, the application of chalk was confined to the stronger lands; but latterly it has been applied with equal, if not greater effect, to the light loams, and even to the sandy soils."

P. 498. " The crops that appear to derive the greatest benefit from the application of chalk, are pease and clover, which are generally rendered more abundant, and improved in quality at the same time. The operation, however, is commonly slow, going on evenly, and for a considerable length of time."

P. 81. " Such farmers in Surrey as lie near the chalk, are very careful to bottom their farm-yards with it; a measure which cannot be too highly commended, and which indeed would pay well, even where the chalk is at a considerable distance."

Lime.—P. 498. " This is obtained by burning either the chalk, or the limestone, that is found near Guildford: most of the lime, however, is procured from chalk; that from the Guildford limestone goes principally to the clays on the borders of Sussex.

" It has already been remarked, that lime is almost universally used in the Weald: indeed, considering the small quantity of manure made on the farms in this district, and the demand which the fallow every fourth or fifth year (according to the rotation) has for a dressing of some
sort,

sort, lime may justly be regarded as the main dependence
of the farmers of the Weald. Hence, on almost every
large farm, there is a kiln for burning the chalk or
limestone; and furze or brushwood is cultivated for that
purpose."

P. 501. "The quantity of lime laid on per acre, varies
with the soil: a kiln of about 400 bushels will lime three
acres well, where the soil is moderately strong, as in the
south-east corner of the county: in the Weald, from 150
to 200 bushels per acre are found necessary: on the sandy
loams, only 80 or 100 bushels are required."

These are accurate traits of management. Strong adhesive soils, I have ever found, require a greater proportion of lime, than those of a looser more friable texture:—a circumstance, this, in the application of lime,
which, I believe, is not generally known; certainly, is not
generally attended to.

Ashes.—P. 506. " In the neighbourhood of London,
great quantities of coal-ashes are used; in the Weald, the
ashes of wood or furze; and in the western parts of the
county, the ashes of turf or peat. They are all principally
used as top-dressings for clover or sainfoin; for the latter,
coal-ashes are preferred, especially if the soil be cold and
close." (?)

" Coal-ashes are laid on at the rate of from forty to
sixty bushels per acre."

Soot.—P. 507. " This cannot be obtained in such quantities or so cheap, now as formerly, owing to the increased
demand for it by the different manufactures of salammo-
niac, &c. It is used as a top-dressing, chiefly for wheat
and young clover: its effects are found to be very much
influenced by the state of the subsequent weather: if it
prove very dry, little benefit, and sometimes rather harm,
results from the use of it. in moist weather it is most
serviceable.

" The price in London is about 1s. per bushel: from
thirty to forty bushels are sown as a top-dressing for
wheat, and about one-third less for clover. A chimney-
sweeper is commonly employed in Surrey to sow it, at the
rate of one halfpenny per bushel, or $1\frac{1}{2}d.$ for two bushels."

Town Dung.—P. 509. " From London are procured immense quantities of stable-yard dung, night-soil, and the
sweepings of the streets; the first is often carried to the
distance of eighteen or twenty miles, and sometimes further, where it is merely an article of back-carriage: all
of them are conveyed up the Thames to the north-western
parts of the county.

" The stable-yard manure procured in London, is in
general

general nothing but long dry straw," (!) "which must require a considerable time and a good deal of management before it is fit to lay upon the ground. The price is 3*s.* or 3*s.* 6*d.* for a cart load of perhaps two and a half cubical yards, which, however, from the state it is in, will probably not weigh 24 cwt. or 7*s.* per waggon load."

Night Soil.—P. 510. " Night-soil, though so evidently a powerful manure, and fitted for almost every soil and crop, does not appear to have been much in demand among the farmers of Surrey till very lately" (?): "the grand depository for it is St. George's-fields."

" The price in St. George's-fields is 7*s.* per waggon load."

Farm-yard Dung.—P. 511. " This can hardly be said to be the chief dependence of the farmers in Surrey, except of those who are too far distant from London to bring stable and other manure from thence."

P. 512. " In Surrey, the general opinion appears to be decidedly in favour of rotten dung; and in order to get it into this state, the long town and yard dung is either frequently turned, or is formed into a compost: the mode of making and managing the latter, will fall to be considered afterwards. The faults of the Surrey farmers in the management of their dung-hills, are those of most other counties: they are unnecessarily prest down by the carts while they are making; and in turning them over, the long dung is not sufficiently broken or torn to pieces, and mixed with such as is more rotten."

P. 513. " In the Weald, farm-yard dung is universally applied to the summer-fallow for wheat: in the other parts of the county, it is used for turnips, wheat after clover-ley, and sometimes for winter tares, where they are meant as a preparation for wheat."

Compost.—P. 494. " The most intelligent and experienced farmers,"—"form mixens, or composts, of all their richest and strongest manures: these composts are no doubt to be met with in almost every county in the kingdom; but in Surrey they are considered much more indispensable, and are in much greater abundance, than in most other counties."

P. 495. " By far the greatest number of these composts are to be found in the more immediate neighbourhood of the metropolis; and here, it is highly probable, the idea of making them first took its rise. Many of the kinds of manure procured from London, are so very powerful, that either the desire to prevent the waste of them, or the experience of their bad effects when spread on unmixed, like common stable dung, would soon lead to the plan of forming composts."—This, I think, is *probable.*

P. 514.

P. 514. " In the management of their composts, the Surrey farmers are very careful and skilful, as well as economical in the materials of which they compose them. The scrapings of the roads, the scourings of the ditches or ponds, the superabundant mould of the head-lands, are carefully collected and mixed up, either with the rich manure from London, with the farm-yard manure, or with chalk, and often with them all."

Herbaceous Manure.—P. 508. " Ploughing in green crops is not now much in use in Surrey: to feed them off on the ground is found to benefit the succeeding crop much more, and to be much less troublesome and expensive. In some parts of the county, however, tares, and occasionally buck-wheat and rape are ploughed in; and I met with one instance in the neighbourhood of Guildford, where a very strong and luxuriant crop of charlock was ploughing in on a thin light soil upon chalk, for wheat."

To those who have read, with attention, the above intelligent notices, concerning the manures in use, in the County of Surrey, it were superfluous to remark that Mr. Stevenson's report of them is mostly satisfactory.

SEMINATION.—*Drilling.*—P. 157. " The drill husbandry can hardly be said to be extending itself, even in that part of Surrey where it it has been practised for some years. It appears to have been introduced, or at least recommended, to the notice of the farmers on the sandy loams in the western division of the county, by the late Mr. Ducket, of Esher, who is well known to have been a strong advocate for drilling all sorts of grain, to have followed it extensively on his own farm, and to have invented many machines for drilling and hoeing the crops.

" At present, the drill husbandry is almost entirely confined to the parishes of Bagshot, Chobham, Ockham, Cobham, Esher, Send, Ripley, Bramley, and the district immediately adjoining, and is seldom practised, except on light loams, or sandy soils. It does not appear to have established itself generally in any part of Surrey to the eastward of these parishes."

ARABLE CROPS.

WHEAT.—This important object of husbandry is treated of analytically, and at an irrequisite length. It is too long, I mean to say, as a report of the practice of a County, and too short as a general treatise on the culture of wheat.

Reasons for its *Cultivation*, in Surrey.—P. 202. " There are several circumstances, which render the cultivation of wheat in Surrey more general and extensive than it is in
many

many other counties. In the first place, the soil of the Weald, or vale land, which forms no inconsiderable proportion of the county, is of such a nature as to require frequent summer-fallowing: where this is necessary, the farmer must have recourse to wheat, in order to pay him for the want of a crop, and for the great expense that he has incurred ; and as lands which most require a summer-fallow, viz. strong wet clay, are peculiarly adapted for wheat, the farmer is led also by this consideration to sow this grain very extensively. In the second place, the general rotation on the light lands brings in a crop of clover after turnips and barley, and of course these lands, which were long deemed unsuitable for wheat, by receiving this crop on a clover-ley, are found to be as productive of this valuable grain as soils of a stronger class. Lastly, the great command of manure which that part of Surrey that lies near the metropolis or the Thames possesses ; and the cheapness of chalk and lime in the other parts of the county, no doubt, induce the farmers to introduce a wheat crop more frequently than they would do if they were not possessed of these advantages."

Extent in Cultivation.—P. 203. " What the extent of land annually under wheat amounts to, it is impossible to ascertain ; and on this, as well as on other topics where there are no grounds for forming a statement or opinion, I shall not hazard a random, a useless, and perhaps worse than useless conjecture."—This is a sound principle of report.

Succession of Wheat.—P. 203. " Wheat in Surrey follows, 1. a complete summer-fallow ; 2. a bastard-fallow after tares, clover-ley, or woad" (Weld); " 3. beans or pease ; 4. clover-ley ; 5. turnips ; and sometimes, but very seldom, it follows oats :"—and, p. 205, " is seldom sown after turneps."

Manure for Wheat.—P. 206. " In the Weald, stable and yard dung, and lime, are used for the summer-fallow : on the clays in the other parts of the county, the same kind of manure, and lime or chalk, are used ; though, as has been already remarked, these clays get by no means their proportion of manure. Sheep are folded on the fallows in some parts, especially where there is a portion of Downs attached to the farm. Five hundred sheep will manure an acre in about seven days. Clover-leys are sometimes manured in the spring ; sometimes in the autumn, just before they are ploughed ; and sometimes, instead of manure being spread upon them, sheep are folded on them, either before they are ploughed or afterwards."

Semination of Wheat.—Time of Sowing.—P. 206. " The
usual

usual months for the wheat seed-time are October and
November: in some parts of the county, and in some
seasons, a considerable part of the wheat is put in during
the month of September."

Methods of Sowing.—P. 207. "Drilling wheat is not
much followed; it is to be met with chiefly in the western
parts of the county, about Bagshot, Send, Chobham, Ripley, &c. and on one or two farms in the south-eastern
part."

"Wheat is either sown broad-cast on the furrow; sown,
and then ploughed in; or drilled. On clay land, the practice of ploughing the wheat in, or sowing under furrow, is
gaining ground."

We are not informed whether the "drilling," which
is practised in those parishes, is done according to Mr.
Ducket's plan, or the seed is passed through a machine.

Produce of Wheat.—P. 216. "The smallest crops of
wheat I heard of did not exceed four sacks, or two quarters" (Winchester measure): "and on the other hand, when
a particular field or district was meant to be recommended
as peculiarly qualified for wheat, the usual expression was,
that it generally produced a load, or five quarters of wheat.
On the rich, deep, friable, calcareous loams, near the northern extremity of the chalk-hills, between Croydon and
Epsom, six quarters have been grown not unfrequently. On
the rich sandy loams near Godalming, a load or five quarters is no uncommon crop: but on the other hand, on the
colder soils, the crop seldom exceeds five or six sacks, or
two and a half or three quarters. In the Weald, this may
fairly be deemed the common crop, except on the drier and
richer spots, which not unfrequently produce a load per
acre. On the 'black-land' the crops of wheat are sometimes very great: but it seems the general opinion in
Surrey, that the calcareous, and even the sandy loams, if
they be deep and rich, produce not only greater quantities
of wheat per acre, than the best clay soils, but also grain
of a superior quality."

RYE.—The subjoined concise, yet intelligent, account of
the culture of this crop, in Surrey, I insert here with
pleasure.

P. 221. "This grain is seldom sown in Surrey, except for
spring-feed for sheep, or for seed. It commonly is put into
ground intended for turnips, or summer-fallow, about the
end of August, or beginning of September. The quantity
of seed is about three bushels: when it is suffered to stand,
it ripens about the 12th or 14th of July: the produce runs
from three quarters to four quarters and a half per acre:
the weight of the bushel is from 56 to 60 lb. The straw,
                                                    which

which is principally bought by the brick-makers, fetches from 50s. to 3l. per load. As green food, it comes in before the winter-tares. Before it begins to shoot up, it is very acceptable and nourishing to sheep; but they dislike it afterwards."

BARLEY.—P. 221. "As it is a very common opinion in Surrey, that barley will not thrive well on clay soils, and as these soils, if they were to be prepared for barley, would require a great deal of time and labour to bring them into proper tilth, the quantity of this grain sown in this county is not very considerable. It is almost entirely excluded from the Weald, and from the stronger soils in the other parts of the county: even soils that are sown with turnips, if they be of a strong nature, are seldom prepared for barley after the turnip crop is eaten off; so that this grain may be considered as confined to the lighter and drier turnip soils—to the calcareous and sandy loams. I heard of one instance, in which, this year (1807), it had been sown on the ' black-land,' below Mestham. The crop was remarkable, producing, *it was said*, three loads per acre: the straw very long, and so firm and strong, as not to be the least lodged, even though the crop was so very abundant."

PEAS. — *Semination.* — P. 231. " Pease are generally drilled about Guildford—in other parts of the county, they are mostly sown broad-cast. Dibbling used formerly to be practised, but it has given way to the practice of drilling. Where they are sown broad-cast, it is considered the better way to plough them in with a shallow furrow, and afterwards to harrow the ground lightly."

Produce of Peas.—P. 232. " In favourable seasons, the crop will run from three to five quarters. It is observable, that calcareous soils are more favourable to the growth of this crop, than soils which have no chalk or lime in their composition. On some of the calcareous ground, even where it lay high and exposed, I was informed that from ten to twelve sacks (five to six quarters) were frequently got."— This is an extraordinary produce.

WELD*.—P. 383. " Woad is sown on the chalk-hills in the neighbourhood of Banstead Downs, where it is found to answer remarkably well. The soil best adapted for it is a thin, and rather poor, chalky loam: it grows too strong on good land.

" It is generally sown along with a crop of barley, on land which has had the preparation of a summer-fallow.

In

---

* Mr. Stevenson has misnamed the plant he was treating of. The material of dying, which is cultivated on the hills of Surrey, is not *Isatis Tinctoria*, or Woad; but *Reseda Luteola*, or Weld.

In order to separate the seed, and to scatter it more evenly
over the surface, it is usual to mix it with ashes : rather less
than a pint is allowed to the acre.

" There are two important circumstances which recommend the cultivation of this plant.

" In the first place, it is found to be a very good preparation for wheat" (?) " on the thin soils, where it is commonly grown ; and

" Secondly, as it is ripe very early in the summer, it can
be sold, and the money for it got in time to help to pay the
expense of the corn harvest.

" It is generally ripe in July, when it is pulled and
bunched."

What I recollect of the Banstead practice, in regard to
this crop, is, that it was chiefly grown among clover;
which, in the spring, before the dyer's weed begins to run
up to seed, sheep will pasture upon, without injury to the
weld ; which is less palatable to them. Weld raised in
this way frequently becomes a profitable crop to a *tenant ;*
but not so, I apprehend, to a proprietor; as the entire produce is carried off the land.

TURNEPS.—Their *Introduction* into Surrey.—P. 243. "As
far back as the memory of one of the oldest labourers in
Surrey would enable me to trace, I found that turnips had
been cultivated in his neighbourhood (about Cheam and
Ewel), nearly to as great an extent, and in his opinion, with
at least as much success as they are now."

The Reporter has extended his section, concerning this
crop, to twentyfour pages ; but without producing much
practical information. A considerable part of the section
is taken up with discussing the controversial point of
whether the *row* or the *random* culture is preferable.—
Having already spoken my sentiments, fully, on that point,
in reviewing the Report from *Northumberland* (the proper
County in which to discuss it) I pass it, here, without further
notice.

Perceiving nothing of novelty, nor of excellence, in this
report of the practice of Surrey, concerning the *cultivation*
of turneps, I proceed to their

Application, there.—P. 260. " The purposes to which
turnips are applied, depend in a great measure on the
distance of the farm from the metropolis; and in some
respects, on the nature of the soil on which they are
grown.

" The greatest part of those in the immediate vicinity
of London, go to the supply of Covent Garden and the
other markets: those at the distance of twelve or fourteen
miles are partly bought by the great cow-keepers, and
                                                    partly

partly consumed by the stock of the grower, or let to such farmers as have not a sufficiency of feed. Turnips beyond the distance of fourteen miles, in Surrey at least, may be considered as grown for the winter feed of stock, unless in those parts of the county which border on the Thames: from these they are often brought in barges for the supply of the London markets, and for the use of the cow-keepers.

" Such turnips as are sold to the cow-keepers, or for the market, are of course drawn ; but unless in these instances, it is by no means common to draw the turnips. They are, however, sometimes drawn and fed on an adjoining ley field, when the soil on which they are grown is wet."

The *Value* of the Turnep Crop, in Surrey.—P. 264. " When turnips are let to be folded off, it is either at so much per acre, or at so much per sheep for the week : about two guineas is the usual price per acre : when a particular field is uncommonly good, or the turnips in general have failed, three or four guineas have been given."

P. 265. " When turnips are sold to be drawn off the field, ten and twelve guineas per acre are very commonly given by the cow-feeders: where they are drawn and bunched for market, they will produce, at 2*d.* per gallon, 26*l.* per acre ; as they are, however, oftener sold for 4*d.* a gallon, the acre may fairly be reckoned worth 40*l.*"

BULBOUS RAPE.—Its *Introduction* into Surrey.—P. 273. " A very few years ago, scarcely an acre of Swedish turnips were to be seen, except on the farms of some gentlemen ; and now, there is scarcely a farmer who grows any considerable quantity of the common turnip, but what has also several acres of the Swedish."

The following *comparison*, between bulbous rape and turneps, is concisely and well drawn.—P. 275. " During the winter they are not considered as equal feeding to turnips : they are then harder, drier, and tougher ; of course they are not so much relished : the cattle or sheep cannot fill themselves on them in so short a space of time, or with so little trouble as they can on the common turnip, and therefore will not fatten so kindly or so soon on them. In the spring, the advantage is decidedly in their favour : the turnips are then hard and stringy, or dry and spongy : while the ruta baga is in its perfection ; more tender than it was in winter, and the juices more easily expressed."

Its general *Application*, in Surrey.—P. 275. " They come in for sheep-feed between the common turnip and the tares or grass. Some farmers give them to their work-horses, but this practice is by no means so common as it deserves to be. Moist food for work-horses is very much wanted
during

during the winter; and if every thing is taken into consideration, the Swedish turnip will be found the most convenient and advantageous."

" SIBERIAN TURNEP."—This is to me, in *name* at least, a
new species of crop, in English agriculture.   Is it the
" Turneprooted Cabbage ;" or the " Kohl Rabi," or " Hungarian Turnep ?"

P. 278. " For the following account of this vegetable,
which has been successively cultivated by Mr. Pennington,
of Lee Place, near Godstone, I am indebted to Mr.
Salisbury, of the Botanic-garden, Brompton, who has witnessed the good properties of it, both at his friend Mr.
Pennington's, and in his own garden."

" The Siberian turnip is a variety between the cabbage
and turnip, but it differs from the Swedish turnip in growing
to a larger size in the root, which is very sweet and nutritious, although equally hardy with the root of the Swedish
turnip : it is superior to this in one important point, as it
produces a greater quantity of foliage in the spring.   The
tops of it branch into a great number of ramifications,
and when full grown, it sometimes reaches the height of
five feet, and covers a space five feet square."

This, I conceive, may be a sufficient notice to practical
men, to try so *promising* a plant.

RAPE HERBAGE.—P. 268. " Mr. Birkbeck, of Wanborough, who cultivates a considerable extent of rape, puts
his sheep upon it more early than is usually done : as they
are suffered to go over the whole field, he finds that they
eat the leaves that grow nearest the ground, and leave the
others untouched till these are all consumed. As soon as he
perceives that all the plants are deprived of the ground
leaves, he takes his flock off the field. Two advantages
result from this management : if these leaves were not
eaten at that time, they would wither, and become useless :
his sheep thus get more food from the rape than they otherwise would do, while at the same time, the other leaves
of the rape are found to grow more rapidly and luxuri-
antly."

If this interesting information is really founded in mature
experience, the incident that gave rise to it may well be
considered as valuable. It is certainly entitled to trial, by
the growers of rape herbage ; which is a valuable species
of fallow crop, on lands that are too tenacious for turneps.

MIXED HERBAGE.—The different *species* spoken of, in the
Report before me, are *red clover, white clover, trefoil, ray-
grass.*   What is said of the two following species is noticeable.

Red Clover.—P. 303. " Clover, as well as turnips, appears
                                                              to

to have been cultivated in Surrey for at least a century*.
They were both most probably introduced, or recommended
to the farmers, by Sir Richard Weston, of Sutton, who,
about the middle of the seventeenth century, published an
account of the husbandry of Flanders, where these crops at
that time formed a regular and constant part of the rotation.   However this may be, the breadth of ground in the
arable part of the Downs and on the northern clays, sown
with clover, as far back as an old man of 82 could remember, was not greater (nor the crop better, in his opinion)
than what is now cultivated.   It probably was later of finding its way into the Weald : at present, it it cultivated
there to nearly as great an extent as in the other parts of
the county.   In the common fields, as might be expected,
it is not often grown."

Trefoil.—P. 310. " It is a very common practice, to sow
a few pounds of trefoil among the crop that immediately
precedes the turnip or summer-fallow : by this means, at a
very trifling expense, some good sheep-feed is obtained for
the beginning of winter."

SAINFOIN.—We are here entering on a valuable article of
report.—*Extent* in Cultivation.—P. 311. " This plant is
cultivated to a very considerable extent in Surrey; the
management of it is in general well understood, the produce
it affords is great, and the merits of it are duly prized.   Its
culture is upon the increase ; and probably, if such a large
proportion of the chalky hills were not continued under the
natural herbage, the Downs would be entirely covered with
it." (?)   " As it is, extensive fields of it may be seen the
whole breadth of the county, from the borders of Kent, at
the eastern side, to the borders of Hampshire, on the western, near Farnham, covering with its valuable herbage large
tracts of the chalky ridge†.

Soil for Sainfoin.—P. 311. " From the experience of this,
as well as of the other counties in England, where sainfoin
is

" * From the following passage in Aubrey, clover appears to have
been cultivated to a considerable extent at the time he wrote his History
(about 1673).   Speaking of Elsted, he says, ' In this parish, and the
parts adjoining, clover-grass has reduced the price of meadow-hay from
3*l.* to 1*l.* per load.'   Aubrey ascribes the introduction of clover to Sir
Richard Weston, of Sutton, in this county, in 1645: he says, he
brought it from Flanders or Brabant.   It is probable, therefore, that
Surrey was among the first, if not the very first district in England, into
which this valuable grass was brought."

" † The date of the introduction of this very valuable plant into
Surrey, I cannot exactly ascertain, but from a passage quoted from
Aubrey (in a note on the article Trefoil), it appears to have been well
known in his time (1673)."

is grown, the great advantage, if not the absolute necessity of a calcareous soil for this plant, is thoroughly and universally acknowledged."

In the calcareous districts in which this valuahle crop has been long in cultivation, the necessity of a *calcareous subsoil*, to make it florish and endure, must have been known for ages past. But not so in the kingdom at large ; where an *impenetrable base*, alone, was believed to be wanting, to secure its successful culture. I claim the credit, if any attach to it, of introducing the essential quality of sainfoin land, to written agriculture. See my YORKSHIRE.

On sowing *Trefoil* Seed with that of Sainfoin.—P. 314. " There is considerable difference of opinion respecting the propriety and advantage of sowing trefoil with sainfoin : this used formerly to be the general practice, but some of the most successful growers of sainfoin are decidedly averse to it."

In evidence of this assertion, however, the Reporter brings forward the subjoined incident.—P. 315. " The following circumstance decidedly proves the impropriety, or at least the inutility of sowing trefoil along with sainfoin. Mr. Birkbeck, of Wanborough, who cultivates sainfoin on a very extensive scale, had been always in the habit of sowing a certain proportion of trefoil along with it; but one year his servant, by mistake, omitted to sow the trefoil on a certain part of a field. The sainfoin on this part flourished much better, and reached to a greater perfection of growth and greater fulness of crop, than the sainfoin that was sown along with trefoil : hence Mr. Birkbeck justly concluded, that the latter might at least be considered as useless, if not as absolutely prejudicial, and therefore for the future he resolved to sow his sainfoin by itself."

But this single incident, unaccompanied by its attendant circumstances, cannot be allowed to be sufficient to set aside the established practice of an extent of country. I have observed the same practice in Hampshire.

That young sainfoin requires some assistance, to keep down noxious weeds, the first year of its growth and the spring of the second year, or to be clean hoed, as turneps, during the same time,—is to me evident, and indispensable to its accurate culture. But I do not think that *trefoil* is its best helpmate. I prefer the Kentish practice, of sowing *red clover* with it; especially within a farmer's day's journey from London; for a reason which will presently appear.

Semination of Sainfoin.—P. 316. " Sainfoin has been sown both in autumn and in spring : the result of the experiments

periments is, that when sown rather early in spring, it is found to answer best. The latter end of the month of March, or the beginning of April."—" It is sown with barley much in the same manner as clover is; *i. e.* after the barley has been harrowed once or twice, the sainfoin is sown, and the ground again lightly harrowed and rolled. As the seeds penetrate through the ground with some difficulty, it is of consequence not to bury it deep, and at the same time to make the ground fine and even.

" *Drilling.*—This is scarcely ever, if at all, practised in Surrey, though there are some advocates for it."

This conveys to me a new idea in the culture of sainfoin. I cannot, however, conceive it to be right to sow it " in rows at the distance of two or three feet"—as the Reporter suggests (p. 317);—but rather at fifteen inches— more or less,—according to the depth of the field of pasturage, and its intended application. If it be right, under any circumstances, to cultivate sainfoin, *alone,* it certainly might be kept clean, the first and second year, at less expence, in rows, than at random.

Making Sainfoin *Hay.*—P. 319. " As soon as ever the sainfoin is in full bloom, it is the proper season to cut it for hay : this is in general done with scythes, with cradles or bows on them. It is suffered to lie in the swaths till it is nearly dried through, when it is carefully and regularly turned over with the handles of the rakes, or with large wooden forks*. If the weather prove favourable, it may then be put up in cocks, and carried the day after the swaths were turned. Great care must be taken not to *over-make* it. The perfection of sainfoin-hay is, when the blossom retains its natural bloom and figure, and when the stalks and leaves are of a clear and healthy green. It is easily spoilt by wet weather."

Application of Sainfoin.—P. 319. " It may be used from the stack, in three or four days after it is put up, if the crop is not very bulky. The best time for carrying it to market is before Christmas ; both the quality and the price are then above what they will in general be, if it be kept till after the new year.

" Very few of the Surrey farmers, who are within 18 or 20 miles of London, consume their sainfoin-hay at home : those at a greater distance give it to their horses principally, and to their milch-cows and cattle. It is in a very high degree grateful and nourishing to all kinds of stock.

In

---

* A long slender pole, somewhat crooked at the thicker or handle end, is the most convenient tool for that purpose.

In London, the hay always brings a better price than clover-hay."

P. 317. " The price of sainfoin hay depends in a great degree upon its being fine."—That is to say—slender stalked ; not " coarse" or thick-stemmed. Hence, the closer the stems stand on the ground, the more saleable will be the hay.—See the above remarks on drilling the crop. Also those on sowing *clover* with sainfoin, instead of *trefoil ;* which is less valuable as forage for horses.

Sainfoin *Seed.*—P. 320. " The management of sainfoin, when the seed is the principal object, is rather difficult. In the first place, the pods, as has been already remarked, fill, and the seeds ripen, at different times, according as they are placed at the bottom or top of the stalks ; of course, it is almost impossible to hit the season when all the seeds are in a proper state of ripeness : and in the second place, the seed very easily falls out, if it meet with rain, or if it be roughly handled during the making.

" When the husks are of a brownish colour, and the seeds feel plump and firm, it is then time to mow it : this is done by the most careful Surrey farmers, only when the dew is on the plants, or at least, not when the weather is either very windy or very dry, since the seeds are very apt to fall out, if the pod is parched by the sun, or the stalk shaken by the wind. The swaths are not turned, for the same reason, if they can be got sufficiently dry without it : when it is necessary to turn them, it is done as gently and carefully as possible, by putting the handle of the fork or rake below that part which contains least seed, while the bottom of the stalk, where the greatest quantity of seed is, rests on the ground, and is turned without being lifted from it. In a good year, and when proper care is taken to prevent the seed from falling out, four quarters per acre may be looked for."

Duration of Sainfoin, on the Surrey Hills.—P. 321. " This seldom exceeds eight or ten years ; at least, when it has stood so long, the broad or oat grass begins to smother it ; and of course, not only does the crop become of comparatively little value, but if it is suffered to continue much longer, the ground gets very foul."

Renewal of the Sainfoin Crop.—P. 322. " The common opinion is, that sainfoin will not bear to be repeated on the same ground, till at least 15 or 20 years have elapsed."

FROM this copious detail of valuable information, it appears that the practice of Surrey is peculiarly adapted to the raising of sainfoin hay, for the London market.—Under this impression, the growers of it wish to fill their ground

as

as full of plants as may be, in order to produce " fine hay."
This may serve to account for the *short duration* of their
crops. The roots, I conceive, are proportionate to the
stems; and are of course unable to penetrate to so great a
depth, in search of their favorite pasturage, as are larger,
stronger-rooted plants.

See my GLOCESTERSHIRE—district, *Cotswold Hills ;* and
SOUTHERN COUNTIES,—district of *Maidstone;* – for further
information, concerning this profitable crop,—on calcareous
lands, whose subsoils and bases are of an open penetrable
nature.

KITCHEN GARDEN GROUNDS.—P. 418. " It is reckoned,
that the whole quantity of garden-ground in Surrey, employed in raising vegetables for the London market, amounts
to about 3500 acres."

HOPS.—P. 325. " It is impossible to ascertain with exact-
ness and certainty, the time when the culture of hops was
first introduced into the parish of Farnham and its neighbourhood, or the circumstances that gave rise to its introduction."

P. 327. " From every inquiry I made, I found that the
extent of ground cultivated with hops was annually increasing in Farnham and the neighbouring parishes. Within
these last 100 years, the number of acres is nearly trebled :
at the beginning of the last century, there were not more
than 300 acres in the parish of Farnham ; now there are
between 800 and 900 acres ; and this year (1807), there is
a greater demand for plants than there was last year. This
is a pretty decisive proof that the Farnham hops, notwithstanding the great expense attending their cultivation, and
the enormous rent of the ground on which they grow, pay
the growers very well.

" Hops are grown in many different parts of the county
of Surrey besides Farnham, and its immediate neighbourhood; but every where else, I believe, they are grown by
farmers : at Farnham, in general, the hop culture is either
the sole, or the principal object and dependence of the
grower."

P. 325. " Farnham was formerly remarkable for its cloth
manufactory ; and while it continued, it is known that the
culture of hops, though it may have been introduced, was
not carried on to any considerable extent. As the manufacture of cloth declined, and receded from Farnham to
some of the neigbouring towns, the culture of hops advanced and took its place.

" It is not easy to determine, when this change in the
occupation of the people of Farnham took place : if we
may credit tradition, confirmed by several corroborating
circumstances,

circumstances, it was about the middle, or rather towards
the end, of the seventeenth century."

Mr. Stevenson enters on the cultivation and after-manage-
ment of hops, in detail, and at great length; having appropriated nearly fifty pages to the subject. His account has
evidently been written, after much previous enquiry and
personal examination had taken place. I have perused it
with attention. I have not, however, discovered any
thing, in Mr. S.'s Report, that materially differs from my
own register of the FARNHAM PRACTICE; which does not
appear to have received any essential improvement, during
a lapse of twentyfive years. I have only to add, that,
if a prior systematized register of it had not been before
the public, Mr. Stevenson's would have been the more
valuable. It appears to have been done with much consideration.

ORCHARDS.—The subjoined account of the orchards of
Surrey, I think, is overcharged. If we except walnuts,
Surrey is not a *fruit* County.

P. 419. " Most of the farms in the county have orchards
attached to them, sufficiently large to supply, in a favourable year, from four to twelve hogsheads of cider; but as
they do not form the principal part of the farm, and the
main dependence of the farmer, they are not much taken
care of."

Walnuts.—P. 443. " This tree also answers best on a
chalky subsoil, though it requires a greater depth of upper
soil than the beech. It is found in many parts of Surrey
of a large size, and very productive, though no where in
any great numbers. When the great value of the timber
of this tree, and the high price which its fruit bears, are
considered, it is rather surprising that it is not cultivated
more extensively on the chalk districts of Surrey.

" A good sized tree, upon a kind soil, will, in a favourable year, such as the present (1807), produce 20 bushels of
walnuts; or, reckoning the bushel to contain 700 walnuts,
14,000 walnuts. I was informed of two trees near Buckland, from which nearly 50 bushels had been got."

GRASS LANDS.

PROPORTIONATE EXTENT of Grass to Arable.—P. 385.
" It has already been remarked, that the county of Surrey
has a much smaller proportion of grass land than Middlesex, and, indeed, than most other counties in England.
It is however thought by many of the farmers, that grass
land is rather on the increase: this, at least, is certain,
that

that there are several very powerful causes operating to reduce the quantity of arable land."

The Reporter sets out in search of those causes. But he does not, to my apprehension, bring them home to the conviction of the reader.—What he has said of them would seem to have risen from the reflection of his own mind, rather than from his survey of the County of Surrey.

MOWING GROUNDS.—P. 389 " By far the greater part, and the most valuable of the meadow land in this county, lies along the banks of the Thames, in the north-western division; in the parishes of Oxted, Tanridge, Lingfield, Crowhurst, in the south-eastern division; on the banks of the Mole, near Cobham; and on the banks of the Wey, near Godalming. There is also some meadow land in the north-eastern division of the county, near the metropolis, about Dulwich and Camberwell, and a little near Petersham, Wandsworth, and Streatham. A few acres are scattered over most other parts of the county; but the proportion both of meadow land and of pasture is least in the Weald, where, from the nature of the soil, and the expense and difficulty of tillage, most grass land would naturally be expected."

Quality of *Hay*.—The following statement is highly interesting.—P. 390. " The quality of the hay varies very much in different parts of Surrey. About Chobham and Bagshot, the meadow-hay has a very fine colour, and, to all appearance, is very excellent hay; but it has been proved by the experience of almost every regiment of cavalry which has been quartered at Guildford, and which, from the appearance of the hay, has been tempted to purchase it, that it possesses very little nourishment; and that in fact, it is much inferior to the hay that is grown on the meadows near Cobham, though the latter does not look nearly so good.

" This curious fact is attributed, and probably with justice, to the different nature of the waters at Bagshot and Cobham: near the former place, the water is evidently very strongly impregnated with *iron:* this must injure the hay: whereas, about Cobham, the water from the Mole is as evidently calcareous; this probably is beneficial to the hay."

GRAZING GROUNDS.—P. 391. " Perhaps the greatest extent of pasture land lying altogether, is to be found on the Duke of Norfolk's estate, in the parishes of Newdigate and Charlwood, in the Weald of Surrey. On this estate, cattle are taken in to graze, from the beginning of May to the beginning of October: the price paid per week depends upon the size of the cattle: the smallest size pay 1s.

1s. 6d.; the largest, 2s. 6d. per week. The land is generally stocked at the rate of one ox to each two acres; but
as there are, almost every week, some taken out, and others
put in, it is not easy to ascertain precisely what number
per acre the land carries through the summer."

DAIRY GROUNDS.—P. 392. "With regard to dairy
grounds, there may be said to be none in Surrey; though
there is reason to believe, that at least a small part of the
butter consumed in London was formerly supplied by it,
at a time when the access to the metropolis from more
distant dairy lands, was not so easy and expeditious as it
is at present."

CHALK DOWNS.—P. 480. "These are to be found on
every part of the chalk-hills of Surrey except the eastern
and western extremities: at the former, the chalk-hills are
extremely broken into vallies, across nearly their whole
breadth; at the western extremity they form merely a
narrow ridge, steep on both sides: at both these extremities, as well as on the more precipitous southern
side, the chalk-hills are almost entirely under the plough,
so that the principal and most extensive Downs, lie either
on the flat or on the northern slope. The most remarkable Downs are those of Bansted, Epsom, and Clandon:
the first was formerly noticed for its sweet mutton, the
last is now considered as affording better feed than any
of the other Downs: probably because it is not stocked
so hard."

" LAYING LAND IN GRASS."—In a section, so entitled,
we find the arduous task of *revivifying old grass lands*
spoken of at extraordinary length. The Reporter calls in
a *friend*, Mr. BERKBECK (see Rape Herbage aforegoing)
to his assistance. But after employing nearly a sheet of
paper, in that difficult service, they leave the matter, *as a
practical subject*, where they found it.—One passage, however, must not be suffered to pass unnoticed.

P. 404. "On the quantity of manure for new lays, the
following *directions* are given by Mr. Birkbeck, of Wanborough.

" 'Turf may be restored to its former fertility; and for
this purpose it is only necessary to observe one simple
rule, viz. let manure equal to the whole exhaustion incurred during the course of tillage, be replaced on the
grass." (!) "To ascertain this, an accurate account should
be kept of the straw and grain produced by each crop.
The same weight of grain and oil-cake consumed by horses,
cattle, or hogs, littered on an equal quantity of straw,
will furnish an equivalent in manure sufficiently exact for
our purpose.

" Had

" 'Had due attention been paid to this circumstance, the plough needed not to have been so scrupulously excluded from our old pastures. In fact, this is the essential point.'

" There can be very little doubt with those who have considered the subject attentively," (!) " that the rule laid down by Mr. Birkbeck is of essential importance, and if it were carefully and accurately attended to, it would go a great way towards restoring a good and permanent turf on land laid down to grass."

Of the many thousands of acres of rich grazing grounds, dairy grounds, and productive hay grounds, that have been violated, and despoiled for a length of years; through the ignorance and rapacity of men of trade turned country gentlemen; the wrongheaded speculations of men of genius without judgment; and the self-interest and artful persuations of designing men,—during the last twenty or or thirty years;—how many have been laid or *attempted* to be " laid in grass"? to be renovated and returned to their former state?—And how many years of plunder did the few, on which attempts may have been made, undergo?—Say ten or twelve, fifteen or twenty.—Set down the medium—fifteen.

An " accurate account" of produce might doubtlessly be kept, during that or a much longer term. But where could the " manure equal to the whole exhaustion" be procured? Or, if raised on the farm, where could it be stored, without losing its essential virtues, during that period of time? Even if it could " be replaced on the grass,"—and the infant crop should be able to rise under it,—it would *still* be fifteen or twenty years before the " TURF" would " be restored to its former fertility."

The mere impracticability of " the one simple rule"— " the essential point," on which the whole machinery of regeneration is proposed to turn—might have been passed over with a smile;—but not so its evil tendency. It is, in truth, a DANGEROUS DOCTRINE;—and right sorry I am that it has been preached up, before the Board of Agriculture; as, there, it is to be feared, it would find listeners. It might be reckoned cleverness and deep policy, in a *tenant* to broach such a doctrine; but it were folly in a *landlord* to drink of it*.

BREAKING UP PERMANENT GRASS LANDS.—Again, we find the Reporter and his friend engaged in the work of deterioration.

---

* The above remark could not be written to offend Mr. BIRKBECK; as I am entirely unacquainted with his rank in society.

deterioration *.   The section " Breaking up Grass Land,"
which is not very long, is chiefly filled with the praise of
" paring-and-burning :"—an operation which most effectually prevents the return of well herbaged sward, for a
length of time, indefinite:—thus completing, in a masterly
way, the work of spoliation.—Not only the *roots*, but the
seeds, of former herbage are, by that promptly destroying
process, annihilated.—Whereas, if perennial grass lands be
broken up with the plow, and subjected to no other operations than what belongs to *tillage*, some of the roots and
seeds may remain alive in the soil—a few years—and assist
nature, IN RESTORING THE TURF.

P. 408. " Paring and burning is an operation so well
adapted to the purpose of converting grass land to a temporary course of tillage, in every view of the subject, that
I have no hesitation in proposing it as the first step, in
all soils and situations." †

After many an ingenious conception and *chemical conjecture!* we are boldly led on to this *logical inference.*—
P. 412. " It seems clear, that the acquisition, however obtained, will be as the quantity of vegetation ; therefore
land which has been pared and burnt, producing larger
crops, will acquire more than fallowed land, to compen-
sate for the loss sustained in the process."

The Writer, however, does not say how long the " quantity of vegetation," *so acquired*, can be induced to *continue*,
under his compulsory process.—Nor what length of years
will be required,—when the accumulated treasures, which a
suite of CARBONATED GRAZING GROUNDS con-
tained, have been thereby dissipated,—before the exhausted lands can be again enriched, and brought back to
their former state of fertility ;—even for the purposes of
ARATION ;—nor how many centuries it would take to raise
them to a state of permanent profit, as PERENNIAL PASTURE
GROUNDS:—such as the measures, above recommended,
effectually tend to destroy.

LIVESTOCK.

Surrey, as Middlesex, is thinly stocked; and the scanty
number it contains are mostly brought into it, from distant
counties.

* Query, had Mr. VANCOUVER those mischievous " Directions" in
his mind's eye, when he drew his admirable inference, concerning the
PRINCIPLES of IMPROVEMENT ?—See p. 351, aforegoing.

† The above, as well as the following extract, is taken from Mr.
BIRKBECK's COMMUNICATION to the BOARD of AGRICULTURE;
from which almost the whole of Mr. Stevenson's section, " Breaking
up Grass Lands," is copied.

counties. Not very long ago, scarcely *a* cattle or *a* sheep was bred within it; excepting a few *diminutive long-horned cattle* (qre. aboriginal?) and some mean native sheep,— which were seen on the heathlands, in the western part of the County.

CATTLE.—P. 519. " From the account which has already been given of the application of the ground in Surrey, it will be evident that of the live stock to which attention is here paid, cattle form a very inconsiderable part. Indeed, if we except the cows that are kept around the metropolis, for the purpose of supplying it with milk; and those that are kept in the more remote parts of the county, for the purpose of suckling calves for the London market, cattle seldom form a standing, regular, or considerable part of a farmer's stock."

Milked Cows.—P. 519. " On the subject of cows that are kept for supplying the metropolis with milk, Mr. Middleton, in his Survey of Middlesex, has treated so amply, and with such abundant sources of information, that it is impossible to add to what he has said, and difficult to advance any thing which will not appear to be taken from his work."

Suckled Cows.—P. 520. " The rearing" (fatting) " of calves for the London market, was once a very favourite and profitable employment in the central parts of Surrey, about Esher, Cobham, Send, and Ripley. The famous Mr. Duckett, of Esher, used to carry it on to a great extent; but from various causes, this practice is on the decline; or at least, is now not carried on to a very great extent, or with much spirit, any where, except in the more retired and distant parts of the county, about Chobham and Bagshot, and in some parts of the Weald."

P. 521. " As each cow brings up more calves than one, it is evident that there must be a great demand for calves: this has given rise to calve-merchants, who attend the different fairs, and purchase calves for the Surrey farmers: the fair at Aylesbury, in Buckinghamshire, is particularly resorted to, as the calves bought there are considered as fattening more kindly, and producing more marketable veal, than the calves from most other places."

Family Cows.—P. 520. " For gentlemen's families, the Jersey, Alderney, and Suffolk breeds are often kept; and by the farmers at a distance from town, the Welsh, Devonshire, Sussex, and Staffordshire: the last in many places are very common, and much esteemed."

Fatting Cattle.—P. 523. " Many of the gentlemen and farmers in Surrey occasionally fatten a few oxen; but none of them carry it on with more regularity, nor to a greater extent, than Mr. Adam, of Mount Nod, and Mr. Coles,
of

of Norbury. The buildings of the former, which are constructed with great regard to convenience, are sufficient to contain 600 head of cattle: they are regularly fed with one pound of linseed, one bushel of grains, and one bushel of chaff, all mixed together; and one truss of hay between eight or ten. Mr. Coles feeds his cattle with oil-cakes and hay, which indeed is the food principally given."

SHEEP.—*Number.*—P. 526. "Sheep are kept in considerable numbers in the middle part of Surrey; upon the chalk-hills; on the sandy loams that lie immediately between the chalk and the Weald, and those that occupy the south-west and west parts of the county, between Godalming and Farnham; on the heaths between Farnham and Bagshot; on the mixed loams that unite the sandy ridge which runs from Godstone to Dorking, with the clay of the Vale; and on the sandy loams intermixed with clay, which lie to the north of the chalk-hills. Such farmers as possess land lying on or near the chalk-hills, are peculiarly well situated for keeping large flocks of sheep: on the Downs, the pasture is remarkably good, and well suited to this animal; and there is no difficulty of finding, among the arable land of this part of the county, soils proper for turnip. In the more immediate vicinity of London, and in the Weald, very few sheep are kept: near London, the land is occupied to greater advantage under a different system; and the soil of the Weald, joined to its low and damp situation, renders it unfit for sheep."

Breed of Sheep.—P. 526. "It is only comparatively of late, that much attention has been paid to the peculiar breed of sheep in this county: the large Wiltshire, in the memory of many still living, occupied entirely the sheep-farms on the chalk hills, where folding or fattening for the butcher were the sole objects; while the singular breed of small ill-formed sheep then entirely occupied the extensive heaths in the west of the county, which they still (though not in so pure a state as formerly) continue to occupy. But there is reason to believe that, before the introduction of the Wiltshire sheep, a small breed, affording remarkably sweet mutton, were generally kept on the hills: for Mr. Evelyn, in his letter to Mr. Aubery, prefixed to the latter's History of Surrey, which was written about 25 years before the end of the seventeenth century, rather complains that the introduction of paring and burning had, by destroying the fine pasture of the Downs, deprived them of their small and sweet mutton."

That letter shows, only, that the *native* breed of Surrey— the greyfaced, greylegged variety, which formerly occupied the commons of England (see NORTHERN DEPARTMENT,)

MENT,) had then (1675-6) been recently banished ; and the tall, heavy Wiltshire breed introduced in their stead. But it is altogether vague to ascribe that memorable change, to " paring-and-burning"!—that is to say, to the deterioration of the hill pastures !—EVELYN, whose works I have had occasion to study with attention, was more the man of learning and fashion, than the country gentleman. The introduction of the Wiltshire sheep, upon the hills of Surrey, was, more probably, a consequence of the introduction of cultivated herbage and turneps, on those hills. The young Wiltshire wedders have ever been depastured on the higher " maiden downs":—a proof, this, that the small, hardy, sweet-mutton breed were not driven from those hills by a want of pasturage !—to make room for a giant race that required vastly more support. See pp. 394, and n. 397.

In 1775, the chalk hills of Surrey were, and had long been, occupied, entirely, by Wiltshire wedders ; and their lower lands, on their northern margin, by Dorsetshire ewes.

P. 527. " At present," (1806) " besides the Wiltshire and Bagshot sheep, the Dorsetshire, South Down, Somerset, or Mendip, the Berkshire, the Romney, and the Merino-South Down, are kept. The South Down, Wiltshire and Dorsetshire, are by far the most common : the last are kept for early lambs ; the Wiltshire are by some preferred for the fold ; and the South Down for the butcher, and for their wool.

" A cross of the Merino and South Down, and of the Ryland-Merino and South Down, is kept by many of the gentlemen, and by some of the farmers, in Surrey."

P. 530 " The South Down sheep in Surrey are not often quite pure : they are generally a little inclining to the Berkshire. The Bagshot sheep also are scarcely ever now found unmixed, the South Down beginning to occupy (either pure, or crossed with the native sheep) even the remote heaths of Surrey. A pure heath sheep is a very ugly creature, with very large horns : it seldom weighs more than 8lb. per quarter

" In some parts of the Weald, where a few sheep are kept, the breed appears to be a mixture of the Welsh and the South Down, or of the Welsh and the heath sheep. Few Leicester sheep are to be seen in Surrey, and the Romney are confined to one or two farmers in the south-east corner of the county."

Outline of *Management.*—P. 532. " Most farmers purchase their lambs at six or nine months old: some breed them. The South Down are bought at Lewes fair; the Wiltshire at Weyhill : both about Michaelmas. The former are usually fatted at two years old: the latter are
folded

folded during two summers, and then fatted the following spring.

" The more attentive farmers carefully separate their flocks, especially if they be large, according to their age, &c. and thus ensure their feeding better, and fattening more regularly, certainly, and quickly. A shepherd is commonly allotted to each flock of 300 or 400: sometimes, but not often, he has 500 under his care. The shepherd's dog, on the Surrey hills, is remarkably sagacious and attentive."

P. 530. " The principal dependence of the farmers for the *food* of their sheep, is on turnips, rape, rye, tares, and trefoil: some put them on the sainfoin in the spring and autumn; but others object to this practice, as very prejudicial, and often fatal, to that valuable plant.

" By sowing the common turnips at different times, and by having also a portion of the Swedish turnip, and of rape, rye, and winter tares, the Surrey farmers are enabled to keep their sheep till the spring is pretty far advanced. If the turnips should fail, or the weather during the winter prove so severe, as to oblige them to bring their sheep into the farm-yard, hay, corn, and oil-cake are then given them, according as the purpose is either merely to keep or to fatten them. It is extremely difficult to get sheep to eat a sufficient quantity of dry hay; this, however, Mr. Birkbeck effected, by cutting the hay fine, and giving the sheep, along with it, plenty of pure water: by this method he got them to eat about $3\frac{1}{2}$ lb. a-piece each day. It is a very common practice with the sheep farmers, to sow trefoil on the land which is to come in for fallow the next year; this, growing rapidly, serves as excellent food for the sheep after harvest; on this, or on the stubbles, where there are no downs attached to the farm, the sheep are kept till the turnips are ready; they are also put upon the clover, where it is not intended to cut it a second time, or to keep it for seed. Where downs are attached to a farm, a great advantage is derived, as the pasture they afford is not only remarkably fine, but it is seldom much injured by the heats of summer."

Folding Sheep, in Surrey.—P. 531. " It has already been remarked, that the Wiltshire are generally used for folding. As the hill-farmers depend principally on folding for manuring their summer-fallow, it is a great object with them to keep large flocks for that purpose, even independently of the profit arising from fattening them.

" Three or four sheep are usually allotted to a square hurdle; and as there are 1030 square hurdles to an acre, the number of sheep sufficient to cover an acre, will amount

to

to about 3500. It is calculated that a flock of 500 will manure an acre in about a week. On the hills of Surrey, the hurdles run from seven to nine feet in length; but they are staked at the average distance of seven feet and a half: allowing three sheep to a hurdle, each sheep will have a space of 18 or 19 square feet: if the sheep are full grown Wiltshire, they are allowed 22 square feet."

House Lamb.—P. 533. " A few years since, Surrey was much celebrated for the number and excellence of the house-lambs, which were sent from different parts of it to the London market; but latterly, not nearly so many are reared, and the practice will probably remove gradually, first to the more remote parts of the county, and ultimately to counties more distant from the metropolis. There are, however, still some farmers who rear a considerable number of house-lambs, about Ewel, Esher, Walton, &c.; though from the increase in the price of labour, and in the first cost of the ewes, the profits are not nearly so great as they were formerly.

" Dorsetshire ewes are the only ones employed for the purpose of rearing house-lambs. They are bought at the Michaelmas Weyhill fair, to which they come, full of lamb, from Devonshire and the adjoining counties. The earliest begin to lamb in October, and they continue lambing during the winter."

P. 534. " The ewes are divided into *mothers* and *dam ewes:* the latter are such as have lost their lambs, or whose lambs have been sold. The *mothers* are suffered to remain in the lamb-house with the lambs all night; they are also brought in to the lambs for an hour in the middle of the day. The *dams* are brought to give suck twice a-day, in the morning and afternoon. It is generally found necessary to put the *dams* into a yoke, while suckling the strange lambs.

" The ewes are fed well, while giving suck, upon grains, chaff, turnips, hay, oil-cake, bran, &c. Chalk mixed up with a few oats, or a little wheat, is given to the lambs, principally to prevent or remove the acidity of stomach to which they are liable. The lambs arc very subject to sore mouths, which arises from the difficulty of cutting their teeth: it has been suggested that the most proper, and probably an effectual remedy for this disorder (of which many of them die), would be to lance their gums, and thus to enable them to cut their teeth without pain or trouble.

" The lamb-house is so constructed, as to keep the lambs separate in distinct pens, according to their age. It is kept very warm, and ought to be well littered frequently with clean dry straw."

Grass Lamb.—P. 535. " *Grass lambs* are also brought up
in

AGRICULTURE.

in considerable numbers about Guildford, Ewel, and in some other parts of the county. Such ewes are bought as will drop their lambs in January. The ewes and lambs are fed on turnips, oil-cake, &c. Great care must be taken not to suffer the lambs to touch the turnips or clover when the frost is on them, as that would inevitably kill them."

" Grass-lambs, of course, do not bring so much at market as house-lambs; but then the trouble and expense attending the rearing of them is not nearly so great. They are ready for the butcher in April and May: the ewes are generally fattened and sold in the succeeding autumn."

PROFIT.—Mr. Stevenson, in this, as in other parts of his work, writes like a man of sense and consideration.—P. 107. " This is difficult to get at, both because farmers, like other people, are not very willing to lay open their affairs; and because many of them, from not keeping their books in a very regular or minute manner, can only tell generally, the gross particulars of their expense and profit."

Nevertheless, he would seem to have felt himself in duty bound to offer some *calculations* on the subject,—as others have done. He has, accordingly, set down sundry sums, as " the expence of stocking a farm of one hundred acres, and of managing it and keeping the family, and paying the rent, for one year." In doing *this*, the groundwork of calculation was within reach. Yet, even in this case, no two men of twenty would bring out nearly the same sum; namely £1077.—And in calculating the " *expence* per acre" of different soils, and under different rotations; then calculating the *produce* of the crops; and, from these data, drawing the " net profit;"—differences of not less than ten, fifteen, twenty, or more, percent, would assuredly be brought out, by different calculators.

What corroborates the idea that making calculations, on the profit and loss of farming, was undertaken, by this writer, as a thing of duty, not of choice, is the ingenuous acknowledgment, which the author has thought proper to make, near the close of his section.

P. 114. " After all, we should constantly keep in mind, that no certainty can be attained on the head of expence and profit."

KENT.

KENT.

KENT, more than any other county, I think, of equal extent, naturally separates into well defined districts.

Nevertheless, among its inhabitants, especially in the eastern parts of the County, its popular divisions are vague and unsettled. Their ordinary denominations are " East Kent" and " West Kent."—The former has its limits, both natural and agricultural. But West Kent is a mere sound, without sense or meaning attached to it;—unless in regard to one article of produce; namely, hops.

The inhabitants of the midland parts of the County, naturally, fairly, and *feelingly*, lay claim to the more central parts, or " Middle Kent;" as will appear in reviewing the Report of it, now under consideration.

Before a natural and agricultural division of the County be attempted, it will be right to notice its more striking natural features. —These are given by two lines of elevated surfaces, which extend lengthway, through the County.— One of them is formed by the eastern extremity of the Chalk Hills of the southern Counties.—This, the main ridge, or " Hogsback of Kent," extends, in a continuous line,—excepting where it is intersected by the streams of water which cross it,—sixty miles ; the Medway and the Stower dividing it nearly into three equal compartments ; the whole chain being co-extensive with the County.

The other is a broken line of irregular Stoney Heights, of minor elevation. These run somewhat parallel with the Chalk Hills ; but are not of equal length, nor equally continuous ; being rather a range of scattered hillocks ; one ridge of a few miles in length, near the midway of the line, excepted.

After viewing almost every square mile of the County, the following appear, to me, as the proper division of it, into agricultural districts ; such, I mean, as an agricultural surveyor ought to examine it under.

I. NORTH KENT.—This division is bounded on the north, by the Thames ; on the west, by the County of Surrey ; on the south, by the line of cliffs, which form the southern confine of the western compartment of the Kentish Chalk Hills ; and, on the east, by the river Medway.

This

This division of the County comprizes the following districts, or subdivisions; namely, 1. The gravelly hillocks and the lower better lands, situated between the Thames and the skirts of the Chalk Hills: a passage of the County which might not inaptly be termed the *Thames-side Lands,* or the *District of Dartford.*—2. *The North Kent Marshes;* which are embraced by the estuaries of the Thames and the Medway; forming the easternmost point of North Kent. —3. The western compartment of the *Chalk Hills.*

II. WEST KENT,—(if the term can be appropriately applied to any part of the County)—has for its northern boundary, the Chalk Hills of North Kent. On the west, it is bounded by, and unites with, the Counties of Surrey and Sussex; on the south, by that of Sussex; and, on the east, by the Weald, or Vale Lands of Kent, and a line extending from the western boundary of the Weald—by the Goudhurst and Brenchley Hills—to the face of the North Kent Cliffs, between Sevenoaks and Wrotham. This infertile—this broken-surfaced, and variously soiled, part of Kent would be best designated by the *District of Tunbridge.*

III. SOUTH KENT.—This is confined, on the north, by the range of Stoney Heights, above spoken of; on the west, by the district of Tunbridge; on the south, by Sussex and the sea; and, on the east, by the eastern compartment of the Chalk Hills.—Its districts are 1. The " Weald," or *Vale Lands* of Kent. 2. The *District* of *Ashford.* And 3. " Romney Marsh," or the *South Kent Marshes.*

IV. EAST KENT.—This valuable quarter of the County is bounded, on the north, and east, by the British Ocean; on the west, by the Valley of the Stower; and on the south, by South Kent and the English Channel.—Its subdivisions are, 1. The *District* of *Canterbury,* extending westward to Faversham. 2. The *District* of *Thanet.* 3. The *East Kent Marshes**. 4. The *District* of *Sandwich.* And, 5. The eastern compartment of the *Chalk Hills.*

V. MIDDLE KENT.—This rightfully claims the remainder of the County;—the Isle of Sheppy excepted. It is bounded, on the north, by the estuary of the Medway, and by the Swale, or narrow strait of the sea, which separates the Isle of Sheppy from the main land; on the west, by the river Medway and the line which is drawn above, as the eastern boundary of the District of Tunbridge, or West Kent; on the south, by South Kent; and, on the east, by East Kent.

---

* EAST KENT MARSHES,—which *now* occupy a considerable extent of space, that heretofore, no doubt, was filled with the tide; *then,* separating the *Isle* of Thanet from the main land of Kent.

Kent.—Its subdivisions are, 1. The *District* of *Sittingbourn* —the rich lowlying lands, situated between the Swale and the Chalk Hills. 2. The central compartment of the *Chalk Hills*. 3. The rich and beautiful *District* of *Maidstone;* or, emphatically, the MIDLAND DISTRICT of KENT.

The *Isle* of *Sheppy* does not well assimilate with any one of the aggregate divisions of the County.

" GENERAL VIEW

OF THE

AGRICULTURE

OF THE

COUNTY OF KENT;

WITH

OBSERVATIONS ON THE MEANS OF ITS IMPROVEMENT.

DRAWN UP FOR THE CONSIDERATION OF

THE BOARD OF AGRICULTURE,

By JOHN BOYS,

OF BETSHANGER, FARMER.

1796."

THIS is one of the very first of the *published* Reports. It is, strictly and literally, a " reprinted report;" Mr. Boys having previously been the *original Reporter:*—a coincidence that has rarely taken place, in the literary career of the Board : notwithstanding it was the ostensible course on which it was proposed to be run.

The QUALIFICATIONS of Mr. Boys, as the Reporter of the agriculture of Kent, are not difficult to estimate. He was not only a farmer, by birth, but, at the time of writing, had been, for a course of years, himself an occupier, on an ample scale. His flock, we are informed, amounted to a thousand head, and his hop grounds to twenty acres. And altho he modestly designates himself an " unlettered" man, he frequently writes with more force and clearness, than many of his *lettered* brethren of Report. The subjoined is his own (?) account of his performance.

‘ PREFACE.

" PREFACE. The original Report having been printed by the Board of Agriculture, and circulated for the purpose of procuring additional remarks, was returned to me by the Board, with a variety of useful hints, observations, and corrections ; of which I have endeavoured to avail myself in this publication, to the advantage, I trust, of those who may take the trouble of perusing it. It is still, however, not so complete as could be wished for ; but a generous and candid public will excuse any imperfections to be found in it, however numerous, and will consider them as almost unavoidable, when it is known that it was originally the work of one individual, unlettered, and immersed in the cares of a numerous family, and an extensive business.

" Neither pains nor expence have been spared to procure information ; and the result is faithfully detailed. Having been brought up under a father who had the reputation of being a good practical farmer, and having been all my life engaged in the cultivation of different soils, and in grazing, I presume to think myself qualified to form opinions on the various systems of husbandry ; but when I recommend any practice, my readers may be assured that I do so, not from theory only, but from my own experience."

It is proper to observe, here, that Mr. Boys's experience evidently appears, from what we see in his Report, to have arisen in East Kent ; his knowledge of the other districts of the County being inconsiderable ; and his account of their practices, are consequently, unimportant ; compared with that of *his own country :*—in favour of which he was, at the time he wrote, unfortunately, and often ridiculously, prejudiced :—a circumstance which serves to lessen the confidence of the reader, in regard to the *authenticity* of the writer's information.

An annotator, upon the original sketch, under the signature of " A MIDDLE KENT FARMER," promptly, and frequently, steps forward, to dispute a point of practice, or to rectify what he considers to be a wrong position ; and is sometimes as promptly answered. The warmth occasioned by those heartburnings, has, it is to be feared, too often warped the true bent of the work.

The way in which the slender knowledge that the Reporter would seem to have possessed, concerning the midland and western districts, was acquired,—is not sufficiently explained.

The number of pages—two hundred and six.

A map of soils—a Kentish plow team!—and a Southdown ram—are the accompanying engravings.

SUBJECT

SUBJECT THE FIRST.

NATURAL ECONOMY.

EXTENT.—P. 2. " The county contains about fourteen hundred square miles, or eight hundred ninety-six thousand acres."

SURFACE.—P. 2. " Two chains of hills run through the middle of Kent, called the Upper and Lower; or, the Chalk and Gravel Hills. The northern range and whole north side of the county are composed principally of chalk and flints ; the southern of iron and ragstone : more westerly, towards Surrey, clay and gravel prevail upon the eminences.

" Below this last range lies the Weald : an extensive and nearly level tract of land, rich and fertile at some places; where fine pasturage and timber are produced.

" The north part of Shepey is high ground ; but it is mostly low and marshy on the south side, where two streams, running into the Swale, form the islets of Elmley and Harty."

DISTRICTS of the *Reporter.*—P. 2. " Thanet had a full claim to the title of an island when the Rutupine Port was in its prosperity; but its pretension to the appellation is now barely kept up by a small sewer communicating with the Stour and the sea. The bed of that once famous harbour now forms valuable tracts of marshes, comprehending above twenty-five thousand acres. Thanet, including Stonar, contains nearly forty-one square miles, or about twenty-seven thousand acres."

P. 5. " That part of the county usually called East Kent, is of two kinds; one very open and dry, the other much inclosed with woods and coppices. The open part lies between the city of Canterbury and the towns of Dover and Deal; and the inclosed part of the tract extends from Dover, by Eleham and Ashford, to Rochester in length, and from the Isle of Shepey to Lenham, &c. in breadth."

Whether the above vague description conveys the idea usually attached to " East Kent," or whether the Reporter has done it in dudgeon toward the man of Middle Kent, for the many sore things he has said of his Report, matters not ; the thing itself being perfectly absurd ; inasmuch as it extends *East* Kent, not merely into the heart of the County, but pushes it two thirds of the way toward its western extreme! thereby depriving Middle Kent of its birthright, and moreover robbing it of its very name ; which is not once mentioned, as that of a distinguished natural division of the County.

P. 6. " All that part of East Kent which lies within the vicinity

vicinity of the towns of Faversham, Sandwich, and Deal,
is mostly arable, extremely fertile, and under the most excellent system of management; which will be described in
its proper place."

These are, legitimately, and honestly, passages of East
Kent. Those rich but no way beautiful passages, with the
eastern compartment of the Chalk Hills, the confined District of Canterbury, and the District of Thanet, are all
that East Kent can rightfully claim. Extending it further,
westward, is robbery.

P. 6. " The Isle of Shepey is separated from the rest of
the county by an arm of the sea, called the Swale, navigable for ships of 200 tons burthen. It is said to have derived
its name from the number of sheep that were continually
feeding on it. It is about eleven miles in length, and eight
in its greatest breadth."

P. 8. " The western part of this county consists of a
great variety of soils and systems of management. It is
much more inclosed than the eastern part, and produces
more timber and underwood.

" The best cultivated is the north side of the district,
from Rainham to Dartford : a tract of five or six miles in
breadth. Parallel to this is a space of like breadth, of exceeding cold, stiff, flinty clay, which is generally ploughed
with six horses : this is the flat top of the chalk-hill that
runs from the sea, by Folkstone, through the county, to
the borders of Surrey, near Westerham. The soil of this
slip of land is nearly alike, and is but of small value, on account of the great expence of cultivation.

" It is the highest land in the county, and is, from thence,
by some called The Hog's Back of Kent. Between this
hill and the borders of the Weald and county of Surrey, is
an inclosed country, with much gentle hill and dale, the
hills shelving in almost every direction, with several varieties
of the ragstone soils. This part produces great quantities of
hops and fruit, with some corn and grass ; also timber and underwood, and has many pieces of common and waste land＊."

Now to deem the above passage *invidious only*, would be
an act of lenity toward its writer. The part of Kent
which lies to the south of the said " Hog's Back"—the
Turnbridge quarter—is the least estimable part of the
County. It is the rich and beautiful district, situated on
the southward of the *middle* division of the Chalk Hills,
which

＊ The inhabitants divide the county into three parts, East, Middle,
and West Kent; and, according to the ancient provincial adage, West
Kent is healthy, but not wealthy ; East Kent is wealthy, but not healthy
but Middle Kent is both healthy and wealthy.
                                        Note by a Middle Kent Farmer.
          " Perhaps more fanciful than true.——*Editor*."

which sends hops, and fruits, and other good things to the
London markets; and which too evidently excited the envy
of the man of East Kent, at the time he drew up his Report. He therefore got rid of it, in the above ungracious
manner.

P. 3. " The *Weald* of Kent, before mentioned, was formerly covered entirely with woods. It has now many small
towns and villages; but is more thinly inhabited than the
other parts of the county, and of course much less cultivated."

P. 9. " *The Weald.* This district of the county was in ancient times an immense wood or forest, inhabited only by
herds of deer and hogs, and belonged wholly to the King.
By degrees it became peopled, and interspersed with villages
and towns; and by piece-meal, was for the most part cleared
of its wood, and converted into tillage and pasture. There
are, however, some woodlands still in their original state."

P. 3. " *Romney-Marsh* is an extensive tract of rich marsh-
land, at the south corner of the county, originally inclosed
from the sea, by a strong wall thrown up between the towns
of Romney and Hythe."

P. 10. " Romney Marsh is a spacious level of exceedingly
rich land, lying at the south corner of the county. Its
shape is nearly that of a parallelogram, whose length from
the foot of the hill at Aldington to the sea-shore, between
Dengeness and Rye, is about twelve miles; and breadth,
from the borders of the Weald of Kent by Warehorn, to
the sea-shore, between Romney and Dimchurch, is nearly
eight miles."

P. 11. " This marsh is defended from the sea by an immense bank of earth (called Dimchurch Wall) of more than
three miles in length. The face next the sea is covered
with common faggot-wood, and hop-poles fastened down
by oak piles and overlaths, which prevent the sea from
washing away the earth. The support of the wall, and the
drainage of this marsh, amount to the sum of four thousand pounds per annum; which sum is raised by a scot per
acre, on the whole level of Romney Marsh."

CLIMATURE.—P. 12. " The proximity to the German
Ocean and British Channel, renders this county very subject to cold sea-winds, which often, near the shore in the
spring of the year, injure the tender shoots of corn and herbage of every kind; especially when, after a few days of
fine warm weather, a north-east wind succeeds.

" The prevailing winds of this county are, north-east
and south-west. When the former sets in and continues
for any length of time, which is often the case in winter,
a severe frost is always the consequence; the air is then
exceedingly

exceedingly keen and sharp; ponds are frozen to the
depth of ten or twelve inches; and turnips are destroyed.
The south-west part of the county is more inclosed; and,
being under shelter of the ridge of hills running from
Folkstone-hill to Wrotham, &c. is somewhat warmer as
to climate; but the soil in this part being much of it a
cold moist clay, the harvest is later than in those parts of
the county which are more exposed to the winds before
mentioned.

" The effect of the climate on Agriculture will perhaps
be best shown, by stating the time when the wheat harvest commences; which, in the most early parts of the
county (viz. the Isles of Shepey and Thanet) is, in a very
forward harvest, by the 20th of July, and in general in the
last week of that month; in East Kent, between Canterbury and Dover, about six or seven days later, according
to soil and situation; and still later, by ten or twelve days,
on the cold hills which run through the middle of the
county."

This may be truly deemed satisfactory Report;—excepting, perhaps, what regards the time of harvest; which appears to be put rather too early.

SOILS.—*Thanet.*—P. 4. " Much of the Isle of Thanet
was naturally very thin light land;" (!) " but the greater
part of it having belonged to the Religious, who were the
wealthiest and most intelligent people, and the best farmers
of the time, no pains or cost were spared to improve the
soil. The sea furnished an inexhaustible supply of manure,
which was brought by the tides to all the borders of the
upland, quite round the island; and most likely was liberally and judiciously applied by the Monks and their tenants;
and their successors to the present time, have not neglected
to profit by their example. Owing to these circumstances,
Thanet always was, and most likely always will be, famous
for its fertility; and the Monkish tale of Thanet's deriving
its superior fruitfulness from its having been the asylum of
St. Augustine, is not so far from the truth as it may at first
appear. Old historians said, ' Felix tellus Tanet sua fecun-
ditate;' and modern writers of husbandry speak of it as one
of the finest gardens in the kingdom.

" In short, is there another district in Great Britain, or
in the world, of the same extent, in such a state of cultivation,—where the farmers are so wealthy and intelligent,
where land, *naturally of so inferior a quality,*" (!) " is let
for so much money, and produces such abundant crops?"

Who, reading the above notice, might not be led to
believe that the rich soils of the " Isle of Thanet" were a
creation of " Monks and their tenants"?—Nothing but a
                                                    mind

mind darkly blinded, or much deranged, by prejudice, could have engendered such an *enthusiastic* idea. The district of Thanet is, *naturally,* a singularly well soiled chalky swell. An inconsiderable extent of its uppermost lands, is somewhat thinly soiled, as are the highest "downs" of other chalk hills. But the soils of the middle and lower stages, and especially of the lowest margin, or base, are, evidently, in their aboriginal nature, deep, rich, calcareous loams; such as are found on the lower skirts of other chalk hills; tho rarely of so good a quality*:—a fact, this, which even the Reporter, in a more lucid moment, would seem to have been aware of.

P. 13. "The bottom soil of the whole island, or what modern writers in husbandry call the subsoil, is a dry, hard, rock chalk. The tops of the ridges are about sixty feet above the level of the sea, and are covered with a dry, loose, chalky mould, from four to six inches deep : it has a mixture of small flints, and is, without manure, a very poor soil. The vales between the ridges and the flat lands on the hills, have a depth of dry loamy soil, *from one to three feet,* with less chalk, and of much better quality.

"The west end of the island, *even on the hills,* has a *good mould, from one to two feet deep,* a little inclining to stiffness; but the deepest and best soil is that which lies on the south side of the southernmost ridge, running westward from Ramsgate to Monkton: *it is there a deep rich sandy loam,* and mostly dry enough to be ploughed flat, without any water-furrows."

Taking it, all in all, the district of Thanet is *naturally* the deepest soiled, most valuable passage of chalk hill, in this island.

Soils of the *other Districts* of East Kent.—P. 13. "The open part of the district between Canterbury, Dover, and Deal, is of various soils, no one parish or farm being perfectly similar in all its parts. The principal soils are, 1st, Chalk; 2d, Loam; 3d, strong Cledge; 4th, Hazel Mould; 5th, stiff Clay. Besides these, there are some small tracts of flints, gravel, and sand.

"The chalk-soils are of various depths; from three to six or seven inches of loose, chalky mould, on a rock chalk bottom, and are mostly found on the tops and sides of the ridges of this district. At some places there is a little mixture of small flints, and at others, of black light mould, provincially called *Black Hover.* This last, in an unimproved state, is the worst land in this district."

P. 14.

* See my SOUTHERN COUNTIES—District, *Isle of Thanet.*

P. 14. The loamy soil is a very dry, soft, light mould, from six to ten inches deep, on a red soft clay, which is good brick-earth, and lies in a stratum of from three to seven feet deep, under which is generally a layer of chalky marl, and then the rock chalk. This soil is very good, ploughs light, and may be worked at all seasons; and produces good crops, if well managed, of all sorts of corn and grass.

" The strong *cledge* is a stiff tenaceous earth with a small proportion of flints, and, at some places, small particles of chalk: it is from six to ten inches deep, on a hard rock chalk, and is found on the tops of the hills. When wet, it sticks like birdlime; and when thoroughly dry, the clods are so hard as not to be broken with the heaviest roll. It is very difficult to work, except when it is between wet and dry. This land, when well managed, and the seasons are favourable for the work, produces good crops of wheat, clover, and oats; but when unkindly seasons happen, and dry summers succeed, it is very unproductive.

" The hazel mould is a light soil on a clay bottom, more or less mixed with flints and sand. It is dry, and forms very kindly land for barley and wheat upon clover lays."

P. 15. " The stiff clay lies on the tops of the highest hills. This soil is generally wet which arises only from the rains in winter; for the springs are above 300 feet deep on the rock chalk. It has at some places a layer of a yellow coloured clay between the surface mould and the rock."

" The flat rich lands in the vicinity of Faversham, Sandwich, and Deal, consist of two sorts of soil; namely, rich sandy loam, with a greater or less mixture of sand; and stiff clay, some of which, in the lower parts, is rather wet. The surface of the first is seven or eight inches deep, with a subsoil, varying in depth, of strong loam, clay, or chalk. *This soil is always ploughed with four horses;*" (yet) "*is very dry and kindly to work at all seasons,*" (!) " and no ridges or water-furrows are required. It produces great crops of wheat, beans, barley, oats, and pease, and sometimes canary and radish.

" The stiff wet clay is that which has a strong clay bottom, or any substance that holds water. It lies low, is subject to land-springs, and of close texture, so as not to admit a quick filtration of water.

" This, when properly drained, and kept cleaned from weeds, and otherwise well managed in favourable seasons, is excellent land, and produces good crops of wheat, beans, and canary; but is generally very expensive to keep in good order."

From the sum of these statements it appears, pretty evidently,

dently, that the various soils of those districts, as of Thanet, are encumbent on chalk; and that the superiorly productive soils, in the environs of Faversham and Sandwich, are deep calcareous loams, similar to those of the lower margin of the district of Thanet, and of other gently sloping skirts of chalk hills.

Soils of the *Isle of Sheppy.*—Sheppy is, still, what Thanet was, formerly,—an appertenance of East Kent.—P. 16. "Almost the whole of this isle is a deep, strong, stiff clay. Some parts are so very sticky in the winter time, that the plough wheels get loaded with dirt, in one mass, so as to form the shape of a grindstone, and are often overturned with the great weight of mould, collected unequally upon the wheels; on which account foot-ploughs are sometimes used. The horses shoes are frequently torn off, by the hinder foot striking its shoe against the heel of the fore one, before it can disengage itself from the soil. The best time to plough these soils, it is said, is when they are thoroughly wet. Some of the upper parts of the island have a few gravelly fields; but those are very wet in winter, and are rather stiff. The chief part of the upland pasture is a stiff clay, covered with ant-hills; it is very wet in winter, subject to burn in a dry summer, and to split open to a great depth. The soil of the marshes is also a stiff clay underneath; originally a sediment of the sea. Its surface for an inch or two in depth is a vegetable mould, much enriched from the land having been thickly covered with sheep for a long series of years."

SUBJECT THE SECOND.

POLITICAL ECONOMY.

APPROPRIATION.—P. 127. "The waste lands, the neglected woods, and the impoverished commons, are striking evidences of the necessity and importance of enquiries like the present; and the legislature will have abundant merit in suggesting to the proprietors of these estates a plan of improvement, from which individuals and the community will derive the greatest advantages.

"In the county there are the following commons, viz.

Blean Common,	Ewel Minis,
Swingfield Minis,	Stouting Common,
Stelling Minis,	Challock Lees,
Rodes Minis,	Baddlesmere Lees,

Chart

Chart Leacon,	Langley Heath,
Hotfield Heath,	Barming Heath,
Hays Common,	East Malling Heath,
Bromley Common,	Seal Chart,
Boxley Heath,	Ightham Heath,
Charing Heath,	Wrotham Heath,
Lenham Heath,	Dartford Heath,
Pinnenden Heath,	Dartford Brimps,
Cox Heath,	Black Heath, &c. &c.

" The whole extent of these commons, I apprehend, does not comprehend more than 20,000 acres. The soil of a few of them consists of a poor cold loam; of others, of a wet stiff clay; but the principal part abounds in gravel and sand. They are in general covered with furze and fern, interspersed with patches of grass; and feed some lean cattle and poor half starved sheep. If they were in a state of severalty, under proper systems of management, they might undoubtedly be made of great value. Inclosures would do much; industry and due attention to the natural produce, and what has been cultivated on similar soils in other places, would do more."

P. 53. " There is no portion of Kent that is occupied by a community of persons, as in many other counties. Our commons for live stock are generally much covered with furze, thorns, brakes, or heath, with a mixture of plots of poor grass-land; the cattle and sheep feeding upon them, are of course in a half-starved state. The total destruction of all commonable rights, by a general act of parliament for inclosing, is an object, in my humble opinion, of the greatest magnitude to the interests of this kingdom in general, and to this county in particular. There have been some exertions for accomplishing a division and inclosure of an extensive common in East Kent, within these few years; which failed for want of unanimity among the persons concerned."

PROVISIONS.—P. 166. "The easy communication between all parts of this county and the metropolis, renders the markets of Smithfield and Mark-lane the regulating medium, by which the prices of all kinds of provisions that are sold in the county are governed. If wheat rises 2s. per quarter at London, it immediately does the same at all the markets in the county; and if buchers meat is plentiful, and falls in price in Smithfield, it soon lowers in the country markets."

P. 167. " *The present prices of Provisions, December,* 1795.—Mutton 6d. beef 5½d. veal 8d. pork 7d. bacon 8d. butter 12d. and good Cheshire cheese 7d. per pound, of sixteen ounces avoirdupois; potatoes 8s. to 10s. per sack of of nearly 200lb. neat; coals 36s. per chaldron of thirty-six bushels; a half peck loaf of best wheaten bread, 2s."

FUEL.—P. 167. "Coals are brought from Newcastle and Sunderland to all the maritime ports of Kent, and from thence are distributed to the interior parts, seldom exceeding 30s. per chaldron in time of peace.

"Faggots of wood are found in plenty in the western and middle parts of Kent."

MANUFACTURES.—P. 173. "The manufactures of this county are very trifling; probably owing to the successful attention generally paid to agriculture and grazing. It has been observed by sensible writers on agriculture, that where manufactures most flourish, the land is most neglected; and this county is an instance of the truth of the observation. There is hardly any county to be named where agriculture is arrived at such perfection, or where there are so few manufactures as in this. There are some, however. At Canterbury, silk has been manufactured to a considerable extent; but it is now giving way to cotton."

"At Dover and Maidstone are manufactories of paper, of all sorts. At Stoner, near Sandwich, and the Isle of Grain, are salt-works. At Whitstable and Deptford are large copperas works; and in the Weald of Kent, bordering on Sussex, are furnaces for casting iron.

"Gunpowder is made at Deptford and Faversham; and at Crayford there are large works for printing of callicoes, and the whitening of linens."

POOR RATES.—P. 39. "The expences of the poor vary so exceedingly in the different parishes throughout this county, that it will be impossible for me to make any exact report on this subject. Some parishes expend no more than 6d. in the pound on their rents, while many others exceed even 5 or 6s. It is a general complaint, that these expences are annually on the increase."

TITHE.—P. 34. "In the Isle of Thanet, the whole of the rectorial tithes are collected, but the vicarial are chiefly compounded for; part is neither collected nor compounded at present, nor has been for some years, owing to a litigation about the right to the tithe of turnips, &c. In the eastern part of the county, the rectorial are almost invariably paid in kind, and the vicarial mostly compounded for, excepting in some instances, where there are disagreements between the vicars and their parishioners.

"The rich lands about the towns of Faversham, Sandwich, and Deal, have their tithes chiefly collected. In the Isle of Shepey, the same."

Nevertheless, in a note p. 37, a clergyman asserts, somewhat sophistically, "There are very few instances of
the

the clergy taking tithe in kind in this county."—To which the Reporter tartly replies—" But they let them to others that do, which is the same thing to the cultivators."

P. 36. "If a fair commutation for tithe could be devised, so as to satisfy all parties, there can be no doubt but that the product of this island, great as it already is, would be much increased by the additional stock of productions from that circumstance.

" There would be another very considerable advantage to the public, in the saving of labour in harvest, by the corn being carried into the occupier's barns in much less time than it is carried into those of the parsonage: the latter being frequently at a great distance from some part of the parish, much time is spent in getting the corn home. The value of the difference of the labourer, between carrying the tithe-corn into the parsonage and farmer's barn, is just so much loss to the public; and if rightly calculated for the whole kingdom would amount to an immense sum. Among the disadvantages to the public in the collection of tithe in kind, the quarrels between neighbours, who perhaps would otherwise be very good friends, is a very material one; and more particularly where the tithe-gatherer happens to be the clergyman; but this is seldom the case in the Isle of Thanet, the tithe there being mostly in lay-hands."

From the adverse notes that stand at the feet of the pages on tithes, as well as from the text itself, it is evident that a degree of animosity existed, at the time of reporting, between the cultivators and the tithe gatherers of Kent: — an unfortunate circumstance which I found to be corroborated, about that time, by the low estimation in which the clergy were held, at market meeting, by the higher class of occupiers, in that County;—comparatively, I mean, with what I have observed, in the rest of the kingdom.

WATER CARRIAGE.—P. 24. " This county possesses advantages superior to any other in point of navigation, from its extensive range of sea-coast, and the two great navigable rivers, the Thames and Medway, besides those of less note, the Stour and the Rother. The two former are navigable for the largest ships to Woolwich and Chatham, and for small craft to a very great distance."

MARKETS.—P. 172. " The chief part of the agricultural commerce of this county, is that of exporting corn to the London markets; very little is sent to foreign ports directly from Kent, though much of the Kentish corn goes abroad, when corn is exported, from the grand receptacle, Mark-lane market.

" At the towns of Maidstone and Chatham, and all others

others on the coast, there are several hoys, carrying from three to five hundred quarters of corn each, which are continually going to London with the produce of the land, and returning with grocery, &c. for the supply of the country.

"The soil and climate of this county being better adapted to the growth of corn than of grass, no cheese or butter is made for exportation, nor a sufficient quantity for the consumption of the inhabitants; the deficiency, therefore, commerce supplies from other parts of the kingdom."

SOCIETIES.—P. 178. "In January 1793, a Society for the encouragement of Agriculture and Industry, was established at Canterbury, under the patronage of Sir Edward Knatchbull, Bart. and Filmer Honeywood, Esq. the members for the county."

P. 181. "Some years since, a society was established at Maidstone, called the Kentish Society, for promoting every branch of useful knowledge through the county of Kent. This was begun under the patronage and support of the late Lord Romney, the Earl of Stanhope, and the present Lord Romney, then the Honourable Charles Marsham. Whether it was by aiming at too much, or from a want of support in subscriptions, that it fell to the ground, I am not competent to say.

"About a year ago, an attempt was made to establish another society at Maidstone, upon less general principles; but joining some other sciences with agriculture. There was a great number of the names of the first of the nobility, gentry, and yeomanry, who, by public advertisement, called meetings at Maidstone, in order to settle the business; but either from want of a full attendance, or of subscriptions, their efforts were not attended with the desired success."

SUBJECT THE THIRD.

RURAL ECONOMY.

TENANTED ESTATES.

ESTATES.—P. 25. "The property in land in this county is very much divided, there being few extensive possessions but what are intersected by other persons property."

P. 26. "The number of yeomanry of this county seems
annually

annually on the increase, by the estates which are divided and sold to the occupiers. There is no description of persons who can afford to give so much money for the purchase of an estate as those who buy for their own occupation. Many in the eastern part of this county have been so sold, within these few years, for forty, and some for fifty years purchase, and upwards." (?)

TENURE.—P. 41. "There are many estates in Kent held by lessees, under the churches of Canterbury and Rochester; and some under the crown; others under the colleges of the universities of Oxford and Cambridge. Many are held on three lives, under fines of renewal as they drop; others under twenty-one years, renewable every seven, on paying a fine as may be agreed upon by the parties, and subject to a small annual rent.

"The value of these leases varies much, according to local circumstances; but it is generally estimated at about fourteen years purchase."

DRAINING Estates.—P. 129. "This a subject of infinite importance to the prosperity of this kingdom. Bogs exist in most of the counties, more or less, and in some to a wonderful extent; the whole of which is convertible to the very best land, by proper management.

"In Kent we have a great many small patches of boggy and spungy lands, formed by means which will hereafter be mentioned. We have also several extensive parcels of marsh-lands, which in the winter months are frequently rendered totally useless, and of much less value in summer. The quantity of these two kinds of wet lands amounts to some thousand acres, the whole of which, at a very small expence, might be improved, in its annual value, at least 1l. per acre.

"Besides these, there is much land of considerable value that might be greatly improved, by a proper attention to the general principles of drainage."

The Reporter, accordingly enters on a didactic discourse of some length, concerning "different kinds of drainage;" which might in the infancy of the art,—notwithstanding its defects, and a few principles erroneously adopted—have had its use; though out of place, in a provincial Report.

SODBURNING.—In the section, "Paring and Burning," we find the following remarks on "Downsharing*."

P. 136.

---

* This provincialism might be deemed corruption worse corrupted:—*Devonshiring—Denshiring—Downshiring.*

A man of Kent, however, might turn the table, and read Downsharing—Denshiring—Devonshiring.

Let the *radical,* and *simplex,* and therefore *truly technical,* term—
SODBURNING—

P. 136. " Of all the improvements in the cultivation of
land that have been hitherto made in Kent, this stands
foremost; some of the very worst land having been made
to produce excellent crops; and poor chalky downs, of
scarcely any value in their original state, are by paring
and burning made to produce *good turnips*" (?) " and
clover, and crops of corn, often equal in value to double
the fee-simple of the land."—Profitable plunder to a
tenant!—Again,

P. 138. " A hundred cart-loads of dung, purchased from
neighbouring towns and villages, at the distance of three
miles from the land, would cost, carriage home included,
ten times the price of downsharing, and yet would not
improve the land more." (!)

These are but a few instances of superlative praise bestowed on downsharing, by the author of the Kentish
Report in different parts of his book. And from *tenants*
" who know what they are about," he has doubtlessly had
many thanks *.

IRRIGATION.—P. 144. " The practice of irrigating meadows, is an improvement of infinite importance ; by which,
many poor grass-lands are made to produce abundant crops,
and good lands are made much more valuable; but I am
sorry to say, the practice has yet very few friends in this
county."

TENANCY.—P. 41. "The leases granted to the occupying
tenants are always for years ; from seven to eleven, fourteen, and twenty-one : fourteen is the most usual term."

RENT.—P. 34. "There are many farms which let as
low as 5s. per acre; and others, at every other price between that sum and 30s.; while some particular fields of
rich land, in the vicinity of great towns, as pasture, garden,
hop-ground, &c. may let as high as 3, 4, or 5l. per acre."

" Perhaps I may not be very wide of the truth, if I
state

SODBURNING—settle the point. *Turf-burning* would be equally technical ; but not quite so euphonious.

Several other provincial terms, in use for this powerful process,
are observable in this volume :—as *paring and burning*—the north-
country phrase for it; *burnbaking* or *beaking*—the Wiltshire dialect;
burning beat, or *beat burning,*—also *skirting, velling* and *skirwinking*—
are in use in Devonshire.—What a confusion of tongues. What in-
technical jargon.

* Some thirty years ago, I was the first (I believe) to advocate,
publicly, the USES of that operation; and to soothe the alarms of
its opponents. Since that time, however, such has been the *burning
rage,* that, during the last ten years, I have deemed it right, as proper
occasions presented themselves, to do my best endeavors to *moderate*
its ABUSES.

state the average rent of the county to be 15s. per acre."
—in 1796.

Paying Rents.—P. 34. " The payments are usually made
half-yearly; that which is due at Lady-day, at Midsummer;
and that due at Michaelmas, at Christmas; generally allowing the tenant one quarter's credit. In some few instances, a half year is given them, paying one half year
under another."

REMOVALS.—P. 41. " The time of entering is generally
on the 10th of October. The barns, and farm-yard for
foddering cattle, are always reserved to the outgoing tenants
until May-day following."

W O O D L A N D S.

THE following notice is twice inserted; namely in
pages 5 and 121.—" The woodlands of the eastern part
of Kent are dispersed principally between the great road
from Rochester to Dover, and the chalk-hill that runs from
Folkstone by Charing to Detling. These woods furnish
the country with fire-wood, *tillers* for husbandry uses, and
the dock-yards with timber for ship-building; but the most
material part of their produce is the immense quantity of
hop-poles cut out for the neighbouring plantations."

At the close of the chapter "Woods and Plantations,"
a folding table is inserted. It exhibits a list of woods
(whether as the whole, or only as a part, of the woods
of Kent, is not expressed;)—showing, in columns, their
names, their proprietors, the parishes they stand in, their
extents, surface soils, the species of trees, and whether
natural or planted, &c.

By whom that table was formed does not appear. It
is not probable that an East Kent farmer, whose knowledge of the woodland parts of the County is evidently inconsiderable, should have been able to furnish those particulars. The following "general observations" on that
table are, probably, by the Reporter.

P. 127. " The oaks are all cut in the flaying season,
for the bark of all sizes. The fencing-poles are either
used whole, or cut into gates for sheep. The hop-poles
are sorted into three, four, or five sorts, and sold by the
hundred. The faggots, or bavins, are made into lengths of
five feet; the best for bakers and house-keepers; and
on the hills they make inferior sorts, called kilnbrush,
which are used for burning lime. Stakes and ethers are
cut out before the faggots are made. In the neighbourhood

hood of Chatham they cut some small bundles of brush and cord-wood, for the use of shipping and the metropolis. The woodlands of the Weald are tithe free."

AGRICULTURE.

FARMS.—P. 31. " The size of farms is generally greatest in the poorest parts of the county. Many small farms, of from ten to fourteen acres each, are found in the richest soils, and few there exceed 200 acres; but where land is poor, there are many as large as 300 acres, and some 600, or more."—I have pleasure in saying that there appears to me much good sense in those remarks.

HOMESTEADS.—P. 29. " There are some few instances of modern built houses for the use of the farmers; but the chief part are very old, large, and ill contrived, the upper stories generally projecting over the under ones. These old houses are, in many parts of the county, built with chesnut, where now no chesnut-timber is to be seen: the offices about them are as badly contrived as the houses themselves. This part of the rural economy of this county stands much in need of a reform. On most of the middle and small sized farm-houses and offices, thatch is the common covering; which is put on, particular in the eastern part, much worse than in any other part of the kingdom that has fallen under my view. The stubble of wheat is raked up for this purpose; which being often done in the winter, when by rainy seasons it is become half rotten, of course cannot last a long time on a building. The farm-houses in the Isle of Thanet are, in general, exceedingly neat and convenient."

COTTAGE GROUNDS.—P. 30. " The cottages are of such various kinds, that it is impossible to give any other account of them, than to say that they are in general comfortable habitations for farming labourers. They are built, some with bricks and tiles; but the greater part, especially of the oldest, with plaistered wall, and are covered with thatch. There are very few but what have a sufficient plot of land annexed to them for the growth of vegetables; and a great many in some parts of the county afford keep for a cow. Those, which have a garden of from twenty to thirty perches, usually let from 2*l.* to 3*l.* per annum, some more and others less, according to situation and other circumstances: those which have land enough to keep a cow, let from 4*l.* to 5*l.* per annum."

PLAN

PLAN of MANAGEMENT.—In his section, " Rotation of Crops," Mr. B. has spoken of the subject, districtwise ; that is to say, separately, according to *his own districts ;* tracing them backward, from east to west ;—the way, we are told by which superior wisdom has ever proceeded.

" *Isle of Thanet.*"—P. 61. " The general system, or plan of management, in the Isle of Thanet, on all the thin light soils, has been, time out of mind, one of four courses, viz. fallow, barley, clover, wheat ; but subject to several variations, which have much increased of late."

But, having mentioned some modern rotations, he continues—" It is to be understood here, that the foundation of all good management, and the system most practised, is the first mentioned of four courses ; and it is by this system, with the plenty of manure from the sea-weed, that great part of this island, which is naturally as poor land as any in the kingdom," (O ! fie,) " is made to produce such excellent crops of corn of the first quality."

Be it here fully allowed, that the " four-course" system of Thanet ; namely *fallow, barley, clover, wheat ;*—with its *exhaustless supply of extraneous manure,* may be continued in perpetuity ;—provided, for " clover," be put *cultivated herbage.*

P. 62. " The deep rich sandy loam before described, and some of the best of the land at the west end of the island, are cultivated under the round tilth system of East Kent, viz. beans, wheat, barley."

Judging from what appears in this report, not a turnep is grown, " in Thanet" !—Hence may we not conclude, that the superior quality of Thanet wheat, and Thanet barley, is to be principally ascribed to deep fertile soil, sea weed, and summer fallows ?

East Kent Plan of Management.—P. 64. " Chalky soil forms a very considerable part of the district under survey. This sort of land cannot be said to be under any settled system of management, for there are almost as many schemes of practice as farmers."

P. 68. " The hazel mould is under different systems at different places, according to the fancy of the farmer, or situation of his land."

P. 69. " The stiff clays on the tops of the chalk-hills are under a four course system of fallow, wheat, beans, barley ; and a very good one it is for such a soil."

The Plan of Management—on " the *Lands* in the vicinity of *Faversham, Sandwich,* and *Deal.*"—P. 69. " The dry loamy soils are cultivated in the round tilth system of East Kent ; namely, barley, beans, wheat. A few oats are sown instead of barley, and pease instead of beans ; and sometimes

times a crop of canary is sown on the bean-stubble instead of wheat."

Isle of Sheppy.—P. 71. " The general rotation here is beans and wheat alternately; and when the land gets foul, or the farmer thinks it wants rest, he substitutes a fallow for the bean-crop, which is done once in six or eight years."

From the aggregate of those various items of information, by a man of practice on a large scale, it pretty clearly comes out, that, in the far-famed husbandry of East Kent, there is scarcely any thing that resembles a " regular rotation of crops:"—the mistic pivot on which we are told, by " modern agriculturists," the whole art of good husbandry turns!

OCCUPIERS.—P. 32. " The occupiers of the small farms in general, work themselves much harder, and fare worse than other labourers, or many journeymen mechanics. Those of the higher class, the large occupiers and principal yeomanry, are a very respectable class of society, and have a great weight in the political scale of the county."

P. 33. " Besides the yeomen, before mentioned, there is an infinite number of farmers, not having or possessing a freehold, who occupy from 40*l.* to 300*l.* or 400*l.* a year. The smaller farmers are in general a very industrious and sober set of men, fare hard, and live with great frugality. The great occupiers, who have property in stock of from 1 to 2, or 3000*l.* live, as they ought, more at their ease; but as to making of fortunes by farming, there is no such thing that ever came to my knowledge; the competition is too great to admit of it; instances have been known of great wealth being left by old farmers, who have never had any other occupation; but then they have, perhaps, had no family, or never spent any thing beyond the expences of a common labourer, so that the fortune has been saved by the simple operation of compound interest; or, perhaps, these persons have held their farms for a long series of years, at a rent of great favour."

WORKPEOPLE.—*Price* of *Labor.*—P. 162. " Labourers per day, of ten hours, from 1*s.* 6*d.* to 2*s.*; thrashing wheat, per quarter* 2*s.* to 3*s.*"

" Reaping of wheat per acre, 8*s.* to 16*s.*; mowing barley and oats, 1*s.* 8*d.* to 2*s.* 6*d.*"

" Mowing grass in the marshes and meadows, 2*s.* 6*d.* to 3*s.* 6*d.*"

Hours of *Work.*—P. 165. " The hours of labour, in summer,

" * This year, 1795 by the badness of the crop, some farmers pay 10*s.* per quarter."

mer, are from six o'clock in the morning till eleven; and
from one in the afternoon, till six in the evening, allowing
half an hour for breakfast, in case that meal is not eaten before six o'clock; and then working till half past eleven; so
that the standard day's labour is ten hours; but there are
few instances in which it is strictly adhered to. In winter,
the time of working for a day is as long as daylight will
permit, making the dinner-time as short as possible.

" Upon the whole, a day's labour is generally much
shorter than formerly, owing partly to the scarcity of workmen, who well know that if one master will not give them
their hire for a short day, another will; and partly to
the inattention of masters and their bailiffs to the hours of
working."

Servants Wages.—P. 163. " Waggoner's wages per annum, and board, 10*l.* to 13*l.*; if a married man, and boards
himself, per week, 10*s.* to 10*s.* 6*d.*; second ploughman, at
per annum, 9*l.* to 11*l.*; third ditto, 8*l.* to 10*l.*; waggoner's
mate, 6*l.* to 9*l.*; second plough-boy, 4*l.* to 6*l.*; third ditto,
3*l.* to 5*l.*; bailiff, 12*l.* to 16*l.*; dairy-maid, 4*l.* to 5*l.*; cook-
maid, 4*l.* to 5*l.*; shepherd, per week, 9*s.* to 10*s.*; women's
wages for weeding, per day, 8*d.* to 10*d.*; children, from ten
to thirteen years old, 6*d.*; value of ploughing an acre of
land, 7*s.* to 10*s.*; a harvest-man for five weeks, with board,
3*l.* 10*s.* to 4*l.*; without board, 5*l.* 5*s.*"

P. 164. " Since the commencement of this survey, the
scarcity of labourers, and high price of all kinds of provisions, have together made the price of labour much higher
than above stated; but some parishes allow corn at a low
rate to their workmen, instead of raising the price; others
raise money for them by assessments; and some pay an additional price for the labour.

" Upon the whole, the price of husbandry-labour is nearly double what it was thirty years ago."

Food of Farm Servants.—P. 84. " The fine white wheats,
especially the hoary white of this county, make most excellent bread of the whole meal, when properly ground and
manufactured in the following manner. To a bushel of
meal, add a pint of good yeast well mixed with two or three
gallons of warm water; stir the whole well together, and
let it work six or eight hours before it is put into the oven.
This is the common farm-house bread of East Kent; but
in some parts, where the coarser kinds of wheat are used,
the broad bran is taken out."

P. 159. " Pork is the chief food of farm-house servants
and labourers in husbandry in this county; and there are
very few of the industrious workmen that do not fat a hog
or two every winter. When hog-corn, such as beans and
pease,

pease, is very dear, the farmers often let their workmen
have a reasonable quantity at an under-price. This tends
to keep up a mutual good understanding between the
farmers and their labourers."

WORKING ANIMALS.—In a section headed, " Horses, and
their Use in Husbandry, compared with *Live* Oxen,"—we
have the following information.

P. 158. " The great supply of draught-horses is from the
midland counties, brought hither while colts and fillies, by
dealers who attend the fairs and markets."

P. 156. " There are many very fine teams, each consisting of four horses, in the hands of the farmers of the Isle of
Thanet and East Kent, some of which were bred here
from a sort that has been long established ; and others are
a cross, between the old Kentish cart-mares and stallions
from the midland counties, or half-bred Flemish ; and within these few years, there have been several very good mares
brought from Flanders, which have cost from 26*l*. 5*s*. to
42*l*. each. Black is the favorite colour ; and there are but
few of any other ; they are from fifteen to sixteen hands
and a half high, with much bone, and good action. They
plough with four in winter, and work an acre and an half
in a day ; and in barley-season with two, and then plough
two acres a day, with a *mate* to lead the horses.

" Many farmers have great pride in their fine teams ;
which are often too fat to do the quantity of work in a day
they ought.

" In the Isle of Shepey, the horses for the plough are
bred principally from a sort that has been in the isle time
out of mind."

IMPLEMENTS.—*Plow.*—P. 45. " The Kentish turn-wrest
plough is almost the only one used or known. Some few
instances of trials of the Suffolk ploughs, which go with
two horses abreast, and are driven by the ploughman, occur,
but they have not been found to answer the purpose of the
farmers of this county, and are in consequence laid aside
for the *native implements ;* which, for all sorts of soils, and
all required depths of ploughing, is the best I have ever
seen and tried."

P. 46. " This implement, altogether, is most certainly
a very heavy one, and, from its construction, must be made
very stout ; as otherwise either the beam or chep will break
with the force of four strong horses, when it comes suddenly against a rock, or any stiff place in the soil, a hard
beaten path, or root of a tree, &c. It is remarkable for
going well among flints and rocks. With these ploughs the
soil may be turned up a great depth, and laid quite flat,
                                                    without

without any kind of furrow being left open; which is a great advantage in a dry soil. They cost, with every kind of tackle fixed for drawing them, entirely new, about 5*l*. 5*s*. each.

"With these ploughs four horses are generally used in East Kent; and there an acre and a half is the common day's work, a little more or less, in proportion to the stiffness or lightness of the soil: but in the western part of the county, from the tenacity of the soil, it is necessary to make the ploughs much stouter, and to use six horses, the plough there being drawn by a long large iron link, called a tow, which comes from the axle of the carriage round the heel of the plough. In that part of the county they seldom plough more than an acre in a day, and sometimes not half so much, even when six horses are employed."

Yet this *enormous* implement—more like a cart than a plow, when seen at a distance—is the idol of the men of Kent!—Let me not be misunderstood.—No man can be more aware, than I am, of its use, in plowing the sides of steep hills; also in working strong deep soils, in which flints or other stones are firmly bedded, especially when such land is worked out of season; also in turning under, and *hiding*, a foul surface for a crop; an operation, this, however which ought rarely to be attempted. But to employ it, in cultivating the level, free-working lands of East Kent, is a species of *idolatry* which nothing but blind bigotry could tolerate.

To wean the Kentish plowmen from the worship of their "native implement," let a *Kentish wrest*, instead of a mouldboard, be placed on an *English* plow; with which, in the East Kent lands, one of the four elephantine horses, now employed, would make equally good work; in lands, I mean that are kept in a due state of tillage.

"*Bavin Tug.*"—P. 49. "In the Weald of Kent, carriages, called bavin tugs, are chiefly used for faggots; and many use them for corn and hay. They carry 150 faggots; each four feet long, and three girt. The hind and fore wheels are fourteen feet apart; by which the length of the carriage is so much, that the load lies very low, and is thereby less liable to be turned over; which otherwise would often be the case in the roads of the Weald:"—And, by the great distance between the wheels, the load is more easily drawn across sloughs; the four, unless where sloughs are very wide, being seldom "mired" at the same time.

MANURE.—*Species.*—P. 138. "The sorts of manure commonly in use in this county, are dung, sheep-folding, chalk, turf-ashes, soot, coal-ashes, sea-weed, woollen-rags, and lime;

lime; with a variety of other manures, too numerous and trifling to be particularized in a general report."

Dung.—P. 139. "Dung of horses, cattle, and hogs, is mixed together in large heaps, and laid in the fields intended to be manured, usually on a layer of fresh earth, a foot or two in depth, dug out of hedge-rows, waste banks, or useless spots of land. When the heap of dung is made up, some persons give it a covering of mould; and it is an excellent practice to keep it moist, and prevent evaporation. After it has lain a month or two to ferment, it is trenched over at the expence of 3s. 6d. per hundred cart-loads; and then, after lying a few weeks longer, it is fit for use."

Sheepfold.—See *Sheep*, ensuing.

Chalk.—P. 139. "Chalk is used to great advantage as a manure on some wet. stiff soils, having no calcareous earth; in quantity from fifty to eighty cart-loads per acre. Its beneficial effects are said to last twenty years, and the value of it is often estimated between outgoing and incoming tenants, when lately laid on, as high as 5l. per acre."

Ashes.—P. 140. "Turf-ashes, if spread on poor chalky thin lands for turnips, at the rate of about twenty cartloads of thirty bushels each per acre, will seldom fail to produce a good crop: and it is well known, that if once a good crop of turnips can be obtained on such poor lands, a good foundation is laid for future improvements.

"Turf-ashes are often used for wheat, and sometimes for other crops; but there is no application of them so advantageous as that of using them for turnips."

Sea Weed.—P. 141. "This is a most excellent manure, being a mass of vegetable matter, strongly impregnated with salt. Immense quantities are sometimes thrown by the winds and tides on the shores of Thanet; from whence it is carted through sloping passages in the cliff to the land.

"When a quantity comes ashore, after a gale of wind, the farmers set all hands to work, to get as much as possible while the tide serves, lest the next should carry it away; and if it happens in the night, they work at it then till stopped by the waters coming on. Some farmers will get up in one tide two or three hundred cart loads. Those who live at a distance, hire small spots of land, of a few perches, to lay the fresh weed upon as they get it; and carry it away to the farm at a more convenient opportunity. It sometimes comes ashore in quantities that amount to several thousand cart-loads; and perhaps all swept away by the next tide. The principal method of using

using it, is by mixing it in layers among the farm-yard dung in the *mix-hills*. It is of great use in helping to rot the dry part of dung carried out of the farm-yard in summer."—This is not a common, but may nevertheless be an eligible, method of using this valuable species of local manure.

Lime.—P. 77. "The tenants" (in the Weald) "are bound to lay one hundred bushels of lime per acre on the fallows for wheat; and generally put on double that quantity.

"This lime is made of chalk, from the hill before mentioned," (Middle Kent hills) "and is brought from the distance of twenty miles to some of the parishes, though there is excellent limestone in the centre of the Weald; and even in the parish of Bethersden, famous for a fine limestone, called Bethersden marble, chalk-lime is preferred; and the chalk to make it is procured from a considerable distance. Chalk-lime is applied to stiff clay-lands, and stone-lime to sandy soils."

I insert this notice, though I may not implicitly rely on its authenticity. It is (with its tautology) twice inserted in this Report. The close of it, if correct, is interesting.

TILLAGE.—*Fallowing.*—P. 57. "On the cold stiff lands on the hills running across the county, from Dover to Wrotham, fallowing for wheat every fourth year, is the general practice. In East Kent, fallows are always made on poor lands, more or less, as occasion requires; in some cases, to get the land clean from weeds; and in others, where weeds do not abound, to make a good tilth for a crop of wheat, if a stiff, and barley, if a light soil. On the very worst soils, where wheat is never sown, fallows are frequently made for oats or barley, and for getting land into fine tilth for rye-grass, or other seeds.

"In the Isle of Shepey, fallows are made every six or eight years for wheat; and in the Weald of Kent, the farmers are bound by the covenants of their leases to make summer-fallows, and to lime for wheat.

"On the clay and stiff soils of West Kent, fallows are usually made for wheat; and in all parts of the county where sainfoin is intended to be sown, a good summer-fallow is invariably made by the best husbandmen.

"When any kind of soil has borne three or four crops of corn in succession, and is become full of weeds, a well made summer-fallow is certainly requisite, not only to destroy the weeds, but likewise to meliorate and invigorate the soil: it is the most certain cure, the speediest, and, in the end, the cheapest."

P. 83. "Many writers on husbandry recommend drilling, with

with a view to keep the land clean by hoeing, and thereby supersede the necessity of making summer-fallows: but those authors should recollect, that if all the crops were drilled, it would require more than treble the present number of husbandmen to perform the operation of hoeing them; and therefore summer-fallows must be continued, until the population is sufficiently increased to clean the land without them."

This is a new argument, in favour of fallowing. But it is not of much force. For it were as easy to cure a scabbed sheep with simple water, as to clean effectually foul arable lands,—such as require a summer-fallow—with the hoe;—be the state of *population* what it may.

Arable Crops.

Species.—P. 79. " The crops most commonly grown in Kent, are wheat, barley, beans, oats, and pease; also hops, canary-seed, radish-seed, turnips, and colewort: these are the principal ones, and are found almost on every farm, having a soil adapted for them."

Wheat.—*Barn Management.*—P. 83. "The thrashing of wheat is performed with a flail on an oaken floor on most farms of 80*l.* rent and upwards; but on smaller farms, on an earthern floor."

Thrashing Mills.—P. 50. " The first, and I believe the only threshing mill in the county, is at Betstranger, which I erected about three years ago."

Winnowing Wheat.—P. 84. " It is universally in Kent, cleaned with a casting-shovel, and flat broom, called a spry, which sweeps off the chaff and white coats with the small pieces of straw that fly among the corn. This method of cleaning corn is certainly the most expeditious and best, where the barn-floor is large, and of a sufficient length: but in a small room, the winnowing machines will do it better, and perhaps cheaper."

Produce of Wheat.—P. 84. " In any county like this, where the soil is so extremely various, it is impossible to make any accurate estimate of the produce of the wheat crop. There are many situations where two quarters per acre are a very good crop; while double that quantity on some others, is but a very indifferent one: twenty-two bushels per acre may probably be nearly the annual average growth."

This produce does not corroborate the repeated representation of the pre-eminent state of husbandry in Kent. It is barely, I apprehend, the medium produce of the kingdom, at large.

Barley.—P. 84. " Barley. There are only two sorts of
this

this grain cultivated; the common long eared English barley, and the short eared sprat-barley: the latter is only sown on some of the richest parts of the soil, where the common kind is likely to grow too stout, and fall."

On the culture of "Thanet barley," celebrated throughout the land, not a syllable is said!

BEANS.—P. 85. "These are usually either drilled, dropped by hand, or boxed, in furrows eighteen inches apart, from three and a half to four bushels per acre, in February and March; in either case they are generally hand and horse-hoed twice, and sometimes three times, and lastly hand-weeded. The crop is reaped about the end of August or beginning of September, and thrashed by a flail, cleaned with the casting-shovel and spry, and then sifted to take out the dirt and small beans. The produce is from two to six quarters per acre, in proportion to the strength of the land and management."

P. 143. "The bean and pea-crop is invariably horse-hoed two or three times; the first, as soon as the rows appear; they are then hoed by the hand along the sides of the furrows, with a plate about five inches wide; as soon as that is done, they are horse-hoed a second time; and if a second hand-hoeing is thought necessary, it is repeated; and then the beans are horse-hoed a third time *with an earthing plate*, to raise the mould against their stems."

PEAS.—P. 90. "All the kinds of pease are drilled in rows, about eighteen inches apart, from the middle of February till the end of March, and sometimes later, when untoward seasons intervene. These crops are cultivated, during the summer, with horse and hand-hoes, the same as the bean crops; and are harvested from the middle of July till the end of September, as they become ripe. They are reaped with a hook, called a podware hook, and thrashed as other crops of corn. The produce is from one and a half to five quarters per acre. Leadman's Dwarf and the Early Grey pease, are thought to be the most prolific."

CANARY SEED.—This, in East Kent, may be deemed an article of farm produce; and Mr. Boys, accordingly, classes it among "crops commonly cultivated."

P. 91. "Canary Seed. There are three kinds of tilths for this crop; viz. summer-fallow, bean-stubble, and clover-lay; the last the best. If the land is not very rich, a coat of rotten dung is frequently spread for it. Whether manured or not, the tillage necessary is to plough the land the first opportunity that offers after wheat sowing is done; and, as soon as the land is tolerably dry in the spring, furrows are made about eleven or twelve inches

apart

apart, and the seed is sown broad-cast, about four or five gallons per acre, and well harrowed in; when the blade appears, and the rows are distinct, the intervals are immediately hoed with a Dutch hoe, and afterwards, in May or June, the hoeing is repeated with a common hoe; carefully cutting up every weed, and thinning the plants in the furrows, if they are too thick. It is cut in the harvest, which is always later than any corn-crop, with a hook, called a twibil, and a hink; by which it is laid in lumps, or wads, of about half a sheaf each.

" The seed clings remarkably to the husk; and, in order to detach it, the crop must be left a long time on the ground to receive moisture sufficient to destroy the texture of the envelopement, otherwise it would be hardly possible to thrash out the seed. The wads are turned from time to time to have the full benefit of the rains and sun; it has sometimes continued in the field till December without vegetating, or suffering any kind of injury.

" The produce is from three to five quarters per acre; and it is sold to the seedsmen in London, who send it to all parts of Europe for feeding small birds, which are kept in cages. The offal of this article is a most excellent food for horses."

MADDER.—P. 101. " This is a plant used by the dyers, which has been *formerly* much cultivated in the eastern part of this county; but I believe is now entirely given up."

TURNEPS.—P. 92. " This plant is more sown with us every year. Thirty years ago, hardly one farmer in a hundred grew any; and now there are few, especially in the upland parts, that do not sow *some* every year."

This is interesting information; seeing how long turneps have been cultivated, in the adjoining county of Surrey. *Thin* calcareous soils, it is true, are not favorable to this crop; owing principally, I believe, to a want of room for the tap roots. But, by collecting the cultivated mold into ridgets, in the Tweedside manner, soils of a moderate depth, as four or five inches, will produce tolerable crops of turneps; provided an extra quantity of seed be allowed; this being a boon, I believe, which all calcareous lands, whether chalk or limestone, require. From the circumstance of only one page being bestowed on this valuable crop by a practical man on a large scale, and that page not very intelligent, we may, I think, conclude that, in 1796, the turnep crop might have been deemed an alien in East Kent.

TURNEP CABBAGE.—P. 104. " Turnip-rooted Cabbage. This kind was first introduced in general culture by the late Mr.

Mr. Reynolds, of Adisham, in this county, for which he obtained a medal of the Society for the Encouragement of Arts and Sciences, many years ago. It is a most valuable plant; and every farmer who keeps sheep, should have a small piece to eat off in the month of April, after turnips are gone, and before there is a plenty of other herbage. The severest winters do not hurt it; and it produces a great quantity of nutritive and wholesome food; it is however an exhausting crop, and expensive to get out of the ground; but its great value, as a plentiful supply of good food for stock, when, in some seasons, there is nothing else to be had, is more than sufficient to counterbalance every thing that can be said against it."

I have inserted the above notice, in remembrance that such an article of culture in English husbandry, had its *entrée* and *exit*, in the eighteenth century. From what I recollect of the " *turnip-rooted cabbage*," it is much inferior to the turnep-rooted, or bulbous, rape,—sillily, because equivocally, called " Swedish Turnip,"—as a fallow crop.

RAPE HERBAGE.—P. 93. " Cole Seed is much cultivated on the poor lands of the eastern part of the county, under the same management as turnips; but it is seldom hoed, and consequently much over-run with charlock. Sometimes, although rarely, it is sown for seed; but is most commonly fed off with lean flocks of sheep."

SAINFOIN.—P. 96. " This is the most valuable of all the grasses cultivated in this county: and is much grown on the chalk-land of the eastern part: it is sown among Lent-corn on clean land, at from four to five and a half bushels per acre; it is mown for hay in June, and its produce is from ten to sixty hundred weight of dried hay, fit to stack, per acre. Those who cultivate this plant should observe, that if it is fed off with sheep, it is very soon destroyed; whereas, if sown on clean dry land, after a good summer-fallow, and preserved from sheep, it will last in the ground ten or twelve years. The aftermath is excellent to feed cattle, and the produce is sometimes very abundant."

GRASS LAND.—*General Remarks.*—P. 105. " The quantity of land in natural meadow, or upland mowing ground, is very small in East Kent, in proportion to the extent of that part of the county, or in proportion to the hay-meadows of many other counties. The greater part of the hay of East Kent, even that which is used for horses, is produced in the marshes, from a want of a sufficient portion of meadow land."

" The other parts of the county have here and there
small

small parcels of meadow-land, some few of which are of good quality ; but in general the hay-meadows of Kent are much inferior to those of many other counties ; and this perhaps may be the reason why there is so small a portion of this kind of grass-land in this county.

" Pastures for keeping small dairies are found on every farm ; but there are no dairy-farms of any great extent in this county. The farmers in the upland parts, in general, desire no more pasture-land on their farms than is neces- sary for the keeping a small dairy for supplying their families with milk and butter, and a little fresh butter for sale. Cheese and salted butter for sale, are seldom or never made to any extent. The markets for corn being so exceedingly easy of access, by means of the navigable rivers and the sea, tillage is thought more profitable than grazing on dry lands; which, if they were laid to grass, would produce but a scanty herbage for cattle.

" The downland sheep-walks, which abound on the chalky hills of East Kent, can hardly be called pasture.

" The marsh-lands are situated along the borders of the rivers and the sea-shore. This sort of grass-land is of a very considerable extent.

" Romney Marsh contains 44,000 acres. Borders of the Stour, about 27,000 acres. Of the Medway, of the Thames, and the Swale, &c. about 11,500. The whole is used either for fattening cattle and sheep, or for breeding of sheep.

" The system of management of Romney Marsh, is that of breeding, rearing, and fattening sheep ; the practice of feeding lean cattle, and even fattening some of the smallest sorts of Welch ones, is only made subservient to the prin- cipal object, sheep-grazing; merely to take off such grass as runs away from the sheep in a growing time; it is always considered extremely bad policy to see much grass on the land among sheep. Every grazier, whose business is com- plete, has two sorts of land ; namely, breeding land and fattening land. The breeding land is stocked with ewes in the autumn, for the winter : every field has such a num- ber placed in it as the occupier supposes it will keep; which is from two to three and a half per acre, in propor- tion to the strength of the field.

" In kindly growing summers it is particularly necessary to keep a strict watch on the grass, that it may not run away from the sheep, and to prevent it by adding more sheep, or any other stock that can be had to keep it under ; for if it is suffered to run from the sheep, they are much injured, and the grass gets coarse. Upon such occasions, cattle are generally taken into keep at very low prices.

" A

"A very few oxen are fattened, which are bought in from the plough-teams of the wealds of Kent and Sussex. They are very large, and have a reserve of the best grass to themselves. From their size, they require a longer time to get fat than the smaller sorts: they usually weigh from forty-five to seventy score each.

"Some of the other marsh-lands of Kent are used nearly in the same manner; others are grazed by Welch bullocks for fattening: and in some parts the graziers buy the lean sheep from the flocks of East Kent, and fatten them for Smithfield, or other markets.

"The land of this county is seldom changed from meadow to arable, or from arable to meadow. The dryness of the soils of the upland parts of the county, occasions the land to be but badly adapted for meadow: when once a field is become a good old meadow, it is held sacred; and it is a common covenant in leases, not to break up old grass-lands."

In this, as in the preceding article, we find much valuable information compressed within a moderate compass. For other remarks on the grass lands of Kent, see *Livestock* ensuing.

The *Downs*, or chalk hill Grass, of East Kent.—In speaking of the arable management of "chalky soil", Mr. B. says, incidentally, p. 64. "much of it is down-land, or sheepwalks; some of which (although no very material part) has been so time out of mind; and some tenants are restrained (very injudiciously) from breaking up those old downs. The practice has been chiefly, when old sheep-walks have been ploughed up, to do it in wet weather, in the midst of winter, when other arable lands are too wet to work with advantage; and the principal inducement has been that of employing the teams when they would probably be doing mischief on better soils:"—A rueful employment!

Hops.—This is the least estimable article of Mr. Boys's Report. How a man who had, at the time of writing, "about twenty acres" of hops under his care and management (N. p. 188.) could send to the Board of Agriculture so flimsey and incorrect an account of their culture, is not readily to be imagined. In an Appendix to the reprinted Report is inserted a paper; headed thus: (p. 186.) "A Note on Hops, by a Gentleman stiling himself a Middle Kent Farmer; inserted in the Margin of the Original Printed Manuscript, circulated for Remarks and Observations by the Board of Agriculture."

In this paper we find some traits of the Middle Kent practice, with a few general remarks on "Hop Farms"; together with many a keen remark on the inaccurate account

count given of the Middle Kent hop grounds; in Mr. B.'s
" original Report."

ORCHARDS.—Nearly the same remark might be made,
respecting this other article of culture, for which Kent has
long been celebrated. But, in this case, an excuse may be
pleaded. East Kent, the Faversham part of it excepted, is
not a *fruit* country. But for the errors and defects of the
Reporter's account of the orchard management of the County
at large, that circumstance is no atonement. For the culture and management of orchards and hops, in middle Kent,
see my SOUTHERN COUNTIES.

LIVESTOCK.

A section, headed " Feeding,"—that is to say *fatting*,
—in which *cattle* and *sheep* and the nature and management of fatting land, or " grazing grounds," in various
districts of the County,—are so intimately blended, so *un*-
digested, and *in*digestible,—that I have deemed it expedient to bring the whole of it forward, in this place.

P. 110. " The system of grazing in the marsh-lands of the
Isle of Thanet and East Kent, is generally to buy in lean
cattle and sheep, and keep them till they are fit for the
butcher. The cattle are principally bought out of the
Welch droves, and the sheep from the fold-flocks in the
vicinity.

" The grass that is mowed for hay is usually set up in
stacks, either in the marshes near a foddering-lodge, or
carried home to the farm-yards on the borders of the marshes,
and given to fattening bullocks, or sold to the inn-keepers
at Margate or Ramsgate.

" The grazing in East Kent, on the upland farms, if it
may be called grazing, is that of feeding flocks of lean sheep
on the downs and seeds, folding them every night. These
are bought in wether-lambs in August, and sold out lean,
when about two years and a half old, to the fattening
graziers. Some farmers of late years, by sowing many
turnips, make their wethers fat, and sell them to the butchers
in the spring.

" The upland pasture is wholly employed in breeding
lambs, or feeding young lean sheep. These fields are generally so poor, as to keep only one or two breeding ewes
per acre, or two or three tegs.

" The inferior parts of the marsh-land are used in the
same way; but the best fatten a great number of sheep, and
many head of cattle.

" The feeding of the grass-lands of the western part of
the county, is done in various ways. Some have dairies of

six

six or eight cows, which are of mixed breeds, between the Staffordshire, Welch, and Sussex.

" Some of the small dairies of three or four cows, have the Welch sort only; and there are farmers who fatten a few Welch cattle on the best of their meadow-land with hay and grass in the winter.

" A flock of sheep under a shepherd, and folded at night, is a very rare sight in West Kent; it is only a very few of the largest farmers who follow that practice.

" Many farmers of this district have small parcels of different sorts of sheep, chiefly either Wiltshire or South Down, for feeding on such grass land as is not used for the dairies, or fattening cattle.

" The *grazing* of the Weald of Kent, is to rear young cattle, which are put out to keep to the Romney-Marsh graziers in the summer. In the autumn, they are taken home to the layers and inferior grass-lands; and in the winter to the straw-yards, or stay out on rough lands, and have straw carried to them; when they are of age to fatten, which is at four years for steers, and three for heifers, they have the best grass with hay. That which is made of rye-grass and clover, is given at the first part of the winter; and the best hay of the farm is used to finish them. Old meadows are always mown for hay to fatten the oxen.

" The inferior pastures are stocked, first with milking-cows to take off the head grass, and afterwards with the lean cattle, or working oxen. A suit of fields are thus fed in rotation during the summer.

" A great number of Romney-Marsh lambs are taken into keep in the winter, on the stubbles, old layers, and meadows; the price of keep is from 2s. to 2s. 6d. per score, per week. These lambs are returned the 5th of April, and in bad winters, frequently go home nearly starved; from which they sometimes die in great numbers when they get into good keep. Great losses are likewise often sustained after a wet autumn, by the rot.

" The layers of rye-grass, and clover, are mown for hay, which is used for the plough-teams and lean cattle; and some of the best is given to fattening bullocks in the beginning of the winter. The old meadows produce great crops of hay, which is of a very fattening quality. Bullocks fed thereon, frequently weigh from forty to forty-five score each; and some old working oxen attain the weight of sixty score, and sometimes much more. The fat oxen are commonly sold between the months of March and June. The sale of them is the chief dependence of the Weald farmers for payment of their rent, and other heavy expences." On

On the *Intercourse* of *Districts,* in regard to Livestock.
—P. 149. (Section " Cattle") " The cattle which are fed in
Romney Marsh, are taken into keep chiefly from those
farmers who keep lambs during the winter. Thus, by a
temporary exchange of stock between the farmer and the
grazier, each party is accommodated; for if the grazier
could not put out his lambs in the winter, he must alter his
present system of grazing ; and the upland farmer would be
very much distressed with his bullocks in the summer, when
his pastures are reserved for hay, or fed with his dairy. The
farmer keeps the lambs about thirty weeks from the beginning of September ; and the grazier keeps the bullocks
about twenty weeks from the middle of May.

" Some graziers buy Welch calves in the autumn, put
them out to keep in farm-yards for the winter, and in the
spring place them among their sheep, where they get fat in
a few months, and weigh from eighteen to twenty-two score
each.

" A very few oxen are fattened, which are bought in
from the plough-teams of the wealds of Kent and Sussex :
they are very large, and have a reserve of the best grass to
themselves. From their size, they require a longer time to
get fat than the smaller sorts: they usually weigh from
forty-five to seventy score each."

Cattle.—*Breed.*—P. 147. " This not being a dairy or
grazing county for cattle, we have no particular breed that
may be allowed the appellation of Kentish Cattle. The
sort bought in by graziers to be fattened for sale in the
marshes of East Kent, are from North and South Wales,
which are brought by the Welch drovers to Canterbury and
other markets; and the chief part of the dairy-cows are
selected from those droves: others are a mixture of those
and home-bred cattle, of various sorts and shapes. The
principal object as to a cow here, is the giving a large
quantity of milk. If a cow, though ever so ugly, is a good
milker, and produces a cow calf, it is often reared for the
dairy."

Stallfatting of Cattle.—P. 150. " Before concluding this
section, it may be proper to observe, that farmers at different parts of this county have been, and still are, in the
habit of fattening oxen, and other cattle, in stalls, on potatoes and hay, or straw ; others on turnips and cabbages, and
hay or straw ; and likewise on oil-cake and hay. By these
means the cattle are frequently made very fat: but it is
generally observed by the most experienced men, that this
system is not profitable, the chief advantage being that of
raising a supply of good manure for the arable lands: a
consideration, which by some is not thought to be of sufficient

cient importance to pay for the risk and trouble of attending stall-fed oxen."

For *Field Fatting*, see *Livestock*, above.

SHEEP.—*Breed.*—P. 150. "Kent has long been famous for a fine breed of sheep, called in the county, Romney Marsh Sheep; but in Smithfield, where great numbers are sold every week, Kent Sheep. They are remarkable for arriving at an extraordinary degree of fatness at an early age, and for producing a large fleece of very long fine wool. These circumstances combined, render this perhaps the most valuable of any breed in the kindom, not excepting the famous Dishley sort, whose wool, confessedly, is very coarse.

"Their carcases and legs are rather long, and bones large, in comparison with some other breeds; they have no horns; and their faces and legs are white.

"The fat wethers at two years old, weigh from twenty-two to twenty-eight pounds per quarter.

"Their wool is the combing sort of the *first* quality," (?) "being very long and fine; the fleeces of the young sheep are about five pounds weight, those of the ewes six, and the fattening wethers eight or nine pounds each. This Marsh is supposed to produce twenty pounds of wool per acre, which, for 44000 acres within the county, is 880,000 pounds of wool, or 3666 packs per annum. But as the greater part of the land has above four sheep per acre at shearing-time, and as the average weight of the fleeces is certainly above five pounds, the annual growth of this Marsh, in the county of Kent, is probably full four thousand packs.

"This is the principal sort of sheep kept in this county. There are, however, many of the upland farmers who keep those of Wiltshire, Dorsetshire, and the South Downs."

P. 152. "Almost the whole of the sheep kept on the upland farms of East Kent, are the true Romney Marsh breed; whose carcases and bones being large, and wool long and heavy, they require rich land and good keep to make them fat. It seems quite contrary to reason and nature that they should be equally adapted to rich marsh-land and poor chalky downs; and consequently they are not so fit for this district, at least the chalky part of it, as the South Down sort, whose natural soil is a fine turf on chalk-hills. Impressed with this sentiment, the surveyor himself has, for these seven years past, kept no other than South Down sheep, and has every reason to be satisfied with them; his flock is about 1000;—400 of which are breeding ewes.

"The sheep in the Isle of Shepey are of the Romney Marsh sort, true Kents. The soil being much inferior to

                                                      Romney

Romney Marsh, the sheep are somewhat smaller; and, from the same cause, their wool is lighter and finer. Some graziers get rams from Romney Marsh; others prefer their own sort, and but very few, if any, pay that attention which it is their interest to do, to the wool of the rams they use. The wethers are fattened at three years old, then weighing from twenty to twenty-four pounds per quarter."

Management of Sheep.—P. 151. " The management of sheep in the different parts of Kent, is as follows:

" In the eastern part, the flock-farmers buy in lambs at Romney Fair, the twentieth of August, at from 12s. to 14s. each, and when they have kept them two years, they either sell them lean to the fatting-grazier, or make them fat themselves on turnips, and pea or bean-straw. Sainfoin and clover hay are generally too valuable at the watering places to be used for that purpose. Oats, and cullings of garden beans, are sometimes given to finish them in the spring."

P. 152. " In West Kent, a flock of sheep under a shepherd, and folded at night, is a very rare sight; it is only a very few of the largest farmers who follow that practice.

" The sheep mostly kept in this district are the South Down sort, bought in wether-lambs, at the autumnal fairs on the Downs, chiefly at Lewes, the second of October. They are kept the first winter on stubble-land, with grass and a few turnips, and on grass and seeds in summer; and frequently are fatted on turnips the next winter, before they are quite two years old: this is become the favourite sort within these few years, and increases annually in this district.

" The other sorts of sheep kept here, are the West Country, from Wiltshire and Dorsetshire; the wethers are brought in at all ages, to be fattened on turnips.

" There are hardly any sheep bred in the Weald of Kent, excepting a few for early fat lambs, of the Wiltshire and South-Down sorts.

" Some of the Wiltshire wethers are bought in to fatten on turnips; and a few South Down wether-lambs are bought in the autumn, and kept on the driest parts until they are two years old, and then made fat for sale on turnips or meadow-lands.

" It has been mentioned that the grand system of management in Romney Marsh, is that of breeding, rearing, and fattening sheep; and it remains only to describe the mode.

" The rams are usually put to the ewes, allowing one to forty or fifty, and sometimes sixty, from the twelfth to the

sixteenth

sixteenth of November, and stay with them about five weeks. The ewes live entirely on the grass, without any hay, during the winter: in deep snow they scrape with their feet, and obtain a subsistence, although they then lose flesh, and sometimes become very poor by their yeaning time. This Marsh produces many twins; but a great number are lost, so that most graziers consider their crop not a bad one, if they wean as many lambs as they put ewes to ram.

"The lambs are weaned the first or second week in August, and very soon after put out to keep to the upland farmers of the county, where they remain till the fifth of April, at from 2s. to 3s. per score, per week. When they return to the Marsh, they are put on the poorest land, or such fields as the grazier thinks want improvement by hard stocking; which is here called tegging a field, and is held to be of great service. These young sheep are placed in the fields in proportion to what it is judged each will maintain, from the fifth of April until August, which is at the rate of from four to eight per acre.

"The wether-tegs in the autumn are removed to the fatting, and the ewe-tegs to the breeding grounds, among the two and three yearling ewes. The wethers remain till July or August following, when, as they become fat, they are drawn out and sold to the butchers at the Marsh markets, or are sent to Smithfield. The two yearling wethers, when fat, at this season weigh from twenty to twenty-eight pounds per quarter; and some of the largest and best fed, a few pounds more. The old ewes, here called Barrens, are put to fattening as soon as their milk is dried after the third lamb, which is at the age of four years, on some of the best land; where they are placed from two to three per acre for the winter. These, in favourable winters, are sometimes made fat and sold in the spring, soon enough for the same field to take in a fresh set of wethers, and make them fat by the autumn; but this can only be done by light stocking."

The following cautions are worthy of attention.—P. 155. "Great caution is necessary in feeding sheep on clover in summer, and on turnips in the first part of the winter, as otherwise they will die in great numbers, by being, what is provincially termed *blown*."—"Attentive shepherds will, in the first instance, take care to feed their flocks so as to prevent this disease, by keeping them from such strong food while they are hungry." A valuable hint.

Folding Sheep.—P. 139. "Manuring with the sheepfold is practised on fallow-lands in the spring months, after
barley

barley sowing, for turnips; then on fallows or clover-lays, for wheat; and when that season is over, the fold is removed to either wheat stubbles or turnips, in order to fold the land for the succeeding crop of barley or oats.

"Two hundred sheep will fold about an acre in a week; the value of which is from 20s. to 30s. in proportion to the time of the year; the last folding in the autumn, next to the ploughing for wheat, being the most valuable."

P. 155. "The practice of fattening sheep on turnips, assisted by oil-cake, corn, hay, sainfoin, &c. is greatly in use among the upland farmers of this county; not so much for the profit by feeding with those articles, as for the great improvement of the soil where the turnips are fed off. The manure from sheep fed on oil-cake and turnips, is reckoned very enriching to the land.

"A great number of fold-flocks of lean sheep are kept by the farmers of the eastern part of this county, of from eight to twenty score in number. These are each attended by a shepherd, who removes the fold every morning to fresh ground, at six o'clock in summer, and at break of day in winter; the flock is then driven away to the most inferior keep at the first part of the morning, and is returned into the fold for two or three hours in the middle of the day, while the shepherd goes to dinner; in the afternoon it is gradually led to the best keep on the farm, that the sheep may return full fed to the fold in the evening."

This is accurate management well described.

PROFIT.—P. 43. "I shall not pretend to give the honourable Board, and the public, a particular and accurate account of the expence and profit of the agriculture of this county: it is absolutely out of my power to make such a statement; and I shall aim only at giving a general idea of the subject.

"The prevailing opinion, for a great length of time, has been, that the average expences of a farm, in the common routine of management, are twice the rent; but my observations of late convince me, that the expence is much more, and often three, four, and sometimes, five times the rent. Generally speaking, he is the best farmer, and makes the most profit, whose expences are greatest, provided his money is laid out with judgment and economy.

"The expence of stocking a farm, and carrying on the business of the year, is from three to four, and in some cases 5l. per acre; and always highest when in the hands of the most skilful and spirited cultivators. The ignorant, timid, and penurious farmer is at the least expence in cultivating his land; but, for that reason, he has the least
produce

produce from it.   Individuals and the state are most
benefited by a spirited cultivation.

"With regard to profit, ten or twelve per cent. *is usually
made* on the capital employed; more or less in proportion
to the skill, spirit, and industry of the agriculturist."

This statement is not sufficiently *explicit.*—Five or seven
per cent. on the capital employed, is by no means a sufficient recompence for skill, diligence, and hard labor of
body and mind, of a man in the middle class of society;
as I have repeatedly shown.   But Mr. Boys does not say
how much *more* the farmers of Kent, *usually make.*

Mr. Boys, shrewdly, and with great truth, and due discrimination, remarks, at the close of his section " Expence
and Profit," (p. 44.) "Where gentlemen take farms into
their own hands, generally speaking, their produce and
profit must be stated at considerably less; for, from a want
of practical knowledge of the subject, and not condescend-
ing to stoop to the minutiæ of the business, they are
subject to various impositions from their tradesmen and
labourers; which occasion much loss of time and profit.
Some instances, however, occur of spirit and great application producing effects creditable to the owners, and
beneficial to such of their neighbours who are wise enough
to follow good examples."

SUSSEX.

SUSSEX.

THE FEATURES of Counties are various as their names.
No two are alike; and there are but few that bear a
striking resemblance of each other. The features of Sussex
are few.—There are only two of any extent:—one of them
broad, almost beyond comparison, in this island. The other
is a range of Chalk Hills ;—a branch,—a narrow ridge,—
projecting from the main body of those of the Southern
Counties;—uniting, on the west, with the hills of Hampshire; the eastern point being cut off, by the sea, at
Beachy Head.

This most southern chain of the Chalk Hills of England
is molded into five links, by the rivers, or brooks, Arun,
Adur, Ouze, and Cockmare, whose narrow valleys separate
them, in like manner, as the Darwent, the Medway, and
the Stower divide the Chalk Hills of Kent.

From Beachy Head, those hills take a somewhat north-
westward direction; and the line of coast a similar inclination to the southward; thus giving room for a tongue
of rich low-lying ground, between the hills and the sea.
This valuable tract of land I have elsewhere named the
Sea-coast of *Sussex*. See my SOUTHERN COUNTIES.

On the opposite side of the same compartment of the
chalk hills—the westernmost—lies the *valley* of the *Rother*
(a branch of the Arun); and, on its northern margin, a
line of well soiled rising grounds, on which the town of
Petworth is situated. This circumscribed, but well defined
passage, I have denominated the *district* of *Petworth*.

To the northeastward of that lightland passage, a pretty
extensive level of strong vale lands are found; mostly
lying within the fortuitous boundary of Sussex; but in
part extending into the County of Surrey. This, at once,
natural and agricultural district, I have heretofore emphatically named the *Weald* of *Sussex;* it being a strongly
marked portion of the wide-spread tract of country, first
above mentioned; the popular, but vague, appellation of
which is the Weald or "Wild" of Sussex; though it contains lands of various descriptions. Of the part which is
now under notice, the *Vale Lands* of *Sussex* might be the
best distinguishment.

Those vale lands form the western extreme of *the
Wild;* its eastern extremity being a similar tract ;—" the
Weald of Kent." The extent of those heretofore truly
wild lands,—an aggregation of forests,—measuring from
west

west to east, (and including the two tracts of vale lands)—is, in length, full sixty miles; and the medium width I *estimate* at fifteen miles. On these dimensions, those forest lands,—the ANCIENT FORESTS of the SOUTHERN COUNTIES,—contain nine hundred square miles. They are principally situated within the political outlines of Sussex; but extend within those of Surrey and Kent.—See the Weald or *Vale Lands* of *Surrey*, p. 253, aforegoing, and the *Vale Lands* of *Kent*, (with the district of Tunbridge) p. 414.

Near the midway of that wide waste of former times, rise a range of elevated heathlands, which divide the waters that descend upon it. Those which fall on the north side of the line tend toward the feet of the chalk hills of Surrey and Kent; and, being collected by the branches of the Mole, the Darwent, and the Medway, are conveyed, by the Thames and its estuary, to the British Ocean. While those which fall, on the south side of the ridge, are received by the Arun, the Adur, the Ouze, the Cockmare, and some smaller streams, and discharged into the English Channel.

In the valleys of those rivers and their branches, lands of various qualities are seen, and large tracts of the ancient woodlands remain.—From HEATHFIELD TOWER, which rises near the center of this singular tract, nearly the whole of it may be viewed, as in a map of nature's delineation.

"GENERAL VIEW

OF THE

AGRICULTURE

OF THE

COUNTY OF SUSSEX.

DRAWN UP FOR THE CONSIDERATION OF

The Board of Agriculture and Internal Improvement.

BY THE REV. ARTHUR YOUNG.

1813."*

THE Writer of the Work, which I am now sitting down to appreciate, may claim a *degree* in QUALIFICATION, which no

* The original Report of Sussex, by the same hand, was among the very earliest of the Board's production; being printed in 1793. But

no other Reporter to the Board of Agriculture, I believe, can arrogate. He is, *legitimately* (to use the fashionable slang of the day) an agricultural Writer; being the Son of the celebrated " ARTHUR YOUNG."

Had the younger Young been initiated in the practice of the sovereign art, on which he has been induced to write, while his mind was sensible to practical impressions; instead of being, reluctantly perhaps, led into the labyrinth of imagination, by the study of " dead tongues,"—the bane of active life and practical knowledge,—he might, by a Survey and Report of the Agriculture of Sussex, " have done the State some service."

The mistake, however, lies with the *choice;* not with the *chosen;*—who appears to have performed his task to the extent of his education; and better, be it put, than an unpractised " man of letters" could well have been supposed to be able to accomplish.

Regarding the MODE of SURVEY that was pursued by this Reporter, we have no direct information. The materials would seem, from what appears in the work at large, to have been collected during repeated *visits*, at the residencies of some men of rank and fortune, who have paid much attention, as amateurs of the first class, to practical agriculture; and the general improvement of rural affairs. I mention, particularly, the EARLS of EGREMONT and SHEFFIELD.—Some professional occupiers, of ability, have likewise contributed their share of information. And, beside the materials thus collected by the Reporter, many notes, some of them of length, which were written, or supposed to have been written, on the broad margins of the original Report,—are inserted;—with replies to some of them.

Touching the *composition* of the Work before me, it is such as might have been looked for, from a man, writing on a practical subject, without previously possessing some length of experience and consideration, concerning it. A want of due discrimination, regarding the subjects proper for particular notice and explanation, is evident throughout:—points that are obvious to practical men, and subjects worn bare in closet husbandry, and, now,

---

But when the octavo edition, which is now before me, was printed and published does not, in any part of it appear. Certainly not in 1813 !—What is of more consideration, the time when the additional materials were *collected* is not declared. The *latest date* which incidentally appears, in the body of the Work, is 1799. (See the article *Grass Land,* ensuing.) But that does not fix the time of publication.— For see the article *Societies,* ensuing.

now, require not the labor of discussion,—are dwelt upon: while matters of importance, to practitioners as well as students, are viewed askance, or passed by unnoticed.

Even the language of the learned divine is not always sufficiently intelligible; frequently diffuse and loose in its construction; and, be it whispered, is seldom *decently dressed.* In very truth, a more "slovenly" written book I have rarely read: not even in toiling through the learned and unlearned Reports to the Board of Agriculture. A want of appropriate arrangement of ideas, and of clearness, ease, and simplicity of expression, is observable in every part of the body of the work;—one instance excepted. The *Appendix,* and a few of the *Notes,* are exemplarily written—are such as a practical man may understand, *at sight.*

The number of pages four hundred and eightyone.

Twenty engravings of implements, &c.

And a base daubing of the "soil of Sussex."

SUBJECT THE FIRST.

NATURAL ECONOMY.

EXTENT.—P. 1. "It contains, according to the mensuration in Templeman's Tables, 1416 square miles, and 1,140,000 acres."

SURFACE.—See Soils, ensuing.

CLIMATURE.—P. 2. "The climate in the western part of the maritime district is very warm, and highly favourable to the powers of vegetation. But upon the bleak situation of the South Downs hills, exposed to the southwest, the winds have been known to strip the thatch off corn-stacks, and the covering from all thatched buildings; and it has sometimes happened, that farmers have suffered considerable losses by the violence of these westerly gales in harvest, blowing the standing corn out of the ear, and doing other damage."

P. 3. "The consequence of this has been, that the greatest part of the buildings in the district are situated in hollow protected situations, in order to shelter them from these distressing consequences."

P. 89. "The wheat-harvest commences, in forward seasons, about the latter end of July; in late seasons, about ten days or a fortnight after."

WATERS.

WATERS.—P. 15. "The chief rivers are, the Ouse, the Adur, and the Arun; they rise in the northern parts of the county, and after dividing the chalk-hills into four or five parts, empty themselves into the Channel; the first at Newhaven, the second near Shoreham, and the third at Little Hampton. Although comparatively small, they render the greatest benefit to the county at large, by furnishing points of connexion for the canals already finished, or in agitation."

SOILS.—*Chalk Hills.*—P. 5. "The soil of the South Downs varies according to its situation. On the summit is usually found (more especially in the eastern parts) a very fleet earth; the substratum chalk, and over that a surface of chalk rubble, covered with a light stratum of vegetable calcareous mould. Sometimes along the summit of the Downs there is merely a covering of flints, upon which the turf spontaneously grows. Advancing down the hills, the soil becomes of a deeper staple, and at the bottom is every where a surface of very good depth for ploughing. Here the loam is excellent, nine or ten inches in depth, and the chalk hardish and broken, and mixed with loam in the interstices, to the depth of some feet, which must make it admirable land for sainfoin.

"West of the river Arun, the soil above the chalk is very gravelly, intermixed with large flints. Between the rivers Adur and Ouse, a substratum of reddish sand is discovered; the usual depth of the soil above the chalk, varies in almost every acre of land, from one inch to a foot. The general average between Eastbourne and Shoreham, does not exceed five inches. West of Shoreham the staple is deeper, and between Arundel and Hampshire the soil is deeper still."

P. 6. "At the northern extremity of these chalk hills, and usually extending the same length as the Downs, is a slip of very rich and stiff arable land, but of very inconsiderable breadth: it runs for some distance into the vale, before it meets the clay. The soil of this narrow slip is an excessively stiff calcareous loam on a clay bottom: it adheres so much to the share, and is so very difficult to plough, that it is not an unusual sight to observe ten or a dozen stout oxen, and sometimes more, at work upon it."

This is the "maam" of Sussex—the "black land" of Surrey—the "coom" of Kent, &c.; and is probably an adjunct—the base—of every chalk hill in the island.

Soils of the *Sea-coast* of *Sussex.* (See p. 453, aforegoing.)—P. 6. "South of these hills is an extensive arable vale of singular fertility. This maritime district, extending

ing from Brighthelmstone to Emsworth, 36 miles, is at first of a very trifling breadth, between Brighton and Shoreham."

The Reporter proceeds to describe the soil, &c. of this singular district; but not, to my apprehension, satisfactorily.—See my SOUTHERN COUNTIES.

Soils of "*the Weald*" of Sussex.—Under this vague head is included, not merely the *vale lands*, or *Weald proper*, of Sussex; but the whole of the *Wild* country, above spoken of;—extending from the confine of Hampshire, nearly to that of East Kent—a distance, as has been said above, of more than sixty miles;—the district of Petworth being immerged in the general mass of mountain, upland, valley, and vale (a singular specimen of chaotic territory); comprizing lands of every description, from the most glutinous clay, to the loosest most barren sand.

P. 8. "The soil of the Weald is generally a very stiff loam upon a brick clay bottom, and that again upon sandstone. Upon the range of hills running through the county in a north-west direction, the soil is different. It is here either sandy loam upon a sandy gritstone, or it is a very poor black vegetable sand on a soft clay marl. A great proportion of these hills is nothing better than the poorest barren sand. St. Leonard's Forest contains 10,000 acres of it, and Ashdown 18,000 more, besides many thousand acres more in various other parts of the county.

"The depth of the sand on those rabbit-warrens is various—full 12 inches in many places: the soft clay, which in its outward appearance resembles marl, is much deeper. In the neighbourhood of Handcross, upon St. Leonard's, this substratum is several feet in depth, as may be seen on the declivity of a new road lately made by Mr. Marcus Dixon. An extensive tract of this unimproved sandy soil, stretching into Kent on one side, and, with some intersection of cultivation, into Hampshire on the other, and calling loudly for improvement, occupies chiefly the northern division of the county. I do not affirm that this unproductive soil is united from one end of the county to the other, since it is broken into and intersected by interventions of the clay district; but it is usually to be met with running east and west at the north side of the county. It is commonly understood to form a part of the Weald, which in its utmost extent comprehends all that district of Sussex at the foot of the South Down hills, or within two or three miles of them. In its more appropriate signification, it has reference to the deep and heavy clay loam district, being bounded to the west by the

the Arun."—No:—The principal branch of the Arun
runs through the middle of the vale lands of West Sussex.
Its waters, excepting what the Rother supplies, are
chiefly collected within the Weald proper of Sussex and
Surrey.

In the "APPENDIX" (apparently written by another and
a better pen) we are favored, in a few words well arranged,
with the subjoined intelligent information, concerning the
central and *eastern* parts of the passage of country, now
under view.

P. 473. " Nothing can be more various than the soil of
the Weald.   In the range of black mountainous land
which stretches from the neighbourhood of Tunbridge
Wells, under the names of Waterdown, Ashdown, Tilgate,
and St. Leonard's forests, the soil is generally bad; a considerable part incorrigible at any expence that will repay
the cultivator, and would be most profitable for the growth
of birch.   But the country between that range and the
South Downs, contains much good land, rich sandy loam,
and fertile clay, generally mixed with some sand: capable
of producing every kind of crop."

Soil of the *Marshes* of Sussex.—P. 10. " Besides the
soils already treated of, there is a large tract of marsh land
adjacent to the sea-coast between the eastern extremity of
the South Downs and Kent.   The soil is a composition
of rotten vegetables, intermixed with sand and other matter,
collected from the floods and filth which settle on the
surface.   In Lewes Level this vegetable mould is at least
twelve inches in thickness.

" In Pevensey Level it is many feet feet deep, and under
it is a very heavy black silt, intermixed with various sorts
of shells.   Water-logs, stumps of trees, and timber, have
been dug from Pevensey Level; trees, each containing
one load, cubic measure, have been taken from Lewes
marshes."

FOSSILS.—P. 10. (" Sect. V. Minerals") "Respecting the
minerals of Sussex, it is not inferior to many in the production of this most valuable material.   Limestones of every
description are to be met with in the *most eastern* parts of
the Weald.   *The Sussex marble,* * when cut into slabs for
ornamenting chimney-pieces, &c. is equal to most in
beauty and quality, when highly polished.   The Earl of
Egremont has several chimney-pieces at Petworth, formed
of it.   It is an excellent stone for square building, and
for paving is not to be exceeded.   It affords a very valuable
manure,

* This belongs to the *most western* part of the County.

manure, equal, and by some thought to be superior, to chalk, and cheaper to those who live near the place where it is dug. It is found in the highest perfection upon an estate of the Earl of Egremont's, at Kirdford, from 10 to 20 feet under ground, where it is in flakes nine or ten inches in thickness. Much of it was used in the Cathedral at Canterbury, the pillars, monuments, vaults, pavement, &c. of that venerable structure, being built of this article, called there the *Petworth Marble*. The Archbishop's chair is an entire piece.

" Besides the limestones of *this*" (?) " district, I shall set down a short account of what I had a more immediate opportunity of seeing, by observing the gradations in the earth, and mineral beds of ironstone and limestone, to the depth of 120 feet, at Ashburnham-furnace";—which is situated toward the *eastern* extreme of the County.

The Reporter speaks, at some length, about those beds of ironstone and limestone. But his *elucidations* are not sufficiently *clear* to the mind's eye of ordinary capacities.

Other Fossils.—P. 15. " Beside the minerals above-mentioned, a vast range of hills, the composition of which is *chalk*, occupy a considerable part of the county, adjoining the coast. *Marl* is dug up on the south side of these hills, in various places. *Fullers'-earth* is found at Tillington, and consumed in the neighbouring fulling-mills; and *red-ochre* at Graffham, and in various places adjoining the sea, as Chidham, &c. much of which goes to London."

SUBJECT THE SECOND.

POLITICAL ECONOMY.

APPROPRIATION.—Under this head, I place the subjoined extract; but without knowing whether the " Wastes," therein mentioned, are or are not, *appropriated*.

P. 187. (" Chapter Wastes.")—" The tracts of land which come under the description of mere wastes, in Sussex, are very considerable; they chiefly occupy the northern side of the county: out of a portion containing, by computation, 500,000 acres, these almost desert tracts take up no less a space than 110,000 acres of it."

FUEL.—P. 413. " Coal or wood, in a few places turf is used. The woods are very extensive; yet the price has greatly increased: great quantities are made into charcoal, and still larger (of the smaller sort) burnt for lime."

The

The Reporter recommends the Rumfordization of cottage fireplaces; in order to lessen the expence of fuel. And an ingenious annotator adds the subjoined notice.

N. p. 414. "I have known a leg of mutton and turnips boiled in a wooden pail. The trick was thus performed : a six feet barrel of a fowling-piece was inserted at the muzzle in the pail, the other end placed against the fire ; the water flowing to the breech of the barrel, the whole was made to boil. *Quere*, might not furnaces and vessels be heated in different rooms by the kitchen-fire only, by means of tubes of cast iron, with a large butt at the end conveniently fitted to be heated?—*Mr. Trayton.*"

MANUFACTURES.—P. 431. "Sussex, in the common acceptation of the term, is not a manufacturing district. Formerly there were very extensive iron-works which flourished in the Weald, but only the remnant of them are at present in existence."

P. 432. "The manufacture of charcoal is an object of some consequence in such a county as Sussex. Large quantities are annually sent to London by land-carriage. The old process in burning has been lately laid aside," (?) "and a new method substituted; as, after various experiments, the powder made upon this new principle, has, upon proof of its strength, been found much superior to that which was made in the old way. And accordingly this ingenious mode has been suggested to Government, by the Bishop of Llandaff, of making the charcoal in iron cylinders, of such a construction, as effectually to exclude the air."

This beautifully simplex apparatus I have seen employed. It is, I believe, understood to be the *invention* of DOCTOR WATSON *. If so, his rapid researches in chemistry,— which gave so much offence to the orthodox, *in learning*, and so little satisfaction to veterans, *in science*,—were not made in vain.

POOR RATES.—P. 455. "The rental of the Weald of Sussex is much affected by the extravagance of the poor-rates; and, comparatively with the intrinsic value of the land, there is no part of the island where it is lett at so low a price : in common years the rate through a considerable district, is at ten shillings in the pound, rack-rents; and during late years of scarcity, they amounted to 25s., and even in some parishes to 35s. in the pound, at rack-rents."—Can this *be*, in a "non-manufacturing district"?

P. 33.

* Now, the *late* Doctor Watson.

P. 33. " From an inspection of the rate-books in various parts of the county, it establishes the fact, of a considerable increase having almost invariably arisen. But this is to be understood as relating to those parishes where houses of industry have not been set up; since, where these have been established (although very recently founded), the contrary has followed. In eleven parishes united at Sutton, in the lower rape of Arundel, though the junction was formed as late as 1791, the rates have diminished."

So short a trial is no proof of the *permanent utility* of " Houses of Industry ;"—otherwise, PRISONS of PAUPERS. While they are closely attended to, by men of influence and leisure, who have pleasure in patronizing *something new*—they may be " found to answer"—the *purpose of parishes ;*—and may be agreeable play places for the young and dissolute.—But, to the aged and infirm, that have been torn from their connexions, and dragged, perhaps, several miles from their native or long-inhabited homes,—perhaps, from their children and consoling friends,—their only solace under their afflictions !—such an arbitrary, unsocial, unnatural plan of treatment is cruel and unwarrantable, in a civilized nation ;—even under the inspection of disinterested and well meaning persons ; and still more so, after the *novelty* of the " Improvement" has passed away, and they are left to the morose usage of an unfeeling superintendant ;—perhaps a *farmer* of the establishment ; whose best interest it must be, to keep them in a state of starvation and filthiness :—in a state altogether unfit for the aged, the infirm, and the unfortunate ; who may have seen, what is termed, " better days." For further remarks, see *Workpeople*, ensuing.

TITHES.—P. 30. " The mode of collecting tithes is variable. In the western parts of the county, the composition which generally takes place, is at the average rate of 4s. 6d. in the pound. The lay impropriators compound by the acre. Wheat, 4s. 6d. ; barley, oats, and pease, 2s. 6d. ; pasture and meadow, 2s. per acre. These tithes, on the whole, are allowed to be moderate and very fair.

" In other parts of Sussex, tithes are higher, and fall with greater weight upon the occupier. About Cuckfield, wheat from 5s. to 6s. ; barley, 2s. 6d. to 3s. In many places they are taken in kind, as Hailsham, &c."

P. 32. " The mode, as at present adopted, of collecting tithes, although perhaps levied with as little hardship upon the occupier as the nature of the case admits, is, without any doubt, exposed to the strongest objections. These have of late been so much and so ably discussed, that a repetition of the complaints would be needless. Certainly tithes

tithes are a heavy deduction from the profit of farming, and an onus of no inconsiderable weight upon improvement. An arrangement of such a nature as to embrace equally the interest of the farmer and clergyman, is the object so much to be wished for."—These well expressed sentiments, I am happy in saying, appear to my mind greatly creditable to the writer of them,—as a clerical man.

INLAND NAVIGATION.—P. 421. " The Arun is navigable from the sea to its junction with the New Cut, 17 miles 3 furlongs; and from thence a company of merchants extended it as far as Newbridge ;"—near the village of Green, which is situated near the center of the Vale Lands, or Weald proper, of Sussex.

P. 422. " The passage from Little Hampton to Newbridge is two days and a half, using a horse : the tide flows 17 miles of the way, and by going through Hardham tunnel, the barges save six hours of time."

" In order to extend the benefit of water-carriage to other parts of Sussex, the Earl of Egremont lately procured an Act of Parliament, enabling his Lordship, at his own sole expense, to make the Rother navigable from its junction with the Arun, as far as Midhurst; and by a collateral branch to Haslingbourne, within half a mile of Petworth."

" By this most useful and public spirited undertaking, many thousand acres of land are necessarily rendered more valuable to the proprietors. Timber is now sent by water. Large falls have been exported which would scarcely have been felled ; and the Government Agents and Contractors have made large purchases, in consequence of a more easy communication to the sea. An additional tract of country is also supplied with lime, from the Houghton and Bury pits."

P. 423. " At least 40,000 ton is annually sent from the Houghton pits, in consequence of Lord Egremont's improving the navigation of this part of the county."

P. 425. " A considerable part of the original plan still remains to be carried into execution : it is, to connect London with Sussex, and to lay open that market to the produce of this county, and receiving its goods and merchandize in return. By a direct communication from Petworth to Guildford, by a collateral branch to Horsham, a very considerable proportion of the county would be benefited : the ground has been surveyed, and the levels taken ; and if ever it should be effected, the value of estates would in many places be more than doubled."—See my SOUTHERN COUNTIES.

P. 426.

P. 426. " It is impossible not to feel great respect, in contemplating the energy of an individual of the highest rank and fortune, animated with such ideas, and expending his income in so meritorious a manner, forming navigations, rewarding industry in the lower classes, improving the breeds of live-stock by bounties, encouraging all useful and mechanical artisans; setting on foot multiplied experiments to ascertain the comparative merit of different agricultural implements; introducing improvements, by extending the knowledge of new plants, animals, or implements, all of them in so many and various shapes contributing their assistance to national prosperity. The thought of one man having been instrumental in the improvement of his country, and still exerting himself in the same career, must be a constant fund of gratification to every benevolent mind; and that long may he live to enjoy the fruits of his labour in the service of his country, is the wish of every man in the county."

ROADS.—P. 416. " The turnpike roads in Sussex are generally well enough executed : the materials are excellent: whinstone; the Kentish rag, broken into moderate sized pieces. Where this is not found, or not used, the roads are not so good; though turnpikes are numerous and tolls high: in some places in the east they are narrow and sandy. From Chichester, Arundel, Steyning, Brighton, Bourne, the roads to the metropolis, and the great cross road near the coast, which connects them together, are very good."

P. 418. " There is such an instance of the benefit of a turnpike-road at Horsham, as is very rarely to be met with : the present road to London was made in 1756; before that time it was so execrably bad, that whoever went on wheels, were forced to go round by Canterbury," (!*) " which is one of the most extraordinary circumstances that the history of non-communication in this kingdom can furnish. The making the road was opposed—for what measure of common sense could ever be started that would not be opposed ! It was no sooner completed than rents rose from 7s. to 11s. per acre: nor is there a gentleman in the country who does not acknowledge and date the prosperity of the country to this road; and the people who were the greatest opposers of it, are now so convinced, that there is a general spirit of mending their cross-roads by rates."

MARKETS.—*Lewes Sheep Fair.*—P. 431. " This fair is annually held upon the second day of October; and it is from hence that the South Down flocks are dispersed over various quarters

* For *Canterbury* read *Caithness.*

quarters of England, as the buyers come from a great distance to attend Lewes upon this day, where large droves are bought up by commission. From 20 to 30,000 sheep are generally collected upon this occasion.

" Previous to this fair, there is one at Selmiston (September 19) upon a much smaller scale. But the principal flocks are drafted and sold previous to either of these fairs, so that a buyer who comes from another county, and examines the sheep upon the day of the fair, is deprived of seeing the finest part of this celebrated stock."

Lewes Wool Fair.—P. 430. " *Lewes Wool Fair, July 26.* This fair was first established in 1786, and the county is indebted to the happy thought which suggested to Lord Sheffield the establishment of such an excellent plan. Before this era, the mode of buying and selling wool was entirely left to chance and uncertainty; and by nobody knowing the fair price, every one sold for what he could get, which necessarily left the seller at the mercy of the stapler; but his Lordship, by instituting this fair, collected the flock-masters together, and a proper price has ever since been obtained."

SOCIETIES.—*At Lewes.*—P. 466. " In 1772 a Society was proposed and established at Lewes, for the Encouragement of Agriculture, Manufactures, and Industry, by John Baker Holroyd, Esq. now Lord Sheffield, and Premiums were offered; but on the breaking out of the war in 1778, it was dropped."

Petworth Meetings.—P. 466. " A fair has been yearly held upon the 20th of November at this place, but was not remarkable till the Earl of Egremont, with a view of promoting the improvement of cattle, by animating the neighbouring breeders to exertions before unheard of, excited a rivalship among them by offering premiums.

" In 1795, Lord Egremont offered a premium of a silver cup to the finest bull that was shown at the fair.

" In consequence of this encouragement nine bulls appeared, and the prize was adjudged to Mr. Thomas Coppard, of Woodmancote.

" This first experiment was so very satisfactory to the farmers, that they agreed amongst themselves to show their stock of bulls and heifers at the next Storrington fair (December 5)."

P. 467. " The first year of the show of cattle turned out so much to the satisfaction of Lord Egremont, that in the following year his Lordship offered the following premiums.

" A show of three and four-year old bulls, and a show of three-year old heifers which have had a calf.

" A

" A *silver cup* will be given to the proprietor of the best bull ; and *ten pounds* to the proprietor of the second best bull.

" *Fifteen guineas* will be given to the proprietor of the best heifer ; and *five guineas* to the proprietor of the next best heifer."

P. 468. " 1797. This year there was a great meeting at Petworth ; and in order the more to stimulate the farmers to exertions of such importance to their own welfare, as well as to the public good, and to give a larger range to the sphere of their ideas by that collision of opinion which takes place in large companies composed of men of all ranks, he has on these occasions filled his capacious mansion with the most celebrated breeders, graziers, and farmers, from various parts of the kingdom.

" Lord Egremont's silver cup, which was this year of the value of fifty guineas, was adjudged to Mr. Harrington ; and the sweepstakes for the best heifer was given to Mr. Marchant."

Lewes Meeting.—" In the year 1797, the Earl of Egremont set on foot a Society at Lewes, for the improvement of cattle and sheep ; rewarding industry among the labouring poor, and distributing prizes to the best ploughmen: and the effect has been such, that although the Society has been established only *six years*,* it has in that short space very materially tended to improve the objects for which it was instituted, and it promises still greater success, by the support it is continually receiving from every quarter of the county."

SUBJECT THE THIRD.

RURAL ECONOMY.

TENANTED ESTATES.

ESTATES.—P. 17. " In so large, populous, and cultivated a county, estates must necessarily vary : the largest does not exceed 7500*l.* a year."

SODBURNING.—P. 197. " This is one of the greatest *improvements* which land is susceptible of receiving." (!)

IRRIGATION.

---

* From this expression, it appears that the volume was not published, until 1803, or perhaps afterward ! What a mischievous trick to suppress the legitimate title page.

IRRIGATION.—P. 222. " On the western side of Sussex, that admirable practice of watering their meadows in a regular manner, is very well understood, and successfully practised. The course of the Lavant river, from its spring-head to Chichester, waters the finest and most productive meadows in the county."—The Lavant is the only calcareous stream, of size, in the county.

TENANCY.—P. 43. " The term of leases every where varies. They are granted for seven, fourteen, and twenty-one years. It sometimes happens that none are allowed, and the tenant depends upon the good faith and honour of his landlord."

RENT.—Of *Chalk Hill Lands.*—P. 28. " The native down, or sheep-walk, is rented at various prices—from 1s. to 8s. 6d. A very large tract of the hills between Newhaven and Shoreham, averages at 5s. 9d. and the arable at 11s.; very rich at 20s. Between Lewes and East Bourne, the Down is 2s. 6d.; arable, 10s. 6d. Between East Bourne and Shoreham, 4s. 1d. On the light gravelly soils, the rent is 12s. 6d. Where the quality is better,"—the rents are from 16s. to 24s. an acre.

Seacoast District.—P. 28. " In the maritime district, rents rise from 20s. to 30s."

Rent of *Grass Lands.*—P. 29. " Grass in the Weald averages at 13 or 14s. per acre, but it is seldom lett by itself."

Of *Water Meadows.*—P. 29. " On the western side of the county, where the admirable practice of irrigating is understood and practised, meadow rents as high as 40s. per acre; in East Lavant, at 25s.; in West Bourne, 35s.; in West Hampnet, meadow, which before watering rented at 5s. per acre, is now lett at 40s. and has been valued as high as 60s.

" The river Lavant, from the spring-head at East Dean to Chichester, irrigates between four and five hundred acres."

Of *Marshlands.*—P. 29. " A large tract of marsh-land adjoining the coast, varies from 20s. to 40s. per acre. Some small parcels rise as high as 50s. and even 60s. Pevensey-level averages at 30s.; Winchelsea, 25s.; Brede, 35s.; Pett, 25s.; Lewes and Lawton, the same; Beeding, 30s.; Arundel rape, 25s."

General Statement of Rent.—P. 29. " I shall conclude this account of the rent of land by the following statement of the rent, produce, and division of the land.

" Down-

	Acres.		£.		£.
" Down land,	68,000 at 7s.	is	23,800 at 3 rents		71,400
Rich arable,	100,000 — 20s.	—	100,000 — 5	—	500,000
Marsh,	30,000 — 25s.	—	37,500 — 2½	—	75,000
Waste,	110,000 — 1s. 6d.	—	8,250 — 1½	—	12,375
Arable and pasture } in the Weald, }	425,000 — 12s.	—	255,000 — 3	—	765,000
Woods, &c.	170,000 — 8s.	—	68,000 — 2	—	136,000
	£903,000		£492,550		£1,559,775

" The remainder is composed of water, roads, buildings, &c.; so that the general rent is 492,500l. or 10s. per acre, including all sorts of land; and the produce 1,559,775l."

WOODLANDS.

EXTENT.—P. 9. " So predominant is the timber and wood of one sort or another in the Weald, that when viewed from the South Downs, or any eminence in the neighbourhood, it presents to the eye hardly any other prospect but a mass of wood. This is to be ascribed to the great extent and quantity of wood; preserved by a custom of a nature so extraordinary, that it is not a little surprising no steps have been taken to put an end to it.

" When this country was first improved by clearing, it was a common practice to leave a *shaw* of wood several yards in width, to encompass each distinct enclosure, as a nursery for the timber, &c. The size of these enclosures being small, must of course contribute to render the general aspect of it woody. Anterior to the Conquest, the Weald was a continued forest, extending from the borders of Kent to the confines of Hampshire, across the whole county of Sussex; and the names of a variety of parishes situated in this line, and evidently derived from Saxon original, attest this fact to the present day. In truth, the forest now remaining occupies a considerable portion of Sussex."

COMPARATIVE VALUE of *Woodland*, with that of *Arable Land*.—On this subject much is written; but, through a want of sufficiently matured knowledge, concerning those rival sisters, I find nothing made out that would add to the value of this register;—even when the aid of *calculation* is called in, to strengthen the force of argument.—For a specimen of *similar* calculations, on the value of woodland produce, see EASTERN DEPARTMENT,—*Secretary's Lincolnshire.*

On the ESTABLISHED MANAGEMENT of Woodlands,—for which

which Sussex has long been celebrated,—I find nothing in
the Reporter's lengthened remarks, in the body of his work,
that demands insertion, here. The only passage of consideration, on that subject, appears in the APPENDIX ; and
that is, pretty evidently, by another hand.

P. 480. " *Lord Sheffield observes*, that a good system
of setting out the tellows or saplings, and of preserving
them when young, and during their growth, would have
rendered the growing timber in this island infinitely more
valuable to the public, and consequently to the individual ;
and he conceives that the timber on his estate would be
worth many thousands more, if he had earlier attended to
the pruning and management of the woods. It is not sufficient merely to leave a great number of young trees, *they
require regular care and training :* if they are left too
thin on the first setting out, they will not thrive, nor become clean lengthy plank timber ; but it is absolutely necessary, as they grow up to thin them properly, leaving at
last after the rate of from 40 to 50 trees on an acre."—
These, let it be said, are masterly remarks.

AGRICULTURE.

F ARMS.—P. 23. " In the Weald, although farms sometimes rise to 200*l.* a year and upwards, yet of this magnitude they are not often to be met with; and in a general
inquiry, a far greater number fall very considerably below
this calculation, insomuch that the average size in this
district is under 100*l.* a year.

" On the South Downs they rise much higher. Many
farmers occupy the greatest part, if not the whole of their
respective parishes, as in Buttolphs, Kingston, Coombs,
Bramber, North Stoke, Bletchington, Falmer, Piddinghoe,
and many others in the neighbourhood of Lewes, East
Bourne, and Brighton. Many of these have marsh-land
annexed to their farms, for the convenience of maintaining
and fattening their oxen, the work for the most part depending upon their labour. A farm of 1200 acres at East
Bourne has 200 acres of marsh ; another of 1260 has 300.
Farms in this district average 350*l.* per annum. In the
triangle formed by Shoreham, Lewes, and East Bourne,
they rise much higher, and on the western side of the Downs
they fall lower.

" In the maritime district they vary from 70*l.* to 150*l.*
Three farms out of five are under 100*l.* rent. In the peninsula

sula of Selsea, rented at 1800*l.* and containing more than 2000 acres, farms vary from 50*l.* to 400*l.*"

HOMESTEADS.—*Building Materials.*—P. 19. "Wherever the quarries are conveniently situated, stone is the usual material for farm-buildings and offices, no less than for gentlemen's seats; and as an excellent building-stone is found under a very considerable proportion of Sussex, it is a valuable circumstance to have materials for building of such a quality.

" On the South Downs, and in the neighbourhood, another material, equally good, is made use of in the construction of houses, which are flints, and a better it is impossible to meet with: farm-houses, barns, stables, out-houses, and, in general, all the buildings in this district, are formed of flint. Tile is much used as a facing for houses, especially in situations exposed to the inclemency of the west or south-west winds.

" I do not know whether this tile-facing for houses is used beyond the limits of Sussex and Hampshire; but it is very prevalent in Sussex," (and in South Surrey) " and in open and exposed situations effectually checks the fury of the storms, and preserves the inside of the house air-tight and dry: they are very common all over the county."

Sheep Yards.—P. 21. " Sheep-yards, or standing folds, are very judiciously constructed on the South Downs. Mr. Ellman has one which contains an area of 50 yards by 20, which is sufficient for 750 sheep, at the rate of one yard and a half for each; so arranged as to contain sheds all around nine or ten feet in width, and across the centre, if the flock is numerous. A rack for hay is placed against the wall which surrounds the whole, and another, a double one, ought to stand along the central shed, for the sheep to feed from in each division of the yard."

OBJECTS of AGRICULTURE.—For a tabled estimate of the values, and the existing states of occupation, of the lands of Sussex, at the time of reporting,—see the article, *Rent*, p. 468, aforegoing.

PLAN of ARABLE MANAGEMENT.—*Vale Lands.*—P. 70. " The most general system pursued on the stiffer or strong loamy clays, is in the following order, and may be considered as the standard for the Weald.

" 1. Fallow; 2. Wheat; 3. Oats; 4. Clover and ray-grass, two or three years; 5. Oats, pease, or wheat."—Suppress the second article, and a better plan of management, for those lands, will not readily be discovered.

A few other " courses" are exhibited, *on paper;* but nothing wearing the resemblance of an *established practice* is seen. The truth is,—in the professional practice of Sussex,

as

as of Kent, of Surrey, of Hampshire, and generally throughout the SOUTHERN COUNTIES,—NO REGULAR SUCCESSION OF
CROPS IS OBSERVABLE.—Every occupier, if not under legal
restrictions, farms by EXISTING CIRCUMSTANCES;
—crops his lands according to the several states in which
they are; so as to provide support for his present stock, or
intended stock; and agreeably to his other OBJECTS in VIEW;
—such as, in his duly considered and deliberative judgement, are the best adapted to the nature and state of his
lands, and his situation in regard to markets, the prospect
of prices, &c &c. &c.

For a *tenant who is master of his business*, or a man of
mature experience who cultivates his own lands, such a
plan of management is doubtlessly the most eligible*:—
not merely because it is conducive to immediate profit;
but by reason of a change and variety of crops enabling
lands to throw out an increase of produce, in future.

To a proprietor, however, who lets his lands, at will, or
a leasor; during the wane of an ordinary lease, such a plan
of management might be found ineligible. But under a
lease, running from three years to three years,—with proper restrictions, after notice given,—the eligibility of such a
plan becomes indisputable; especially on *mixed-land farms.*

WORKPEOPLE.— *Wages.*—P. 404. " The wages of servants vary from 7*l.* and 8*l.* to 11*l.* a year. Task-workers
will earn upon a medium from 1*s.* 6*d.* to 2*s.* a day; perhaps
the average is 2*s.* or near it. The weekly labourers from
16*d.* to 18*d.*†

" The price of labour is above the medium of many other
counties; in the neighbourhood of the sea are seen many
old labourers, as the young and active find smuggling a
a more lucrative employ, which is very successfully pursued in Sussex. At Rye and Hastings, Bourne, &c. it is
highly flourishing, whilst the health of the inhabitants is
injured, the revenue defrauded, and labour extremely high.
It has been computed, that the revenue in this line of
country is cheated to the amount of 80,000*l.* per annum:
between 3 and 400,000 gallons of gin, rum, and other spirits,
are annually smuggled into this district. The principals
engaged in the business have about 10*s.* 6*d.* each night:
the common men a guinea a week; and in the conveyance
from the vessel to the shore, from 2*s.* to 7*s.* per night:
12,000 gallons of spirits have been landed in a week at Dun-
geness, in Kent. Light goods from Flanders, into Sussex
and

* For a novitial occupier, not yet out of leading strings, it may be
well to " go by line and rule."

† At what period of time? In 1793, 1797, 1799, or 1803?

and Kent, 105,000*l.* a year, upon which the profits have been so high as 30,000*l.*

" This great consumption of spirits is very pernicious to the labourers, and equally injurious to the farmers: but the cheapness of gin recommends the sale of it, and unlicensed gin-shops are without number.

" The price of labour in Sussex, is in some measure according to the local situation. The standing price is lower on the western side of the county than it is in the eastern: it has advanced in half a century about thirty per cent."

On the *Condition* of Workpeople, as *Members of the Community.*—P. 411. " Most clearly the wages of labouring families are inadequate to support them in that comfortable condition which they are entitled to expect: it is evident from the general increase of rates; but far more so to any man who thinks it no disgrace to visit the dwellings of the poor: their clothes, their bedding, diet, fuel, and cot; and when the interior of the cottager's house is inspected, will it be made a question whether labour and provisions are upon a par? 'Tis absurdity to question it. A labouring family, honest as they may be, and industrious as their strength and activity renders them (if numerous), it is hardly possible they can be maintained upon the present wages of labour with ease and comfort."

And, in a section entitled " Poor," Mr. Young enters, at large, on the discussion of that very important subject of agricultural report; and treats it in a way which is not only, creditable, to his diligence, as a professional guardian of the poor, but to his feelings, as a member of the same community.—*There,* we perceive his sentiments and his language in unison with his subject;—at once perspicuous and instructive.

P. 436. " I shall set out with observing, that the present state of this class of people is in many parts of England inferior to what every humane person would wish, and much below that condition which they may reasonably expect in so wealthy a community. Too many of their houses are the residence of filth and vermin; their dress insufficient; their minds uneducated, uninstructed; and their children, from insufficiency of earnings, trained to vice; their daughters to follow the easy road to prostitution."

P. 437. " It will be worth inquiring into the state and price of the following articles:

" 1. Expences; 2. Earnings; 3. Cottage; 4. Food; 5. Dress; 6. Friendly Societies; 7. Charity; 8. Houses of Industry.

" These circumstances involve their maintenance and support: let us then compare the income with the expenses of industrious labouring families in Sussex, and examine
                                                              whether

whether the wages are not absolutely inadequate to support them honestly in their calling. For this purpose, the annual expenses and earnings of several labouring families must be stated, and a medium year is the fairest for calculating the account, because during the last three years, the price of provisions has fluctuated too much to strike an even balance in any one of these years; for if the account had been averaged according to the valuation of the necessaries of life during this period, such a table would have exhibited too severe a picture of distress. The following account was made with great accuracy and correctness."

In pursuance of that laudable undertaking, a table of " Expenses and Earnings of Six Families of Labourers, by the Week and by the Year, in the Parish of Glynde, Sussex, 1793," was constructed.—Of that table the subjoined extract forms the first column. It is headed, " No. 1, eight persons," namely, " a man, his wife, and six children; the eldest twelve years old, the youngest two years old."

P. 439. " Expenses per Week:

	£.	s.	d.
Bread or flour,	0	6	8
Yeast and salt,	0	0	6
Pork, or other meat,	0	2	0
Tea, sugar, butter,	0	1	7½
Cheese,	0	0	10
Soap, starch, blue,	0	0	6
Candle,	0	0	4½
Thread, worsted,	0	0	7
Total,	0	13	1
Per annum,	34	0	4"

P. 440. " To the above amount of expenses per ann.	34	0	4
Add rent, fuel, clothes, lying-in,	8	14	0"
" Total expenses per ann.	42	14	4*"
P. 440. " Total earnings per ann.	28	12	0"
" Deficiency of earnings,	14	2	4"

By the above statement, it is shown that a labourer his wife and eight children earned no more than two thirds of their

" * According to the expenses of the boasted houses of industry in Norfolk and Suffolk, this, instead of 42 l. 14 s. 4 d. would have been 65 l. 4 s."

their expences. Another family, " No. 3, six persons,"
namely, " a man his wife and four children—the eldest
fifteen, the youngest three years old,"—nearly earned the
whole of their expences; the deficiency being only 6s. and
2d. a year.

The subjoined account of the CHARITABLE DONATIONS of
the EARL of EGREMONT are well entitled to a place in this
register.

P. 445. " Of all the duties which we owe to society, charity
is the first. There are various ways in which the exercise of
this virtue may contribute its assistance to the poor; but
certainly the best method is when it operates to the promo-
tion of industry. In this manner the relief of the poor in
Sussex has been taken up by Lord Egremont. The great
utility which results to the community at large, from holding out rewards to the poor and industrious among the
lower ranks, and from discouraging, as much as it is possible, every propensity to idleness, long since induced his
Lordship to distribute to the sober and industrious, bounties in clothes, which are intended to serve for the encouragement of active industry, at the same time that it
might operate as a check and discouragement of the idle,
by cutting off all hopes of such being recommended as
objects of charity. For such a plan to have its fullest effect,
by rendering it known to the great mass of the people, it
was necessary to circulate the following certificate, describing the age, sex, &c. of the person who may be entitled to
the bounty, upon application to two respectable persons
(not parish officers), for if it rested with these, it might
tend to defeat the very end for which the bounty was intended, as the officers might recommend any persons as
objects of the charity, in order that they might not any
longer apply to the parish for relief. Here follows the form
of the certificate.

" We the undersigned inhabitants of the parish of Petworth,
do recommend *Mary, the wife of William Ayling*, a
poor person resident within the said parish, being of the
age of 47 years, and having six children living at home,
under the age of twelve years, as sober and industrious,
and a proper object to receive the Earl of Egremont's
bounty of clothes. Dated this 25th day of February,
1799.

(Signed)　　{ WILLIAM WOUT,
　　　　　　{ ISAAC IRELAND.

" The above recommendation is to be signed by two
respectable housekeepers living in the same parish with
the party recommended. And to prevent any abuse of the
charity, it is earnestly requested that no person will sign
this

this paper, unless he perfectly knows such party, and is fully convinced that in all respects he or she is a proper object of the bounty.

" The number of families that partook of this bounty for the last year, was as under:

Parishes.	Numbers.	Children under Twelve.
Stopham,	5	25
Fittleworth,	18	68
Petworth,	74	190
Tillington,	28	82
North Chappel,	14	36
Green,	6	22
Kindford,	19	57
Lurgershall,	8	18
Ambersham,	3	11
Sutton,	1	3
Lodsworth,	2	7
Wollavington,	1	5
Bury,	2	8
Egdean,	3	8
Wisborough-green,	1	6
Cold Waltham,	1	0

186

" Besides this bounty (which is very much increasing), of the strongest Yorkshire cloth, Lord Egremont constantly distributes three and four times a week, good soup to the poor of the neighbourhood, made of barrelled beef, Scotch barley, and potatoes, besides regaling between three and four hundred families at Christmas with beef and pork pies.

" A surgeon-apothecary (Mr. Andrew) lives in Petworth-house, for the express purpose of attending upon the poor of that and the neighbouring parishes gratis. All who come under his care, are treated in the best possible manner: if a limb is fractured, it is set; if physic is wanted, it is administered, as there is a complete apothecary's shop and surgical apparatus at hand.

" In 1795 his Lordship sent an expert woman to the British Lying-in Hospital, to pass through the qualifications requisite in the business of midwifery, preparatory to her settlement at Petworth.

" Another woman has been settled in the neighbourhood, for the sole purpose of inoculating the children of the poor."

The following sentiments, concerning the existing poor laws of this realm, are likewise truly welcome.

P. 453. " On the subject of the poor laws and management

ment of the poor, Lord Sheffield, who has had upwards of thirty years' experience of their effect, is fully aware of all the difficulties which have arisen from the abuse of them, and the misconception of their great object; and he considers all the deviations from the principles of the law of Elizabeth, as promoting the mischiefs which now embarrass us. The original law of Elizabeth was excellent in principle, but a false interpretation, and bad execution of it, and above all, the nonsense of sentimental *economists*, who never comprehended its spirit, have rendered it a great nuisance, highly oppressive of the landed interest, and crippling of the resources of the country. He observes, that a kind of system has been established, of relieving the the poor, by no means supported by law. The statute of Elizabeth was well imagined, and answered all the purposes intended; it merely gave a power to the parish officers to provide for the lame, blind, and impotent, and to set the idle to work; which was peculiarly necessary at that time, as there was a number of idle, needy, and disorderly people, who used to receive alms from the monasteries, previously to their dissolution, and of soldiers and mariners, who were turned loose after the defeat of the Spanish Armada. But it has been so much misconstrued and abused, that it has, in a great degree, destroyed a provident spirit on the part of the lower ranks, and promoted the neglect of their families and children, by suggesting notions that the parish is obliged to maintain, not only their children, but themselves also; thereby leading them to look to other means of subsistence than their own industry, than which a greater mischief cannot be imagined. Unfortunately an ill-judged conduct on the part of those who were not aware of the views of this excellent law, and who never had a practical knowledge of the country, has encouraged these evil consequences, which are becoming highly calamitous."

WORKING ANIMALS.

HORSES.—P. 376. " The horses employed in the husbandry of the county, have nothing in them which deserves particular notice. Considerable numbers are annually bought up at the fairs and markets, which come from other places."

OXEN.—*Breeds.*—The ordinary breed of working oxen is that of the County.—Lord Egremont works " Hereford, Sussex, Devon, and a mixed breed between Hereford and Sussex. The Hereford breed appears to be the best of the three, when pure, for the two objects combined, of working and fatting; but the mixture of half Hereford and half Sussex, are equal." p. 264.

" Lord

" Lord Sheffield prefers the blood bay, such as he has seen of the Devonshire breed.

" A principal reason for preferring the cattle which he now rears is, that they make the best working oxen. The coarsest kind of Sussex grow too heavy for work soon after six years old, and are very slow; but the kind which Lord Sheffield raises, step out better and faster than horses, and do the same work, for he never employs more than four for any purpose."—p. " 466."—476.*

Mode of *Working* Oxen.—P. 278. " The mode of working their oxen in this county has, from the earliest ages, been the established one of bows and yokes, both single and double. Oxen in collars are a late improvement. A wide difference of opinion amongst practical men exists, with regard to the best method of using oxen, in yokes, or in collars."

Different opinions, on this point, are brought forward; but nothing decisive is made out, in favor of either practice; until we reach the close of the section; where a report of Lord Egremont's mature practice would seem to decide in favor of the yoke.

P. 282. " Lord Egremont has worked his cattle each way, and in road and field work, upon a large scale; and his experience fully confirms the general opinion, that the old established mode is superior to the new method, and that any number in yoke are equal to an equal number in collar."

In the *Appendix*, however, we find the like experience of another noble lord casting some considerable weight into the opposite scale.

P. 466 (476). Lord Sheffield " has only two cart-horses and eighteen working oxen, who are harnessed like horses, have bridles, and are accustomed to be led."

Those two varying practices may have grown out of different circumstances. Lord Sheffield, using so inconsiderable a number of horses, is constrained to employ his oxen in every work of husbandry; whether with plow or cart, and whether on broad roads, or in narrow ways; in which the beasts of draft are obliged to draw singly. Whereas, in my Lord Egremont's practice, oxen are principally, I believe, employed in *plowing;* and I have long been convinced that, in *this* operation, and on land that will bear the tread of oxen, double, the yoke is preferable to harness; especially when oxen are driven with reins.

Having been thus incidentally led, to endeavor to clear up an important point in the practice of aration, I will not
hesitate

---

* A slovenly error of " the press"! pervading a succession of pages.

hesitate to suggest, to those who employ oxen in the various works of husbandry, to enure them, in early training, equally to the double yoke and chain, and to the collar or single yoke and traces; and equally to work with each other, and with horses, as circumstances, and the multifarious labors of a farm, may require.

The *Food* of Working Oxen.—In Lord Egremont's practice.— P. 264. " When at straw in the winter, they work three days in a week; for instance, his Lordship has now thirty-four, being twelve three-year olds, ten four-year olds, and twelve of all ages above that, as they happen to be good for work. And here it is to be observed relative to turning off from work, that when an ox will not bear hard work and hard food, he may on an even chance, if put to feed, fatten as well as one that would stand work and hardship much better, as the qualities of fattening well, and bearing hard work, are distinct. But the perfection of breeding is to have such as will do both; and the free temper and willingness in work of an ox, may make him be thought tender, and unfit for labour, if due attention is not paid to this circumstance.

" Those thirty-four oxen are at oat-straw, with no other food, and sixteen of them are worked every day; and I could not but remark the very good order they were in; none of them complaining, by their appearance, of any want of better food. This straw system holds till about the 10th of February; then hay is given, to prepare them for the fatigue of spring-sowing; the hay system lasting till May, when they are turned to grass."

In Lord Sheffield's Practice.—P. 476. " They have never any food but grass or straw, until they begin to work hard in the spring, when they have hay cut with their straw."

Years of Work.—P. 233. " The age when the generality of farmers turn off their oxen from work, is at six years old. They will sometimes work them another year; but if we take the county upon a medium, we shall find that the far greater proportion send them to the grazing account at six. The proper time when cattle fatten to the best advantage, is a matter undecided in the opinion of some of the best judges in the county; yet it is a point that deserves ascertaining, for it is very necessary to know at what age they decline in the working state. It is affirmed, that young beasts are much more profitable for fatting than older ones, as the union both of growth and fat pays better than fat alone. We know that cattle will continue their full work long after the time they are usually sent to graze, and perhaps to greater profit than when they were young. At six, they are turned off; at seven, slaughtered; although

at

at ten or eleven, he is greatly to be preferred to the work of a four or five-years old steer, and the additional labour would probably out-balance any injury he might receive by more than three years' work; not that the cattle would be damaged by any alteration of this kind, for the greatest injury is effected in their growing state; and this ceasing at six, an ox cannot receive any damage which is not over-paid by his work. Lord Egremont has a pair of Sussex oxen in the eleventh year of their age, which, for seven years, have done as much ploughing and carting as any two horses in the county. His Lordship is now fattening those beasts, and they thrive very kindly, and more so than younger beasts in general. With half a summer's grass after taken from the collar, and an autumn's rouen, they were, without other food, sent to Smithfield, and sold for eighty guineas: a remarkable fact, bearing directly on the question of age and long work."

P. 264. Lord Egremont " works them three, four, or five years, that is, from three years old to four, from four to five, from five to six, from six to seven, and from seven to seven and a half, being in this last case put to fatten after the wheat season. But his more common system is, to work them four years and a half, and then fatten."

P. 476. Lord Sheffield " often works them, when they are hardy and do the business well, till they are upwards of twelve years old. He has proved the fallacy of the notion, that if worked hard to that age, they will not fat well; he used two of his largest oxen beyond that age, without ever sparing them, and within one year they were fatted with oil-cake to the great weight of nearly 210 stone each. Such of his oxen or steers as prove clumsy or short-legged, he sells or fats."

IMPLEMENTS.—Plows.—P. 55. " The wheel-plough most common, is the Kentish turn-wrest."

P. 56. " This tool, which is not very well adapted for any thing except always throwing land the same way, and consequently doing well on steep hills, or for laying land to grass without a furrow, is in this county a great favou-rite. This is universal. Whatever plough we find in any county, is sure to be called the best in the world.

" In the maritime division of this county, a one wheel-plough is much esteemed; it is generally drawn by three horses in a line."

MANURES.—For a novel comment on *Yard Dung*, see *Wheat*, ensuing;—and for *Sheepfold*, see the article, *Sheep.*

Chalk.—P. 199. " This is in great request, and used in quantities from 800 to 1600 bushels per acre."

Lime from *Chalk.*—P. 202. " This is an article of the
greatest

greatest consequence where chalk is procured in such abundance, as all the farmers use it very plentifully to manure
their crop, chiefly for wheat. But the present use of it
renders the expense so heavy, and the repetition so rapid, as
to put the effect of liming in a very questionable point of
view. The farmers generally lay it on their fallows from
80 to 120 bushels, every fourth or fifth year, and some use
it every third year."

P. 203. "*As* the chalk-hills extend no further than East-
Bourne, in order *therefore* to supply the rest of the county,
the chalk is shipped in sloops from the Holywell pits at
Beachy-head, from whence it is carried to the Bexhill,
Hastings, and Rye kilns: here it is burnt into lime, where
the farmers come with their teams and take it away at 6*d.*
per bushel. In this trade 16 sloops are considerably employed from April to the month of November. Nine of
these belong to Hastings, and seven to the port of Rye.
The total quantity consumed at these kilns, for one year,
amounts nearly to 633 sloop-loads of chalk, each containing
550 bushels, or about 350,000 bushels."

Lime from *Stones.*—P. 205. " Besides the lime burnt
from chalk, another great supply from limestone is drawn
from the bowels of the earth, in the Weald.

" Of this the Earl of Ashburnham is almost the sole proprietor, and the greatest lime-burner in all the kingdom ;
the spray-faggot of all his extensive woods being cut down
as fuel for his kilns."—A plate and verbal description, of one
of the kilns, are given.

P. 208. " The two sorts of limestone in use are very different in the effect which the fire has upon them. The one,
a grey stone, is a mass of marine shells, and the exuviæ of
sea animals: this will at first bear the necessary degree of
heat without danger; is very tough, and will open a little
without flying; but, upon fire being continued too long,
will vitrify. The other is a blue stone, very much inclined
to crack and fly to pieces, and requires great attention, to
prevent the stone forming the arch, from breaking and letting in the kiln. By continuing fire too long, and too
fiercely, it runs into a powder, although it does not vitrify
like the other: it is a much stronger cement than the grey,
or chalk."

This is probably the " blue lias" of the west of England
and other districts ;—properly, *clay stone;* as it is usually
found embedded in clay, in various parts of the kingdom ;
and in Glocestershire, is known by the name of " claystone." It is liable to burst in the kiln with the report of
a gun ; and burns to a sulphur-colored lime. As a cement,
in " water-work," it is nearly equal to terras; and is frequently

quently carried to a great distance, in different parts of England, for that purpose. It probably lies, in a state of neglect, in many places; through the want of that peculiar property being known. My principal motive, this, for bringing it into view, here.

It usually rises in broad slabs, about five or six inches thick; the body of the stone being of a dark-blue color; but is generally coated with white. It is mostly of a smooth even texture; with frequently, however, the remains of a few minute broken shells. It is commonly found in flat vale districts, under very cold clayey lands; and, mostly, a few feet beneath the surface. Coltsfoot abounding is a strong indication of it. It is observable in the faces of sea cliffs, on different parts of the coasts of this island, in alternate strata with thick seams of clay;—its invariable adjunct, I believe.

P. 210. " The great demand for lime in the eastern parts of the Weald, induced the Earl of Ashburnham, a few years since, to set about a method of drawing up the limestone from under ground, for the supply of the neighbourhood. This great undertaking he has most successfully accomplished, and the neighbouring farmers for many miles round, are now supplied from his works.

" The lime-works are situated in a valley in the centre of Orchard-wood, Dallington-forest, &c. The shaft by which we descended is four feet by five, boarded, with ladders for the men to go and return from their work, which is 80 feet deep, more or less: through this the stone is drawn up in barrels, of 5 cwt. to each, one descending while the other ascends. The whole machinery is moved by a horse, and is the same with that generally used in collieries."

P. 211. " The kilns begin working in April. In 1792, the account stood thus:

April,	6000 bushels.
May,	8000
June,	26,000
July,	25,000
August,	21,000
September,	10,000
October,	9000
November,	6000
	121,000 bushels.

" Respecting these lime-works, it is impossible not to admire the spirit with which his Lordship entered upon this arduous undertaking, by sending for miners and artificers

tificers skilled in the operation of mining: his success has corresponded to the spirit which first animated his endeavours, and he now reaps the fruit of his labour, in creating a supply for the neighbouring farmers, which before was to be had but in small quantities, and that at a dearer rate, or it was obliged to be brought from a distance."

Marl.—P. 212. " In the maritime district, this excellent manure is in great abundance a few feet under the surface. It is to be preferred when it contains much of that greasy kind of soapiness, which has worked such wonders in various parts of this district. Great exertions have been used in marling these fertile soils."

This was, at the time of report, a recent discovery of high importance to this naturally valuable little district. See my SOUTHERN COUNTIES—District, *Seacoast* of Sussex.

Sleech.—P. 218. " Sleech, or sea-mud, is not uncommonly used as manure in the neighbourhood of the sea: they spread from 12 to 1300 bushels of it for wheat; but the land has been too frequently dosed with it, to render it any longer answerable. It is inferior both to marl and chalk."

TILLAGE.—*Fallowing.*—To this topic the Reporter has repeatedly turned his attention, in the course of his work. His sentiments concerning it, however, savor of the closet, rather than of the field of practice.

ARABLE CROPS.

WHEAT.—*Manure.*—In the following strictures, we perceive the profundity of this Reporter's researches into philosophic agriculture; and the scientific manner in which he conveys his discoveries to the public.

P. 80. " There is about Eastbourne, Jevington, &c. a bad custom on the arable lands of that neighbourhood, spreading in July forty large loads of dung per acre, to be sown with wheat at Michaelmas; and they leave it till then on the surface, exposed to the sun and wind. Upon what system they can follow this custom, it is difficult to conjecture. If they would reflect on the fact of the volatile alkali being the food of plants," (!) " and that one of the principal causes of the fertility resulting from dung, is its containing that evaporative salt, surely they would think that some experiments on this point would not be undeserving their notice. If they will try the effects of spirits of hartshorn applied to common-field earth in a garden-pot, they will presently be convinced of one fact" (which?); " and if they then expose some of the same spirit to the atmosphere in a plate, they will soon understand another
fact

fact not less important" (what?): " these two trials are very easily made; * and he who tries them will not be ready afterwards to expose his dung-hills one moment longer than necessary."—Ha! ha!

Semination of Wheat.—Are we to conclude, from the subjoined notices, on hand-hoing, (which we are informed is " most generally adopted" (?), that wheat is seldom, or never, *drilled*, in Sussex ?—P. 87. " This operation of hand-hoeing wheat is disapproved by Mr. Ellman, who never hoes his white corn, having given it up from a conviction that his crops were never benefited by the practice ; but on the contrary, that it always did mischief." Again, " I have heard excellent farmers declare, that if a man would pay for the hoeing their wheat, they would not permit the operation, being convinced that it did more harm than good."

These can scarcely be the *unqualified* sentiments of " excellent farmers." They are doubtlessly intended to be confined to *full, even crops* of wheat; and not to be extended to the thin weedy parts of an irregular crop.

Treading Wheat Land.—P. 88. " Mr. Kenward, of Fletching, uses six and eight oxen in drawing a light pair of harrows ; and he remarked, that they were not, on such occasions, used either at harrows or ploughing for the draught ; but for the treading on such of the Weald lands as tend pretty much to sand, or rather a sort of soft abraded stone. He named a farmer who could get no wheat, until he drove all his oxen, cows, and sheep, repeatedly over his land, directly after sowing."—If it be meet to sow wheat on such land, the expedient hit upon is admirable.

P. 89. " Upon dry soils subject to poppy, Mr. Ellman, of Shoreham, ploughs his tare and rape land for wheat, the beginning or middle of September, to sow the wheat the middle of October. The harrowing kills the poppy ; and in putting in the seed, he likes to tread much with oxen, or with sheep. A neighbour treads his with oxen in March, which he thinks better against poppy, than doing it at sowing."

Barn Management of Wheat.—P. 90. " Thrashing the wheat is every where performed by flail-work, and cleaned either with a shovel and broom, or by winnowing-machines. Three instances occur of thrashing-machines having been erected, namely, that of Sir Richard Hotham's, at Bognor, which has been out of repair ; Mr. Pennington's, at Ashburnham ; and the Earl of Egremont's, at Petworth."

Produce

* To what end ? Why, to prove, by a *novel* method, that the whole world of vegetables live, grow, and have their being——*in sal volatile.*

Produce of Wheat.—A gradation of products are exhibited, in this report; rising from twelve to fiftytwo bushels, an acre.—The subjoined notice further shows the almost wonderful fertility of the seacoast of Sussex.

P. 93. " One of the most extraordinary *experiments* that was made in this county, was by the father of the present Mr. Car, of Bedingham, who upon a piece of land" (31 acres) " that had been left by the sea at Bishopstone, tried how often in immediate succession it might profitably be sown with wheat; *not* so much from an *experimental* intention, as from the *circumstances* arising in the trial." (!) " The first crop was seven quarters; the second, the same; the third, six ; the fourth, fifth, and sixth, each five quarters, upon an average."

BARLEY.—*Produce*.—P. 99. " The produce may be estimated to vibrate from three to six quarters. Perhaps the average is four quarters."

PEAS.—P. 102. " Pease are much cultivated in Sussex, especially on the South Downs, and along the maritime district. The common preparation is to sow them after one ploughing, either upon a wheat, barley, or oat-gratten; the land is ploughed from four to five inches; four or five bushels of seed are sown. The produce is very various— from two and a half to four, and even five quarters per acre. They are often drilled ; many farmers preferring this method to the common one of broad-cast."

P. 222. " Mr. Woods hoes his pease by fixing together two five-inch hoes at three inches asunder (between which a drill passes), in such a manner, that a man draws it after him. Of this work one man will hoe an acre per day."—For the origin of the " double handhoe," see the MINUTES of AGRICULTURE.

BUCKWEET.—P. 128. " Mr. Davis had one year eight acres of buck-wheat at Bedingham, which his shepherd fed with the flock when in full blossom, for two hours: all were drunk ; the glands of three were swelled quite to the eyes ; none blown ; but were staggering and tumbling. On hogs it had the same effect : bleeding made the sheep worse ; however he lost none." Q. By the buckweet, or weed of poppy?

HOPS.—P. 129. " In the eastern part of Sussex, they are much cultivated."

P. 131. " The parish of Salehurst contains the largest plantation of hops in the county ; between three and four hundred acres."

It may be observed, here, that the hop culture of Sussex is confined to the two extremities of the County. In the western extreme, it is conducted according to the Farnham practice ;

practice; and, in the eastern, conformably with that of Middle Kent :—the body of the County separating, widely, those two (in many particulars) varying practices.

POTATOES.—*History*, in Sussex.—P. 115. " It is upwards of twenty years since the first introduction of them into the Sussex husbandry, for fattening bullocks."

Application of Potatoes.—P. 120. " The chief use and object for which they are cultivated in Sussex, is the fattening of bullocks. Mr. Mayo has entered largely into this practice, and with uniform success, for upwards of twenty years, and is decided in the conviction of the profit of it. He fattens every year six oxen, two steers, and four cows or heifers. They complain at Battel, that they have no hay good enough to fatten a bullock ; but with potatoes, all difficulties vanish."

" Mr. Fuller has fed many sheep till they were quite fat, upon potatoes, and has kept to the practice. Mr. Mayo has fed horses with them, and with success ; and Sir Charles Eversfield fed all his horses upon them at Horsham."

P. 124. " The late General Murray was in the constant habit of feeding a very large flock of sheep on potatoes; they were given in a manger: 710 ewes in winter, ate one-third of a ton of hay, and 22 bushels of potatoes, every day, which is a quart to each. He used potatoes for fattening sheep, as well as for lean stock ; 196 fat wethers ate 14 bushels and 1 cwt. of hay daily : it may be reckoned 14 bushels for 200 sheep."

TURNEPS.—Their *History*, in Sussex.—P. 107. " The cultivation of this very valuable root is thoroughly well understood ; and the high degree of importance which is attached to it in the economy of a flock farm, renders it an object of the last consideration among the South Down farmers. Turnips for many years have been cultivated in this county, and with increasing success."

Hoeing Turneps.—In the following report of the practice of Mr. Ellman (whether of Glynde or of Shoreham is not said) may be caught, if patiently perused, a good practical idea.

P. 108. " Mr. Ellman observes, that in hoeing with the common Norfolk hoe, more of the weeds are drawn together than are cut up, and if rain come, most of these weeds shoot again ; but his own hoe, the blade of which is but an inch *wide*, effectually cuts up every thing, whilst the weeds and earth pass freely over it, at the same time that none of the earth is collected. This hoe ought by all means to be used on turnip farms, where the soil is inclined to be light and sandy, but on those of a heavier tendency, the hoe should be *wider*."

This *misepithet* produced, on the first reading, a ludicrous effect ;

effect; it thereby appearing that Mr. Ellman hoed his turneps with *one-inch hoes!* the blade of a hoe, as the blade of a sword, is spoken of by its length and *breadth.* Who ever heard of a wide sword? This by the way.

Mr. E. has merit in forming *new* hoes with *narrow blades,* for free working soils; as we are led to conceive, by the above extract. It is well understood that an old worn-down hoe makes the best work among *weak seedling turneps,* in such a soil. But a turnep hoer generally makes one hoe serve for all purposes; and soils of a " heavier tendency" require a stronger blade.

Much depends on *setting* a hoe. If the handle and the blade form a sufficiently acute angle, a good workman will not draw the weeds into heaps; unless on very foul ground, in moist weather; and, under these circumstances, fewer plants will regain roothold, in heaps, than when they remain erect, on the ground where they grew :—as, in this case, every fibril that has been severed from the main roots, will *strike,* and regain the soil; whereby young plants will continue to grow, and scarcely experience a check by the hoeing.

By the Reporter's representation, or misrepresentation, of his friend's practice, *it would seem* as if Mr. E. cleared his arable lands from *charlock,* by raising his own turnep seed; *or* by plowing his turnep fallows " four or five times, in the month of June;" when, unless in a " dripping season," scarcely a charlock seed can be induced to vegetate.

P. 108. " The attention which Mr. Ellman has given to eradicate weeds, is another instance of good management. *Kilk* or charlock, is the most destructive foe to which the chalk hills are liable, yet a *blade* of it is never visible upon his farm; whilst between Lewes, Eastbourne, and Brighton, almost every farm is overwhelmed with this weed. His neighbours have been frequently surprised at seeing his turnip crops upon land similar to their own, and apparently with similar management, whilst they are not able to grow any. This has been a frequent object of remark; but there are some circumstances in his management which will explain the reason. Mr. Ellman pays great attention in saving his seed, by transplanting some of the largest and roundest turnips in his garden, and in rejecting all those large ones which indicate any hollowness in the crown of the plant, which forms a cavity for the rain to lodge on it, and thus cause the turnip to rot. By constantly sowing such seed, which he annually saves, he contrives to get fine crops; and by setting them out very thick, he raises very heavy ones. He begins to sow early, and raises several pieces in succession. His turnips are this year (1797) upon rye-grass,
which

which he folds in spring; he then ploughs in June four or five times for turnips, hoes twice, setting them out very thick, remarking at the same time, that the small crop and thick one will exceed the other considerably."

But even this passage, if deliberately read, will not be found destitute of useful information.

Folding off Turneps, with Sheep.—P. 111. "In folding his sheep, Mr. Ellman draws them out of the ground two or three days before the sheep are turned into the field; by this method, which begins to be general, the turnips lose their watery property, and the sheep thrive on them much better.

" Similar to this is the practice of Mr. Carr, who, in folding his sheep, draws up all the turnips within the fold, a day or two before the sheep are allowed to enter, in order that the turnips might wither, and evaporate their water. The reason is, that when the sheep ate them without this precaution, many were lost." (?)

Drawing Turneps, for Cattle.—P. 239. " *Turnips* are chiefly cultivated upon the flock-farms for sheep; but it is a practice in various parts of the county to draw the largest for the bullocks. When they are given upon an empty stomach, the cattle will blow; but never when hay is mixed. Mr. Milward observes, that when they are given to the cattle fresh drawn from the field, his oxen are liable to the flux; but taken up before-hand, no food is better, as the watery nature of it is removed; but, in order to carry this into execution, he adopts the method of stacking, taking special care of guarding against the frost; and this very spirited cultivator never found his oxen thrive so well as on dried turnips.

" The custom of drawing them two or three days previous to giving them to cattle, is very prevalent about Lewes, Brighton, Shoreham, &c. Mr. Ellman constantly practises it."

CULTIVATED HERBAGE.

RYE HERBAGE.—P. 101. " Rye is much cultivated on the South Downs as food for sheep. It is sown in August and September; the earlier, the better it is. In spring, when other food is scarce, and in the lambing season, ewes and lambs are turned into it: a certain portion is hurdled off for this purpose."

RAPE HERBAGE.—P. 106. " Cole is deservedly in high repute amongst the flock farmers of the Downs. It is sown either with tares, or by itself, as food for sheep; not frequently for seed. Ewes and lambs are wattled upon it in spring, and it is generally allowed to be most efficacious and highly nourishing to the young lambs."

P. 107.

P. 107. "Mr. Gilbert sows ray-grass with his rape for
sheep, on Down land; one gallon of rape-seed, and two
of ray-grass. The rape is fed off first; and after that the
ray-grass rises and affords a spring bite. June and July
is the usual season for putting in this crop."

TARE HERBAGE.—P. 104. "The cultivation of tares is well
understood, and in many parts successfully practised.
They are used for cattle, horses, and sheep; and sometimes hogs have been folded upon them. From two to
three bushels are sown upon the subbles in autumn, and in
the spring they are wattled off with sheep."

"*They*" (?) "have on the South Downs an admirable
practice in their course of crops, which cannot be too much
commended; that of *substituting* a *double crop of tares,
instead of a fallow for wheat.*" (!) "Let the intelligent
reader give his attention to this practice, for it is worth
a journey of 500 miles." (ha! ha!) "They sow forward
winter tares, which are fed off late in the spring with ewes
and lambs; they then plough and sow summer tares and
rape, two bushels and a half of tares, and half a gallon
of rape; and this they feed off with their lambs in time to
plough once for wheat."

One plowing, in autumn, and that a seed plowing (of
course to be immediately harrowed, and thereby *sealed up*)
we are here requested to believe, is the best substitute
for a whole summer's fallowing!—that is to say, for three,
four, or five *open* plowings, with intervals of time between
them, to allow the sun and wind to destroy the *roots* of
weeds, and summer showers to promote vegetation, and
thereby to destroy the *seeds* of weeds.

It may sometimes, perhaps, be found *convenient*, to have
recourse to such an *expedient;*—as to assist a needy sloven;
or to enable a shifty tenant to force a crop of wheat on
foul land, in the last year of a term. But let it not be
named, as a "substitute" for TILLAGE;—*in a course of
practice.*

MIXED HERBAGE.—P. 149. "The artificial grasses in the
highest request, and chiefly cultivated, are red and white
clover, trefoil, and ray."

P. 150. "The course in which these artificial grasses
are introduced, is generally with barley and oats; sometimes with wheat in spring."

GRASS LAND.

On PRODUCING Grass Land.—In a section headed "Clover,
Trefoil, and Ray Grass,"—from which the two last extracts
are taken,—we find an *ingenious* but, in a great measure,
futile scheme, ill drawn,—concerning the operation of
converting

converting arable grounds to a state of permanent herbage, or grass lands.

P. 150. " The cultivation of our best natural grasses has been long called for, and lately recommended by that elaborate botanist, Curtis, and by many others, as likely to turn up a very valuable acquisition. No branches of the art of agriculture are less understood, than a right knowledge of the properties of our grasses, and the soil congenial to each. Till very lately, they were entirely neglected, excepting ray, and one or two others, all of them inferior to many of those in a natural state.

" As there is undoubtedly a particular period when the grasses are in a proper state for mowing, and as that state is most probably about the time of their flowering, should all the under-mentioned grasses be found, upon fair trial, to deserve cultivation, the following diagraph would seem to divide them into proper assortments to be sown together; supposing the fields or meadows where they are to be sown, to be principally intended for hay. If an assortment for *three* crops only be desired, the brackets on the right hand will shew the division. If *five* crops are required, the brackets on the left hand will direct to the assortment: in the division of *three* parts, the first crop will be fit to cut early in June; the *second* about Midsummer; and the *third* about the middle of July. In the division of five *parts*, the *first* will be ripe about the latter end of May; the *second*, the beginning of June; the *third*, about Midsummer; the *fourth*, about the beginning of July; and the *fifth*, the middle or latter end of July.

" The *annual meadow, vernal, smooth-stalked meadow, small fescue, dogstail, yellow oat,* and *fine bent,* seem to be best adapted for the feed of sheep; the rest for the larger kinds of cattle;—the *soft brome, smooth-stalked meadow, smaller fescue,* and *yellow oat,* are partial to dry soils;—the *vernal, foxtail, rough-stalked meadow, quake-grass, meadow-fescue, soft grass, meadow-barley, catstail,* and *marsh-bent,* flourish most in moist soils; and soils of an intermediate quality, as to moisture and dryness, will best suit the remainder.

1 { Annual meadow (poa annua), flowers first week in May. Vernal (anthoxanthum odoratum), flowers second week in May. Foxtail (alopecurus pratensis), flowers second week in May. Soft brome (bromos mollis), flowers third week in May. } 1

Smooth-

2 {
Smooth-stalked meadow (poa pratensis), flowers fourth week in May.

Rough-stalked meadow (poa trivialis), flowers first week in June.

Smaller fescue (festuca ovina, rubra, duriuscula,) flowers first week in June.

Quake-grass (briza media), flowers second week in June.
} 1

3 {
Rough cocksfoot (dactylis glomerata), flowers second week in June.

Tall oat (avena elatior), flowers second week in June.

Meadow fescue (festuca pratensis), flowers third week in June.

Darnel (lolium perenne), flowers fourth week in June.
} 2

4 {
Dogstail (cynosurus cristatus), flowers fourth week in June.

Yellow oat (avena flavescens), flowers first week in July.

Soft grass (holcus lanatus), flowers second week in July.

Fine bent (agrostis capillaris), flowers third week in July.
}

Meadow-barley (hordeum pratense), flowers third week in July.

Catstail, (phleum pratense), flowers third week in July.

Marsh-bent (agrostis alba), flowers third week in in July."
} 3

Let us examine the structure and bearing, of this design; and thence endeavor to ascertain how far it is *practicable.*

To simplify the enquiry, we will suppose five fields, of similar soil, to be sown agreeably to the " five-crop" system, which is set forth in the above diagraph. It may readily be admitted that such of the seeds, sown, as were natural to or culturable in the given soil, would rise; and doubtlessly delight the eye of the cultivator,—*the first year.*—The second year, some resemblance of the first might be discernible. But the third, fourth, or fifth year,—from an invariable law of nature that each species, or distinction of land, shall encorage the species of herbage that are most congenial to it,—the five fields would be found to send up the same, or nearly the same, crop of herbage.

Let it be admitted, however, that no such alteration
would

would take place; but that the very plants that were sown would hold quiet possession of the ground, to the end of time; and then consider how *five hay times* would answer the husbandman's purpose.

In the existing practice of the island, hay time falls between turnep seed-time and corn harvest. Now, in the Southern Counties, on which the sublime conception would seem to have descended, the bustle of the former cannot well be closed before the first week in July, and the latter frequently commences in the wane of the same month.— Haytime is, in every district, confined within a limited space of time, and is ever a work of precipitation. Yet if we believe in the foregoing *diagraph*, it ought to last from "the latter end of May" to "the latter end of July;" that is to say, two months. "Two months!"— a practical man might exclaim:—"Why, two or three weeks is all the time we can conveniently spare for our *meadow haymaking.*—Our *sown grasses* will sometimes break in upon our turnep sowing; but this we cannot always help."

This circumstance is chiefly occasioned by the early growth of *ray-grass*. Hence, this most valuable of the gramineous tribe comes somewhat too early, *as a hay crop,* for modern husbandry. In the more southerly parts of the island it is sometimes ready for the sithe, the latter end of May, or early in June. Nevertheless in the diagraph under view, *lolium* stands the last of the list of " artificial grasses" proper to be sown for the *third cutting !*

I dwell not on the "botanical arrangement of plants," in this *extolled* diagraph; lest a minute examination of it might tend to show a want of sufficient knowledge of the subject,—in the *graphist*.

A GENERAL REMARK on producing permanent Grass Land.—That a variety of nutritious grasses and legumes ought to be made use of, in attempting to execute a plan of that intention, with the view of doing our best endeavor toward assisting Nature,—in propagating such species as may be suitable to the given soil and situation,— is, I will presume to say, assuredly right.

There is nothing new in this idea. It has been acted upon ever since " HAYSEEDS" have been used for that purpose; which they probably have, for a century past; and a better plan, perhaps, will not be discovered, for a century to come :—PROVIDED a well herbaged hay ground, of a nature similar to the land to be sown, be carefully weeded, in the manner of corn crops, from time to time, during the early stages of its growth; and the swaths carefully

AGRICULTURE.

fully looked over after the crop is mown.—PROVIDED,
also, that different parts of the herbage, so freed from
noxious plants, be cut in different states of ripeness, that
the seeds of the nutritious herbs may be saved in a state
of maturity. And PROVIDED, of course, that the several
parcels of hay be thrashed, as they become sufficiently
dry for the operations (without being heated in bulk);—
the different products of seed be intimately blended by
sifting them together;—and carefully stored till the season
of use:—whether this may be in the autumn, the spring,
or the summer months, next ensuing.

MOWING GROUNDS.—*Oiling Hay.*—This is something
new.—P. 153. "The following singular and interesting
method of applying linseed-oil on hay-ricks intended for
fattening beasts, merits the attention of the curious. It
was communicated by the Earl of Egremont.

"SIR,

"I received your letter in regard to oiling hay. I made
practice of it about three years; but always choose to
do it when the weather is fine, and can get it up without
taking much rain. My method is, when stacking the hay,
to take a water-pot, and sprinkle over every layer very
lightly a quart of linseed-oil to a ton of hay. I find that
the hay comes out of the rick very moist and very clammy:
fatting beasts and fatting sheep are very fond of it, and
thrive upon it very fast. I think it not proper to give it
to horses, or milch-cows, as I think it is too hot. I wish
it not to be reported in my name, as I did it for my own
security.

"Your most obedient humble servant."

PASTURE GROUNDS.—On the *upland* pastures, we find
nothing of consideration; except what relates to the *sheep
downs;* for which see *Sheep,* ensuing.

The *Marshlands* of Sussex.—P. 148. "Besides the natural pasture and meadow-land, are several thousand acres
of marsh-land, either situated along the coast, or in the
neighbourhood of the rivers which empty themselves into
the sea. These marshes perhaps are to be ranked amongst
the finest of their kind that are any where to be met with;
and the conduct of the grazier in the management of the
fertile level, is the direct reverse of that unsystematic
policy which is the guide of the upland farmer in the arrangement of his grazing land.

"Very considerable improvements have been effected
of late years in the marshes. The brooks or levels have
been, and are now, sometimes subject to be flooded with
the

the violent rains which periodically flow from the hills, but more particularly in the winter. If, as is sometimes the case, these inundations take place in summer, the whole produce of the land for that year is lost by the stagnant muddy water; and no cattle will taste the herbage that year. The tide is another evil sometimes complained of, as the banks are not every where put into a proper state of defence against the incursions of the sea. An act was however obtained a few years ago, for widening the channel near Lewes, and making a shorter cut to the sea; and it has essentially benefited the Lewes and Laughton Levels."

P. 156. " In the Level of Pevensey, cattle were universally preferred to sheep. The marsh ground about Winchelsea and Rye, as it wants fresh water, has been thought better calculated for sheep: these grounds are universally stocked with them; and the general rule is, to have no more bullocks than what are sufficient to keep the pasture fine, which is usually one to three or four acres. Pevensey having plenty of water, was considered as better adapted for oxen. It should seem as if this circumstance had governed the custom of the two marshes: the soil and rent are nearly the same; yet there are very few fortunes made in Pevensey, but many about Winchelsea and Rye; and this is attributed to sheep being found to turn out so much more profitable than oxen.

" But throughout the whole range of Pevensey Level, it is to be observed, that the number of sheep have been very much increased of late years. Graziers have now discovered, from the late rapid advances in the single article of wool, and the still increasing demand for it, that sheep pay far better than beasts, whilst the loss is comparatively less."

" Men are generally employed in the Levels to mow down the over-grown herbage, as it grows rank, and sheep or cattle are not inclined to feed upon it."

P. 157. " The increase in the quantity of sheep annually pastured, is to be accounted for from the good management of the grazier in laying his lands dry, by opening and keeping clean the ditches, and making drains at proper times to receive the superfluous waters."

Preserving Pastures, for Spring Food.—P. 155. " That admirable practice, of reserving the *rouen* for the pinching part of the spring, when all artificial provender fails, and before the young clover and other grasses have begun to throw out their shoots, is hardly known in the county. The Earl of Egremont has usually some portion of the Home-park wattled off for this reason, either for his Lordship's different

different flocks, or for the deer; and experience has declared the beneficial effects of it, for now he has it in his power to apply the hay for other purposes, and save a considerable consumption by the deer.

"1799. His Lordship has continued this practice to the *present* moment, and with increasing success. He is now practically convinced, through a variety of severe and open winters, that the resource of *rouen* is one of the most important that can be secured on a farm. It is also a constant practice with Mr. Ellman, at Glynde, and Mr. Sherwin, at Petworth. Mr. Ellman usually saves 40 acres."

P. 269. "I saw four oxen, two of which are ten years old, which his Lordship bought of my father; and two others coming eight years old, feeding upon rouen in January, through the severe frost of the end of December, and without having a mouthful of any other food, and thriving well : a very satisfactory proof how much rouen is to be depended on, even in such a season, and of the great profit attending it. The advantages of kept grass can hardly be exemplified in a clearer manner than in this practice ; for no slight portion of the profit throughout the scale, arises from the cheapness of this food. The calves entirely depend on it for the first winter : they have some the second also, though at straw ; and the winter previous to fattening, the oxen are put to it, to improve them. Its value is best ascertained by supposing its absence; for then hay must be the substitute ; and the expense of that food, if reckoned at what it would sell for, every one knows to be extremely great. I had the pleasure of seeing Lord Egremont's whole crop of lambs thriving admirably on this food also, without the addition of any other ; a very severe frost leaving his turnips rotten, and yet the farmer free from all anxiety. Rouen defies the season, and places the flock-master on velvet."

LIVESTOCK.

GENERAL OBSERVATION.—P. 226. "The breed of Sussex cattle and sheep, and the system upon which they are founded, form the most distinguishing feature in the husbandry of this county."

CATTLE.—P. 226. "The cattle must unquestionably be ranked amongst the best in the kingdom; and had Bakewell, or any of his associates, adopted the middle horned breed, either of Sussex, Devonshire, or Herefordshire, in preference to the inferior stock which the reputation of his name, and the mysterious manner in which his breeding system was conducted;—had he, I say, gone to work with any of the above-mentioned breeds, it would have contributed

buted to exalt the superiority of his stock beyond the power of local prejudices to remove."—All this *I* stedfastly believe.

P. 228. " In treating of the management of Sussex cattle, with a view to greater clearness, the first object to be considered is, the division of the subject; and this raises an inquiry into the purposes for which cattle are bred in this county. This is the leading question, and it will materially tend to elucidate the arrangement, by considering cattle under the three purposes of, I. Beef. II. Dairy. III. Work."

The Reporter's motto, while " elucidating the arrangement" of his subject, in this case, would seem to have been —" the last shall be first, and the first last." BEEF, whether of steers or heifers, aged cows or working oxen, is the looked for END of cattle.—It were equally *lucid*, in treating of the subject, *Wheat*, to commence the enquiry with its ultimate, BREAD.—This by way of apology for pursuing my own plan of arrangement, in preference to that of the work before me.

Breeds of Cattle, in Sussex.—The native or established Breed of the County.—P. 229. " Sussex cattle are universally red; for wherever any other is found, it may be depended upon that the breed is stained with foreign blood."

P. 231. " Mr. Ellman, of Glyd, has given us his experience of cattle, summed up in the following description of a thorough-bred Sussex ox. It should be observed, that these points were approved by several other intelligent breeders. A thin head, and clean jaw; the horns point forward a little, and then turn upward, thin tapering, and long; the eye large and full; the throat clean, no dew-lap; long and thin in the neck; wide and deep in the shoulders; no projection in the point of the shoulder, when looked at from behind; the forelegs wide; round and straight in the barrel, and free from a rising back-bone; no hanging heaviness in the belly; wide across the loin; the space between the hip-bone and the first rib very small; the hip-bone not to rise high, but to be large and wide; the loin, and space between the hips, to be flat and wide, but the fore-part of the carcass round; long and straight in the rump, and wide in the tip; the tail to lay low, for the flesh to swell above it; the legs not too long, neither thick nor thin on the thigh; the leg thin; *shut well in the twist;* no fulness in the outside of the thigh, but all of it within."

Other Sorts.—P. 250. " The other sorts of cattle to be found in Sussex, are a small breed brought by Welsh drovers, which, by crossing with the native breed, have very much injured the Sussex stock. The Alderney, Norman, and Jersey breed of cows, are to be found all over this county.

county. Lord Egremont has some of the cows, and a very fine bull, of that breed."

Breeding Cattle.—Breeding Stock.—P. 260. " The breeding system of this district is entitled to considerable attention, and is a most profitable branch in the management of live-stock. The cows are in proportion to the farmer's occupation, and all, or nearly all the calves are reared, which are kept in succession for work ; so that a farm of eight cows will have six calves, six-year olds, as many two-year olds, four three-year olds beginning to work, four four-year olds, as many five-year olds, and as many six-year olds. Upon some farms, the calves reared are, los excepted, equal to the number of cows : females are sufficient to keep up the stock of cows ; and if other females remain, they perhaps change them with a neighbour for males. Others again spay the females, and work them as oxen."

Choice of Parents.—P. 273. " Crossing is universally practised. It is very strongly believed, that without this custom, the breed would infallibly degenerate ; and in conformity to this-notion, the Sussex breeders every year or two change their bulls; consequently this practice is in vogue, for the mere sake of crossing ; and it has contributed to the deterioration of the stock. Bulls are seldom to be met with above three years old ; so that, with this system, a man scarcely knows what his young stock will turn out. Mr. Ellman, in support of this opinion, gives it as the result of experience, that it is necessary in all kinds of animals : that it is, of course, better to cross from a finer stock than their own ; but, if they have been long in one blood, it will be better to take a cross from a worse breed, rather than not change, as the mere crossing will be advantageous enough to induce this conduct. And it is thought that this observation goes more pointedly to the means of improving the health of the animal, and the disposition to fatten, than either to shape or colour."

This is ill-termed *crossing*. It is rather enriching the blood of an established breed : whereas crossing, in its true sense, I conceive, is mixing it with the blood of an *alien* breed ; and thereby, most likely, deteriorating it ; and in the end, if continued, annihilating its essential characteristics ; let their peculiar excellencies be what they may.

How unfortunate for the progress of science and the useful arts, when they happen to be publicly treated of by writers who have not maturely studied them. No two principles of action can be less alike, than that of improving a select *native* breed of domestic animals, by further selecting the most valuable of its individuals, male and female, for the purpose of propagation ; and that of deteriorating

riorating—or destroying—it, *as a distinct breed*, by mixing its blood with that of an *alien* variety.—This is intended, not as a *pointed* but as a *general* remark.

If a breed, whether of cattle or sheep, that has been long enured to the soil and climature of a district, is so innately bad, as not to be improvable without admixture (a circumstance, I believe, which has rarely occurred) ;— *and* another variety of superior value that has long inhabited the same or a very similar species of soil and situation, can be procured, at a moderate cost,—banish the former, altogether, and replace it with the latter :—as the occupiers of the Western Chalk Hills of the Southern Counties are now changing the Wiltshire-down, for the Sussex-down, breed of sheep.

Rearing Cattle, in Sussex.—P. 261. The calves " universally suck the cow from ten to thirteen weeks, are cut at seven weeks, and are weaned by being shut up ; and having a little grass given them, till they have forgotten the dam, are then turned out to pasture. The first winter they are well fed with the best hay ; after that with straw, except after Christmas, while working, when they have hay, but straw alone till they begin to work."

Dairy of Sussex.—P. 253. " The material object in the cattle system of Sussex, is the breeding and rearing of stock for working and fattening. The concern of the dairy is but a secondary object in this system.

" Upon many farms, nearly as many fat oxen are annu ally sold as there are cows kept. 3*l.* or 4*l.* in the product of the dairy, had much better be lost, than an indifferent ox bred.

" In quantity of milk, they are not to be compared with some other breeds, as the Holderness, Suffolk, &c."

P. 254. " A good cow will give 5 lb. of butter in a week in the height of the season ; and six will make from 30 to 40 lb. of cheese in a month, of skim-milk."

Making up Butter.—The following novel idea, concerning this important operation in a butter dairy, I transcribe from a *note, by Mr. Trayton.*

N. p. 258. " I am inclined to think this useful aliment of butter suffers greatly in its quality and durability, in the ordinary process of making up. The error I would point out is, the admission of water (warm or cold), both into the churn, and in the heating and making up. Water is well known to be a great dissolvent ; at least if it be not essentially so, it serves *in vesiculi* as a conductor to air, which is universally such. Fresh butter then, in consequence of imbibing water, and water being saturated with air, is always in a progressive state of decay. Not so when water is is excluded : its obginous parts are admirably calculated to secure it from putrefaction ; and I am almost positive, that butter might be made with as little trouble as the present method, to keep the whole year fresh and sweet, without the least particle of salt, solely by the exclusion of water. I was witness some years ago to a piece of butter being taken out of the churn in very warm weather : there might have been water put in previous to the churning, and I believe there was, but it had none afterwards : a part of this butter was used for making ointment, the remainder was set by and forgot ; a fortnight afterwards, it was discovered to be as fresh and sweet as ever, though it had never been salted. I have heard it spoken of a notable old housewife famous for good butter, that she always kept the floor of her dairy dry. The custom is exactly the reverse at present in those parts, many pailfuls being thrown down in the hot weather, which will assuredly rise again in steam, and affect the milk with its humidity."

For the mode of *fatting* cattle, see *Grazing* aforegoing. And for remarks on *Working* Cattle, see p. 476, aforegoing.

On a *Disease* of Cattle.—P. 285. " South Down receipt for hoved bullocks is, a quart of lintseed-oil, which vomits them directly, and never known to fail."

Markets for Cattle.—P. 246. " Smithfield is the greatest market for the sale of Sussex cattle, which is well supplied with fat oxen from this county, where they are deservedly held in the highest estimation. They go at all times of the year ; but the grazier endeavours to bring his beasts to the pitch, so as to be enabled to meet the demand when it is probable there will be the greatest call for prime beef, which is from Christmas till May. After this the market declines."

SHEEP.—This section may not inaptly be termed the great work of the volume under review. It fills five sheets of letterpress : one sixth of the book.

The beginning and the ending, thereof, are alike the theme of comparison, between the favorite " South Downs" and the other fashionable breeds of the day. Mr. ELLMAN of Glynde sustains the principal character ; " his cousin Mr. Ellman of Shoreham," acting a subordinate part. This is not said in light derision of Mr. JOHN ELLMAN of GLYNDE ; who is entitled to much praise ; as having been principally instrumental, in *promulgating*, and, for some purposes, *improving*, a valuable breed of sheep.

No *public character*, perhaps, ever set out with less promising auspice,—saving the intrinsic merit of his subject,—than did " John Ellman." By perseverance, however, he acquired *oratory* sufficient to engage the attention of of fashionable breeders of sheep; as a still greater man had done before him.

Turning back a sheet of desultory discourse, concerning the comparative merits, and specific claims, of the favorite variety, we arrive at some more direct information, respecting the superior qualities which belong to the

Breed of South Down Sheep.—About the "form, color, and hardiness," of this breed, much is said. I perceive nothing, however, that calls for particular notice, here; excepting what relates to "the length of the neck." Indeed, we search, in vain, for plain, intelligent, *general description* of the breed under report.

P. 293. "The true South Down sheep are polled, and when very well bred, have a small head, and clear neck, which are very essential points; the length, indeed, of the neck, is a matter in dispute among the breeders. Mr. Ellman, who certainly has brought his flock to a high degree of perfection, thinks the length of the neck no demerit; and other breeders, who look for fine wool more than form of carcass, think it a merit, as the surface produces more wool, and that of a fine quality. Others, on the contrary, prefer a short neck, because it is thought that lambs that are spear-necked, are free of wool, and not so well able to bear severe weather; and long necks are inclined to long carcasses."

The *true South Down!*—Surely not: the true, the *legitimate* South Down sheep would be better described by—"the head and neck thick and short." *

For an instance of the *want* of *hardiness*, in the smart, modernized breed, see EASTERN DEPARTMENT—*Kent's Norfolk*. And for *general remarks* concerning them, see the same volume; article, *Secretary's Norfolk*.

For the purpose of *growing wool*, the best of the modern variety have received some considerable improvement †. As mere pasture sheep, for well soiled, well sheltered uplands, they are equal, I believe, to some of the other puffed and pampered breeds of the kingdom. But for the profitable purpose of braving bleak barren hills, by day, and manuring arable lands, by night,—their fitness is "now no more." It were as fitting to put an arabian courser into the shafts of a dung cart, as a delicate, highblooded, fashionable "South Downer" into a sheepfold.

On the *spareness of diet*, which is held out as belonging to this breed, we have the following remarks:

P. 302.

*For a description of the *genuine* South Down breed, see my SOUTHERN COUNTIES.

† Attend, however, to the next extract.

P. 302. "It is a part of the subject which depends entirely on the quantity of food eaten, and it is very necessary and requisite to know the usual allowance of food, artificial as well as Down, in several distinct flocks, from which it will appear, that the food eaten is comparatively small in this part of the kingdom; and it must impress other Counties with a very high idea of South Down sheep.

"A tenantry flock * belonging to Denton parish, consisting of six hundred breeding ewes, has no other provision but the native Down (seven or eight loads of hay excepted) for the whole year: no green food. This flock lives upon the hill the greatest part of the year, very nearly indeed the whole of it: at lambing time it is taken away; and it is observed, that *no where is finer wool found;* and is an instance in favour of the quality of the wool depending upon the sort of food, and as strong a one to shew, how small a quantity of food serves to winter this flock."

P. 304. "The native Down is stocked in proportion to the quality. Glynde and Ringmer Down, measuring 1100 acres, now maintains 5000 sheep and lambs for six months in the summer, and 2500 in the winter, exclusive of artificial provision.

"Upon the whole of those accounts, a superiority is immediately discovered over other breeds, in the small proportion of food allotted for the maintenance of such numerous flocks. It is to the excellency of the breed, in union with the happy state of the Downs, to which this circumstance is to be attributed; and partly to the beneficial arrangement of arable and pasture. In all seasons, recourse is had to the Downs for food; and it is admirably well calculated for the purpose. If the proportion of stock to ground is extended over all the South Downs and the contiguous land, so as to comprehend a tract of 150,000 acres, the stock of sheep upon this surface, from authentic accounts, is estimated at 270,000 in summer, and 220,000 in winter; a rate of stocking which is not to be exceeded in any other part of England, marsh land alone excepted."

Near the close of the Reporter's long, long, article, we find a loosely given account of some experiments instituted by the EARL of EGREMONT, in 1795, with different breeds of sheep; to the intent of ascertaining "the proportion of food to mutton, offal, and tallow, live and dead weight, &c. &c." p. 361.

Nothing

* A parish or township flock; of course *unimproved;* the "true old sort;"—and listen to their merits!

Nothing, however, is made out, *in the report of those experiments*, to prove or even to strengthen the foregoing suggestions, concerning the comparatively short allowance of food, the South Down breed require. Nevertheless, the PRINCIPLES, on which those EXPERIMENTS were conducted, are very ingenious ; and, under *scientific superintendence* and *intelligent Report*, a course of similar experiments might bring out results of great importance, in the propagation of domestic animals.

We may, I think, be allowed to conclude, from what appears in this Report, that the large " proportion of stock to ground," which is so confidently spoken of, in different parts of it, is more owing to the superior excellence of the " native downs," than to the breed of sheep that are depastured upon them.

On the *comparative sale value* of the favorite breed, are the subjoined remarks.

P. 305. "This is another point which ought to impress upon the world an high idea of the merit of this breed of sheep: the advance in the prices of the flock proves it in the most satisfactory manner, and marks the improve-it has received.

" The superiority of one flock over another, may be gathered from the difference of value in the sale of the produce: thus estimated, the success of some few breeders have been felt and acknowledged: the difference in the price is the quantum of improvement: and the constant unbroken rise of late years in the prices of sheep and lambs, denote certainly the merit, and probably the demand for the breed. And no where shall we see such accounts of the profits of flocks, that will bear to be compared with the prices on the Downs. Such an incessant demand has existed for the breed, that the advance in the value has excited much emulation: price has done the whole."

The panegyrist, when he wrote those remarks, does not appear to have been aware that *fashion* had much ado, in exciting the "incessant demand," proudly mentioned :— which did not arise so much from the specific, inherent, intrinsic value of the animals, as from a *temporary* demand for them :—which temporary demand, when the *rage* for them shall have cooled, when the several districts, for which they are peculiarly adapted, shall be fully stocked, and the surplus number which the wind of fashion may have blown into districts for which they are unfit, shall have returned into the market, it may, perchance, be overstocked ; and a *discount*, instead of a *premium*, on their intrinsic value, may take place.

Some

Some observations, touching the *modern improvement* of the breed of sheep under notice, I welcome to a place, here; as they accord with my own sentiments concerning them;—but ill assimilate with the general tenor of the article under review.

P. 297. " In the form of the sheep, great room is open for improvement. It is only in a few of the best flocks, that much attention has been paid to the carcass. The quality of the wool has been the first object, and points of greater consequence neglected.

" The improvement of the South Down sheep in the last twelve years, though considerable, is not to be attributed to the general spirit which prevailed in the county, so much as to the skill and intelligence of a few active individuals, who first set improvement afloat.

" Such are the ideas which have been pretty much afloat since this breed has been improved. It remains for further experience to ascertain, whether they are not in the way to be carried too far; a point suspected by some persons;—whether the hardiness of the old breed will not gradually be lost in the modern improvements."

The *Number* of Sheep kept in the County of Sussex.—P. 372. " We have a most correct account of the number of sheep in the county, including the horned flocks on the western, and the Romney on the eastern side, by referring to the Custom-house entries.

	No. of Sheep.	Weight. Tod.	Lambs.	Tod.	lb.
Chichester	60,983	4537	13,381	444	0
Arundel	30,942	2805	9852	219	5
Shoreham	28,245	2280	10,782	189	11
Brighton	43,258	3182	24,866	336	12
Newhaven	45,605	3247	18,566	278	21
Eastsbourne	30,638	2207	8274	124	13
Hastings	13,118	1098	4555	95	28
Bexhill	11,785	1351	2271	41	14
Winchelsea	9627	1392	3816	42	2
Rye	67,544	8801	21,242	952	13
	341,745	30,900	113,605	2714	23
	113,605			30,900	

Sheep & lambs 455,350   Tod of wool 33,614

" This includes all the sheep that are registered, and nearly all that are kept in the county."—We are not informed of the year in which this account was taken.

Breeding Flocks.—P. 307. " Mr. Ellman's flock consists
of

of about five hundred breeding ewes, each ewe (barrens
and refuse excepted) produces three lambs, lambing at
two, three, and four years old, and when four years and a
half old, he sells them off, to go into other flocks. The
general practice has been, to sell them to the graziers,
in the Weald of Sussex and Kent, who fatten both the
lambs and the ewes the following summer; but Mr. Ellman
has for some years, found a better market in the great
demand in other parts for his sheep, and he expects that
this will continue to be the case, till the South Down
sheep are generally known. He usually saves for store
about two hundred and twenty ewe lambs, which gives
him an opportunity to refuse about fifty-one each year.
His ewe lambs at Michaelmas are sent out to keep in the
Weald, amongst the small farmers, till the following Lady-
day, when he takes them home, and flocks them at night,
till they are a year and a half old, when they are put with
his breeding ewes. He always takes sixty of his best
ewes, and puts them to his rams of the best shape, and
finest wool, and saves the rams from them*. But the usual
way is to give about fifty ewes to one ram, and to put all the
rams into a flock at a time, which he very properly condemns, for several reasons. After having taken out sixty
ewes, he then puts three of his next best rams into the flock,
and about five or six days after, he adds two more, and
continues to add two every four or five days, till the whole
are put in, by which means his best rams have the most
ewes. He begins to put them to his flock about the 25th
of

" * What I mean by the best wool, is a thick curdly wool, with
depth of staple, and even toped; such wool as will best defend the
sheep in bad weather, and will not admit the water to penetrate, as it
does a thin, light, loose wool. I have found from many years experience, that sheep in the same flock, of the former descriptions, will
keep themselves in better flesh, than those of the latter.

" When I change my breed, which I think it absolutely necessary to
do, I get some neighbour to let me take out fifty of his best ewes (of
the former description) and put my best ram with them, and I save
ram lambs from them. By following the above practice, and drafting
thirty or forty refuse ewes every year, I have got my flock tolerably
good, both for shape and wool. The farmers on the South Downs, a
few years since, were taught by the wool buyers to believe, that it was
not possible to increase the quantity of wool, without decreasing the
quality, an opinion which was not grounded in truth. For by adhering to the rule above-mentioned, I believe I grow the heaviest
wool between Brighton and East-bourne, and sell for the highest price
on the South Downs.

" I do not put more than eleven rams to five hundred and sixty ewes,
so, by saving twenty ram lambs every year, have an opportunity of
refusing eight or nine.—*John Ellman.*"

of October, and lets them continue with the ewes about five weeks, from first to last.

"They are folded at night, throughout the year, except for a month or five weeks after lambing, which is the latter end of March, or beginning of April, and the lambs are well covered with wool when born. If the ewes are well kept, one third of his flock will bring twins. The lambs are weaned at twelve or fourteen weeks old. Mr. Ellman never puts ram lambs to his flock. His cousin, at Shoreham, some years puts no other: the former carefully avoids his ewe lambs taking the ram; but this is no general rule. Neither ram nor ewe lambs should be allowed to copulate."

Principles of *Breeding.*—P. 309. " In the principles of breeding upon those hills, *exchanging the rams* every third, fourth, or fifth year, is the practice almost unanimously agreed upon. It is found to be most essentially necessary in preserving the health, size, and bone of the flocks."—This is what has, previously been termed " crossing." See p. 496, aforegoing.

Same page.—" Crossing the South Down breed with other sorts, has been very sparingly practised. Spanish rams have been introduced into some few flocks. Lord Sheffield, first introduced the Spanish breed into the county: the wool of his Lordship's flock was considerably improved by it. The few breeders on the South Downs who have tried it, found two capital defects, not to be compensated by any improvement in the wool, tender constitution, and bad shape."—Here, we recognize *crossing* in its true sense. —And again, p. 477. " Above 30 years ago Lord Sheffield gave 50 guineas, a large price at that time, to Mr. Bakewell, for the use of one of his rams; the ewes were of the South Down breed, and the cross appeared *at first* to have answered well; but he soon found that he had sheep of no character; the lambs appeared larger, but weighed little more than South Down, and the wool was very indifferent, being neither long nor short."—This is a happy illustration of crossing.

P. 361. " In his" (Mr. Ellman's) " ideas of breeding, deduced from long observation, he is of opinion, that what he calls the *stain* of the breed, is for some years difficult to remove. A ram and ewe both with fine wool on the breech, will in an ordinary flock, very probably produce a coarse breeched sheep; but if they have been well bred for several generations, then there is good reason (and not else) to rely on the progeny."—This well known truth, here well defined, serves to show the lasting mischief which may be entailed on a pure breed, by a mixture of alien blood.

The

The *Management* of *Store Flocks.*—On this, a principal work of sheep farming, I have found it difficult to discover, in the chaotic mass before me, even a passage, (unless on folding) that is entitled to transcription. The following short notices may have their use.

P. 310. " The best time for this operation is, eight, ten, or twelve days old. Mr. Ellman cuts off the tails of his lambs at the time of castration : thus a considerable quantity of blood is lost, which he considers as preventing the part from the gangrene."—This practice is not less eligible for being pretty common ; tho not universal.

P. 314. " Mr. Ellman of Shoreham, generally gives his sheep hay, in hoar frosty mornings. He finds that it preserves them from the *gall.*"

P. 353. " Mr. Ellman has a practice, which he thinks answers to him : it is, to clip off the coarsest of the wool on the thigh, and dock a month before washing and shearing, which he sells as locks; the quantity is about 4 oz. per sheep; it keeps them clean and cool in hot weather."—And may assist, perhaps, in the sale of the fleece.

Folding Sheep.—In moveable folds.—P. 346. " Undoubtedly, one of the most valuable practices ever established on the South Downs, and the universal attention paid to it, shews how well adapted the breed is to support bare keep and distant folding; for the position of great numbers of farms, in this respect, is such, as to put the flocks to the severest trials.

" The practice upon the Downs, it appears, is, to fold upon the arable lands: in the winter, upon such as are intended for pease, oats, or turnips. At this season, two folds are thought necessary; one on the Downs, where the sheep are penned in rainy nights, when the arable lands are too wet for them to set on. The early part of the summer, they fold on such lands as are intended for turnips; after which, upon lands which are in rotation for wheat. It is not a common practice to fold upon pasture land, although Mr. Ellman frequently does it soon after lambing time. Folding begins soon after lambing, when the lambs are about a fortnight old, and continue folding, except in very wet weather, till the ewes begin to lamb again ; and it may be said that, during the lambing season, they are penned either in the standing fold or in the pastures. But this is Mr. Ellman's mode of management, and not the usual practice of the county, since some of the flockmasters allow their sheep to lay out of the fold on the Downs for three or four months during winter.

" 1. *Space.*—Mr. Ellman states, that a flock of 500 sheep will pen 28 square perch each night, which is 50 acres in a year;

year; allowing them to be left out of the fold two months in the year, which is a fair estimate for the best farmers.

" 2. *Value.*—This is in proportion as the farmer considers the profit of the fold. It varies from 35s. to 42s. per acre, which for 500, is from 87l. 10s to 100 guineas for the 50 acres, which, if we take the average at 94l. for the flock, the annual value of the fold will be, per head, 3s. 9d. and a small fraction: at 100 guineas, it is 4s. 2½d per head. Of what great consequence the fold is to the farmer, when the value of it is found to be so high!

" 3. *Stock.*—All the sheep, excepting the fat stock, are regularly folded: these are never folded."

In fixed Folds.—P. 349. " In Mr. Ellman's management of his flock, there is a circumstance which should be more universally attended to; not indeed that he is singular in it. He has two or three yards well sheltered, for the sheep to lie down in at night, in very rainy and stormy weather. One contains, including the sheds, 355 square yards. The sheds around it are about four yards wide, and the whole thoroughly well littered. These yards are extremely warm, and preserve many lambs in bad weather; around the whole circumference is a rack for giving hay."

Fatting Sheep.—P. 325. " The South Down wethers are generally turned off to fatten from one to two years old. It is considered as bad policy to keep for profit more than two years and a half; and indeed it is usually allowed, that they pay better at one year and a half old, than at any other age."

Wool.— P. 354. " The weight of the fleece is various, and depends much on the food: about East-bourne it is light; upon rich food it is, of course, heavy—two pounds and an half is the average."

A *Disease* of Sheep.—P. 336. " Hoving, or bursting with eating luxuriant plants, clover, rape, &c. Mr. Ellman remarks, that they are never subject to it when the food is wet from rain or dew; an erroneous idea, very common. He always chooses to turn into such crops at such a time; but when quite dry, and the leaf at all withered from a hot sun, the danger is considerable. The remedy: half a pint of lintseed-oil to each sheep, given with a horn, which vomits them directly, and never known to fail."

SWINE.—P. 381. " The hogs of Sussex are either descended from the large Berkshire spotted breed, or from a cross between that and a smaller black, or white breed."

The following experiments on *fatting* swine are very ingenious; but not well reported.

P. 385. " Lord Egremont has tried a great variety of hogs, and made many experiments, to determine the most profitable

profitable food, which is barley; the white hog for store and grazing, is the best he has yet tried. They are killed after summer grazing in the park; and it is a most advantageous method: no corn is given: nothing but grass. They are turned out in May, and in October and November brought to the slaughter-house, and die good porkers. This is a curious experiment, and deserves further trial.

" In this experiment the hogs ranged over an extensive park."—This must be a mistake.—That experiment was made in a suite of fatting deer paddocks ; and altho the *pigs* had " no corn" *given* to them, they might pick up the *crums* which fell from the mangers of the deer. See my SOUTHERN COUNTIES.

P. 386. " In another trial made, they were confined in a cage, exactly fitted to the size of the animal, which was augmented as the hog grew larger; and no more space allowed him, than what was sufficient for him to lie down upon his belly."—Of the *result* of this trial no mention is made.

" As there were some hogs that *we* wanted to keep over the summer, seven of the largest were put up to fat on the 25th of February; they were fatted upon barley meal, of which they had as much as they could eat. Some days after, the observation of a particular circumstance" (?) " suggested the following experiment : a hog *nearly* of the same size as the seven, but who had not been put up with them, because they appeared to be rather larger, but without weighing them, was confined on the 4th of March, in a cage made of planks, of which one side was made to move with pegs, so as to fit exactly the size of the hog, with small holes at the bottom for the water to drain from him, and a door behind to remove the soil. The cage stood upon four feet, about one foot from the ground, and was made to confine the hog so closely, that he could only stand up to feed, and lie down upon his belly. He had only two bushels of barley-meal, and the rest of his food was boiled potatoes: they were all killed on the 13th of April, and the weights were as follow : (8 lb. to the stone.)

	st.	lb.
The hog in the cage	13	2
The other hogs, all of the same breed	12	2
	12	3
	11	2
	11	4
	11	4
	11	2
	12	2

" The

" The hog in the cage was weighed before he was put in: alive 11 stone 1 lb.; he was kept five weeks and five days, and then weighed alive 18 stone 3 lb.; he had two bushels of barley-meal, and about eight bushels of potatoes. He was quite sulky for the two first days, and would eat nothing.

" This is a most singular result, and as the hog thus confined was so much superior to all the others, though not equally fed, it can scarcely arise from any other circumstance but the method adopted: it is exteremly curious, and deserves to be farther examined in a variety of trials."

RABBITS.—P. 391. " This stock is the nuisance of a county; they flourish in proportion to the size of the wastes, and are therefore productive in Sussex. From Horsham forest and Ashdown, &c. considerable quantities are sent to London."

POULTRY.—*Cramming Fowls.*—P. 391. " North Chappel, Kindford, &c. are famous for their fowls. They are fattened here to a size and perfection unknown elsewhere. The food given them is ground oats made into gruel, mixed with hogs'-grease, sugar, pot-liquor, and milk; or ground oats, treacle, and suet; also sheep's plucks, &c.; and they are kept very warm: they are always crammed in the morning and at night. They mix the pot-liquor with a few handfuls of oatmeal; boil it: it is then taken off the fire, and the meal is wetted, so as to be made to roll into pieces of a sufficient size for cramming: the fowls are put into the coop two or three days before they begin to cram them, which is done for a fortnight, and then sold to the higlers. They will weigh, when full grown, 7 lb. each, and are sold at 4s. 6d. and 5s.; the average weight 5 lb.; but there are instances of these fowls weighing double this.

" Mr. Turner, of North Chappel, a tenant of Lord Egremont's, crams 200 in a year. Many fat capons are fed in this manner; good ones always look pale, and waste away." (?)

FISH.—P. 393. " This is an object of some consequence in Sussex. The ponds in the Weald are innumerable; and numbers of them date their origin from that part of the county having once been the seat of an extensive iron manufactory, which has now deserted the country; and the mill-ponds now raise large quantities of fish. A Mr. Fenn, of London, has long rented, and is the sole monopolizer of all the fish that are sold in Sussex. Carp is the chief stock; but tench and perch, eels and pike, are raised. A stream should always flow through the pond; and a marley soil is the best. Mr. Milward has drawn carp from his marl-pits 25 lb. a brace, and two inches of fat upon them, but then he feeds with pease. When the waters are drawn off and re-stocked, re-stocked, it is done with stores of a year old, which remain four years: the carp will then be 12 or 13 inches long, and if the water is good, 14 or 15. The usual season for drawing the water, is either autumn or spring: the sale is regulated by measure, from the eye to the fork of the tail. At 12 inches, carp are worth 50s. and 3l. per hundred; at 15 inches, 6l.; at 18 inches, 8l. and 9l.: a hundred stores will stock an acre; or 35 brace, 10 or 12 inches long, are fully sufficient for a breeding pond."

PROFIT of FARMING.—There is much good sense in the following remarks. P. 44. " To draw up any detail of the the expenses and profit of farming with accuracy and precision, such as may be relied upon as a medium standard for the whole county, is, I fear, a task so difficult of execution, that it may be thought to border upon impossibility. No farmer, for obvious reasons, will lay open to the view of others a detail of his business; and observation alone is absolutely insufficient, and never to be depended upon. It must be founded on documents, and collected from registered accounts."—Nevertheless, some pages of calculations are offered on the subject.

E N D

OF THE

SOUTHERN DEPARTMENT.

THE

PENINSULAR DEPARTMENT

OF

ENGLAND.

SOUTH-WESTERN

OR

PENINSULAR DEPARTMENT

OF

ENGLAND.

THIS DEPARTMENT of England, which is at once *natural* and *agricultural*, I have described, in the Introduction to these volumes.

'THE SOUTHWESTERN DEPARTMENT. The situation of this extremity of the island is remarkable. It stretches away from the main body, in a narrow headland, or peninsula, nearly two hundred miles in length, into the western sea; which is its common boundary; unless where it joins the extremes of the western and southern departments.

'The natural characters of its area are likewise singular. The midland and the western parts of it, are chiefly composed of SLATE-ROCK HILLS: a species of country which is unknown, in the rest of the kingdom; excepting a comparatively small district of its northern department; and excepting the insulated hills of Charnwood, which rise near its center! Indeed, the surface, almost throughout the department (its northeastern angle excepted) is of a singular cast: namely, tall, steepsided hills, severed by narrow valleys; the hills being, in most instances, productive to their summits.

'Its agricultural distinguishments are not less remarkable. The DAMNONIAN HUSBANDRY is as foreign to the practice of the kingdom at large, as the lands on which it has been nurtured are to those of its other departments.'

For DIGESTED DETAILS of the ESTABLISHED PRACTICES of this Department; with MINUTES on my own practice within it; and with TRAVELLING JOURNALS, on viewing its more interesting passages; together with RETROSPECTIVE REMARKS, on the Department at large,—pointing out its distinguishing characteristics, and suggesting the manner in which

which its striking peculiarities of practice, probably, had
their rise;—see my RURAL ECONOMY of the WEST of
ENGLAND.

THIS DEPARTMENT comprizing little more than two Counties,—Cornwall and Devonshire, with the western quarter
of Somersetshire, and a very small portion of Dorsetshire;
—and the Reports to the Board of Agriculture, concerning
it, being very few, and of secondary consideration, (one of
them excepted);—I have deemed it proper to include my
abstract of them, in the same volume with the more important information afforded, by those from the SOUTHERN
DEPARTMENT. The quantity of valuable matter which I
have been able to extract from the Peninsular Reports is,
I perceive, too inconsiderable for a separate publication.

THE REPORTS to the Board, that require examination and
abstraction, relative to this department, are
    Fraser's and Worgan's, from Cornwall.
    Fraser's and Vancouver's, from Devonshire.
    Billingsley's West Somersetshire.
    The small portion of Dorsetshire, which extends within
the Peninsula, has been noticed, in reviewing the Reports
from that County; and will be mentioned, again, in speaking of Devonshire.

                                        CORNWALL.

CORNWALL.

THIS peninsular extremity of the island might be familiarly described, as a rugged heap of rocks, rising abruptly out of the ocean ; whose waves wash it on every side ; excepting the eastern ; on which it is bounded by the river Tamar, that separates it from Devonshire.

Along the middle of this wrinkled horn, is stretched a chain of mountain heights, with narrow precipitous valleys, on either side of them ; by which their waters are conveyed, principally, to the English Channel ; but in part to the Irish Sea.

As the valleys descend they acquire width ; and, toward the seacoast, some of them spread wide, with flattened bases, and fertile soils, well adapted to cultivation. And a few well soiled plots are found at a greater distance from the sea.

But the lands bearing that description are inconsiderable in extent, comparatively with those of an opposite nature. It may be said, without risk, I think, that Cornwall comprises a greater proportion of *inarable lands,* than any other English County.

"GENERAL VIEW

OF THE

COUNTY OF CORNWALL.

WITH

OBSERVATIONS ON THE MEANS OF ITS IMPROVEMENT.

By ROBERT FRASER, A. M.

MAY, 1794."

THIS is one of the original sketches that were hastily sent in, presently after the birth of the Board. It was printed in May 1794. The materials for it were, of course, collected during the winter months of 1793-4 ; and the MS. hurried to the press, early in the spring ;—as the Reporter himself intimates.

The number of pages—seventy.

NATURAL

NATURAL ECONOMY.

EXTENT.—P. 12. Mr. Fraser makes out, from " Martyn's original survey," the total extent of Cornwall, to be " 758,484 acres"—nearly 1200 square miles.

SURFACE and SOILS.—P. 13. " On the sea shores and the vallies, near the banks of the great rivers, are the chief and almost only seats of cultivation. The higher grounds exhibit, in many parts, the appearance of a dreary waste. The roads of communication with the neighbouring country pass chiefly *through* these higher grounds, or large and extensive commons, and exhibit to the traveller a rude prospect which impresses him with a more unfavourable opinion of this county than it in general deserves. For although the higher lands have little to please the eye, the number and variety of beautiful and well wooded vallies, left me only to regret that the season in which I visited them did not allow me to enjoy their beauty in full perfection. While the strata of the rich and fertile soil, with which the lands of this county frequently abound, invited a more minute examination than my time could possibly afford."

P. 23. " So great is the variety of soil in the county of Cornwall, that to describe it with correctness, would require an history of every parish. I shall just point out the general distinctive characters. Throughout the higher lands, almost generally the upper stratum of soil consists of a light black earth, intermixed with small gravel, the detritus of the granite or growan. Hence they call this soil by the name of *growan*. This soil, on the tops and sides of the mountains, is very shallow, and even on many of the more level and flat extensive wastes, of no great depth. Its natural produce is a thin short heath, and the dwarf or *Cornish furze*."

P. 25. " A great part of the soil of Cornwall consists of a kind of slaty earth, the detritus of the softer species of the schistos. This kind of soil is found in many parts of the west and south-west, near the sea shore, stratified in regular strata : it is also found more inland, in patches. It produces excellent crops of wheat, and particularly of barley. It also makes an excellent compost with the more viscuous earths, sand, &c. as I have seen successfully practised at Clowance, the seat of Sir John Saint Aubyn.

" In the eastern part of the county, there are two very fertile districts which abound with this species of soil. One of these districts is on the north, and the other on the south

south side of the range of mountainous grounds we have described.

" The northern district is on the banks of the Alan and Camel towards Padstow, and from thence west on the one hand as far as the parish of Cuthbert, or on the other north-east to Lanteglos.

" In the south, on the banks of Fowey, around Menabily, the seat of Philip Rashleigh, Esq. from that river, extending eastward, skirting Bodmin Downs to Liskeard, Saint German's, and to the banks of the Tamar, below Hengston, this soil prevails, stratified in many places with reddish and hazle loams.

" These two districts are very fertile. The northern produces immense crops of barley, and may be justly called the Granary of Cornwall. It is from thence, the miners of the west are chiefly supplied with that grain. On the south, plentiful crops of wheat as well as barley are produced. They grow wheat in the northern district, but in the south they have the advantage of procuring lime from Plymouth, which would be very expensive in the north: this they use as a preparation for wheat.

" Besides these two districts, is a very rich tract of land on the banks of the river Fal, around Tregothnan, the beautiful seat of Lord Falmouth, extending to Grampound and Trewithen, the seat of Sir Christopher Hawkins, &c. round by Tregony to Roseland. Another district of excellent fertility is to be found on the river Hel, around Trelowaren, the seat of Sir Cary Vivyan, Anthony, St. Kevran, &c. towards the Lizard Point.

" In the hundred of Stratton, on the north-east of the county, around the town of Stratton, and towards Morwinstow, there is a district of good land, although the greatest part of this hundred consists of waste and boggy land. Towards Penzance also, on the south-west, there is some land which produces very large crops of potatoes and grain.

" In general, the more internal parts are only cultivated in patches, and these surrounded by uncultivated wastes and commons. The most remarkable of which are those extending from near Launceston, almost to Bodmin, and to the south and south-east of this borough. In the parish of Saint Agnes, and the neighbouring mining parishes in the west, there are extensive tracts of waste lands. On the south, towards the Lizard, there is also an extensive tract of waste, called GONHILLY DOWNS."

CLIMATURE.—P. 29. " In Cornwall, the air is milder in winter than in the more internal parts of England, and cooler in the summer months. From its being open to the vast Atlantic ocean, without the intervention of any land almost

almost to the coast of America, it receives the whole force
of the south-west winds, which are remarked to blow, in
general, throughout Great Britain four-fifths of the year.

————Madidis Notus evolat alis
Terribilem picea tectus caligine vultum
Barba gravis nimbis, canis fluit unda capillis
Fronte sedent nebulæ rorant pennæque sinusque.

" This character which the south wind has had in all ages,
it preserves in full force in Cornwall. The air is thereby
more full of moisture, and frequently subject to fogs, but
they are not unhealthy. Ray-grass is earlier than in more
internal parts of the kingdom: the winters very open, last
winter for the only time these five years were the gentlemen
able to procure ice to fill their ice-houses."

" Myrtles grow every where" (?) " in the open air, without the aid of green-houses."

MINERALS.—The natural riches of Cornwall were, in
days of old, hidden beneath its hard-featured surface. But,
during a length of time which history is unable to measure,
they have been sought after,—the principal part, probably,
dislodged,—and scattered over the face of the globe. A
remnant of them, however, is still left; as the annual products of the several mines, that are now worked in the
County, fully testify.

Tin has ever been its most valuable treasure; and, as
Mr. Fraser (who I have understood held an appointment
under the Lord Warden of the Stanneries) has furnished
some interesting information, concerning the mines of
Cornwall,—I will here insert a few extracts on the subject;
—to endeavor to make up for the deficiency of information,
regarding the more immediate subjects of enquiry.

P. 14. " THE MINES of CORNWALL consist chiefly of tin,
copper, and some lead. The strata in which these metals
are found, extend from the Land's End, in Cornwall, in
a direction from west to east, a very considerable distance
into Devon, to the furthest part of the Dartmore Hills.
These strata consist chiefly of the various species of the
schistus, here called killas, and of the granite or growan."

Tin Mines.—P. 15. " Formerly immense quantities of
this metal were found in the county of Devon, and in the
eastern part of Cornwall; and innumerable ancient work-
ings are to be seen on Dartmore, and the adjoining country;
and in the east of Cornwall. In Devon, of late years,
several ancient works have been resumed, and some new
discoveries made, of which we shall give some account in
the survey of that county. In the eastern part of Cornwall
some old works have been lately resumed on Hengston
Down, and Linkinhorn parishes, which formerly produced
                                             considerable

considerable quantities of tin, and promise well to the present adventurers; but at present the chief seat of mining lies to the westward of St. Austle. From hence to the Land's End, the principal mines are to be found in various strata, extending along the northern coast, keeping a breadth of about seven miles.

" Polgooth, the most considerable of the tin mines in the county, lies about one mile and a half west of St. Austle, and has produced, on an average, the last eight or nine years, about two thousand five hundred blocks per annum. This mine remains still as rich as ever. Some others there are working in this neighbourhood, but not of much consequence.

" In the parish of St. Agnes, and its adjoining parish Perranzaboloe, there are a great number of mines, the joint produce of which is very great.

" Kenwin, Kea, and Gwenap, afford considerable quantities of tin. In Gwenap is the mine called Poldice, very ancient and deep. It has yielded sometimes one thousand blocks yearly. It may now with more propriety be denominated a copper mine. In this, and many other tin mines, when they get to a great depth, the tin wears out, and leaves a lode or vein of copper.

" Huel Virgin is another instance of this kind; but as it produces, at her greatest depth of one hundred and sixty fathoms, some tin mixed with copper, I have enumerated it amongst the former. In Redruth, from Huel Pever, a portion of Northdowns and some other parts of the parish, tin is produced. In this parish the ancient mine of Treleigh Wood, though long neglected, will probably be worked again. In Wendron, north-east of Helstone, the tin mines are numerous; and though not individually large, the ancient and present quantities are high. Between Helstone and Marazion, are the tin parishes of Sithney, Breague, Germo, &c. &c.

" Immediately beyond Penzance, is a tin mine worked under the sea. The shafts through which the miners go down to work, is situated nearly one hundred yards below highwater mark. During the greatest part of the flood and ebb tides, if the works were to give way, they would be exposed to inevitable destruction. Further westward from Penzance, there are only small scattered mines, until you come to St. Just, in which stands Cape Cornwall, one of the western promontories. In this there are several mines, the ancient and present produce of which is very considerable. North and north east of Penzance, to St. Ive's Bay, are many mines, and generally much tin, but not at present so productive as of late years: from hence, little, until you reach St. Agnes again.

" I have thus given a general view of the tin mines in the county. I shall also just enumerate the stream works, by which is meant the operation of washing the soil in the vallies, which is found to contain tin in the form of small particles or grains, supposed to be the detritus or abraisions from the greater lodes, either at the first formation of the earth, or subsequent revolutions.

" These are principally in the parishes of Lanlivery, Lux-ilvan, St. Blazy, St. Austle, St. Mewan, St. Stephens, St. Columb, St. Enoden, and Ladbrook, east and north-east of Truro, from five to twenty miles. The principal stream mine in the county is at Carnon, about half way between Truro and Penryn. West of this there are few stream mines.

" All tin ores are brought into metal *in the county* in blocks of from two hundred and three quarters, to three hundred and three quarters each, which are carried to the different coinages held at four stated periods in the year, and not saleable until there passed and marked with the arms of the Dutchy by the officers appointed for that purpose under His Royal Highness the PRINCE OF WALES, to whom there is a duty paid of four shillings per hundred weight, on all tin so coined.

" PRODUCE OF THE TIN MINES.—The annual produce of tin for seven years from 1786 to 1792 both inclusive, has been about 22,000 blocks, amounting nearly to 10*l.* 10*s.* per block, exclusive of duties, in the whole affording a produce of 330,000*l.*

" From the stream ore is produced generally what is called grain tin, amounting to 5 or 600 blocks per quarter, and sometimes more. The superior price of this tin above the common tin at different times, has been from four to twelve per hundred weight.

" Native gold has been found in some stream works, and also, but more minutely, blended in some mines of tin."

Copper Mines.—P. 19. " The produce of the whole of the copper mines amounts to about 40,000 tons of ore, yielding on an average about eleven three-fourths in the hundred, and consequently producing about 4,700 tons of copper. The greatest part of the copper ores are sent out of the county to be smelted, and the price is very variable ; but taking the ore at 8*l.* per ton, the produce of the copper mines will amount annually to about 320,000*l.*

" There are several old mines now unwrought, and which seem to carry a probability of being at some future period renewed. But it is necessary to observe, that many of the
present

present are become so deep and expensive, that they cannot be expected to continue many years; and that it is likely the setting on of those supposed worth being renewed, may not take place until the present deepest and most expensive are given up."

Lead Mines.—P. 19. " There are also some lead mines in different parts of the county, but they are not much worked at present, nor is their produce great, although the ores in general, I am informed, produce a pretty considerable proportion of silver."

Miners.—P. 20. " I found it difficult to arrive at any very accurate estimate of the number of people employed in the mines of Cornwall. Some stating the number of men as high as 22,000, others not more than 8 or 9,000. Including the streamers, who are a distinct body from the miners, the number of men, women, and children, employed in raising the ore, washing, stamping, and carrying it, amount to about 16,000: of these there are from 12 to 14,000 men capable of bearing arms, who are as brave and hardy a race of men, and as much attached to the happy constitution under which they live, and the illustrious family on the British throne, as any description of individuals in the the kingdom*."

Profit of *Mining.*—After mentioning some fortunes, that have been made by mining, the Reporter informs us, p. 22, " In general, the mining business is considered as a lottery, in which there are more blanks than prizes; but these prizes sometimes are so very high, that they excite people to adventure, without making any very accurate calculation of the probability of loss."

POLITICAL

" * From the miners having occasionally given interruptions to the peace of the county, people who are strangers to their dispositions, might be apt to conclude that they were not so loyal, or peaceable set of people. That is far, however, from being the case, their insurrections are almost uniformly on account of either the actual dearness of grain, or from the apprehensions of approaching scarcity. But although they have frequently, from the real pressure, but more often ill grounded apprehension of approaching want, behaved with unpardonable irregularity and violence, yet they have been found, on different occasions, ready to follow the gentlemen of the county to Plymouth, or such other places as their services were required for the defence of the country; and, I am persuaded, that if any such occasion should again present itself, they would be found equally ready to turn out, according to their motto, ' one and all,' in support of their Sovereign and their Country."

POLITICAL ECONOMY.

APPROPRIATION.—For some account of the wild lands of Cornwall, see *State* of *Cultivation*, ensuing. But nothing explicitly appears, as to whether they were, at the time of reporting, *appropriated*, or otherwise; unless so far as relates to the rights of the Duchy.

RURAL ECONOMY.

ESTATES.—P. 31. " The Dutchy lands are still by far the most extensive of those belonging to any proprietor in the county. The lands of the other proprietors are very much intermixed with the dutchy lands, and with each other. Property is very much divided ; there are very few who possess, of landed rental within the county, more than 3000*l.* per annum, exclusive of under ground profits."

Mr. Fraser gives his readers a general view of the lands belonging to the Duchy of Cornwall; whether they are included within the County, or lie scattered, in various parts of the kingdom. Information, this, which concerns not the present enquiry.

TENURES.—See *Farms*, ensuing.

WOODLANDS.

P. 59. "There is a good deal of coppice wood in the county of Cornwall, but little timber. Formerly the tin was smelted only with charcoal ; and this made them cut down their woods, and keep them in coppice; so that there is not a great quantity of timber; although, from what is to be seen around the seats of many of the nobility and gentlemen, there is no doubt that timber will thrive as well in many parts of Cornwall as in other counties.

" The nine ancient parks belonging to the dutchy of Cornwall, were all of them covered with large forest trees, and a great quantity of coppice wood. But, when in the reign of Henry VIII. they were disparked, agreeable to the plan he had adopted, throughout the kingdom, for
encouraging

encouraging agriculture, the wood was mostly destroyed; and what remained, has, by want of care, dwindled almost to nothing; and by some mismanagement, the royal intention of rendering the ground more profitable, by being turned into tillage, has never answered.

"There were formerly, also, some extensive forests which are now covered with the sea, particularly between the Ram-head and Loo, and between St. Michael's-Mount and Penzance.

"In many of the vales on the Tamar, Alan, Camel, Fal, and Fowey, there are considerable quantities of coppice woods, and a good deal of planting, and some old timber, particularly at Tregothnan, Carclew, Port-Eliot, Anthony, Tehidy, Clowance, &c.

"At Trevetho, Mr. Pread has taken a great deal of trouble to raise his plantations, in a situation where they are exposed to both the south-west wind, and also the northerly winds, being the highest ground between the Bristol Channel and St. George's, in that part of the county.

"After making a great number of unsuccessful experiments, at a great expence, in order to find out some hardy plant that would shelter the more tender trees, he was led to try the pine-aster fir, from observing that this tree grew well spontaneously, from some cones which happened to be accidentally scattered in one of the fields near his house. The pine-aster is not a valuable wood, nor is the form of the tree beautiful; but it has been found to stand the sea air surprisingly without being injured. This tree Mr. Pread plants on the highest parts, and very thick in the outer rows of the plantations, and within he plants oak, ash, elm, plane, &c. all of which flourish extremely well under this shelter."

AGRICULTURE.

STATE of Cultivation, in Cornwall.—P. 56. "Those lands in England are denominated waste, which remain in their original uncultivated state, although in many parts of them sheep and cattle are pastured, by those who are entitled to rights in common on those wastes. In Cornwall, as nearly as I have been able to calculate, the proportions of waste and cultivated land stand thus: one-third part of the county is under a regular course of husbandry; one-third is in furze crofts, which are only broke up once in twenty-five or thirty years; the remaining third is wholly

wholly uninclosed, consisting of *marshy grounds*," (?) " intermixed with rocks and mountains, and in the west, with extensive tracts of waste land, almost plains. This third and last part is almost wholly dutchy land."

P. 58. " I am persuaded that there is, at the very lowest calculation, 100,000 acres of waste lands in this county, which may be valued at seven shillings and six-pence per acre, which would produce an annual rent of 37,500*l.* per annum, and leave a sufficiency of turbary for fuel, if properly regulated."

FARMS.—P. 31. " Farms are in general very small. In the eastern and more fertile parts, rents, in general, do not exceed thirty or forty pounds per annum; the greater part not above ten or fifteen pounds per annum; some few are as high as 100*l.* and from that to 200*l.* per annum. All the farms are generally on leases of lives. In the western and mining districts they are very small indeed, chiefly cottage holdings."

OCCUPIERS.—P. 13. " Cornwall possesses the happy advantage of a numerous and public spirited body of gentlemen, who are alive to the improvement of their native county. The people of Cornwall also possess a great degree of perspicacity and acumen; they attend to new improvements: if they find them successful, they are not slow in imitation."

PLAN OF MANAGEMENT.—P. 33. " The management of the land is uniform; here and there an exception will be found. The whole is convertible, sometimes into arable, and sometimes pasture. Arable is sown with wheat, barley, or oats, as long as it will bear any; and then grass for eight or ten years, until the land is recovered, and capable again of bearing corn."

" The best farmers take only one crop of barley after wheat, and lay down with grass seeds, which they dress with dung and earth, and after four years break up again; but in general, with all those lands that are at a distance from their farm-yards, they pursue the same negligent mode above described. They sow them with oats, or barley, as often as they think it will pay the expence of the tillage; and very often, when they have little more than the seed returned, which so impoverishes the land that it cannot be broke up again to any advantage, but remains in furze and brambles for twenty-five or thirty years, reducing it to a dry gritty substance, little more than a caput mortuum.

" While truth demands that I must state this process as the general routine of managing the land in the county of Cornwall, it is also but justice to state, that there are many who pursue a liberal and enlightened course of husbandry, and

and instead of running out the land in the mode I have
described, perceive the advantages arising from supplying
it with proper manure, and introducing green crops between
the crops of grain."

WORKING ANIMALS.—P. 34. "Horses and oxen are
generally both used for the plough, throughout this county
as well as Devon. The country very hilly, not admitting
the use of carts, the horses are wanted for some carriage
or another, and are almost always under the pack-saddle.
The plough team is sometimes four oxen, and sometimes
only two, with always one or two horses as leaders before
the oxen, with a man or boy to drive them."

P. 46. "We have already mentioned that carts are not
made use of in this county. Every thing is carried on
the pack-saddle," (no) "for which both horses and mules
are used. Mules have lately come greatly into use, particularly for carrying and recarrying the produce and
supplies of the mines; for which great numbers are
wanted, and they sell at a very high price. Sixteen,
eighteen, and twenty guineas are given for a mule. The
common horses are small, but very hardy, and well adapted
to a hilly county."

MANURE.—P. 36. "In the eastern part of Cornwall, near
the sea, and the rivers, they bring lime-stone from Plymouth, which they burn with culm from Wales, and use
each as a preparation for wheat. Afterwards the best
farmers use a compost of sea sand, pilchard salt, dung,
and the rotten slaty earth, as a preparation for turnips;
afterwards lay down with barley, for grass seeds. They
use from eighty to one hundred bushels of lime, and from
one hundred and fifty to two hundred horse seams of
compost.

"The manure produced from the bruised and decayed
pilchards, and the Bay salt already used in curing the
pilchards, and declared by the salt-officers unfit for farther
use, is purchased by the farmers, and consisting of oil, salt,
and putrified fish, is a most excellent dressing for land.
It is purchased from eight-pence to one shilling the bushel,
consisting of two *Winchesters*, or sixteen gallons.

"This is the best of all manures, and the cheapest, as it
goes farther than any other; is lighter in carriage, and
lasts very long. It is mixed like lime, with *earth sand*, in
various proportions, as it is easy or difficult to be procured,
from forty to sixty Winchesters, to one hundred and fifty
or two hundred seams of sand and earth; it is left to
ferment and incorporate with the sand and earth, and the
whole frequently turned over and mixed, before it is laid
on the land.

"After

" After a dressing of this kind for barley, on some lands near the Lizard I have been assured that ninety bushels of barley, Winchester measure, have been produced on an acre, statute measure ; and that it is not uncommon to have from seventy to eighty bushels ; seventy-five bushels they consider as a middling crop. Such a surprising fertility may, perhaps, hardly be credited, but it is supported by undoubted authority."

ARABLE PROCESS.—P. 33. "The process they pursue is, in general, by paring and burning the surface of the ground. The land is then dressed with the ashes, and a compost of sea sand, earth, and the scrapings of lanes, in which they throw straw to collect the soil and moisture : to this they add the dung which they save in the farm yard, or which they purchase from the adjacent towns. Their chief dependence is on the sea sand."—Rather say the broken shells of the sea beach.

CATTLE.—P. 45. "Their cattle are chiefly of the North of Devon kind. Although the breed is not kept up in its greatest perfection, yet they are very much in request, and are sold off in great numbers for fattening. Their milch cows are therefore kept chiefly for the sake of rearing young stock, the dairy being very little attended to."

P. 46. "They have a small sort of cattle on the commons, and in many other parts, which they call the *Cornish breed*, which, when fat, do not exceed five or six hundred weight."

SHEEP.—P. 46. "The common sheep in Cornwall are the same as the *neat breed of Devonshire.*" (!) " They have a small species of this kind of sheep in Gwithian, which have very small tails, and a very well formed animal, and small boned."

"A GENERAL

"GENERAL VIEW

OF THE

AGRICULTURE

OF THE

COUNTY OF CORNWALL.

DRAWN UP FOR THE CONSIDERATION OF

THE BOARD OF AGRICULTURE

AND INTERNAL IMPROVEMENT.

By G. B. WORGAN.

1815."*

THIS REPORT has been brought out to public view, under peculiar circumstances. Mr. Worgan's manuscript having been deemed unsatisfactory, the Board appointed three men of " long experience in practical agriculture— natives and inhabitants of Cornwall"†,—to *revise* it. The subjoined extract forms the close of an address to the Board, by the revisers; giving a plain and appropriate Report of the trust reposed in them.

P. viii. " We beg to add, that we believe Mr. Worgan to have been very diligent in collecting materials for his Work. It happened however unfortunately, that he was obliged to perform the greater part of his Survey during winter, by which he not only endured much hardship, but was also forced to take many things upon trust, of which at a more favourable season, he might have been an eye witness. We have taken great liberties with his manuscript, and generally suppressed what was deemed redundant; but

after

---

* The Survey was taken in 1807-8: a prefix to the Report, by Mr. Worgan, is dated, " Bodmin, November, 1808"; and a revision of it, in May 1810. In what year the book was printed and published is doubtlessly known to its printer and publisher. The title page of the copy which I received, in March 1816, is evidently *younger* than the rest of the book.

† Amateurs of a superior class, probably, rather than professional men.

after considerable erasements, alterations, and additions, a large portion of the original is preserved; and to obviate the inconvenience of notes and references, we have in some measure identified ourselves with Mr. Worgan in the body of the Work; taking care that wherever we have made observations, or stated facts, for which we alone are answerable, the initials of our respective names are subjoined.

We are, Gentlemen, with much respect,

Your obedient humble Servants,

ROBERT WALKER.

JEREMIAH TRIST.

CHARLES VINICOMBE PENROSE.

Cornwall, May 1, 1810."

Mr. WORGAN'S QUALIFICATIONS are not so fully set forth, as are those of his judges. By incidental expressions, it appears that Mr. W. was, or recently had been at the time of his Survey, an occupier in the County. He rarely, however, brings his own practice, or his own opinions, forward; —appearing to be most desirous to give a faithful account of the best practice of the County; which is, I conceive, the true principle and business of Report.

His MODE of COLLECTING INFORMATION appears to have been, principally, by a *pedestrian tour* through the County; —the fatigues and privations attending which are not passed unnoticed. To his own observations he has fortunately been able to add much valuable intelligence,—liberally furnished by professional men of the higher class, and well informed amateurs.

Fraser's original Report is not once named!

The number of pages, of the body of the book, one hundred and eightyeight, with an index.

The number of engravings fifteen, together with some wooden-cut diagram. The plates are *neatly* done; and are doubtlessly intended, in those picture-fancying times, " to sell the book",—by raising its price from *five* (its letterpress value) to *twelve* shillings.

A map of soils; properly distinguished by the graver; not by colors.

NATURAL ECONOMY.

EXTENT.—See the original Report.

SURFACE.—P. 5. " The whole county of Cornwall, with a very few exceptions, is remarkable for inequality of surface; ascents and descents follow in rapid succession. Some of

of the hills are very steep, and tediously prolong a journey.
The great post-roads being carried many miles together,
over rugged, naked, and uncultivated heaths and moors,
the traveller is impressed with a more unfavourable opinion
of the county than it deserves."

CLIMATURE.—P. 3. "The general character of the climate of Cornwall, like all other peninsulated situations
lying far to the southward and westward, is inconstancy as
to wind and rain ; and mildness as to heat and cold. Nor
is it so subject to thunder storms as some inland counties
are."

" The cause of more frequent rains in Cornwall than in
other parts of England, is, that for three-fourths of the
year the wind blows from the intermediate points of the
west and the south, which sweeping over a large tract of
the Atlantic Ocean, collects and brings with it vast bodies
of clouds, which, being broken by the narrow ridge-like
hills of the county, descend in frequent showers: but it may
be remarked, that the rains in Cornwall, though frequent,
cannot be said to be heavy or excessive, and perhaps the
quantity may not exceed that of other counties."

P. 5. " *Snow* seldom lies more than four or five days on
the coast; and a skaiter may sometimes pass a winter in
Cornwall, without being able to partake of his favourite
amusement. A kind of languid spring prevails through the
winter, which brings forth early buds and blossoms, raising
the farmers' and gardeners' expectations, to be too often
disappointed by blighting north-east winds, in March, April,
and even sometimes so late as May.

" With respect to the effects of the climate on the human
race, it may be said to be particularly healthy and genial,
and there are numerous instances of longevity."

WATERS.—P. 14. " Nature has been bountiful in her
supplies and distribution of this blessed element in Cornwall, sufficient for every purpose of life. Springs are abundant on the high, as well as the low grounds, which, gli-
ding away to the vallies, unite, and form numerous streams,
rivulets, and some not inconsiderable rivers.

" The most considerable are the Tamar, the Lynker,
the Looe, the Fowey, the Camel or Alan, and the Fal."

SOILS.—P. 8. " The soils of Cornwall may be arranged
under the three following heads:

" 1st, The black growan, or gravelly.

" 2d, The shelfy, or slaty.

" 3d, Loams differing in texture, colours, and degrees of
fertility.

" To attempt to specify these soils severally, with their
endless combinations and adventitious differences, would be

a

a hopeless task, as in the same field they are frequently found to vary exceedingly, in the proportion of their several constituent parts. The first consists of a light, moory, black earth, intermixed with small particles of the granite rock, called *growan*, from grow, a Cornish word for gravel."

P. 9. " The shelfy, or slaty, soil, forming the second class, is by far the most prevalent. It is distinguished by this name, from having a large proportion of the schistos, or rotten slaty matter, mixed with the light loam of which its soil is composed. When the substratum is a schistos, or soft slate, there is a considerable difference in point of fertility, according to the disposition of its laminæ; for, if flat, the surface is more retentive of the manure; but if on its edge, it forms what they call a greedy hungry soil, allowing the manure to wash down through it."—This, let it be said, is valuable Report.

P. 10. " *Loamy Soils.*—There are some very rich and fertile patches of these soils, interspersed in different parts of the county; the low grounds, declivities, banks of the rivers, and town lands, are composed of them. Some of these are incumbent on a subsoil of clay, and partake, more or less, of it in their composition, forming clay loams."

FOSSILS.—P. 12. " Both on the north and south coasts of the county there are quarries of slate, which form excellent covering for houses. The famous quarry called Dennybole, near Tintagel, on the north coast, is supposed to afford the finest slate in England. There are other slate quarries, particularly in St. Neot's, St. German's, and Padstow, but of inferior quality.

" In some parts are strata of freestone, which, in quality, approach to the Portland stone; these are of great value as materials for building, as is another stone of a coarser texture—the moorstone, or granite."

MINERALS.—P. xi. " Of the great variety of mineral and fossil productions for which Cornwall has from time immemorial been so famous, a few only are enumerated, Professor Davy having undertaken to draw up in a distinct work, a Mineralogical Survey of his native County."

POLITICAL ECONOMY.

APPROPRIATION.—P. 46. " Though there be no case, till very lately, of enclosure by Act of Parliament in the county; yet there are numerous instances of parcels of land

land being taken up from the waste, and enclosed with temporary dead fences, for the purpose of securing two or three crops of corn; after which the land is consigned to waste again."

P. 104. " The coarse or uncultivated wastes of this county, though, as elsewhere, of much less value than the enclosed lands, have yet their appropriate uses. A hardy race of herds and flocks depasture the coarse herbage of the more level parts ; goats climb and browse the rocky summits, and the wild conies feed and burrow among the sandy hillocks. The lands in Cornwall, which come under this description, bear striking marks of ruggedness and deformity. Viewing these lands with an agricultural eye, they present a wide field for speculation. The pasturage of the moors, downs, and *crofts*, as the waste lands in Cornwall are called, is generally considered to belong to the tenantry, in the right of some manor or lordships, to which such wastes are appurtenant; and consequently, as in most cases of common lands, the pasturage is by no means equal to the stock.

" A practice has prevailed in this county for many years past, and still prevails, of breaking up detached parcels of the waste lands, paring and burning, sometimes liming or sanding them, and after taking as much corn as they will carry, letting down the temporary fences, which had been raised to secure the crops, and then suffering them to run to waste again, in tenfold worse condition than they were in a state of nature."—This practice has formerly been common to the West of England; and still is continued in different parts of it.

P. 106. " Mr. Wallis, Secretary to the Cornwall Agricultural Society, has favoured me with the following remarks on waste lands.

" ' It is computed that there are in Cornwall, at least from 150,000 to 200,000 acres of unenclosed waste lands, which are appropriated to no other purpose than a scanty pasturage for a miserable breed of sheep and goats throughout the year; and about 10,000 acres to the summer pasture of cattle and sheep: the principal and most profitable tract of these waste lands extends from south to north, between the towns of Liskeard, Bodmin, Camelford, and thence to within a few miles of Launceston; particularly those called Roughtor, Temple, and Alternoon Moors: some of these wastes are stocked in the summer by large flocks of sheep and cattle, which are taken in to pasture by the tenants of the neighbouring farmers, from about the middle of May until October, at 2s. to 21s. per head for neat cattle, and 1s. to 3s. per score for sheep. Herdsmen
are

are employed by these tenants to look after the flocks during these months, whose business it is to restore them to their owners, at the end of the time agreed on.

" ' The sheep pastured on these moors will not remain there healthy during more than a month or two at a time, but become what is called moor-sick, and are removed into the inland country, when the change of a few weeks renders them fit to return to the moors again.

" ' These wastes also produce some furze, and excellent turf, which are the chief fuel of the neighbouring inhabitants.'"

FUEL.—P. 160. " The principal article of fuel in the western parts of Cornwall is turf, furze, and Welsh coals; in the eastern part, hedge and coppice-wood, and coals.— With the poor in Cornwall it may be said, this necessary article of comfort is scarce, and many of them are obliged to take a great deal of pains to collect a scanty burthen of miserable furze (a short kind called the Cornish) from the commons."

MANUFACTURES.—P. 165. " These are very few and inconsiderable; some coarse woollen, several paper, and a carpet manufactory, make up the principal."

For the evil effects of *spinning mills*, see *Poor Rates*, ensuing.

MINING.—P. 179. " The observations which perpetually occur against mining, as an obstacle to improvement, amongst over-jealous friends to agriculture, require some animadversion. Where the mines are situated, they undoubtedly spoil some good land; but the mines are generally situated in the poorest part of our county. In spite however of these natural disadvantages, every where in the neighbourhood of them may be seen excellent crops of corn, crops produced by the labour and savings of the industrious miner; on spots which, in any other county, or under any other circumstances, must have remained in a state of perpetual barrenness: and the fact is, that some of our greatest improvements in agriculture, have been made by profits from the mines, and from the trade which they create and maintain."—For their effect on the poor rates, see below.

POOR RATES.—P. 33. " These, as in other parts of the kingdom, have been some years on the increase."

" In the mining parishes the estates have been so burthened with poor-rates, in scarce seasons of grain, or when employment for the miners has failed, as to be of little value to the proprietors, and the remedy has been resorted to, of calling upon the hundred for aid.

" Carding and spinning were formerly found profitable employments for the female poor; and to the total decline

of

of this business must, in some measure, be attributed the progressive increase of the rates in this county."

P. 166. " From the few manufactures in the county, the poor are not numerous, excepting in the mining parishes; nor are the rates heavy, if compared with those of many other parts of the kingdom: from 2s. 6d. to 3s. in the pound of the rental, may be about the usual rate of the county; but in the mining districts, the poor-rates are very high, sometimes up to 10s. or 12s. in the pound; however, the land proprietors who have been benefited by the mines, have of late years been obliged, by contributing to the rates, to lighten the oppressive burthen."

P. 178. " The serious increase of the poor-rates, especially since the decline of the carding and spinning employment, and since so many burthens have been thrown on it for raising soldiers and seamen, and for the support of the families of militiamen, must operate as a check to improvement."

TITHE.—P. 32. " The great, or sheaf tithes, are for the most part the property of laymen, and are by them farmed out to persons called proctors. The small tithes, which comprise all tithable things, except corn, are in the hands of the Clergy, who in general compound at 1s. to 1s. 6d. in the pound of the rent, for vicarages; and for rectories, where the great tithes also belong to the clergyman, from 2s. 6d. to 3s. 6d. in the pound. In general it may be observed, they are compounded for on very moderate terms, when held by the Clergy; when held by a layman, they are sometimes taken in kind, but generally valued, and agreed for in the field about the time of harvest "

MARKETS.— *Surplus Produce.*—P. 165. " It is generally supposed, that Cornwall is deficient in its produce of wheat, in proportion to its inhabitants; but of barley, oats, and potatoes, it grows much more than it consumes. A great many neat cattle, pigs, and some sheep, are driven annually out of the county."

Weights and *Measures.*—P. 180. " Divers weights and measures prevail throughout Cornwall, to a mischievous and vexatious degree, and are productive of much inconvenience, perplexity, and error. They are a snare to the ignorant, a handle for the artful, and equally injurious to the individual and the community. Of all those who have regard to fairness and justness in their dealings, a uniformity of weights and measures is the universal and ardent wish.

" Corn is sold in the eastern parts of Cornwall by the double Winchester of 16 gallons, and in the western parts by the treble Winchester of 24 gallons; oats by the hogshead

head of nine Winchesters; but with some farmers, the
double Winchester will run 17 or 17½ gallons. Again, if a
farmer in the eastern part of Cornwall buys a bushel of
seed-wheat from the western farmers, it will run short a
gallon or two by the eastern measure. Butter is generally
sold at 18oz. to the pound. The customary perch for land-
measure is also 18 feet; but this is giving way to the statute
perch of 16½ feet."

SOCIETIES.—P. 180. " The Cornwall Agricultural Society
has been frequently mentioned in these papers. It was
established in the year 1793, has been supported with great
spirit, and been attended with very beneficial effects in
the encouragement of agriculture throu*hout the county;
and it has never been in a more flourishing state than at
present."

RURAL ECONOMY.

TENANTED ESTATES.

ESTATES.—P. 17. " Property is very much divided,
subdivided, and vexatiously intermixed; consequently the
proprietors of lands are numerous. Some few accommodations of interchange have conduced to the concentrating
landed property, forming those desirable estates, bounded
within ring fences, always to their greater profit and improvement. The size of estates varies greatly, perhaps
from 20 acres to 500 acres, very few exceeding 400l. per
annum."

TENURES.—P. 18. " The tenure of the land in Cornwall
is generally freehold, excepting lands of ecclesiastical cor-
porations, and ancient duchy land, which is equivalent to
copyhold in fee, held under the Duke of Cornwall, subject
to a small annual rent."

Life Leases.—P. 19. " There is a very considerable proportion of the lands of Cornwall now held by the tenantry
under these leases; but it is certain, that the number of
new grants, or renewal of old ones, is on the decrease; and
seldom take place, excepting under some peculiar circumstances affecting the particular estate, or from some particular motives, arising from the situation of the proprietor."

SODBURNING.—P. 118. " This process is, with much propriety, arranged under the head of Improvement. The
general opinion throughout this county is, that a more
prompt and efficient improvement cannot be devised; and
                                        accordingly,

accordingly, it is the usual and prevailing preparation, for the conversion of old tough lays and furze or heathy waste grounds into tillage.* The process commences with paring the surface of the land, and the operation is performed, either with the common plough, the beating-axe, or the skimming spade. The plough is used for lay grounds, the two latter implements for coarse grounds."

For the process of burning after the plow; see the head, *Turneps*, ensuing.

IRRIGATION.—P. 131. " The county of Cornwall, almost every where presents a surface well adapted to this greatest and cheapest of all improvements. Almost every farm is by nature thrown into slopes and declivities, and very few are deficient in wholesome fertilizing springs and rivulets. Most of the soils are calculated to receive very beneficial effects from this mode of improvement; the declivities of the grounds favour that nimbleness of the current required, and the porous shelfy substrata allow of their being quickly laid dry. These local advantages are not overlooked nor neglected; a great many intelligent spirited agriculturists adopt the practice of irrigation, which may be said to be already extensive, and is still extending."

P 89. " I am happy to see that the watering of meadows is becoming more common in Cornwall."

From these notices, we may pretty safely judge that irrigation is not much practised, by professional men, in Cornwall.

MANAGEMENT of ESTATES.—P. 17. " The management of great estates is generally given to attornies, acting as stewards. As professional men, they are certainly among the most respectable any county can boast ; but, without the assistance of a land surveyor, they must be very incompetent judges of the value and management of estates ; the most eminent are aware of this, and are beginning to act accordingly. Some landlords, when their estates are to be new let, set a value on them, and let them for a term of years by private contract ; but the most usual custom is to let them by public survey to the best bidder, he giving security, if required, for the payment of the rent, and the performance of the covenants."

TENANCY.—P. 34. " The rack-rented farms are mostly held for terms of fourteen years, a few for twenty-one years, and still fewer for seven.

" The time of entry, in the eastern part, Lady-day ; in the western, Michaelmas."

RENT.

* Yes: in that case, it is, in reality, a valuable *temporary improvement*.

RENT.—P. 32. " The rental of the whole county may
fluctuate between 5s. and 50s. per acre, of farms properly
so called.

" Circumstances which affect rents, beside quality of
soil, and aspect, are, their vicinity to sea-sand and to market-
towns."

WOODLANDS.

WOODS.—P. 98. " Whoever confines his travels in
Cornwall to the route of the main roads, will perhaps be
impressed with ideas of its barrenness ; but if the traveller
will made a little deviation from the beaten dreary tract,
he will frequently be repaid by rich woodland scenery. In
the valleys and dells, and on the steep-sided hills, which
form the banks and shores of the rivers and creeks, woods
and coppices abound."

COPPICES.— P. 98. " The coppices are all of the common
oak, and are usually cut from twenty to thirty years'
growth, selling from 20l. to 60l. per acre. The principal
source of profit is the bark, which now sells for 11l. per
ton, and is purchased by tanners in the county. Some of
the wood is converted into poles for farm purposes; but it
may be said the greatest part is charred for the use of the
blowing-houses, and domestic purposes; the brushwood is
sold for fuel. No instance of a copse being grubbed, has
occurred to the Surveyor."

AGRICULTURE.

FARMS.—P. 31. " The divisions and subdivisions of the
lands in Cornwall, as such as may accommodate every
description of men, who for business or pleasure, are disposed to employ their capital in rural concerns ; from the
barton of three or four hundred acres, down to the mere
cottage-holding of three or four acres."

HOMESTEADS.—P. 23. " Many of the old farm-houses
throughout the county are built with mud walls, and
covered with thatch of wheaten straw."

P. 24. " The modern farm-houses are built upon a more
liberal plan, the walls of stone, and the roofs of slate."

" The plan adopted in these buildings is, to throw every
convenience possible under one roof. The building is called

a

a chall-barn; the ox and cow challs being under the chamber for thrashing the corn."—This plan is well adapted to a side-hill situation.

COTTAGES.—P. 26. " It may be truly said, these are very humble dwellings indeed ; of the same materials as the old farm-houses, with only two or three apartments, the upper one immediately under the thatch. I had occasion often, in my dreary walks, during my Survey, to take shelter in some of these miserable dwellings, and found the poor inhabitants busy in placing their bowls, crocks, and pans, to catch the waters pouring in at the roof."

These form a contrast with the cottages of West Devonshire, and of Wales ;—a sister of Cornwall.—Those above described, must surely be the temporary huts of miners. Yet what follows would seem to mark them as permanent dwellings.—" However, the meanest cottage generally has that great source of comfort, a garden, attached to it."

FENCES.—P. 46. " The fences may be divided into three classes. First, Stone hedges, which are principally in the *western part*, and upon the sea coast. Secondly, Earth hedges, capped with stone, brush-wood, &c. chiefly used on the moors, and country round Camelford, to the north. And thirdly, Hedges planted with thorns, hazel, and other brush-wood, or trees, and formed generally of earth alone, faced with sods, or stone. This is the common fence of the eastern part of the county, and is also used, though not universally, in every part."

OBJECTS of HUSBANDRY.—P. 53. " Cornwall not being a dairy country, and the generality of the farmers having an idea, that there is nothing like corn in sacks, for making money, they are very fond of the plough ; and consequently the tillage for white crops is large : perhaps it may be hazarded, that full one-third of the cultivated lands are under the plough."

PLAN of MANAGEMENT.—P. 55. " The general course of crops, in the county of Cornwall, is extremely reprehensible ; there is no circumstance evinces the truth of this assertion more, than the wretched, exhausted, foul appearance of the grounds, laid down with grass-seeds ; nor can it be otherwise, after having been cropped with corn, as long as they will bear any.

" I might mention a few, nay, perhaps many instances, in opposition to this impoverishing system."

WORKPEOPLE.—*Wages.*—P. 159. " The agricultural labourers in Cornwall may be arranged in four classes—farmservants, parish-apprentices, day-labourers, and a class, who do not steadily engage themselves with any master, but take bargains of work of every kind, and wherever they offer.

offer. The women, every where in the county, perform a
large share of the rural labours, particularly the harvest-
work, weeding the corn, hoeing turnips, potatoes, &c. attending the thrashing-machines ; by the latter business they
have more employment in the winter than they formerly
had.

" The prices of service and labour may vary a little in
different parts of the county, but the following is nearly
the average :—the farm-servants have from eight to twelve
guineas a year, and their board ; maid-servants from three
to four pounds per annum. The price of labour, of the
hireling class, may be stated from nine to twelve shillings
per week, with the privilege, which is a very general one,
of a limited supply of corn for the consumption of his family,
at a fixed rate, considerably under the market price. The
women have from sixpence to eightpence per day."

Food of Workpeople.—P. 160. " The most common food
of the labouring class is barley bread with tea, and salted
fish. The pilchards, which are caught in great abundance
on our coasts in the autumn, and cured for foreign markets,
supply our poor also with wholesome and nutritive food ;
they are salted in the months of August and September,
and thus are preserved throughout the year ; they give a
relish to the breakfast or tea, and are eaten with potatoes at
the other meals of dinner or supper.

" Many of the labourers, however, who gain better
wages, or who are not burthened with large families, use
wheaten bread, and are able to indulge in some meat for
their pasties, as well as for their suppers, after their daily
labour is done. They have an advantage also, from the great
plenty of fish with which the markets abound. Indeed, the
poor are in general better fed and clothed than in most
other counties."

WORKING ANIMALS.—P. 146. " In no county does the ox
stand in higher estimation for all kinds of work, than in
Cornwall. Oxen are every where to be met with, drawing
the butt, the wain, and the waggon, on the roads; in the
fields, the plough and the harrow. They are brought to the
yoke and bow, at about the age of three years, and worked
to the seventh or eighth year ; they are shod, or, as it is
provincially termed, *cued,* are extremely docile and active,
going at a full trot with the empty carriages in the bustling
seasons of hay-time and harvest, and driven by a little boy,
who chears and excites them in their labour by the song and
the goad: bulls in some few places are worked with oxen.
A plough team generally consists of four, some of six, or of
four with a horse to lead."—See *Horses,* ensuing.

IMPLEMENTS.—*Wheel Carriages.*—The Reporter speaks,
at

at large, on "Wheels;" but touches lightly on "Horse-and-Crooks," or *packsaddle carriage;* which, unless on the sea-coasts, is the most practical mean of conducting the business of arable farming. See Fraser, on this topic, aforegoing.

True it is, however, that wheel carriages are much more used, in Cornwall, than in West Devonshire; where the " Cornish wain" and waggon might, in many instances, be adopted.

The distinction, between *Cornish* and *English* carts and waggons, lies in the former having *no bodies:* the bed or bottom of the carriage has *no sides;* each wheel having only an arch of wood bending over it; equally to prevent the load from bearing upon it, and to defend the load from its action. A *top load,* as of hay or corn, is not only conveniently loaded, but, by its lying low, is less liable to be overturned, on the sides of hills, than one which is more elevated.

The other carriage contrivances—the *sledges* and *slide butts* of Cornwall, resemble those of West Devonshire.

Plows.—P. 42. " The turn-wrist ploughs are in common use throughout this county" (?); " indeed the hillyness of the land makes them indispensable; nor do any people know better how to make good work with them."

I wish Mr. Worgan had given the history and contruction of the turnwrist plow of Cornwall. I have long recommended the use of such an implement in West Devonshire, and it seems somewhat extraordinary that the circumstance of its being in " common use," in Cornwall should not, there, have been known. It was, in 1807, perhaps, of recent introduction.

MANURE.—*Pilchards.*—P. 123. " The maritime situation of Cornwall presents the farmer with three valuable manures, fish, sea-sand, and ore-weed. We will speak of these respectively.

" In some years the farmers who live in the vicinity of fishing towns, have an opportunity of buying the *bruised and small pilchards;* these being deemed unfit for market are rejected, and called ' caff;' four cart-loads, of twelve bushels, are considered as the proper quantity for an acre. The usual mode of management is to bury the caff in a pile of earth, deep enough to secure it from dogs and hogs, adding to the pile a sufficient quantity of sand, well mixing and turning all together, after having lain some months. Without this practice, the fish would not decay sufficiently for perhaps a year or two. The fish are sometimes used alone; they are then spread thinly over the ground before the plough, and turned under furrow. I have been told,

that

that one pilchard, cut up small, will amply dress one square
foot of ground. They used to be sold for about 9s. or 10s.
a butt-load" (cart load); " they are now risen to 15s. or
20s. per load. *The bruised fish*, immediately from the cellar doors, are considered as infinitely preferable to *the refuse
of the salted fish.*

" The fishery having of late years been greatly checked,
by the failure of the foreign markets, considerable quantities of fish have been converted to manure ; but this is to
the great loss of the adventurers: if, however, the bounty
which has been granted to merchants on the export, was
extended to all fish taken by adventurers in seins, and sold
for manure, it would enable the proprietors to put out their
seins for the express purpose, and thereby both the interest
of the fisheries, and the advancement of agriculture, would
be greatly promoted ; and, it is presumed, that the influence
of the Honourable Board would be well employed in obtaining this great national object. The old salt which has
been used for curing the pilchard, and judged to be no
longer fit for that purpose, is advantageously applied for a
barley or a turnip crop,—twenty to thirty bushels per acre.
It is commonly hand-sown, in the manner of corn ; and it
should remain on the land five or six days before the seed
is sown. It is best adapted to light lands, particularly
furze-crofts.

" Twenty bushels per acre have been strewed over grass
lands, and over a wheat crop, in the month of March, with
evident advantage. The price of this salt used to be six-
pence per Winchester bushel, which weighs 84 lb. and is
called a *gun*, but cannot be had now under tenpence or one
shilling.

" Another article of manure is obtained from this useful
fish—this is the liquor which drains from it while under the
process of curing, consisting of blood, brine, and some oil
which escapes, and which is caught in pits ; the diligent
farmer carts this away in casks, for the purpose of pouring
over and mixing with his piles of earth and sand, which it
greatly enriches."

Sea Weed.—P. 125. " The most approved management
of this excellent manure is, to carry it fresh from the shores,
and spread it on heaps of earth, then to cover it with sand ;
after lying in this state some time, it is completely incorporated, by turning and mixing it with the other ingredients,
which make together a rich compost. If the wrack is
suffered to lie in a heap by itself, it heats, and becomes
so extremely putrid, as to attract flies, and generate mag-
gots.

" Some farmers carry the plant alone, in small heaps,
over

over a field they intend for barley, spread it, and turn it immediately under furrow; for if they are not diligent and cautious in this work, the sun and the wind exhale its rich moisture; it shrinks almost to one half, and is then little worth."

Sea Shells, or *Sea Shell-Marl*; improperly named " Sea Sand;" which, without the shells, or the mucilage which appears to be formed from them, is of inconsiderable value, I believe, as manure.—P. 126. " Here is another inestimable treasure which Cornwall derives from her great extent of sea coast. Long experience has proved, that sea-sand is a fertilizer of the soil; good for corn, causing it to kern, or corn well, as well as for pulse and roots, and excellent for pasture. It is in such estimation with farmers, as materially to affect the value of estates, according to their nearness to, or distance from, this manure. It is frequently carried fifteen miles inland. Cornwall has perhaps a greater variety of shelly sands than any other county in Great Britain : Dr. Borlase enumerates thirty-two different kinds. It is in greater plenty, and, in general, of superior quality on the north coast than on the south; but there are very few places where one kind or other may not be had.

" The relative degrees of the fertilizing powers of sea-sand depend on the different proportions of calcareous and animal matter of which it is composed, but its effects on soils are mechanical, as well as chemical. There is indeed mixed with some sand, a slimy earthy matter, the recrement of leaves, wood, and perhaps animal remains; this, I believe, is what they call *lig*, or *liggan*, and has been found to be a good manure for potatoes. That sand which is in highest estimation is taken up about Falmouth Harbour, in Carrick Road; it is a coral sand, and of large size, effervesces strongly with acids, and lies longer in the ground, in an undissolved state, than any other. This sand is much in use about Truro, Probus, and the vicinity. There is also a much finer sand taken up at the mouth of the harbour, less calcareous, and less in request. All along the north coast, from the Land's-End to Bute Haven, the sands are very good, containing a large proportion of shelly fragments.

" *Application.*—When sea-sand is applied alone as a dressing, which is sometimes the case, both on grass and arable lands, they call it a clean sanding; but the most usual method is, to mix it in the compost with earth and dung. The quantity used per acre will depend on the ability of the farmer, and the distance he has to carry it. Three hundred sacks, of sixteen gallons each, is deemed a good sanding for a Cornish acre, and it is applied in all the intermediate quantities, even down to thirty sacks."

P. 128.

P. 128. " It is computed, that upwards of 54,000 cart-loads of sand are carried from Padstow harbour only, and that the expense of land-carriage of sand, for the whole county, amounts to upwards of 30,000*l.* per annum."

Lime.—P. 128. " The only places where limestone is found in Cornwall, and burnt for manure, are in the parishes of South Petherwin and Veryan; the former is an old work, and, about half a century ago, the lime was much used in the neighbourhood of Launceston; it is still carried on.

" The Veryan limestone was discovered on the lands of the Rev. Mr. Trist, in 1796, and has been wrought by him ever since, both for manure and masonry."

ARABLE CROPS —P. 57. " The corn crops cultivated in this county are wheat, barley, and oats; the avena nuda of Ray, in Cornwall called pilez, is also sown in small patches in the Western District; it bears the price of wheat, and is used for fattening pigs, or for rearing calves.

" The green and root crops, commonly cultivated by the farmers in Cornwall, consist of red and yellow clovers, tre-foil, and rye-grass (called eaver in Cornwall), turnips, ruta-baga, potatoes, and in some instances the flat-pole, or drum-head cabbage."

Mr. Worgan has spoken, at some length, on the culture of those crops. I perceive in his account, however, very little of consideration, that differs from the West Devon-shire practice, which I have described in detail; and, to re-peat it, here, would be an unnecessary encumbrance on my present Work.—What little *variation* of practice which I may find, in Mr. Worgan's Report, I will notice, in this place.

WHEAT.—*Succession.*—P. 59. " Wheat too frequently succeeds a crop of barley; in this case, the barley stubble sometimes receives a manuring of earth and lime, or com-post, which have been collected and mixed during the sum-mer round the hedges of the barley field; this is carried out and spread upon the stubble, and after one ploughing, the wheat is sown and harrowed in."

NAKED OATS.—P. 66. " *The Avena Nuda, provinci-ally called Pilez, or Pillas.*—The culture of this grain is confined to the western parts of Cornwall, and it is gene-rally the farewell crop to a piece of ground that has been completely exhausted of vegetable food by preceding crops of potatoes, wheat, and oats. This plant grows something like the oat, but the straw is much finer, almost as good as hay; the grain is small, about the size of a shelled oat, and weighs as heavy as wheat per bushel; it is excellent for feeding poultry and pigs. One gallon of pilez mixed with

with 20 gallons of potatoes, makes a rich fattening mess for pigs."

P. 67. " This grain has been chiefly grown in black, moory, moist soils; the tillage, culture, and harvest, the same as for oats."

TURNEPS.—P. 67. " The commencement of the grand preparation of the land for this crop, is announced early in June, by the whole district being enveloped in smoke, exhibiting at once the very general establishment of the turnip culture throughout the county, and the almost universal assent as to the utility of the practice of paring and burning for them : many farmers would despair of success in the attempt to get a crop, without their beat ashes, nor do they think the benefit is confined to the turnip crop only, but shrewdly anticipate its good effects in one or two succeeding crops of corn. The ground, which is generally a lay from four to seven years or more old, having been stripped or velled, is dragged, harrowed, and rolled, then briskly harrowed a second time with two horses, which operation (provincially *running tabs)* is executed with a rapidity that would astonish the farmers in those counties where they use three or four heavy fat snail-paced horses. Here, a boy mounts one of the two light horses used, for the purpose, and keeps them at a smart trot until the earth is entirely shaken from the roots, and the weeds are made light and fit for burning ; and now all hands, men, women, boys and girls, with short-headed rakes, having long wooden teeth set about three inches asunder, begin at the leeward side of the field, and rake the light well-harrowed tabs into small heaps; a wad of straw, or a bit of furze, is put into each heap on the windward side, and just before they go to dinner, they set fire to all the heaps got together in the morning. In the afternoon the business of raking, priming, and firing, goes on until a late hour in the evening, for it is a kind of harvest work, bustle bustle, for a month or six weeks.

" They are very careful that this process of incineration shall be carried on by a smothered heat, so that the roots appear rather charred, than consumed by flame."—In this particular, the men of Cornwall have much merit.

CULTIVATED HERBAGE.—P. 83. " A mixture of red clover, from 5 lb. to 8 lb., of trefoil from 2 lb. to 4 lb. and from six to ten gallons of rye-grass, or eaver, are the grass-seeds most usually sown with either barley or oats in the spring, for a hay crop the next year, after which, the lands are left in lay during two or three years. Many farmers add to the above, from 2 lb. to 4 lb. of white clover, and some few, a pound or two of rib-grass, by way of providing for the deficiency

ficiency of pasture when the red clover fails, which it naturally does after the second year."

GRASS LANDS.—"Natural Meadows."—P. 89. " The lands in Cornwall which come under this description, are to be met with in the vicinity of towns and villages, on sheltered slopes, in valleys, level and moist situations, on the banks of the great rivers ; and most farmers select a field or two near their homesteads, which they appropriate to the feeding their calves, or milch cows, early in the spring."

Natural Pasture.—P. 89. " The natural pastures consist of the uncultivated lands, which in Cornwall are distinguished by the names of moors, downs, crofts, and wastes. Nature has clothed them with two species of furze ; with ferns, heath, and the poorer kinds of grasses, which are depastured by cattle, sheep, and goats ; to the latter of which animals a great proportion of the coarser lands, particularly in the mining districts, are adapted."

" *Cultivated Pasture.*"—P. 90. " These are such as have borne two or three successive crops of corn, with the last of which grass-seeds have been sown : they remain as pastures from two to three, or five years, before they are again broken up for corn."

HOPS.—P. 83. " Have been much grown in Roseland, but the culture is on the decline : the duties increasing, and hops from Kent and Hampshire finding their way here, the Cornish hop-grower is discouraged ; for except he can sell at 15d. per lb. it is a losing crop ; half a pound to a hill is a great crop."

ORCHARDS.—P. 93. " In sheltered situations, many of the farms are furnished with orchards ; but I am sorry to find, that in some of the western parts of the county, the orchards have of late years been very much neglected, and that the cultivation of them in general does not prevail so much as in Devonshire."

It is a well established fact, I believe, that the climature of Cornwall is ungenial to orchard produce ; unless in the more sheltered parts of its eastern quarter.

HORSES.—P. 153. " Few horses in Cornwall are kept for ostentation, or to live in idleness and luxury. The gentleman's horse often disdains not to draw the cart or the plough, when not wanted for the coach or the chariot, thus the produce of his labour far exceeds his maintenance. The farm horses are excellently adapted to the hilly surface of the county ; they are rather small, but hardy and active, and it may be truly said, they eat no idle oats. Most farmers keep up their stock, by breeding a colt or two annually ; but I believe that one eighth of the horses used for the saddle

saddle and draught, are brought into the county by eastern dealers."

CATTLE.—*Breed.*—P. 140. " The native cattle of Cornwall are very small, of a black colour, short horned, coarse-boned, and large offal; very hardy. There are certainly cattle now, in different parts of the county, which partake of the above qualities. I have met with black cows and bulls of a small size, weighing perhaps from three to four hundred."

This is, to me, peculiarly interesting intelligence. It sufficiently shows that the three more mountainous portions of this island have been, beyond the ken of history or tradition, inhabited by *Celtic tribes,* and *black cattle:*—while the lower, more genial and fertile parts, have been occupied by different races of men and animals.

It has been said, with what degree of truth I cannot affirm, that, in every mountainous tract of Europe, a dialect of the Celtic language is spoken.—May we venture to suggest, on such slender evidence, that the CELTIC TRIBES were, aboriginally, the *natural,*—or, by long-established habits, in far distant times, became the *voluntary* INHABITANTS of MOUNTAINS; and that black cattle and goats have ever, or long, been their accompanying domestic animals?

P. 139. " Two opinions prevail in Cornwall, on the breed of cattle for slaughter; the one is, that symmetry of shape, proportional length, breadth, and roundness, with a fine bone, thin hide, and small offal, with the colour of a blood-red, form the basis on which the properties of health, hardiness, and an aptitude to fatten, principally depend. The prime North Devon cattle comprise these essentials, in a degree sufficient to satisfy any breeder or feeder of reasonable expectations.

" The other opinion is in favour of the boney system. ' Give me,' says the still prejudiced farmer, ' a snug tight bullock, with a stout frame of bone, to build my flesh and fat upon; and a good thick hide to keep out the cold and wet: they be strong and hardy, Sir, cost little or nothing in keep, range the moors, live and thrive on furze and heath in summer, and in winter too, with a little straw; get as fat as moles when put on turnips; the butcher likes 'mun (them); they tallow well, and hide tells in the tanner's scale.' Such is the colloquial information you will get from the more rustic sons of agriculture, who form a pretty numerous class in Cornwall. As to Leicestershire lines of beauty, they tell you, in homestead plainness, ' they won't do here;' and to argue with them, would be taking the bull by the horns."

There appears, to me, to be more good sense and practical knowledge

knowledge, in those remarks, than the Reporter of them would seem to be aware of. The occupiers of the Cornish mountains, having nearly lost their native breed, require a hardy race to repair their loss;—such as they can rear on mountain pasturage;—not a dainty animal that requires soft and sweet herbage, to gratify its palate, and pamper its delicate constitution.

Markets for Cattle.—P. 138. " The markets in the different districts have some influence in governing the size of cattle, large meat not being so saleable as smaller. A bullock of from three to five hundred weight, is more marketable than one of eight or nine hundred weight. The larger breed of cattle, of which there are great numbers in Cornwall, are annually sold to graziers and contractors; to the former, in store state, to be driven into Somersetshire, or other grazing counties; and to the latter, when fattened on turnips or summer grass, to be slaughtered at Plymouth for the Navy."

Here, we perceive the true economy, or plan of management, of the Cornish cattle farmer. He rears cattle on mountain pasturage, to be fatted on the marshlands, and other rich grazing grounds, in more genial climatures.

On the circumscribed plots of low lands, in Cornwall, let the occupiers choose their own plans of husbandry.

DAIRY.—P. 140. " It has been already stated, that the dairy does not constitute a very important department in the husbandry of Cornwall. The cows appropriated to this use, are mostly of the Cornish or Devon breeds; there are also many Jersey und Guernsey cows, their milk yielding a cream of a richer colour and quality.

" My intelligent informant, Mr. Sickler, tells me, that in the western part of the county, from the river Hayle to the Land's End, the greater part of the high land is appropriated to the keeping of cows; the soil is the black growan, the farms from 20 to 60 acres of grass land, with large portions of waste, which are called crofts; these crofts are kept up all the summer for the cows, into which they are not turned till about the first week in November, and remain there until about three weeks before they calve, when they are brought to the fields, which having been kept up, are now full of grass: this feed, with an oaten sheaf now and then, serve to raise their milk; but they have no other dry meat, nor turnips through the winter, while in the crofts; the grass there being plenty and of good quality.

" The farmers whose property these cows are, and who also keep them in the above manner, have nothing to do with their produce excepting the calf; for should a farmer
possess

possess twenty cows, he lets them, nearly all out, to labourers and poor people, at 6*l*. or 8*l*. per cow, for seven or eight months; four, six, eight, or ten cows to each person. The hirer pays his cow-rent by milk and butter, for which he finds a ready market and sale in this populous district. When a cow approaches her time of calving, the farmer is obliged to take her, and provide the person with another, flush in milk. These cow-renters generally have a piece of ground allotted them by the farmer, on which they grow potatoes; with these, and with the scalded milk which has yielded cream for the butter, they fatten a great many young porkers."

Mr. Worgan touches on the Cornish method of *making butter*, from *scalded cream*. But I perceive nothing in his account that would add, beneficially, to the practice of West Devonshire.

SHEEP.—*Breed.*—P. 148. " Curiosity induced me to see what they still call the true Cornish breed of sheep: the animals pointed out to me as such, have grey faces and legs, coarse short thick necks, stand lower before than behind, narrow backs, flattish sides, a fleece of coarse wool, weighing about two or three pounds, of eighteen ounces; and their mutton seldom fat—from eight to ten pounds per quarter.

" From the various crosses which have been made by rams, introduced at different periods into Cornwall, of the Exmoor, Dartmoor, North and South Devon, Dorset, Gloucester, and Leicester sorts, a pure Cornish sheep is now a rare animal."

P. 151. " On the towans, or sand-hillocks upon some parts of the north coast, Peran-Sand, Gwythian, Phillack, and Sennan-Green, they have a small compact sheep, the mutton of which is of a peculiarly superior flavour, weighing about eight pounds per quarter; the fleece is of finer wool, approaching the quality of South Down; the fleece may weigh two or three pounds. The grass of the towans is of a short sweet nature; but in the mornings and evenings innumerable small turbinated snails come out from the sand, on which these sheep *seem* to make a delicious repast, and on which *it is said* they get fat. I saw them myself eating these snails."—This is *interesting* information.

" The mongrel flocks that live upon the downs, heaths, and moors of this county, summer and winter, are a hardy race, weighing about 10 or 12 lbs. per quarter; the mutton very good; bearing fleeces from 2 lb. to 4 lb. each, of moderate quality; some have horns: they are not nice in feeding, for I have seen them cropping the furze and the heath, as well as depasturing the grasses; they are as active as
deer,

deer, and if they cannot leap over a fence, they will contrive to creep through it."

P. 150. " Only two breeds of sheep, distinct and of pure blood, have been observed by the Surveyor in this County, the Leicester and the South Down."

Folding Sheep.—P. 152. " Very little folding: certainly nothing worth mentioning, in the practice."

Washing Sheep.—P. 152. " Sheep are not washed in this county: early in the spring their tails are trimmed, to keep them clean."

GOATS.—This is a species of livestock, which abounds more, in Cornwall, than in any other district of the island; not excepting Wales. Goat's flesh is, or was a few years ago, an ordinary article of butchers' meat, in the Cornish markets.—In the Report which I am now closing, they are merely mentioned, incidentally, in speaking of mountain pastures. See p. 544, &c. aforegoing.

SWINE.—P. 155. " A large white, long-sided, razor-backed pig, I have been told, was the true Cornish breed: this has been crossed by the Devon, Suffolk, and Leicester breeds, which have taken off length and sharpness, and added breadth and depth; a mixture of Chinese and Suffolk, is another variety."

" I have to observe, in honour of the swinish race, that notwithstanding the general jumble, I have, in my progress thought this county, met with very few bad pigs; they are all of them good grass-eaters, orchard and lane grubbers," (!) " and with this liberty of ranging, and a little kitchen offal, keep themselves in good store condition."

After enumerating different varieties of Cornish pigs, the Reporter adds, as from his own experience,—p. 156. " All these sorts are good graziers, living well in the house on cut grass, and a little wash once a day."

DEVONSHIRE.

DEVONSHIRE.

THE COUNTY OF DEVON is strongly marked with NATURAL DISTRICTS.

1. NORTH DEVONSHIRE :—an extensive and valuable tract of country; bounded by the Bristol Channel, on the north; and, on the south, by the wild lands in the environs of the mountain height of Dartmore.

2. The FOREST of DARTMORE and its ENVIRONS : a barren blotch which occupies a wide space, toward the center of County.

3. WEST DEVONSHIRE:—situated between the Dartmore Hills, and the western bound of the County. In natural and agricultural characteristics, it assimilates with *East Cornwall;* the two forming the adjacent valleys of the Tamar and the Tavey; and comprizing a well defined district,—whether in an agricultural, or in a mineralogical view.

4. SOUTH DEVONSHIRE,—or the "South Hams." This district occupies the southern limb of the County. It is bosomed by the sea, from the mouth of the Teign, eastward of Torbay, to that of the Tamar, at Plymouth. Its northern boundry is the skirt of the Dartmore mountain ;—its north-eastern point being cut off, by the Haldown and Mamhead hills, from

5. The VALE of EXETER :—The garden of the west. This rich, beautiful, and genial district, is singularly well defined :—on the west, by a line of infertile heights ; on the north, by the extended environs of the forest of Exmore; —on the east, by the Blackdown hills, which sever it from Somersetshire, and, thence, by a continuation of tall steep sided hillocks to the English Channel; which bounds it on the south.

6. EAST DEVONSHIRE.—This minor portion of the County assimilates with the western extremity of Dorsetshire; in like manner as its opposite extreme unites with East Cornwall; the four points forming two well defined natural districts; the limits of that which is now under notice being the line of hills, last mentioned, and the western termination of the Chalk hills of the southern Counties. It is strikingly marked by its steep-sided, flat-lopt, *table hills,* separated by narrow, and, in some instances, fertile valleys. Its principal agricultural product is that of the *butter dairy.* —See DORSETSHIRE; article, *Dairy.*

" GENERAL

"GENERAL VIEW

OF THE

COUNTY OF DEVON.

WITH

OBSERVATIONS ON THE MEANS OF ITS IMPROVEMENT.

By ROBERT FRASER, A. M.

MARCH, 1794."

THE ABOVE can scarcely be deemed a fair title, for an agricultural survey that is prosecuted, professedly, by *Counties*. It covers more ground than it can rightfully claim. The pages to which it is prefixed give a tolerable "General View" of the *South Hams*, and "some account" of the *Forest* of *Dartmore*, in Devonshire; but certainly not of the County at large. What little is said of North Devonshire, East Devonshire, and the Vale of Exeter, ought to have been suppressed. Even what is reported of the two first named districts, is so ill digested, and so full of incorrectnesses, as to render difficult the task of abstraction.

The subjoined is the *unstudied* apology offered by the learned Reporter,—or, judging from the *manner* of it, by an officious friend,—for the inadequacy of his performance. —It appears in a *detached* "Introduction."

"The zeal *which* I felt to promote, to the best of my abilities, the important objects for *which* the BOARD OF AGRICULTURE was constituted, led me to undertake the survey of two districts, *which*, from their great extent, the variety of objects to investigate, added to other circumstances with *which* it is needless to trouble the Board, must necessarily render my Report not so complete as I could have wished. I hope, however, that it will meet with that candour and indulgence of *which* it stands so much in need."

In a section, of one page,—headed "the Midland and Northern Districts,"—the Reporter, himself, apologizes for his neglect of those most interesting parts of the County.— P. 65. "Having said so much on the Southern and Western Districts, I shall be under the necessity of being very short

in

in my account of these districts.   The lateness of the season, and my being obliged to go to Cornwall, prevented me from making an extensive tour through this part of Devonshire, a great part of which, I am informed, is *extremely beautiful and romantic.*"

I do hope that CAPTAIN FRASER, whom I formerly knew as a friend, will not take unkind the requisite animadversions of a Reviewer.—His education, early habits, and turn of mind, well befitted him for various employments; but certainly not for the difficult undertaking that was imposed upon him, by his inconsiderate countryman.

The number of pages—seventyfive.

A *well lined* map of the County; to show its prevailing soils, &c.

NATURAL ECONOMY.

E XTENT.—P. 8.—Mr. Fraser computes the extent— " from Don's map, with the aid of the surveys made for the *new map of Devon,* by Mr. Tozer,"—to comprize " 2,552 square miles ;" and adds—" I think, therefore, that Devon may be computed at about 1,600,000 acres."

CLIMATURE.—P. 9. " The distinguishing characteristic of the climate of Devonshire is mildness."

" This mildness and temperature of climate is more particularly felt in winter."

P. 10. " From this advantage in point of climate, there is little interruption to vegetation in time of winter.   It has the appearance almost of a perpetual spring.   In the south of Devon, the snow seldom lies on the ground in severe winters more than three or four days.

" In the high grounds of Dartmore, and in the northern parts of the county, the climate is not entirely so mild ; but the difference is not so great as the inhabitants themselves apprehend.

" On Dartmore and the high grounds adjacent, snow continues in severe winters, sometimes ten days or a fortnight, but seldom longer."

SOILS.—The " Map of the Soil of Devonshire;" which is prefixed to this Report, does credit to its draughtsman ; in as much as it gives a tolerably just idea of the natural division of the County, into *more fertile* and *less fertile* lands.   But the sweeping tracts of " dunstone"—" clay"— " white chalk"! (lined as strong loam) and " strong loam" —serve only to induce an erroneous conception of the soils

of

of the several districts, which they are made to cover.—An extraordinary intermixture of lands prevails, throughout the County.—In the letterpress, it is true, some attempts are made to separate the intermixed lands; but rarely with due effect.

The subjoined passage, I conceive, is the only one capable of conveying useful information to my readers.—Speaking of " red marl loam," the Reporter says,

P. 12. " This singularly rich stratum has a marked, but irregular progress, through different parts of this district;" (South Hams) " which I shall beg leave more particularly to describe.

" It begins in Plymstock, near Plymouth; from thence it holds its course to Yealmpton, Modbury, Aveton-Gifford, Ugborough, Ermington, Harburton, Ashprington, Stoke Gabriel, Paington, Marldon, Cockington, Coffenswell, King's Cerswell, Combeinteign Head, Stokeintein Head, Teignmouth, Bishopsteignton, Mamhead, Powdersham, Exminster, North Tawton, Bow, Collumpton, Clysthaydon, Broadclyst, Broadninch, and several other parishes adjoining the east."—The truth is—this valuable variety of land is found in all the more fertile parts of the County.

POLITICAL ECONOMY.

APPROPRIATION.—A considerable porton of this brief Report relates to the *Forest* of *Dartmore;* considered as part and parcel of the DUCHY of CORNWALL.

Its existing state, in 1793-4, and the improvements to be made in it, are the topics of discussion. The first object of the writer, it pretty evidently appears, was to show that the duchy lands were, then, of little or no value,—either to the community, the duke of Cornwall, or to those whose domestic animals they maintained, nine months in the year. And the second, to point out their capabilities, as a wide field of improvement.

Neither of those designs, however, has, to my comprehension, been fulfilled. And having looked, in vain, for incidental remarks, concerning those wild lands, which might tend to correct, corroborate, or add, to my own, on the same important subject, I pass over the ground, in silence; lest I should otherwise be inadvertently led into expressions of censure *.   The

* For my own account of the existing state, and means of improvement, of Dartmore and its environs, in 1804,—see my WEST of ENG-LAND; Ed. 1805.

The only information that I have gathered concerning the general head now under consideration, that can, I conceive, be useful to my present Work, is the following passage; which I insert, here, on the judgement of the Reporter.

P. 65. "From the best information I could obtain, it appears to me that fully one fifth part of the county of Devon is waste land which would amount to 320,000 acres; all of which, except perhaps, some part of Dartmore, is capable of improvement."

RURAL ECONOMY.

ESTATES.—P. 17. "The freehold property of the county of Devon is very much divided, perhaps more than in almost any county of England. The large tracts of country granted to the ancient barons, have been subdivided amongst their descendants, or sold, so that, a few families excepted, there are no very great proprietors, but there are a great number of gentlemen of easy independent fortunes, who pass their time chiefly on their own estates, and live in great harmony with each other, and with the respectable yeomanry in their neighbourhood."

TENURES.—P. 16. "In general, throughout the whole of the county of Devon, the land" (of the larger estates) "is occupied" (held) "by tenants for the terms of ninety-nine years, determinable on three lives."

P. 18. "Leases on lives afford an irregular kind of income to the proprietor, and the holder frequently pays so great a proportion of his little capital for the purchase, that he has only a small sum left, not perhaps sufficient to stock and work it with advantage. When these leases also hang on one life, it tempts the tenant to run out of the ground, from the apprehension of being obliged to pay a fine, on renewal, equal to the improvements he may have made.

"On the whole, I found that the people in general are very desirous to possess themselves of leases on lives, from their considering it as a more permanent and independent species of property."

TENANCY.—P. 17. "These life-estates are frequently let out for terms of seven, fourteen or twenty-one years, but many occupy their own."

AGRICULTURE.

AGRICULTURE.

FARMS.—P. 17. " Farms in general are small, from twenty to forty acres being the common run of the holdings in this county. Of late, the farms are beginning to increase, and one farmer is sometimes found to occupy two, three, or more, of these tenements ; but I found very few farms exceed two, or at most three hundred acres."

OCCUPIERS.—P. 17. " In the South Hams in particular, the respectable class of yeomanry is more numerous than in any district of England I have seen. They live in great comfort, and exercise without parade, that old English hospitality which the refinements of modern manners have banished from many other parts of the kingdom. I observed with much pleasure, the attention they paid to their various dependants around them, and their kindness to the poor."

PLAN of MANAGEMENT.—P. 20. (South Hams.) " The greatest part of the land in this district is under a course of husbandry; scarcely any of the land is kept wholly in grass, but is alternately under grain and grass, and no part is kept unbroken up by the plough, except the water meadows. The rotation of crops for this purpose, varies according to the skill and industry of the farmer."

WORKPEOPLE.—P. 43. (South Hams.) " Wages are one shilling a day, and a quart of cyder. In harvest, the wages much the same, with as much cyder as they chuse to drink."

IMPLEMENTS.—P. 43. " Carts are little used for the purposes of agriculture."

MANURES.—P. 22. (South Hams.) " In the southern part of this district, they are at a considerable distance from lime, and they therefore make use of *sea sand* * as a substitute for lime, to the amount of one or 200 seams per acre (each seam contains two bushels) which they mix with earth, the scrapings of the lanes, mud from ponds, bottoms of the ditches, &c. and above all, when they can collect it, with rotten dung, to the amount of about 120 seams each ; all of which is generally carried on horses backs: on account of the country being hilly, carts are very little, or not at all, used, for the purposes of agriculture.

" The best farmers spare no labour or expence, to collect these different manures, and mix them with each other with great care. This compost of dung, mud, and sea sand,

is

* See *Cornwall*, p. 541, aforegoing.

is reckoned a most excellent manure, and more lasting than the composts with lime."

TILLAGE.—" *Skirting and Beat-burning*."—This operation is, in its effects, much the same as " paring and burning." But being performed by *implements* of *draft*, I here consider it as a kind of tillage, and insert Mr. F.'s slight sketch of it.—P. 21. (South Hams.) " This process, which, I believe, is peculiar to Devon and Cornwall, has been uniformly practised in this part of Devonshire for near 300 years; and whether the farmer intends to sow wheat or turnips, this is the uniform mode of breaking up grass lands.

" Skirting is properly a sort of half ploughing, as *two or three* inches of surface of the ley is left unturned, and is covered by the furrow, cut very thin, with the grassy side downwards; so that the grass side of the furrow, and the narrow balk which is left unturned, being in contact, soon rot by the fermentation of the sward. If for turnips, it is turned thin about Midsummer, and is immediately worked; if to lay to rot for wheat, in the fall of the year it is turned a little deeper. The operation is performed by a wing turned up the furrow side of the plough-share, which cuts the furrow the breadth the farmer chooses; generally about four inches and a half.

" This operation is sometimes, also, performed by spading, or pairing with a breast plough; sometimes, also, with a *mattock*. But skirting with the plough is generally practised. The best time for this operation is before Christmas, if the grass can be spared: the winter frosts bring it into fine order, but in general it is done in summer.

" After laying some time, it is cross cut with the plough and well worked with harrows, and either left to rot, or again harrowed and rolled with much care and labour, until the broken sod is made very light, and the earth shaken from the grassy roots and weeds, which are then raked together by hand into heaps, and burnt, which process is called *beat burning*."

CATTLE.—On this, the most valuable species of domestic animals,—taken all in all,—I find nothing that is satisfactory.—I copy the following passage; as it requires correction.—P. 32. (South Hams.) " They are of the *short horned* breed, and have been in the south part of Devon from time immemorial. The best of this breed are excellent milkers, and answer well for either work or fatting. The oxen are generally turned off to fat at five or six years old, and run up to eight, ten, and twelve hundred weight. These cattle are larger and heavier than the North Devon breed, the beauty of which is so famed and well known, throughout the kingdom."

The

The South Ham breed of cattle,—if that district can be said to have one,—differs as much from the true shorthorned variety of the North of England, and the South of Scotland, as it does from the longhorned breed of the Midland Counties. The cattle seen in South Devonshire are mostly bought in, from the Cornish mountain, and Dartmore-side, breeders; who can rear them until they become fit for work, or the dairy, much cheaper than the arable occupiers of the South Hams. In a general view, they appear, either as an unimproved, or as a deteriorate, variety of the North Devonshire breed.

SHEEP.—P. 33. (South Hams.) "There are to be found in this county both the polled and horned sheep. The polled sheep, generally called nott, or knott sheep, are of a large size, with long combing wool; shear on an average about eight pounds each. More attention has hitherto been paid to the wool, than to the carcass. The wether sheep run from fifteen to thirty pounds a quarter; the average about seventeen pounds a quarter."

" GENERAL VIEW

OF THE

AGRICULTURE

OF THE

COUNTY OF DEVON;

WITH

OBSERVATIONS ON THE MEANS OF ITS IMPROVEMENT.

BY CHARLES VANCOUVER.

1813." *

THIS is the fourth Report, by Mr. VANCOUVER, that has come under my examination,—and the sixth time I have

* At the head of a column of errata (chiefly verbal) stands the subjoined notice.

P. xi.—"*Lymington, Hants,* 1st. *Oct.* 1807. From the Author's itinerary engagements in a distant part of the kingdom, there was an absolute impossibility of conveying the proof-sheets for his examination, without creating a delay in the execution of the work, which was much wished to be avoided by the Honourable Board. The consequence is the following Errata, which he requests the reader will take the trouble of correcting with a pencil, before he enters upon the perusal of the work."

have found it requisite to bring his performances forward,—in the course of the toilsome—though rarely irksome—work, which I am now bringing to its close.

What I have said of Mr. V.'s Report of *Hampshire* (p. 302, aforegoing) is applicable to this of DEVONSHIRE. It is strikingly characterized by a waste of words; and a perplexing arrangement of ideas.—As a literary composition, it resembles those modern performances, that are rapidly written, for the amusements of general readers;—rather than a well considered work, to convey instruction to practical men. The descriptions are mostly too diffuse; covering pages, where sentences, only, were required. Well sounding words glide from subject to subject, in the same paragraph; without the required points. Long periods, ill pointed, are intolerably teazing. The attention is engaged in discovering the meaning of the words, when it ought to be estimating the justness of the ideas which they are meant to convey. By this chaotic style of composition, unassisted by an index, the business of reference and research is precluded.

In an "Introduction,"—from which the subjoined is an extract,—the author thus speaks of his performance.—P. v. "In prosecuting an inquiry of this nature, it may be proper to observe, that the Surveyor enters on the examination of the agricultural practice and general interests of the county, with a mind totally unfettered by any opinions or practices prevalent in its rural, commercial, or manufacturing departments. So little indeed has his attention been engaged of late years in the consideration of rural improvements (unless on the great scale of cutting down the woodland, and clearing the forests in Kentucky) and the interests of a community necessarily connected therewith, that on the commencement of the present Survey, he found it necessary to re-peruse, with considerable attention, the two Reports he formerly had the honour to prepare under the sanction of the Honourable Board, on the Agriculture of Cambridgeshire and Essex, before he entered upon the present inquiries. This recurrence to former labours, has tended to disperse the confusion of ideas which pressed upon his mind, in his endeavours to retrace impressions which once interested, although from lapse of time and other engagements, became in a manner disregarded."

North Devonshire, would seem to have been Mr. Vancouver's principal STATION; and that being the only agricultural district of the County that I have not maturely examined, I have bestowed especial attention on Mr. V.'s Report of it. In what he has written of the other districts,

I

I have found very little to add to my own accounts of them;
not much to corroborate ; and nothing to contradict.

The number of pages four hundred and eighty.

A map of the County; *colored,* to show the different
varieties of *soils :*—the veins of *limestone,*—deposited
beneath them, being judiciously marked *with the graver;*
distinguishing those pointed out, by Mr. VANCOUVER, in
North Devonshire, &c. from those of the South Hams,
&c. which were previously marked, in a similar manner,
on Mr. FRASER'S map :—a valuable addition, this, to a
map of the soils of a County or District.

Twenty or thirty other *engravings !*—of much less consideration ;—though some of them are well drawn, and
well executed ; and, by *some purchasers,* will *therefore* be
admired, perhaps extolled; "as the best part of the book"!

NATURAL ECONOMY.

EXTENT.—P. 1. " The most modern calculation ex-
tant (or at least such as has been within the reach of
the Author of this Report), assigns an area of 1,595,309
statute acres, or 2493 square miles, including water-
courses, for the surface territory of the county."

ELEVATION.—P. 278. " The relative heights of the most
prominent and lofty points upon or near the Forest," (of
Dartmore) " with well known eminences in the surrounding country, must afford considerable satisfaction, as the result of data deduced from the trigonometrical survey,
conducted by Colonel Mudge, and to whose politeness
the Surveyor is much indebted for the important communication. These heights are all in reference to the
common level of the sea. Where they are returned certain, there can be no appeal beyond this statement; and
where the return is made probable only, it will, in most
cases, be found within a few feet of the existing elevation,
and, at all events, sufficiently accurate for our purpose.

	Feet.
Butterton Hill, near Ivy Bridge, ...	1201 certain.
Rippon Tor, east of ditto, ...	1545 ditto.
North end of Cawsand Beacon, ...	1792 ditto.
Highest part of Dartmoor, called Caw-sand bog, ...	2090 probable.

Summit, 5347 feet.
3

Mean height of the Forest of Dartmoor, 1782 feet.
" The

" The height of well known hills in the country below, and within reach of the moor-winds, are,

	Feet.
Black Down, near Tavistock, ...	1160 certain.
Highest land, near Modbury, ...	600 probable.
Little Haldon, ...	811 certain.
Great Haldon, ...	800 certain.

Summit, 2211
3

Mean height of the most commanding situations in the country below Dartmoor, ... } 737 feet."

CLIMATURE.—*North Devonshire.*—P. 4. " The climate here, although very indulgent in respect to many parts of England, is by no means comparable to the temperature which characterizes the seasons in the southern parts of the county."

Yet it is related, in the succeeding page, that " the Dutch broad-leaved double-flowering myrtle, as well as the more delicate aromatic and narrow-leaved sorts, constantly flourish in the open air, and are found not unfrequently to constitute a part of the garden hedges." And we are further told, in p. 7, that rock cantelope melons—in size and flavor equal to any raised under glass (in Bidiford or its neighbourhood) were produced " in the open air."—I have not, I confess, been so fortunate, as to see or hear of any thing to compare with those extraordinary circumstances, in the most favored situations, near the southern coast.

SOILS.—The subjoined are *Mr. Vancouver's districts of soils;* taken from his *map.*—See aforegoing.

1. " North Devon."
2. 2. " Free or dunstone."
3. 3. " Moor lands."
4. "South Hams; dunstone, limestone, slate and clay."
5. " Granite gravel."
6. " Red sandy loam, marl, grout and dunstone, including the flints of Haldon and Woodbury."
7. " Chalk,* flint, sandstone, limestone, &c."
8. " Dartmore Forest."

The part of *Exmoor Forest,* which extends within the
fortuitous

* A few fragments that have been scattered from the Dorsetshire Hills.

fortuitous limits of Devonshire, wears the same *color*, on this Reporter's map, as the more valuable lands of " North Devon."—That bleak, black, barren margin of the forest appears as *green* as the land of myrtles and melons.

Not only the soils of Devonshire; but the other prominent subjects, belonging to its natural, political, and rural economy, are reported by the above-enumerated *Districts;*—are, of course, repeatedly brought forward; without, perhaps, furnishing the reader with any increase of information; changes of well rung words being his only recompense.

The section, " Soil," by passing, in effect, through *seven distinct Reports*, is lengthened to two sheets of letterpress. I have bestowed some time on examining it; and the following are the particulars which, I conceive, are proper for insertion, here.

P. 11. (North Devon.) " In those places where the upper parts of the rock are of a splintry texture, rising below in rhomboidal or cubical fragments, exhibiting in their fracture a dun, or rather liver-coloured appearance, and the small stones on the surface are found to be encrusted with a brown, or rather yellowish kind of ochre, it is generally called free, or Dunstone land.* Here the soil is of a good depth upon the shillot; is of a bright hazel colour, of a tender friable nature, and generally esteemed to be the best corn land. When the rock crops out in very thin lamina of a smooth and glossy appearance, with a rotten shivery fracture, it forms the basis of the soil or surface-mould, the subsoil of which is continued to various depths, according to the resistance the under stratum of shaley rock may have presented to the slow decomposing process which this species of rock seems gradually to be undergoing, and thence forms a stratum of brown-yellow, or blueish-coloured clay, corresponding in colour with the rock below, and from which all the clayey parts of this country are unquestionably derived.

" The soil here, from the coolness and moisture of its bottom, is generally considered more favourable to the culture of grass than of corn. The surface of the un‧ enclosed and extensive moor-lands or commons, which occupy so large a proportion of this district, lie generally at a greater distance from the shillot or shaley understratum before described, than in the cultivated parts of the district. In some instances, the substratum of the wastes

---

* *Good land* (deep rich soil, on absorbent subsoil) might be deemed the best definition of " Dunstone."

wastes is formed of a hard and durable species of whin
and freestone mixed with white acre (that is, quartz), and
a species of granite gravel, covered with a strong growth
of black heath, rooted in a thin staple of dry brown peat
lying immediately on the rock, and from which it is pared
by the inhabitants for the purposes of fuel. Where water
has been arrested on the sides of hills and low places,
peat, to a greater or less depth, has been produced; but
in no instance is the quantity of peat or turf to be regarded as considerable."

P. 15. (North Devon.) "The land between the Taw
and the Torridge rivers, bounded southwardly by the
parishes of Wear Giffard, Henshaw, Yarnescombe and
Atherington (and formed by a continuation of the same
ridges, although considerably lower, which mark the leading features of the country lying east of the Taw river),
consists with little variation of a well stapled, tender, grey,
and brown loam on the shillot, shaley, and schistus rock,
and well calculated for a system of convertible husbandry.
Upon the low grounds a stratum of loam or brown potter's
clay occurs between the surface soil and the rock, and
which at Fremington is of a considerable depth, and much
used in the coarse potteries of Barnstable and Bideford.
Westward of the Torridge, and through the parishes of
Northam, Bideford, Abbotsham, Alwington, Littleham and
Land-cross, the same general character of country continues, although the soil occasionally varies from a grey and
brown loam to that of a light red or cedar-colour, and lying
on a deep stratum of rubbly loam, highly shaded with, and
partaking of the same hue."

The subjoined passage is extracted from " District II.
Free Dunstone." It stands at the head of the section, and
may be fairly considered as a proper specimen of the lands
of that district.

P. 16. " The soil in the parish of Little Torrington, consists of a loose free loam of a good staple, on a deep rubbly
subsoil. At Frithlestock it abates considerably of this good
quality, and in many places is found to consist of a moist
grey loam on a tough yellow clay, much better adapted to
the culture of oats than of barley. Through the parishes
of Monkleigh, Buckland Brewer, the free or Dunstone
soil prevails, occasionally varied with small veins of a
cedar-colour on a substratum of rubbly loam, in which
there are sometimes found black flints or firestones, particularly in the parish of Buckland Brewer. This bright
hazel-coloured land, generally denotes a favourable disposition for the culture of wheat, barley, oats, turnips and
clover."

It

It were difficult to discover a *specific difference*, between the many-soiled lands, described in the two last extracts, to warrant the *distinction* by which they are separated. Those extracts, which immediately follow each other, rather serve to show that they inseparably belong to one and the same natural district ; and, indisputably, to the same agricultural district. There is no line of demarkation between them;—other than what the painter has been pleased to draw.

P. 20. (District II. " Dunstone Land.") " The soil in the parishes of Shepwash, Buckland, Filleigh, Petrockstow, Marland, and Langtree, may be divided into three classes : the first consists of a loose friable loam of a good staple, lying upon the schistus rock ; the second, a well stapled reddish brown loam, on an understratum of rubbly clay, which is found finally to rest on a hard shillot rock, breaking up into excellent building stones ; the third class chiefly occupies the vallies and low grounds, and is composed of a thin grey loam, on a subsoil of white, yellow, and blue clay."

Here, no " dunstone land" appears :—it being a variety of land, it would seem, which is rarely to be met with in District II. ; judging, I mean, from the few instances of its being mentioned, in the thirteen pages-set apart for that section. Even the red loam, which is pretty common in North Devonshire, is more frequently, I think, noticed ; but not once (if I mistake not) in " District I. North Devon."*

To a man who is desirous to purchase an estate, or to rent a farm, of a particular description of land, in the County of Devon, Mr. V.'s details may be highly useful ; to assist him in the search. But, to the agricultural public at large, their value is less considerable. I therefore refer those, whom they may particularly concern, to the work itself.

FOSSILS.—*Limestone.*—This truly estimable fossil abounds in Devonshire :—not in extensive ranges of heights, as it is found in many parts of the island ; but rather in " veins," or narrow lines, with little elevation, above the adjacent lands.

In tracing those lines, and marking them on his map, Mr. Vancouver has much merit, and deserves well of the County. Mr. Fraser set the example, and made a valuable beginning, in the southern districts ; but Mr. Vancouver has greatly extended the search ; and has, I apprehend, pointed

* Those notices are creditable to Mr. Vancouver, as a *Surveyor and Reporter of soils ;* but not so, as a *delineator of districts.*

pointed out the principal places in which limestone may be raised, in the several districts of the County.

Wood Coal.—" Bovey Coal."—Of this peculiar fossil, Mr. Vancouver gives an interesting account.—P. 70. " After following a western branch of the Bovey river from the commons of Widdecombe in the Moor, we descend into a plain bounded on the north by a range of craggy hills in the parish of Bovey Tracy, and westwardly by the high lands of Ilsington and Heytor rocks. In this plain or valley is found rising to the surface, and with a gentle dip or inclination to the southward, distinct strata of a fossil substance called Bovey coal. This lies in several parallel seams at the distance of six or eight feet from each other, and to the depth of 60 feet."

P. 71. " The Bovey coal exhibits a series of gradations, from the most perfect ligneous texture to a substance nearly approaching the character of pit coal, and which by exposure to the air breaks into thin laminæ, assuming the appearance of the grey or common schistus rock of the country, but in which are indistinctly to be traced the original fibrous vegetable of which it was composed, and which is generally the roots and trunks of the *pinus sylvesiris*, or Scotch fir ; the former being distinguished by the workmen as root; the latter as broad coal, flattened into parallel layers by the compression it has undergone; and frequently rising to the thickness of a large folio volume. The upper strata of these veins are of a greyish colour, and resemble a mass of the shaley rock ; the lower assuming a black coal colour, and showing between its leaves, but particularly on its transverse fracture, the same smooth glassy appearance common to stone-coal. The root coal has a broken and wavy texture. On examination of some of the roots of the bog timber in the neighbouring morass, a faint smell of turpentine was still retained, and the turpentine appeared in an inspissated state between the fibrous substances of the wood; hence there is reason to suppose that, next to the woody fibre, resin is the substance that, in vegetables passing to the fossil state, most powerfully resists alteration, but which once effected, becomes the substance whence bitumen is produced. Among the clay, but adhering to the coal, are found lumps of a bright yellow resinous earth extremely light, and so saturated with petroleum, as to burn like sealing-wax, and when not carried too far, to produce an agreeable and aromatic vapour. This, by analysis, appears to have, resin 55, asphaltum 41, earthy residuum 3. Large pieces of the board and root-coal have been taken up at different depths in the Stover plantations, and at the distance of
about

about two miles from the present coal-pits. This substance
is also found diffused in very small pieces through all the
beds of potters' clay in the parishes of Teigngrace and
King's Teignton."

Mr. V. attempts the rationale of this extraordinary fossil.
His ideas concerning it are very ingenious; but do not
bring conviction to my mind   I am well acquainted with
the site of the Bovey coal quarry, and the surrounding
country.

Pipe Clay.—Bovey Pits.—Mr. Vancouver notices a use to
which the refuse clay is put.—P. 43. " The waste clay dug
out of these pits is converted into a beautiful white durable
brick, by the admixture of about one-third part of sand.
The clay is first dried in the open air, and then pounded and
mixed dry with the sand, and afterwards worked and tempered together. It is necessary the bricks should be well
dried before putting them in kilns."

Iron Stone.—P. 54. " A considerable quantity of very
rich ironstone is annually sent from the neighbourhood of
Combe-martin to Mr. Raby's iron-works at Llenethy, in
South Wales."

MINERALS.—On this division of the natural economy of
Devonshire, Mr. Vancouver is less intelligent, than on the
two which precede it. Prosecuting the search, *by Districts;*
—and picking up, here and there, items of information,
without afterward *classing* them, so as to place, in separate
points of view, those which pertain to the *different species
of metals*, that are raised, or were raised at the time of
survey, in the separate parts of the County;—the chaotic
aggregate becomes unpleasant to examine; and, in a degree,
unprofitable to the student, who looks for something of the
nature of scientific information.

POLITICAL ECONOMY.

APPROPRIATION.—P. 271. " It seemed a very desirable object, on the commencement of this Survey, to
ascertain with as much correctness as possible, the extent of
waste land belonging to the respective parishes in this district: to this end, very particular inquiries were directed in
all the different parishes; but so extremely vague and contradictory were the accounts received, together with the
doubts entertained of the moors, in many places, being
appurtenant to particular estates, or open in common to all
the inhabitants, that the subject at length became much
confused,

confused, and involved in contradiction, and it was judged better to pass over those inquiries, and direct the attention more fully to the quality of such wastes, let their boundaries and extent be what they may, or the right of ownership in them be in whom it would."

P. 272. ("North Devon.") "According to the prevalence of drought or moisture in the surface and substrata of these wastes, their herbage and common covering is found to vary, and may generally be divided under the following heads:

"The first, of a soil formed of a tender light coloured loam when dry, but when moist, assuming a brighter brown colour, and lying upon a brown and grey clayey subsoil, veined and mixed with portions of small rubbly or argillaceous gravel. This land is always covered with a close and sweet herbage, on which the sheep are found to lie very hard, and to keep it constantly pared down. Through the loose veins of under-strata, springs occasionally rise, creating small spots of rushes, and a few square yards of boggy ground; its surface is otherwise free from any incumbrance of furze, fern, or heather, and seems as loudly to demand, as it appears willing to requite the labours and fostering care of the skilful husbandman.

"The second denomination of these wastes may be called furze and fern lands: a portion of granite gravel is always found to have place in the composition of their soil and substrata. This is generally of a drier nature than the one just noticed, and seems well adapted for a system of barley and turnip husbandry.

"The third class is that where a dwarf growth of heath or heather is found, but which is nearly smothered and eaten out with a variety of coarse aquatic grasses. The soil is here generally composed of a dark moor or vegetable mould, lying on a close and deep stratum of blue and yellow clay, intermixed with a coarse argillaceous rubble, and a reddish coloured clay or fox-mould, equally retentive of, and generally charged with an undue proportion of moisture.

"A fourth class is composed of a red spongy substance, answering, in all appearance, the character of a red Irish bog. This is always kept highly saturated with water, and is found of various depths, on a substratum of peat, which again ultimately rests on a compact bed of white, blue, and yellow clay. By conducting the improvement of this class in the manner its nature and situation demand, very great advantages must inevitably result, not only from the undertaking itself, but its effects on the
surrounding,

surrounding, and even more remote districts, will gradually be felt, and found to prove highly beneficial to them.

" The last class of wastes necessary to notice in this place, is, that where the surface is composed of a dry, inveterate brown peat, of two or three inches in depth, and lying immediately on the granite and whinstone rock, or rather the loose flat stones answering to such characters. This peat having all the appearance of the red bog in a dried and compressed state, is seldom found to yield any thing but a strong luxuriant growth of ling, or black heather, and which is generally pared close to the stones or rock, for the purposes of fuel. In this appropriation, this class may be said to have attained the very acme of its nature, as it appears to be invincibly opposed to every effort of improvement by planting, or by any other means for the purpose of cultivation.

" The ancient moorlands in the district will be found very nearly to agree with the description given in Class No. 3, with the addition only of their surface generally having been left under ridge and furrow, and consequently bearing evident marks of a former cultivation.

" The present value of these lands may in general be rated at from 4s. to 6s. per acre. It will be difficult to affix any thing like a standard value for the intercommonable lands, but on considering the relative value of the different classes, and placing the two last at 0, unless for the purposes of turbary, the preceding ones will rank at five, eight, and twelve shillings per acre, and all applicable to the purposes of feeding sheep and store cattle. No doubt can possibly be entertained as to the propriety of enclosing and cultivating these old moors and waste lands ; but until some farther disposition is manifested in the country to improve and cultivate such as are already held in severalty to particular estates, it will be idle and fruitless to suggest any measures for enclosing and cultivating those intercommonable lands, which at this time occupy so large a portion of the area of the district."

P 278. (Dartmore.) " The forest of Dartmoor rises with a bold majestic grandeur over all the surrounding heights, which compose an extremely rough and broken region in this part of the county of Devon. After attaining the summit of this waste, it is found to spread generally (at least in comparison with the leading features of the country below) into an extended plan, and so much of this stupendous eminence as is called The Forest of Dartmoor, is divided by certain meets and bounds from the commons belonging to the surrounding parishes, and which, by calculation from the map of the moor, made by Mr. Thomas
Gray,

Gray, in 1796, is found to contain 53,644 acres. This forest belongs to His Royal Highness the Prince of Wales, as appurtenant to, and parcel of the Duchy of Cornwall.

" The duty of the Surveyor on this occasion is deemed to be exclusively confined to the examination of the native properties of the forest, and how they may be most effectually and permanently improved to the public benefit, the advantages of the revenues of the Duchy, and above all, to the melioration of the climate of the moor, and consequently to that of the country below."

Neither in the Reporter's description of *his* Dartmore,— nor in the means of improvement which *he* proposes,—can I perceive *that* Dartmore which I have traversed, again and again, in different directions; and seen from different points of view, I apprehend, every square mile of its surface. Nor can I discover any thing peculiarly applicable to its melioration ;—the draining of its bogs excepted ; and this is a species of improvement which is, now, pretty generally understood.

MANUFACTURES.—Formerly, different branches of the woollen manufacture,—mostly, it would seem, of the lighter kinds,—florished in different parts of Devonshire ; and some of them have lingered on to the present time. *Women* have, there, been employed, as *weavers*, during a length of years.

The mischiefs of complicated *machines* of manufacture, that are worked by water and children, to the exclusion of women, are shown in the following extract.—P. 464. " The want of employment for the females, particularly in the western parts of the county (and where they are not so much in the practice of making bone lace as to the eastward), is very much felt and complained of. About fifteen years since, it is notorious, that a good spinner would earn 3s. 6d. per week ; her time is now, through the general failure of that employment, too frequently spent in rummaging about for a few loose sticks in order to procure a scanty supply of fuel."

In the Vale of Exeter, *lacemaking* still florishes.

FISHERIES.—P. 75. " The *herring* fishery which was formerly carried on in these parts" (N. Devon.) " to a considerable extent, is now, from the caprice of that animal in forsaking the shores of the district, in a great measure lost, not only as a valuable supply and change of food for the inhabitants, but as an object of no small moment in curing for exportation."

P. 76. " A few herrings are still found to frequent the coast in the fall of the year, but they are very small both in size and quantity, and even this supply is equally uncertain."

The

The *salmon* fisheries, too, have declined, in the north, as in the west, of the County;—owing, as the Reporter imagines, to the nefarious practice of destroying the young samlets, in their passage from the breeding grounds to the sea. And to that unpardonable crime, the decline is no doubt, in some measure, to be ascribed.

SEA EMBANKMENT.—At the mouth, and on the banks, of the joint estuary of the Taw and the Torridge, an extent of unembanked *saltings*, or mudbanks open to the sea, and of a superior quality, is said to be ripe for embankment.

This is a subject to which Mr. Vancouver has paid much attention (see EASTERN DEPARTMENT—*Waterlands* of *Cambridgeshire*) ; and his observations concerning it, in the volume under review, are entitled to transcription.

P. 299. " From the attention which the author of this Report has had an opportunity of paying to the nature and formation, as well as to the mode of embanking, cultivating, and appropriating salt-marsh in this country, Ireland, Holland, and America, no instance has occurred, or come within his knowledge, of any improvement being made on a crude, tough, black sea-mud. This substance when dry, is the most rigid and untractable of all argillaceous compounds ; on the contrary, salt-marsh, properly so called, when ripe and ready for embankment, is the mildest, most temperate, and permanently fruitful soil of any in the universe; and which before its embankment is, or should be raised to nearly, if not quite, the height of the ordinary flow of the spring-tides. The sea-mud, on the contrary, is covered every twelve hours with a depth of twelve or fifteen feet of pure, or nearly so, sea-water, and when embanked, lies perhaps a little above the line of low water mark.

" In proportion as all embankments from the sea have been made between these points of high and low water mark, they have answered or disappointed the views of the undertaker. Throughout all the seven townships of Marsh-land in Norfolk, the whole of which at different periods have been rescued from the sea, the earliest embankments, and those in the interior of the district, are uniformly lower in their general level, and of an inferior quality, to the level of country enclosed by a line of embankments made at a subsequent period. In this manner, the latter embankments continue on still higher plains to the present line of sea-coast, where the last of any importance that has been made, was effected by Captain Bentinck a few years since, by the enclosure of a very large tract (perhaps) twelve hundred acres. This lies upon a higher level than the interior enclosures, and soon after its embankment was esteemed by far the best of all.

" Throughout

" Throughout all the embanked marshes of Cambridge-shire and Lincolnshire, a premature enclosure from the sea has never failed to disappoint the expectations from the enterprise. Had the lots below where the new Custom-house is built in Dublin, been left open to the tidal-waters (and which are there very turbid, and highly charged with sediment) from the end of the north wall and towards the sheds of Clontarff, and the expense of the enclosing mounds and walls been applied in continuing the north wall in a line nearly parallel with the south one, the waters of the Liffy, thus confined in their descent, would have scoured out and preserved a deep channel for their discharge into the bay of Dublin, and perhaps contributed to the removal towards deeper water, those bars so justly dreaded and so highly injurious to the shipping and commercial interests of that important city: at all events, the navigation and access to the port must have been greatly benefited by a work of this nature; and at this time, or perhaps a few years hence, such a deposition of sediment would have been made by the unrestrained flowing of the tides over what are now the old enclosed lots, as to have rendered them equally rich and fruitful with some of the most favoured spots in the neighbourhood of that metropolis.

" These observations may be considered as rather foreign to a report on the agriculture and internal improvements of the county of Devon; but the Surveyor has been led to the discussion, in order to illustrate his idea of the dif-ference between salt-marsh, ripe and fit for exclusion from the sea, from that which may be prematurely enclosed, and also of embankments made with a view of enclosing portions of invincibly steril and shear sea-mud."—Those are well matured remarks which bring conviction to the mind, at sight.

ROADS.—The following description of a *washway road!* is welcome to a place, here. See my MIDLAND COUNTIES, on *such* roads.

P. 371. " As to the application of water, as a means of preserving, it has been so far beneficial (if such it may be called) as to wash and scour away every particle of clay or loam which would have tended to unite the loose stones together, and wear them down to a more even and regular surface than is at present exhibited by most of the side-hill roads and lanes in the country. As there are but few wheel carriages to pass along them, the channel for the water, and the path for the pack-horse, are equally in the middle of the way, and which is altogether occupied by an assemblage of such large and loose stones only, as the force of the de-scending torrents have not been able to sweep away or remove."

SOCIETIES.

SOCIETIES.—P. 439. " An Annual Meeting of the South
Devonshire Agricultural Society is alternately held at Tot-
ness and Kingsbridge. Neither this Society, however, or
that formerly instituted in North Devon, are kept up with
that spirit, perseverance, and liberality, which the nature
of such institutions require, and by which they are conducted and preserved in other parts of the united kingdom."

RURAL ECONOMY.

TENANTED ESTATES.

ESTATES.—P. 80. " If we except a few individuals,
who, in reference to others, may be considered as owners
of large estates, the landed property in this county will
appear to be very much divided; a large proportion of it
being in the hands of a respectable yeomanry, and other
estates belonging to the sees of Exeter, York, and Salisbury, the Dean and Chapter of Windsor, the Universities,
and the Duchy of Cornwall, forming no inconsiderable part
of the whole county."

TENURES.—*Church Leasehold.*—P. 84. " The church
property, consisting of tithes and demesnes belonging chiefly
to the see of Exeter, are frequently held in perpetuity by
the nobility and gentry of the country, renewable with
certain or arbitary fines: these are justly considered valuable possessions, and are by them disposed of in such a
manner as comports with the general arrangement of their
other property. An indulgence is sometimes given, and
formerly went to a far greater length, enabling the widow
of the last surviving tenant to the church-lands in possession, to hold over the estate so long as she remained unmarried; but as this in some instances led to intrigues of
a loose and disreputable nature, great care is now taken
by the Bishop, and those who have the management of
these affairs, to prevent in future any disgraceful abuse of
such humane and generous concessions."

Life Leasehold.—P. 81. " The mischievous consequences
inseparably connected with, and resulting from, the want
of agricultural knowledge in those who have the direction
and management of such estates, and who, to cover the
want of the necessary qualifications of a land agent, most
commonly advise the proprietor to grant those lifehold
tenures so frequently heard of in Devonshire and South
Wales,

Wales, are more injurious and extensive than is generally apprehended."

IRRIGATION.—This operation is repeatedly mentioned, *incidentally*, in different sections of the work. Mr. Vancouver appears to be fully aware that much depends on the *specific quality* of the *water*, applied to the purpose of irrigation. He speaks highly of the waters of the Mole and the Bray;—two brooks in the northern part of North Devonshire. But he does not specify the substrata out of which they issue. Indeed, his ideas on the subject, at the time he wrote, were, it is evident, insufficiently mature, to write on it with profitable intelligence.

MANAGEMENT of ESTATES.—The following remarks are so justly made, that I willingly give them a place, here.— P. 80. " It is believed, that in no part of England are the care and management of estates so generally deputed to the superintendance of attornies and other unqualified persons, as in the county of Devon: in what view their education, professional pursuits, and habits, can be deemed qualifications for the important duties of land agent, is not easily to be understood; particularly, as the essential endowments of the latter are so widely different from those of law agents, whose exclusive attention should be directed to the title. Different, however, are the qualifications for a land steward, for it is to him, and him only, that we must look for projecting, directing, and carrying into execution such works as the nature of the estate requires, and by the most economical and judicious means, effecting the permanent improvement of his employer's property."

TENANCY.—*Covenants of Repairs.*—P. 88. " The repairs of the farm-houses, such as walls, floors, roofs and doors, are usually done by the landlord; all others, except the finding of stuff for gates, rails, and posts, are performed by the tenant; it has, however, been generally noticed, that the tenant for years keeps his occupation in repair, being first put in that condition by the landlord at the commencement of the lease. The cottages are also generally kept by the tenant farmer in repair."

WOODLANDS.

ON *woods*, whether of timber or coppice, I have detected, in the Report under examination, nothing that demands particular mention.

On the practice of *propagating woods*, I arrest the subjoined

joined passage; which I know contains much truth.—P. 263.
" It would afford the author of this Report much pleasure,
to be able to dwell at some length on the principal articles
of this section; but so little attention has been paid by the
inhabitants of this district," (North Devon.) " in the culture of forest trees, that excepting those plantations only
that have been made by Lord Fortescue, on the old lime-
works at Filleigh, the plantations of Mr. Basset, of Water-
mouth, and a small grove chiefly of the pine tribe, raised
by the Reverend Mr. Sweet, of Kentsbere, the cultivation
of deciduous or ever-green trees is seldom seen extending
beyond the pleasure-grounds or homesteads of the inhabitants; where they have been planted for the purpose of ornament, a little shade, or shelter."

Under the present head, may be mentioned the well
matured EXOTIC TIMBER GROVES of Mamhead; which
stand on an elevated stage,—facing the east,—on the western
bank of the estuary of the Exe.

P. 260. " In Lord Lisburne's park, at Mamhead, the
ever-green oak, *acacia*, or black locust of North America;
the double flowering ash, wainscot, or white oak of North
America; cork tree of Portugal, Russian moss, and Ame-
rican red oak, seem all to flourish with peculiar excellence;
as do also the cedar of Lebanon, spruce, Scotch, and silver
firs, with many other native and exotic plants of great variety."

AGRICULTURE.

FARMS.—P. 100. " It is extremely difficult to speak
with any degree of certainty on a subject in which there is
so wide a range for the striking an average, with respect
to the extent of the occupations of a country, which vary
from 10*l.* to 400*l.* a year; in general, however, it may be
stated, that persons who come within the description of
what may be called farming tenantry of the district, rent
or otherwise occupy from 200 to 300 acres of land, the
greater part of which is subject to a system of up-and-down
husbandry, and to which is generally attached a small proportion of permanent pasture, and of marsh or meadow-
land."

OCCUPIERS.—The subjoined extract evinces much natural
good sense; and extensive knowledge of the superior class
of English farmers.

P. 430. " With regard to a farther dissemination of knowledge

ledge among the farmers, however fashionable it may be to stigmatize them as ignorant and obstinate, because they do not adopt the wild theories and hypothetical opinions of modern writers on husbandry, still, so far as the observation of the Surveyor extends generally, he has met with but few instances of that invincible ignorance so commonly asserted, or of any judicious and actual improvement being made clear to the judgment of the farmer, that he has not gradually and ultimately adopted. In truth, the farmer has by far too much at stake, to be easily seduced from the course of husbandry pursued by his forefathers, and which, by his own practice, has yielded to him the means of raising his family, paying his rent, tradesmen's bills, and meeting the parochial payments, to forego the certain means of procuring these supplies in order to pursue a different system of management, dressed up in all the parade of science, and altogether in a language he does not comprehend ; but let the advantages of a superior management be once demonstrated to his understanding by a series of beneficial results, and there is an absolute certainty of his soon becoming a convert to the better practice."

OBJECTS of HUSBANDRY. — " *North Devon*." — P. 139. " The proportion of tillage to the enclosed grass-ground in this district, may be stated as one part in eight, that is, seven parts of enclosed grass-ground to one part in corn, or in preparation for it by fallow, turnips, and potatoes ; out of this seven-eighths, there is estimated to be only one-eighth under permanent pasture, marsh, and meadow; hence seven-eighths of the whole enclosed country are subject to a convertible system."

P. 209. " It has been already observed, that about one-eighth part of the enclosed cultivated lands in this district are annually under corn crops, or in preparation for them. The remainder will always be found lying in permanent pasture, or subject to such a course of tillage as the caprice of the occupier may choose, either as to the time he may keep the land open, or the course of crops he may employ it with."

WORKPEOPLE.—*Servants.*—P. 361. " The general rule in hiring servants, is to engage them at Christmas, to come home the Lady-day following, and to continue in service until that time twelvemonth. The usual wages to the head man, or carter, is 10*l.* per annum, with board, washing, and lodging. The inferior departments of his establishment are often filled by parish apprentices."

Parish Prentices.—P. 359. " Some difference of opinion was met with in the course of the Survey, as to the general utility of this system, but the reasons stated for its continuance

ance appeared so much to outweigh what was urged against
it, that in the judgment of the Suveyer, he can neither
withhold his concurrence to the general principle, or
forbear to recommend its adoption in other parts of England."

Laborers.—P. 361. " The wages of the out-door labourer
is 7*s.* per week, winter and summer, and from a quart to
three pints of drink daily; even in hay-time and harvest,
these wages are not increased, although the additional exertions at those seasons are amply compensated by board,
and very extraordinary drinks and sittings over ale and
cider. To these wages must be added the standing supply
of bread-corn; of wheat at 6*s.* and barley at 3*s.* per
bushel."

Hours of Work.—P. 363. " The hours of work are from
seven to twelve, and from one to between five and six."—
This *idle* custom is not confined to North Devonshire.

On the *Education* of Farm Workpeople.—P. 465. "From
the first dawning of that gracious benevolence which issued
spontaneously from the bosoms of their present Majesties,
in promoting the instruction of the poor by the establishment of Sunday Schools, the Surveyor has looked forward
with a sort of dread to the probable consequences of such
a measure. If the illumination of the peasant mind would
make him more moral, better satisfied with his state and
condition of life, and on all occasions more desirous of
excelling in the exercise of those duties his peculiar situation in society dooms him to perform, much private satisfaction and public benefit would naturally result from such
institutions. This however can easily be demonstrated as
not likely to be a consequence of thus opening the peasant
mind to a contemplation of situations in life, that can have
no other possible effect than that of rendering him dis-
satisfied with his own. That this is an incontrovertible
truth, is clear, from the conduct of the peasantry of Ireland;
all of whom but slightly acquainted with the English language, are instructed to read and write; and thence springs
the cause of that general restlessness of character, and of
the numbers that annually ship themselves as redemp-
tioners to different parts of the United States of North
America."

And well it is, for Ireland and America, that they do so.
The one is overstocked with the class that furnishes workpeople; the other wants enlightened workmen. Of slaves
and savages it has enow.

The *unlettered* Irish stay at home,—to riot, plot, and
murder;—to commit acts of " treason, stratagem, and
spoil;"—*or* emigrate to England,—to revel, awhile, in out-
rage,—and be hanged.   After

After some other groundless arguments, the Reporter sums up, *in Italics*,—and with the aid of foreign tongues,—in the following *ultra-royal* manner.

P. 468. "*In short, the peasant's mind*" (this is *Russian*) "*should never be inspired with a desire to amend his circumstances by the quitting of his cast ;*" (this is *Hindoo*) "*but every means the most benevolent and feeling heart can devise, should be employed to make that situation as comfortable and as happy to him as possible ; and to which end nothing more essential could contribute, than by exciting a general emulation to excel in all their avocations, even to those of breaking stones for a lime kiln, or for repairing the highways.*" Hear ! Hear !—this is *English*.

Good Heaven!—And is there an Englisman (or a Dutchman—they are brothers in sentiment) with nerve enough to write the two first lines above quoted ! ! ! He surely could not know that many men of " the brightest genius," and,—who are much more estimable members of a community,—many GREAT AND GOOD MEN have, *in England*, been moulded and nurtured in the "*peasant cast*" !

Fortunately for society, *in England*, the writer's exotic notions have not taken root. Seminaries, for civilizing the children of the laboring classes, have been rapidly encreasing, under the " gracious benevolence" of ROYAL PATRONAGE, since his *barbarian* doctrine was promulgated.

In a civilized nation, EARLY SCHOOLING tends to reclaim children from *savage propensities ;* and to prepare them for *civilized society ;*—inculcates a PROPRIETY of BEHAVIOUR,—one of the very first lessons a child should be induced to learn,—*in a civilized nation**.

Attendance in a school enures children to a requisite degree of restraint, and a division of time ; employs their minds, and prevents idleness, and other vicious habits, from taking root:—thus tending to raise them to the rank of RATIONAL BEINGS.—While the unfortunate offspring of indigence, that are suffered to loiter away their early days, on commons, in lanes, and bye places, acquire habits, of indolence and pilfering ; give a loose to their own wills, and unrestrained tempers; commit acts of MISCHIEF ; and add to them the GUILT of LYING (the seedbud of FRAUD); to skreen them from correction.

The discipline of a well governed school impresses, on youthful minds, SUBORDINATION, INDUSTRY, PATIENCE, and its consequent, PERSEVERENCE ; and thus *habituates* them to RECEIVE INSTRUCTIONS. WORKING

* In the *savage state*, savage manners may be deemed a virtue ; as being, *in that state*, conducive to self-preservation.

WORKING ANIMALS.—*Horses.*—P. 353. "A small snug breed of horses, between the pack and larger cart horses, are getting much in use in different parts of the county. The former are out to grass all summer, and generally wintered upon very coarse hay: so long as they are kept steadily at work, they are allowed about half a peck of oats per horse daily, but as the work abates their allowance of corn is lessened also."

P. 354. "In the less hilly parts of the county, where one and two horse carts are more commonly in use, a larger breed than those above noticed is preferred."

For Working *Oxen*, see Cattle, ensuing.

IMPLEMENTS.—*Carriages.*—P. 125. "In the hilliest parts of the county, horses are only used for packing lime, dung, and all other purposes, for which wheel-carriages would in a less hilly district be far more appropriate; it is only in the less broken parts of the country that one and two-horse carts are found to supply the labour, and to carry in common from 8 to 12 cwt."

In the section, "Winnowing Machines," we discover some account of *packsaddle furniture*, used in *horse-back carriage.*—P. 127. "The long crooks generally affixed to the pack-saddles, for the purpose of removing corn, hay, straw, turf, or faggots, from such hills and side-lands as are deemed inaccessible to wheel-carriages, are formed to correspond with the curve of the pack-saddle, to descend rather below the line of the horse's girth, there to curve outwardly, forming a bottom of from twenty inches to two feet in width; thence rise with a small inclination inwards, and to the height of about two feet eight inches, or three feet, above the line of the horse's back and withers. Within these crooks, which are placed two on each side of the pack-saddle, there is no difficulty in laying on any load, equal to the strength of the horses. Stronger and shorter crooks are used for the purpose of transporting boards, poles, and small sticks of timber; and, for the carriage of stones, gravel, and dung, strong wicker baskets, opening at bottom, and sufficient to contain one hundred-weight and a half of short or rotten dung each, are most generally used; the lime is either packed in bags on horses' backs, or carried loose in two or three-horse carts, holding from 20 to 25 bushels each."

MANURE.—To this essential agent of practical agriculture, the Reporter has not assigned either *chapter* or *section*. In his "Conclusion," it is brought forward, as an *article:*—not with the view of describing the *species* in use, and their *management*, in the County under Report; but to receive some immature remarks (not altogether his own,

own, it would seem) on the *operation* of *manures in general.*

ARABLE CROPS.—To this main subject or division of *agriculture*, the Reporter has paid much attention ; having filled seventy pages with readable matter, concerning it.—After repeatedly examining it, however, I have not been able to select a page that I think will add to the value of this Register. The more instructive particulars of information which it contains, are before the public ; and, I presume to judge, in a better form.—In the culture of WHEAT, in *North Devonshire,* the practice of " beat-burning" would seem to be less prevalent,—and that of " rotting the spine" more in use, than in the southwestern parts of the County.

The only passage, that I have marked for extraction, relates to an extraordinary effect of *soil,* on the *color* of the FLAX CROP.—P. 208. " It is curious to notice the difference in the colour of flax cultivated on the grey loam, from that which is produced upon the red land ; for a permanent pink shade accompanies the latter, which no bleaching, washing, or chemical preparation yet discovered, has been sufficient to discharge, or obliterate in the slightest degree its native hue. So little, indeed, has the bleaching operation any effect in removing this colour, that it seems rather to increase and to shew itself more strongly as the operation is continued."

I have only to remark, on this notice, that red land, perfectly similar, in outward appearance, to that which is seen in various parts of Devonshire, is prevalent throughout England. Yet I never observed, nor heard of, its communicating a kindred hue to flax, or a permanent tinge to cloth. I do not mean, by these observations, to *contradict* Mr. Vancouver's notice.

ORCHARDS.—P. 236. " As cider is found to be the most general beverage of the inhabitants, it is reasonable to expect that much attention is paid to the cultivation of orchards. In this district, however," (North Devon.) " although a leading consideration among the farmers, and where there are many very good apple-orchards, they do not seem to form so principal an object of agricultural economy, as in other parts of the county."

GRASS LAND.—P. 209. " The low-lands by the sides of the rivers, and other smaller streams, are too frequently, through the mistaken avidity of the occupiers, broken up for the purposes of tillage, and in their first operation spaded and burnt in the same manner as the other grasslands lying upon a higher level."

P. 213. " The best feeding land in this district is unquestionably

questionably in those enclosures that lie permanently on the green side; and for the first two, or perhaps three years, such fields as have undergone the operation of paring and burning, and have not been too far exhausted afterwards by the usual succession of corn crops: but neither the permanent herbage, nor the maiden bite of the artificial grasses and white clover, which seem very much to flourish so long as any force from the ashes may be remaining in the ground, are supposed to be equal to the grazing of a cow beyond nine score per quarter, apportioning about two acres of the summer's pasturage to each cow; and the field carrying during the remaining seven months, after the ratio of about one sheep and a half, or at farthest, two sheep per acre."

CATTLE.—*Breed.*—P. 325. " The country watered by the river Bray, and on the northern branches of the Mole, appear to have attained the highest proof, and to form the most perfect of their species. The superiority of this breed for grazing or for draught, is amply demonstrated by the demand, and very high prices they bring after their work is done, either at home or among the Somersetshire graziers; but for the uses of the dairy or for milk, it is a breed by no means held in general estimation, as their aptitude to look well (without being fleshy), is derived from the peculiar nature of the animal, which disposes its secretions in the accumulation of fat, rather than in the production of milk. For the purposes of labour, this breed can no where be excelled for docility, activity, or hardihood, in proof of which no stronger circumstance can be adduced, than that it is a common day's work, on fallow land, for four steers to plough two acres with a double-furrow plough, and that a general use is thus made of them, and for most of the other purposes of draught in the country where they were originally found; and in others to which they have been since transplanted."

P. 327. " The full-sized North Devon cow, when fattened to its frame, will not exceed eight score per quarter; and the ordinary average of its ox, at five years old, and equally well fattened, must not be rated higher than three score per quarter above the weight of its fattened mother."

Elegant representations, of the cow the bull and the ox of " North Devon," appear among the engravings *given*, in the volume under review *

In

---

* Very dissimilar to that which is given! of a " Devon Bull," in the *Cornwall* Report;—and of which, a *grazier* would say, " though not *so viewly*, is of a more *useful* sort."

In page 214, it is said, "the native animals of the dis-district;" (North Devon.) "among all their other good qualities, are certainly not to be recommended for the dairy."—Yet we are told, in the next page, "The ordinary produce of milk per day, for the first twenty weeks after calving, is three gallons, and is equal to the producing of a pound and a quarter of butter daily, by the scalding process. The scalded skimmed milk is valued at $1\frac{1}{4}d$. per quart, either for cheese-making, or feeding hogs. The sum of the trials procured to be made on the milk in several parts of this district, gives an average of twelve pints of milk to ten ounces of butter. When cheese is to be made (but in which manufacture there does not appear to be any superior excellence in Devonshire), great care is taken that the milk is not heated so far as to produce bubbles under the cream.

"Although these general statements will be found con-siderably short of the average produce from cows of a larger size, and probably much better adapted for the pail, still there are not wanting instances of what must be regarded as extraordinary produce among the North Devon cows.

"In the neighbourhood of Molland Bouceaux, a single cow, judged to be rather less than eight score per quarter, within three weeks from the time of calving, yielded, in seven successive days, seventeen pounds and a half of butter; several of the meals of milk were measured during this time, which gave an average of fourteen pints per meal: instances also occurred in other parts of the dis-trict, of two pounds of butter per day being obtained from cows within a short time after calving; and it is particularly clear in the recollection of a gentleman in the neighbourhood of Bishop's Tawton, that some years since a cow of the common red breed, after her second or third calf, which she had between Michaelmas and Christmas, yielded, without any particular attention being paid to food or treatment, during a considerable time of the en-suing winter, two pounds and a half of butter per day" (!); "this cow living at the time in common with the other dairy cows, which were permitted in the day time to range over all the old pasture-grounds, and regularly foddered morning and evening with hay in the same field."—After this, let no one revile the Devonshire breed of cows, on account of their being deficient in dairy produce!

The *Show Fair* of this Breed.—P. 384. "The fair of Barnstable is supposed to be one of the best cattle-fairs in the kingdom; it is held about the middle of September, when those who are desirous of viewing the most perfect

of

of the breed of North Devon cattle, will never fail of being
very highly gratified. Great Torrington, and all the large
towns in the county, afford fairs for cattle, horses, &c."

Leading Breeders.—P. 328. "At the Right Hon. Earl
Fortescue's; Sir Bourchier Wrey's; ——Ackland's Esq. of
High Bray; the Rev. Mr. Quarterly's, of Molland; Mr.
Stoneman's, of Woodhouse, near Torrington; Mr. Nickoll's,
of Heanton-Court house; Mr. George Burdon's, of Har-
wood ; and at many other gentlemen and respectable farmers
in the district of North Devon, the most beautiful specimens
of this justly esteemed animal". (the North Devon bull)
" are always to be met with."

Rearing Young Cattle.—P. 326. "The rules generally
pursued in breeding and raising this valuable animal, may
be considered as follow. Many judicious observations have
been made on the preference given to Michaelmas calves
to those that drop the latter end of February; notwithstanding the additional expense and care required in nursing
them through the winter. The greater number of calves,
however, fall between Candlemas and May, and some much
later ; but among the best breeders, such late calves are
not so generally approved of. The usual mode of raising
them in this district, is to let the calf suck as much as
it will three times a day for the first week; then bring it
to the finger, and feed it with warm new milk, in like
manner for three weeks longer.

" This is the ordinary treatment for the first month, and
the calf is then fed for two months longer, twice a day,
with as much warm scalded skimmed milk as it will drink ;
when, gradually abating its morning and evening meals,
at the end of four months the animal is weaned from all
milk draughts, and left to itself. Small portions of finely
pounded linseed cakes are often used, and recommended
to be mixed with the skimmed milk, particularly in the
first period of its being given in the place of new milk."

Working Cattle.—P. 330. "It has been already noticed,
that the steers of the district are always worked as far
as occasion may require. Their labour begins at two years
old, when they are broke in and worked gently for the
ensuing twelvemonth; from three to four, but more frequently to the ages of five or six, they are put to all the
ordinary labours of the yoke; and their day's work at
plough or harrow, is usually performed in a journey of
about eight hours, during which time the plough-boy has
a peculiar mode of cheering them on, with a song he continually chaunts in low notes, suddenly broken, and raising
a whole octave."

Disposal of *Worked Oxen.*—P. 329. " The usual practice

tice in this district, is to sell the steers, at four or five years old, to the graziers in the county of Somerset, who feed them for a supply to the Bath, Bristol, and London markets."

SHEEP.—" *North Devon.*"—P. 338. " The *native* sheep of this district is the *Exmoor*" (?) " a horned animal, with a moderately-long staple of wool, which heretofore, and before the cloth manufacture fled from this county into Yorkshire, was much used by the clothiers of North and South Molton, Cullumpton, Thorverton, Tiverton, and other places in the county. The fattened wethers of this breed, at three years old, will usually weigh about 15 lbs. per quarter, and average four pounds and a half of washed wool to the fleece; worth at present about thirteen-pence per pound."

The above notice stands at the head of the Reporter's section, "Sheep;" which is closed by a table, exhibiting more than twenty different *varieties*,—" native," " neighbour," " distant," " foreign,"—that were found in the County, at the time of his survey:—most of them *mongrels,*—otherwise—*crosses.*—The four " native breeds" are thus described.—

P. 352. " Exmoor, horned, white legs and face, with a moderately long staple of wool, pure.

" Dartmoor, ditto, ditto. !!*

" South Devon Nott, with brown face and legs, long wool, pure.

" Bampton Nott, white face and legs, short wool, pure."

The other " pure" breeds are the Dorsetshire and the South Downs. The rest are of course *impures.*

Markets for Sheep.—P. 384. " The fair of Bampton is the most remarkable of all for sheep, and where a most excellent show is always to be met with, on the first Tuesday in November."

SWINE.—P. 355. "The native hog of this country grows to a large size, stands high upon its legs, lengthy, of a large and coarse bone, flat-sided, and in its store state seldom seen in any thing like tolerable condition."

P. 356. " The proportion of fat to lean, or in other words, of pork to bacon, in the above breeds, may be thus stated: the native country hog, when well fed, will produce for one pound of pork, one pound and a quarter of bacon. This, crossed with the Leicester or Hampshire breed, will produce for three-quarters of a pound of pork, one

---

* In the *native breed of Dartmore,* there are scarcely two individuals alike. Some with horns, others without; having only *knots* where horns usually stand. Viewing them in the mass,—there are horns of every size and shape; and faces and legs of every hue.

one pound of bacon. This cross again varied by the Chinese, will in two-thirds of the time, produce for two-thirds of a pound of pork, one pound of bacon."

I have transcribed the above passage; notwithstanding it is written in a language that I do not quite understand.

PIGEONS.—The subjoined extract is much clearer to my comprehension, though it may seem to extend beyond the limits of credibility. It shows, in strong coloring, the mischiefs which an ACCURATE CULTIVATOR is liable to, through the want of a sufficient law, to guard his property from what is, at present, *unpunishable theft.*

P. 357. " These birds often fly to a great distance for their food, and when they can find corn to eat, seldom prey upon any thing else. They begin to eat corn about the middle of July, and rarely want the same food at the stacks, in the straw-yards or in the fields, until the end of barley sowing, which is about Old May-day, and which includes a period of 280 days, or better than three-quarters of the year; the rest of the time they live upon the seeds of weeds and bentings. It is somewhere stated, that in England and in Wales there are 20,000 dove-houses, averaging about 100 pair of old pigeons. We will take this estimate at three-fourths, which will equal 1,125,000 pair of dove-house pigeons in England and Wales. These, to speak moderately, will consume (with what they carry home to their young) one pint of corn per pair daily, and which for 140 days, being half the period they are supposed to subsist upon corn, amounts to 157,500,000 pints of corn consumed annually, throughout England and Wales, by these voracious and insatiate vermin, for in no other light can they possibly be viewed or considered by the Agriculturist. The amount and value of this consumption, when brought into bushels, and averaged at the present price of wheat, rye, barley, oats, beans and pease, and assuming that an equal quantity of each corn is thus consumed (but which is far from being the case, as the wheat is not only the most inviting, but by far the most exposed to the ravages of these birds, both at seed-time and preceding harvest) will stand thus: 157,500,000 pints = 4,921,875 Winchester bushels, which at 6s. per bushel, the present average price of the grain and pulse before enumerated, amounts to 1,476,562l. 10s. value of the agricultural produce of the country annually consumed in this manner; a circumstance most respectfully submitted to the consideration of the Honourable Board of Agriculture, in comparison with the true and natural value of these birds, as a luxury for the table, their dung for the use of dyers, or the purposes of manure. To this statement is to be added

added the irreparable injury they commit in seed-time, picking up every grain of seed wherever they alight, and the corn trod under and also beaten out by their wings before harvest."

For another instance of *animated* strictures, on the same side of this unsettled point, see NORTHERN DEPARTMENT,— *West Riding of Yorkshire.*—And for a striking evidence produced, on the opposite side,—see MIDLAND DEPART-MENT,—*Parkinson's Huntingdonshire;*—in which these companiable domestics are styled "an encourageable species of fowls."

As a moderator, in this matter, which is by no means unimportant, I will just observe—that, *in seed time*, pigeons are much less hurtful to the husbandman, than is generally imagined. They neither "scrape" like the pheasant, nor "joll" like the rook. They merely, I believe, pick up the grains of corn which lie exposed to the eyes at the surface.—Nevertheless, on the near approach, and during the early part, of *harvest*, pigeons become truly noxious, in a corn country. At that consecrated season, there surely ought to be a heavy penalty, leviable on those who suffer them to fly abroad;—or a law to render it allowable to treat them as *birds of prey*, at that time,—by those whose property they may be destroying.

Viewing the propensities and effects of a flight of pigeons, *the year round* (the time of harvest *perhaps* excepted) they might, I think, be truly termed the *slovenly farmer's friend.*—The seeds of *weeds* are their *natural food.*

This, however, furnishes not any good argument against the suggestions, above offered. Slovenliness—the propagation of weeds—might well be made a legal disqualification from the occupancy of arable lands,—as being an inveterate enemy of the community.

WEST

WEST SOMERSETSHIRE.

IN DIVIDING the territory of England into AGRICULTURAL DEPARTMENTS, the COUNTY of SOMERSET extends, *unnaturally*, into three of them.

NORTH SOMERSETSHIRE, which borders on the vales of Glocestershire and North Wiltshire, forms an inseparable parcel of the WESTERN, or DAIRY Department. WEST SOMERSETSHIRE is equally inseparable from the SOUTH-WESTERN or PENINSULAR Department. And the remainder of the County, which borders on South Wiltshire and Dorsetshire, naturally unites with the SOUTHERN Department.

WEST SOMERSETSHIRE, at the present period of time, comprizes two distinct formations of territory.—The one ABORIGINAL,—as left by the convulsion of elements,—the other ALLUVIAL; having been formed by floods and tides, since the surface of the island was molded as it is, at present.

The ALLUVIAL DEPOSIT,—the WATERLANDS,—have been principally caused by the feculencies of two distinct rivers,—the BRUE and the PARRET;—with which,—obstructed and thrown back by the tides and eagres of the Bristol channel,—two distinct compartments, or "levels," of valuable lands, have been formed. These levels are separated,—unless toward the mouths of the rivers,—by a natural embankment,—a tall narrow ridge;—the Polden Hill.

The level which is situated on the NORTH side of that line of separation, is named the "BRENT MARSHES," from a *steep* conical hillock which rises near their center: or "the Brue and Axe Marshes"; the Brook, Axe, passing along their northern margin.

The sub-divisions of those alluvial lands which lie on the SOUTH side of that barrier, bear the popular name of "SEDGEMOORS", as King's Sedgemoor, West Sedgemoor, &c. &c.:—names, doubtlessly, attached to them while they lay in a moory, sedgey state. But, at present, by an increase of alluvial matter, and, more latterly, through the aid of drainage, the principal part of them are become of a valuable marshland quality.

Hence, in speaking of those two extensive levels of marsh land, I will denominate them by the NORTH or

BRUE

BRUE MARSHES, and the SOUTH or PARRET MARSHES;—those rivers passing nearly through their centers.

The ABORIGINAL or DRY LANDS, of the western point of Somersetshire,—not inaptly divide into DISTRICTS:—as, the *seacoast* of *West Somersetshire*, that occupies its northern margin;—the *Exmoor, Brendon*, and *Quantoe Hills*, which form a line nearly along the middle of this heterogeneous passage of country;—and the *Vale* of *Taunton*, a rich and beautiful District, situated to the southward of those hills, and having for its southern confine the Blackdown Heights of Devonshire.

The only REPORT of Somersetshire is that of Mr. BIL-LINGSLEY, of Ashwick Grove, in that County;—of whose QUALIFICATIONS, as a rural Reporter, I offered some re-marks, in the WESTERN DEPARTMENT, and, again, in p. 233, aforegoing.—Mr. B., on many occasions, has evinced a superior strength of mind, with a bias toward rural *im-provements*. But there is very little, in his Report, which shows that he was, at the time of writing it, *a well ex-perienced practitioner in agriculture*. His silence, nearly, on practical subjects, is therefore a mark of his good sense.—As a *commissioner* of " *inclosure*," and as an *engineer*, in matters of *drainage*, Mr. Billingsley would seem to have had some considerable experience. Hence, on those subjects, he is full of useful intelligence; as will be seen, in his account of the Waterlands of Somersetshire.

The number of pages, which relate more particularly to WEST SOMERSETSHIRE, are seventytwo.

IN ABSTRACTING the matter of these pages, I will, first, take into consideration the alluvial lands; and, afterward, what relates to the more western part of the County; viewing the whole of the latter as one aggregate district.

THE WATERLANDS OF
THE WEST OF ENGLAND*.

THE NORTH OR BRUE MARSHES.

GENERAL DESCRIPTION.—P. 166. " *Brent Marsh* is that portion of land comprehended between Mendip-
hills

---

* For ample information, concerning the Waterlands of the *eastern* part of England, see the EASTERN DEPARTMENT.

hills and Polden-hill on the north and south, Bridgwater-bay on the west, and extending to Wells and Glastonbury on the East.

" This marsh may also be divided into two parts, separated by a tract of elevated land, on which stand the parishes of Allerton, Mark, Blackford, Wedmore, &c. Through the Northern level runs the river *Axe*, emptying itself into the Bristol Channel at Uphill; and through the Southern the river *Brue*, emptying itself into Bridgwater-bay near Burnham.

" This country has been heretofore much neglected, being destitute of gentlemen's houses, probably on account of the stagnant waters, and unwholesome air; but of late many efforts have been made to improve the soil, by draining and inclosing, under a variety of acts of parliament. The benefit resulting therefrom has been astonishing. The rhynes and ditches necessarily cut to divide the property, together with the deepening of the general outlets, discharge so much of the superfluous water, that many thousand acres, which heretofore were overflown for months together, and of course of little or no value, are become fine grazing and dairy lands; to the great emolument of the individual possessors, as well as the benefit of the community. The quantities thus inclosed in Brent-Marsh, within twenty years past, under authority of parliament, are as follows:

	Acres.	
Wedmore and Mear	4,400	together with 1,100 acres of turf-bog as yet unimproved.
Compton-Bishop ...	300	
Glastonbury	1,500	Ditto 300 ditto
Westhay, &c.	1,700	Ditto 1,000 ditto
Mark	2,000	
Huntspill	1,200	
Shapwick	100	
Blackford	900	
Wookey	900	
Westbury	450	
Bleadon	400	
West-Pennard	250	
Eddington	1,000	Ditto 400 ditto
Stoke and Draycot	800	
Nylands	350	
Wells	1,150	
	17,400	2,800 of turf-bog.

" Of these seventeen thousand four hundred acres, six parts out of seven are cleared of stagnant water, and rendered

dered

dered highly productive: on the turf-bog but little improvement has hitherto taken place. * There remain about three thousand acres to be inclosed, which (the turf-bogs excepted) will complete the division of all the moors within the Brent-Marsh district. It is not to be understood, that the local drains, under such a variety of acts, and at such different times, can have the most perfect influence on the country; particularly when it is considered, that the river Axe has no barrier to the tide, which flows several miles, and choaks the lower part of it with *slime*, to such a degree, that many thousand acres adjoining the upper parts of the river are, in consequence thereof, very much injured. Were a barrier, with proper sluices, erected near the Bristol Channel, some of the most considerable windings of the river shortened, and the shallow parts deepened, not only the moors, but the *old inclosures*, would be benefited thereby, to the amount of at least five thousand pounds per annum.

" The river Brue drains a much more considerable part of Brent-Marsh than the Axe, and has a barrier to the tide (which rises there no less than twenty feet in height) with sluices therein, at Highbridge; but its foundation, and the apron and cills of the sluices, are at such a height above low water mark, that the drain is very imperfect, and the lowest lands, which lie some miles up the river, are frequently incommoded by the land floods.

" On the confines of the Brue are two heath or turf bogs: one on the north side containing about three thousand, and the other on the south containing about six thousand acres.

" On these bogs scarce any pasturage at present grows.— They are a composition of porous substances, floating on water, and imbibing it like a spunge. They are observed to rise with much wet, and sink in dry weather. The principal use to which they are appropriated is that of fuel to the surrounding parishes."

SOILS.—P. 173. " The soil of these moors may be comprehended under four divisions :

" 1st. Strong, dry, and fertile clay, of a considerable depth.

" 2dly. Red earth, of various depths, from one foot to six feet, covering the black moory earth of the heath.

" 3dly. Black moory earth on the surface, with a substratum of clay at various depths.

" 4thly, and lastly. The turf-bog.

" The first of these descriptions of land may be considered

---

* Ten thousand sheep have been rotted in one year in the parish of Mark, before the inclosing and draining took place.

sidered as of the best quality, being highly productive, and particularly so in a wet summer. If shut up early in the spring, it will produce from two to three tons of hay per acre. Its value may be estimated from two to three pounds per acre, and it is for the most part devoted to grazing.

"It is no less remarkable than true, that this land will fat sheep nearly as well in the winter as the summer, if not stocked more than one to an acre."

P. 177. "Some of this clay land, when tilled, has been known to produce ten or twelve successive crops of wheat, without an intervening fallow or fallow crop. I was shown a field in the parish of Mark, which had growing in it the *nineteenth* crop of wheat; and I verily think the produce was not less than fifty Winchester bushels per acre. No manure had been put on it during the whole time, save the contents arising from the cleansing of the ditches. The stubble was mown every year, and carried off; two ploughings only were given it, after which the wheat was sown in the months of November or December, under furrow, in eight-furrow ridges, after the rate of two bushels and half per acre, chopping the clods, and smoothing the surface of the ridge with a spade.

"The average produce per year, for the whole eighteen years, was estimated to exceed thirty-five bushels per acre."

P. 178. "The second description of soil found in this district, namely, a strong red earth over a pure clay, possesses also many good qualities; it is neither subject to injury from an excess of wet weather, nor does it burn in a drought.

"This soil, formed by a deposit washed from the hills, may be considered as a fine vegetable mould, and, if tilled, is capable of bearing a variety of crops in the highest perfection. Its value is about forty-five shillings per acre, and its produce of hay about two tons.

"Black moory earth is the third sort of soil found in this level, and on it extraordinary improvements have been effected, by covering the surface with a thick coat either of clay or red earth.

"In its natural state it is in a great measure unproductive, yielding scarcely any herbage, save carnation grass, rushes, and other aquatic productions."

P. 180. "The last species of soil is *the Turf Bog.*

"The surface of this soil is of a light, spungy, tough texture, full of the fibrous roots of plants, and withal so matted together, that a spade or knife must be made very keen to penetrate it. Immediately under the turf, or sward, is found the vein of black moory earth, so unlike in its nature to the peat which lies underneath, that when cut with it, and dried, it will fall off and separate from it.

"This

" This mould is of good quality, and will bear both natural and artificial grass in great abundance. It is also an excellent manure for clay or any other heavy land. This black moory stratum is from one to two feet in thickness, and underneath is found the peat, which is from three to fifteen feet in depth.

" Under the peat is a bed either of clay or sand; the peat is full of flaggy leaves and hollow stalks of rushes. These vegetable matters are accompanied with a substance like pitch, of a bituminous nature, which lies between the stalks of the rushes and the leafy remains, and constitutes the inflammable part thereof. It is used as the common fuel of the country, and makes a clean and pleasant fire, particularly well adapted to the purposes of the dairy. An acre of land will furnish an immense quantity, insomuch, that in the parish of Catcott it has been sold, for a term of twenty-one years, as high as thirty pounds."

MANURE.—P. 177. " The only manure ever put on these lands, is the contents of the drains and ditches; and this, with judicious management in the method of grazing, is sufficient to keep them in unabating fertility."

FENCES.—P. 175. " The division of property, on these lands, is effected by ditches eight feet wide at the top, three feet and half wide at the bottom, and five feet deep."

IMPROVEMENTS.—P. 169. " As it is an object of the first importance to the country to have the bogs perfectly drained and consolidated, I shall endeavour to suggest a plan whereby this desirable effect may, in my opinion, be attained.

" The cause of the inundation and drowning of this level arises from the outfalls being choaked up either by the collection of sea-mud in the river, or by the elevated land lying between it and the Bristol Channel. Of course, nothing more is necessary than a removal of those obstructions to the outfalls, which will open a free passage and quick current to the land water; this being effected, the turf-bogs, which are now five or six feet higher than the adjacent land, would subside, and the porous earth become consolidated, and fit for all the purposes of vegetation."

Mr. B. has inserted " a PLAN for the more effectually draining the turf bogs and flooded lands, near the rivers Brue and Axe, in the county of Somerset;"—with a diagram to show the inequalities of surface: thus furnishing a scientific guide to their drainage. The map and levels by " William White, Surveyor, Sand, near Wells, 1794."

Same page.—" By the levels thus delineated, (the accuracy of which, I think, may be depended on) it appears, that the spring-tides are nearly on a level with the surface

of

of the turf-bogs, and that by the proposed outlet an additional fall of ten feet will be acquired. Such a drain, reduced to an inclined plane of a foot in a mile, would, in all probability, discharge all its stagnant waters."

" The present outlet at Highbridge is not only of insufficient depth, but is situate so far *inland*, that the slime and mud choak up the river, and the current is not rapid enough to dislodge the same.

" I am aware that many of the proprietors of land in Huntspill, Mark, &c. will object, under an idea that their lands will be made *too dry*, and that in the summer season their stock will be destitute of water. But this objection, and indeed every other drawn from the apprehension of a too liberal discharge of water, may be obviated, by *placing hatches at the different bridges*, which will be necessary both for public and private accommodation.

" An improvement of such magnitude cannot be effected without the authority of parliament; and all persons receiving benefit must be burthened with a rate proportionate to the advantages derived. This assessment may be made by commissioners duly appointed, but subject to an appeal to the court of quarter-sessions; and the drains, when finished, should be put under the view of the court of sewers.

" I will now endeavour to give a hasty sketch of the probable cost, and subsequent improvement: but in this I do not pretend to accuracy; suffice it to say, that the apparent benefit so far exceeds the utmost latitude of expence, that no solid objection can lie on that head.

" *Brent-Marsh and the River Axe Drainage.*

" DR.	£.
To act of parliament, gaining consents, &c.	400
To sluice at letter *a* near the river Perrott	600
To twelve miles of new drain, average depth fifteen feet	12,000
To lowering river Brue three miles	1,500
To purchase of land	2,000
To bridges, hatches, &c.	2,000
To sluice on the Axe near Hobb's boat	500
To one mile and half of new drain	1,500
To lowering the river Axe six miles	1,000
To purchase of land	1,000
To commissioners, surveyor. &c.	2,500
	25,000
To balance of profit	331,250
	£.356,250
	" CR.

"CR.   £.

By 9000 acres turf bog improved, at the most
moderate computation, 15s. per acre, making
6750l. per annum, twenty-five years purchase   168,750
By 15,000 acres of flooded land improved 10s.
per acre, or 7500l. per annum, twenty-five years
purchase   187,500

                                                 £.356,250

"On the side of the river Axe, the expence of a compleat
drainage would not exceed five thousand pounds; and there
can be no doubt that the low lands near Axbridge, Cheddar,
Nyland, Draycot, Rodney-Stoke, Westbury, &c. would
be improved at least four thousand per annum. As a farther stimulus it might be urged, that the air would be rendered more healthful, and the exhalations which now rise
from so large a body of stagnant water, and are wafted by
the winds to the high corn-lands of the Mendip-Hills, to
their great detriment, would be unknown.

"Were the turf-bogs reclaimed and made productive, I
think this district might be considered as one of the most
fertile in the kingdom."

P. 173. "The profit which has attended the improvement already practised during the last twenty years is, I
should think, a sufficient incentive. Scarcely a farmer can
now be found who does not possess a considerable landed
property; and many whose fathers lived in idleness and
sloth, on the precarious support of a few half-starved cows,
or a few limping geese, are now in affluence, and blessed
with every needful species of enjoyment. Disorders of the
body, to which the stagnant waters heretofore subjected
them, are now scarcely known: and the inhabitants for the
most part arrive to a good old age."

P. 174. "The vast advantage resulting from the inclosure of the waste lands in the parishes before enumerated,
is so manifest, that whoever runs may read.

"A moiety of the manor of Wedmoor might have been
purchased, about twenty years ago, for twenty thousand
pounds. It is now worth seven thousand pounds per annum.
The improvements in Huntspill, Mark, Mere, Glastonbury,
Eddington, &c. &c. are nearly similar. In the latter hamlet,
single rights of common, when inclosed, have been sold for
more than eight hundred pounds; and all this without any
concomitant inconvenience. At first the scheme was highly
unpopular, and its first promoters were on the eve of falling
a sacrifice to popular fury and resentment, but by coolness
and perseverance they weathered the storm: all parties
                                                     are

are now satisfied, and acknowledge the wisdom of the measure."

P. 178. " The deficiency of this soil arises from the want of tenacity. The best means of improvement is *compleat draining*, and after that a liberal covering with clay or red earth ; these will freely incorporate with the soil, and make it sufficiently firm. After such improvement, no kind of land is more productive, particularly in a dry summer.

" I have this year seen land of this description, spring-fed till the 12th of May, yield by the 24th of June two tons of hay per acre; and Mr. Lax, on his farm at Godney, has, for five years past, kept twenty cows and a bull throughout the year on thirty-five acres of land. His plan is to winter *hayne** fifteen acres. This, on an average of seasons, is fit to be stocked the beginning of April, and is fed till the 12th of May. By this time the remaining twenty acres are in sufficient strength to take the cows, and will keep them till the after-grass of his mown ground is fit to receive them ; then the unfed grass in the summer-leaze is *skimmed*, which yields from five to ten cwt. of hay per acre ; this is given to the cows when they are dry, namely, in the months of December and January. After they have calved, which is from the beginning of February to Lady-Day, they are supplied with the best hay ; here are more than thirty tons of hay produced, so that twenty cows cannot possibly want winter provender.

" Not many years since this farm was part of an extensive moor, inclosed by Act of Parliament, and was purchased by Mr. Lax, of the Commissioners, at fifteen pounds per acre, to which add five pounds per acre for draining and claying, making in the whole twenty pounds per acre, at five per cent. the rent will be twenty shillings per acre."

Before closing his valuable observations, concerning the *drainage* of the NORTH MARSHES, Mr. B. enters, further, on their *agricultural improvement*. But not in a way, I conceive, which can demand particular attention, in this place.

THE SOUTH OR PARRET MARSHES.

GENERAL DESCRIPTION.—Mr. Billingsley, or his Editor, or the Board's literary manager, has made a palpable mistake, in describing this compartment of the Waterlands of Somersetshire.

On quitting the aboriginal or upper grounds of what Mr. B. terms the " Midland District" of the County, he
says,

" * It is *old* English," (from *hay*, a *hedge*), " and found in all books and laws relating to forests."

says, p. 166, " Hence we descend into the marsh or fen-
lands, which are divided into two districts, namely, *Brent-
Marsh*, and the *Bridgwater*, or *South-Marsh*."

And having described the *North Marshes* and their general improvement, in the masterly manner, above set forth,
we are led to a division of the work, conspicuously headed
" the South Marsh ;" which he thus proceeds to describe.—
P. 188. " The South Marsh is bounded on the North-East
by Polden-hills, on the South-West by the river Parrett, on
the North-West by Bridgwater-bay, and on the South-East
by Ham-hill, &c."

Now, this is only one moiety, or a certain portion of one
moiety, of the South Marshes ; namely, that part of them
which has gone, for some length of time, by the name of
" King's Sedgmoor." The other moiety of the South
Marshes,—tho the *better* half of them, I believe,—is not
directly noticed, in the Report under view ; unless in a
summary way that will be shown. The river Parret forms
the boundary line, (which extends in a southeast and north-
west direction) between the two, otherwise, undivided
moieties.

This wide-spreading level of waterformed land, which
measures, by the maps of the County, not less than one
hundred square miles in extent, (sixtyfour thousand acres)
is situated between the Polden line of hill, on the north or
northeast, and the Curry Hills (the Limestone Heights travelled over between Taunton and Langport) on the south.;
and extends from nearly the foot of the Quantoc Hill, on
the west, to the skirts of the Ham Hills (the Limestone
Downs passed over between Langport and Somerton) on
the east*.

Hence, the information, comprized in Mr. Billingsley's
Report, concerning " the South Marsh," requires to be considered

* I had an extraordinary opportunity of viewing the situation and
outline of this wide extent of alluvial land, as well as those of other
more confined " moors" of Somersetshire,—in travelling through the
County, by the way of Castle Cary, Somerton, Langport, and Ilminster,
in October, 1799, when they were inundated !—deeply covered with
water. This was, *to me*, a most *interesting* circumstance. I thereby
saw, in reality, a strong resemblance of what I had previously conceived and related, must necessarily have been, when their sites were
unobstructed inlets of the sea ;—when the tides, from the Bristol Channel, filled the spaces which the Marshlands now occupy.; and forced
their way, up what was, *then*, the *estuary* of the Parret, to its probable
head, at Seaborough, situated at the foot of Beaminster Hill :—thus
approaching the tides of the English Channel, at Bridport, within a
very few miles ; which, then, formed the narrow isthmus, or neck of
land, that connected the western peninsula with the mainland of
England.

sidered as regarding "KING's SEDGMOOR," only ;—not as relating to the South or Parret Marshes, at large.

"KING's SEDGMOOR."

GENERAL DESCRIPTION.—P. 188. " That part thereof which lies nearest the sea is higher than the interior part, owing to the great deposit of sea-mud left at the high spring-tides for ages past ; and it is also better drained, in consequence of being near the outlet, where the greatest fall of draining exists. (This observation also extends to the lands of Brent-Marsh.)

" The river Parret is the principal drain of this marsh. It has no *barrier*, and the tide flows up as far as Langport, filling its banks, and frequently penning the land-floods over the moor, and meadows adjoining ; so that near thirty thousand acres of fine land are frequently overflown for a considerable time together, rendering the herbage unwholsome for the cattle, and the air unhealthy to the inhabitants."

P. 189 " About the year 1680, King James laid claim to the soil of this moor, and formed the design of improving it by a compleat drainage ; but so perverse were the owners of the adjacent lordships commoning with their cattle on it, that they opposed the scheme with all their might ; and discerning that they could make no justifiable claim to the soil, offered to assign to the king four thousand acres, in lieu of his right thereto, and to lay out the residue, being nine thousand five hundred and twenty-two acres, among their lordships ; which being accepted of by the king, there were allotments then made to each manor according to the following proportions :

Names of Manors.		Acres.
" Dunwear	To the heirs of Sir Robert Chichester, &c.	346
Stawell	To Sir John Stawell	274
Sutton-Mallett	To John Mallett, esq;	234
Bawdrippe	To Walter Long, esq;	218
Brogney	To Thomas Muttlebury, esq; ...	70
Middlezoy	To R. Warr, esq; Sir R. Strode, &c.	567
Moorlynch	To the heirs of Mr. Floyer	354
Highham	To Henry Lord Gray	708
Netherham	To the heirs of Sir Ed. Hext ...	264
Beere	To Sir William Courtney, &c. ...	229
Aishcotte	To Sir Thomas Cheeke	526
Horsey	To Sir George Horsey	370
Chedzoy	To Earl Pembroke	411
Weston	To Sir Peter Van Lore, &c.	582
		5153

Names of Manors.		Acres.
	Brought forward	5153
" Othery	To Sir Edward Trent, &c.	428
Somerton	To Tho. Hill, esq; James Rise, esq; and Burgesses, &c.	1505
Graynton	To the heirs of Mr. Watts	291
Pitteney	To Earl Northamton, and Sir J. Hanham	569
Compton-Dunden	To Sir J. Strangway, and Baronet Portman	548
Walton	To Sir Thomas Thynne	540
Street	To Andrew Whittington, &c.*	488
	Total acres	9522
	Besides for the king	4000

" *Memorandum.* That these allotments are rated proportionably, after the rate of two hundred and eighty-two acres of the moor (by the perch of fifteen feet) to every hundred acres of the severals.

" In the reign of King William, a similar attempt was made. An act was obtained for draining it, but by some means or other its operation was entirely frustrated. This projected and useful improvement lay dormant till the year 1775, when it was revived by Mr. Allen, then member of parliament for Bridgewater. Sanguine of success, and highly impressed with the idea of its importance, he purchased a large number of rights, and having obtained a signature of consents, went to parliament; but not having interest enough in the house to stem the torrent of opposition, all his delusive prospects of profit vanished, and he found himself left in a small but respectable minority. Though Mr. Allen met with so warm an opposition, yet there were not wanting many lords of manors interested, who expressed their decided approbation of the measure, in a *general point of view*, but objected to the mode by which it was conducted, and to the men who were the ostensible movers in the business.

" After this defeat, nothing was done till the year 1788, when a meeting was held at Wells to take into consideration the propriety of draining the said moor, and dividing it into *parochial allotments.* At this meeting Sir Philip Hales presided; and after much abuse and opposition from the lower order of commoners, who openly threatened destruction to those who supported such a measure, the
meeting

* Dugdale.

meeting was dissolved without coming to any final determination.

"The leading idea was, however, afterwards pursued, with great assiduity, by Sir Philip, and his agent Mr. Symes of Stowey; and by their persevering industry, and good management, matters were brought into such a train, that application was made to parliament in the session of 1790, for leave to bring in a bill for draining and dividing the said moor into parochial allotments, among thirty parishes and hamlets therein stated; and also among such other parishes as may prove a right to feeding the same. In the spring of 1791, this bill passed into a law; and the commissioners, acting under the powers thereof, held their first meeting at Bridgewater in June 1791."

IMPROVEMENT of King's Sedgemore.—P. 192. "I have been thus particular in stating the progress of this business, merely to shew the impropriety of calling publick meetings, with a view of gaining signatures of consent, or taking the sense of the proprietors in that way. At all publick meetings of this nature, which I ever attended, noise and clamour have silenced sound sense and argument. A party generally attends with a professed design to oppose, and truth and propriety have a host of foes to combat.

"Whoever, therefore, has an object of this kind in view, let him acquire consent by *private application;* for I have frequently seen the good effects thereof manifested, by the irresistible influence of truth, when coolly and quietly administered; and it has frequently happened, that men, hostile to your scheme, have, by dispassionate argument, not only changed their sentiment, but become warm partizans in that cause which at first they meant to oppose.

"This never could have been done at a publick meeting; for after men have once joined the opposition, their pride will not permit them to retreat.

"How far the commissioners appointed under this act have discharged their trust, time will shew; but the general opinion of their conduct seems to be flattering; and those who at first supposed that the act carried with it the seeds of its own dissolution, are brought to confess, that the present appearances are highly promising.

"It cannot but be supposed, that in the investigation of four thousand and sixty-three claims, (of which only one thousand seven hundred and ninety-eight are allowed) and in making compensation for a large portion of land, necessarily cut through in making the great drain, many causes of offence must be given; but, I trust, neither partiality, negligence, nor corruption, can be imputed to them; and

if

if they have erred, it has been an error of the head, and not of the heart.

" Previous to the present drainage, this moor emptied itself into the river Parrett, some miles above Bridgewater, and the fall from the moor was very trifling. Hence it followed, that the least flood covered it with water, and in that state it frequently remained many months. It was at first suggested, by many people whose abilities the county held in high estimation, that nothing more was necessary for the purpose of draining the moor, than the opening and widening these old outlets; but it occurred to the commissioners, that such a partial and ineffectual mode of procedure could not produce a radical cure. They therefore set themselves about to discover a convenient place of discharge lower down in the river, by which a greater and more rapid descent might be gained.

" An old sluice, called Dunbald Clize, presented itself as the desired spot; and on levels being taken by Mr. White, an eminent surveyor, it appeared that an extraordinary fall of nearly ten feet could be acquired; and that the descent from the upper part of the moor to this outlet, (a distance of about twelve miles) was nineteen feet, or about one foot and a half in a mile. The only objection which could be brought to the measure, arose from a consideration of the great expences which must be incurred by cutting through two miles and a half of elevated land.

" No alternative, however, presented itself. It appeared that this plan must be adopted, or the work would be incomplete. Justified therefore by the concurrent opinion of Mr. White, and of Mr. Jessop, (whose advice was taken) they proceeded boldly; and having erected at a great expence, and under numerous difficulties, (arising from the morassy nature of the ground on which it was built) a strong substantial *sluice*, they proceeded to make a channel or cut fifteen feet deep, ten feet wide at the bottom, and fifty-five feet wide at the top.

" It is impossible to describe the ridicule which this undertaking excited. Some thought the commissioners mad; others, and by far the majority, ascribed the boldness of the plan to the liberality of the proprietors, in allowing the commissioners three guineas per day for attendance and management, and drew this sage conclusion, that the work would never be finished, but would be protracted till the expences *would equal* the value of the moor.

" Uninfluenced by letters, or by menaces, the commissioners persevered; and they have the satisfaction of seeing the principal difficulties overcome; and of hearing those very men, who were most violent against the measure, acknowledge

knowledge their error, and candidly confess that the work is well executed, and promises to be effectual.

" It may be necessary, by way of instruction to others engaged in schemes of the like nature, to state, that had the drain been made less wide at the top (and the opponents insisted that it should have been only twenty-six feet wide) it would have collapsed, or fallen together; as it was, there were numerous and alarming slides, the repairing of which cost a considerable sum, and there can be no doubt, but something of this kind will happen for years to come; for the substratum, at the depth of sixteen feet, is so soft and morassy, that it gives way to the superincumbent clay, and rises up in the middle of the drain.

" This cut from the Dunbald sluice to the moor (a distance of about two miles and a half) cost four-pence per cubic yard, or in the whole about three thousand two hundred pounds; and the parochial drains, which were twelve feet wide at the top, four feet wide at the bottom, and six feet deep, cost on an average two shillings and seven-pence per rope (twenty progressive feet.) Expensive as this undertaking inevitably must be, yet the benefit resulting from it will most amply repay; for without saying any thing of the injury done to the health of the inhabitants in the circumadjacent country, and which this drain, by rendering the air more salubrious, will totally remove; we may fairly state, that the probable improved value cannot be estimated at less than four hundred and fifty thousand pounds*.

" The total amount of the expenditure is now ascertained; and it may give some satisfaction, if I inform my readers the sum total thereof. The following statement of the account *Dr.* and *Cr.* will approach pretty near the truth; but let it be understood, that this calculation is made under the idea of *parochial subdivisions*, without which little benefit will result either to the publick or individuals. The principles which I have, in my report on the North-East district, fixed as *data, incontrovertible, viz.* That all commons, however rich and fertile the soil, are unproductive of profit, in consequence of *overstocking*, must be here adhered to; and this argument is equally applicable to old inclosures. Let a farmer put *ten* head of cattle into a given piece of ground where only *five* should be depastured, and the cattle will be of less worth after the grass is consumed, than they were before: Of what value then is the land?

" KING'S

" * If we add to this the capital necessary to stock this moor, the publick utility and importance of the undertaking will be more strongly manifested. J. B."

" King's-Sedgmoor.

Dr.	£.	s.	d.
" To act of parliament, and all other incidental expences	1,628	15	0
Interest of money borrowed	3,239	4	11
Commissioners	4,314	7	8
Clerk	1,215	19	0
Surveyor	908	12	6
Printers	362	6	3
Petty expences	575	11	1
Land purchased	2,801	4	11
Drains, sluices, bridges, and roads	15,418	2	8
Awards and incidentals	1,160	0	8
	31,624	4	8
To which add for subdividing in each parish	28,000	0	0
To original value of the moor, say 10s. per acre, at twenty-five years purchase ...	150,000	0	0
	209,624	4	8
Profit	365,375	15	4
	£ 575,000	0	0

Cr.			
By 12,000 acres, at 35s. per acre, and 25 years purchase	525,000	0	0
By improvement of 4000 acres of adjacent land, at 10s. per acre	50,000	0	0
	£.575,000	0	0

" The above is the real expenditure taken from the commissioners books, and about seven hundred acres have been sold to discharge the same.

" N. B. Had the commissioners been empowered to sell land at the commencement of the business, the expenditure would have been reduced five thousand pounds by the difference in the interest accompt.

" This is not the only improvement, for by the addition of such a quantity of rich and productive grass land, the upland inclosures, and common fields, may be greatly advanced in value. In short, it is difficult to point out all the benefits likely to accrue from this grand but arduous undertaking; beside, though the original value of the moor per acre is stated to be ten shillings, this is done merely with a view to give the arguments against the inclosure the greatest weight; and perhaps it would have been more

just

just to have stated its value at five shillings per acre, or even less than that, for a right of stocking could be rented for half a guinea per year.

" Nor is the improved value at all exaggerated. On the contrary, I am confident it will exceed thirty-five shillings per acre; for even in dry summers three tons of hay per acre have been cut on inclosed lands adjoining or near the moor, the soil of which lands is in no respect better than that of the moor."

"Other Sedgmoors."

P. 197. " Besides King's-Sedgmoor, there are other similar tracts of land on the adjacent rivers Tone and Yeo, on which no improvement has yet been attempted, namely, Normoor, near North-Petherton; Stanmoor, Currymoor, West-Sedgmoor, &c. near North-Curry; West-Moor, near Kingsbury; Wet-Moor, near Muchelny;* amounting in the whole to about ten thousand acres, independent of many thousand acres of low flooded inclosed lands, which might be greatly improved by judicious draining.

" Many of these moors are superior in their quality to King's-Sedgmoor; and the example now set before them will, I trust, remove the mist from the proprietors' eyes, and make them see, in a true light, their own and the public interest."

THE

ABORIGINAL LANDS

OF

WEST SOMERSETSHIRE;

COMPRIZING THE

VALE OF TAUNTON, AND ITS ENVIRONS.

NATURAL ECONOMY.

SURFACE.—P. 263. " Quantock, Brandon, and Dunkry-Hills, may be noted for their wild and rugged scenery; and the part which is called *Dunkry Beacon*, is the highest land in the whole county."

CLIMA-

" * Most of these moors are now (1797) inclosed or inclosing."

CLIMATURE.—P. 263. " The climate, particularly of that
part which is called the *the Vale of Taunton Dean*, is
peculiarly mild and serene ; and the soil highly fertile and
productive. The eye is agreeably relieved by a judicious
mixture of arable and pasture ; and if it be contrasted with
some parts of the Northern District, it may emphatically
be called the Land of *Canaan*.

" There are, however, certain parts North-West of the
said vale which are mountainous, and subject to that mu-
tability of weather, and moisture of air, generally found on
elevated situations."

SOILS.—Of the *Vale of Taunton.*—P. 264. " The soil
is a rich loam, interspersed in some places with clay, as
part of Bradfield, Buckland, North side of Wellington,
part of Sampford, Hill-Farrence, Ninehead, Oake, and
Heathfield ; and in other parts with sand, or a lighter
mould ; as Kingston, Bishop's-Lidiard, Halse, Fitzhead,
Milverton, Langford, Thorne, and Runnington."

Of the *Seacoast Districts.*—" The soil of some part
of this district is but little inferior to that of the former ;
but the hills and forests are for the most part left in a
state of nature."

POLITICAL ECONOMY.

APPROPRIATION.—P. 286. " In an agricultural survey of the county of Somerset, it will naturally be expected that particular notice should be taken of the forest
of Exmoor ; its vast extent, and capability of improvement, render it an object well worthy of attention.

" This forest extends from north to south about eight
miles, and from east to west ten or twelve ; containing,
according to an accurate survey lately made, about nineteen thousand nine hundred acres."

Mr. B. enters on a description of this forest ; and makes
proposals for its improvement. I perceive nothing, however, in his observations, that appears, to me, either sufficiently instructive, or interesting to the public, for extraction.

P. 289. " Besides Exmoor, there are several hundred
acres of uncultivated land around Dunkry, and on Quantock and Brandon hills."

MANUFACTURES.—P. 295. " About a century ago the
woollen manufactures in the town of Taunton were in a
very flourishing condition, and of course some of their
benefits

benefits devolved to the agriculturist ; but of late years the warmth of party at the elections of their representatives in parliament has run so high, that it has not subsided from one election to another ; by which means manufactures declined, and have been removed to Wellington and other places. So that it may fairly be inferred, that if the right of election to members in parliament has been injurious to any borough in the kingdom, it has been so to this."

P. 296. "Though the trade of Taunton has declined, yet considerable manufactories are carried on at Wellington, Wiveliscombe, and other places ; and many thousand hands are employed therein."

RURAL ECONOMY.

TENURES.—P. 268. "The major part of the five hundreds of Taunton Dean, consists of customary lands of inheritance, held under the Lord Bishop of Winchester, paying an annual rent. These customary lands pass by surrender, paying to the lord fines and heriots on alienations. There are also many singular customs within the manor, difficult to be understood even by the tenants themselves. The descent is called that of *Borough-English*, with some variations. The wife is heir to her husband ; and it is no uncommon thing for a widow, on the death of her husband, having children by him, to marry again, and carry her estate into her second family, to the disinheritance of her first."

AGRICULTURE.

WORKPEOPLE.—P. 294. "The price of labour, throughout the whole district, is nearly the same, viz. Men, through the year, one shilling per day and beer ; women, for weeding and common work, six-pence per day ; and for mattocking the wheat and hay-making, eight-pence per day."

WORKING ANIMALS.—P. 291. "Oxen are principally used, and are for the most part worked in yokes."

P. 293. "The oxen of this country are large, well made, and beautiful animals. They are almost all red. They are yoked at three years old, and worked till they are five or six, when they are sold to the graziers, at prices from ten pounds to twenty-two pounds each ox."

ORCHARDS.—In a note, by R. P. appendant to the chapter

chapter "Orchards," of this Report, I find a few particulars, on *cidermaking*, that are new to me; not having
met with them, either in the Glocestershire or the West
Devonshire practice. The process is well described—concise, yet clear; and although the Writer's theory may be
unsound, his practice, fortunately, does not bear upon it.

N. p. 282. "In part of this county, the art of making
sweet rich *cider*, which sells from three to five or six
guineas per hogshead, is reduced to a system; and there
are some persons who, on being furnished with a sufficient
quantity of apples, undertake to make and carry it through
the whole process at the price of fifteen shillings a hogshead. But the method of doing this they endeavour to
keep a profound secret. The Writer of this note, who is
in possession of this method, and has practised it successfully for his private use, desirous that all makers of cider,
who think it worth their attention, may profit by it, takes
this opportunity of making it more generally known:

" The apples being ripe, but not rotten, and all of the
same sort, that the fermentation may be more uniform,
grind and press them moderately, but by no means closely.
Pour the liquor into a tub to kive, and when the brown
head (which will rise on it sooner or later as the weather
is more warm or cold) begins to crack, and the white froth
appears in the cracks level with the surface of the head, it
must be drawn off in order for tunning into your vessel. At
this time a great deal of feculence is thrown to the top, as
well as deposited at the bottom, and if the liquor is continued longer in the tub, the head will sink, the bottom
rise, and a strong fermentation take place, which it will
be difficult to subdue, and which carries away the sweets.
Proceeding in your operation, tun into a hogshead vessel
three pail-fulls or about fifteen gallons of this cider. This
done, burn in the vessel a strong match made with nearly
a quarter of a pound of stone brimstone, stopping the bung
as close as possible, that none of the fume may escape.
When the match is quite burnt out, open the bung, and
immediately pour in four ounces of sweet spirit of nitre.
Put in the bung tight again, and roll the vessel strongly
for near half an hour, by which time the smoke of the
match will be destroyed and taken up by the liquor. Then
set the vessel in its place, fill it to within a finger's breadth
of the top, but no higher, and let it stand till the month of
February. In this month it will be coming fine, and must
be watched attentively, and examined frequently by a peg
in the barrel. When perfectly fine, it must be immediately
drawn off and tunned into the same vessel, after washing
out the lee, burning also at this racking a smaller brimstone
match

match. It is directed to be drawn off *immediately* when quite fine, because a very few hours produce an amazing alteration. It becomes turbid and foul, the" (a) " second fermentation is commenced, *the sweets fly off*," (!) " and all the preceding trouble is rendered of no effect. R. P."

LIVESTOCK.—P. 291. " The stock of Taunton-Dean, is principally neat cattle and sheep ; the former of the *North Devon*, the latter of the *Dorset* breed, both excellent of their kind. Many graziers prefer the oxen bred in this district to those of Barnstaple, South-Molton, Torrington, &c. and the sheep are considered as equally profitable with the Leicestershire breed, which have been introduced, but do not gain ground.

" The dairy farmers are accustomed to take in sheep to keep during the winter, viz. from the beginning of October and November, to the 5th of April; the usual prices are, for hog sheep five shillings, and for ewes seven or eight shillings per head. The Dorsetshire flocks are greatly improved by this custom, and the price of keeping is on the advance."

SHEEP.—P. 292. " There are two sorts of sheep in this country, the one a native breed, without horns, well made, and covered with a thick fleece of wool, weighing in general seven or eight pounds; the other a small horned sheep, called Exmoor sheep, bought, when hoggits, at South-Molton market. The first is a valuable sort, not much unlike the Leicester breed; and their fleeces may be considered as a most profitable article to the breeder, as they sometimes reach even the weight of twelve pounds."

P. 293. " The second sort are kept on the forest of Exmoor, or the adjoining hills, for two or three years, merely for the annual profit of their fleeces; the weight of which seldom exceeds four pounds. They are fattened on turnips, and sold without their wool. Weight of carcase from fourteen pounds to eighteen pounds per quarter."

IMPROVEMENTS.

AT THE CLOSE of his Report, Mr. Billingsley inserts— " a recapitulation of the Hints for Improvement, already suggested in the preceding pages, with some additional remarks."

But before I enumerate the subjects of improvement which Mr. B. conceives the County to be capable of receiving, I will place, here, his well expressed sentiments, concerning the RURAL PROFESSION.

P. 297.

P. 297. " Very few gentlemen of landed property in this
county have shewn that attention to the advancement of
rural œconomy, or to the improvement of agriculture,
which a science of such importance merits: this is the more
extraordinary, as their own interest is so deeply involved,
and as great examples have been shewn them by the nobility
and gentry of other counties, and even by Majesty itself.

" It is no uncommon thing for untitled gentlemen to ap-
prentice the younger branches of their family to trade, for
five or seven years: And why not to agriculture? It cannot be because the former is a more respectable occupation
than the latter. I rather think, it is because the acquire-
ment of knowledge in the one is considered as more difficult than in the other. The general opinion seems to be,
that any one may become a farmer: How egregiously are
they mistaken who think thus! I have known both, and
can truly say, that more experience, care, assiduity, patience, and attention, are requisite in a farmer, than in a
tradesman of any description whatever."

The following are the heads of Mr. B.'s proposed improvements.

1. " Inclose and cultivate all Waste Lands susceptible of
Improvement, and divide and inclose the Common Fields."

2. " Where Lands are situate on bleak and exposed eminences, improve the climate by judicious and extensive
plantations."

3. " Wherever marl, lime, or chalk, can be procured
within a reasonable distance, neglect not a liberal use
thereof; and if destitute of such resources, be careful to
make as much dung as possible by folding sheep, housing
all sorts of cattle, preserving urine, collecting woollen rags,
malt-combs, ashes, horn shavings, bones, &c. &c."

4. " A regular and well-conceived rotation of Crops."

5. " Enlarge the upland corn farms; erect proper buildings and conveniencies for the shelter of the cattle in the
winter months, thereby inviting substantial and well-informed farmers, of more enlightened countries, to settle
upon them."

6. " Improve the Stock by a judicious selection of Males
and Females for breeding; and be particularly careful to
choose a Male handsome in those points wherein the Female may be deficient."

7. " Lessen the number of Horses, and encourage the
use of Oxen."

8. " Amend the Publick Roads."

9. " Encourage the use of such ploughs, and other instruments, as are best calculated to expedite work and do
it well."

10. " Sow early in exposed and cold situations, and be particularly careful not to plough or harrow in wet weather."

11. " Destroy Rats and Mice."

12. " Introduce Threshing Machines."

13. " Let all Unmalted Corn be sold by weight."

14. " Grant Long Leases."

15. " Sow more Sainfoin on the stone-brash lands, and on all other soils congenial thereto."

16. " Roll all Grass Land once a year at least, with a heavy roller, and abstain from ploughing your Arable Land in wet weather."

17. " Set all Pease and Beans in lines from North to South, and hoe them twice at least."

18. " Devote at least one quarter part of your Turnip Land to the Ruta-baga or Swedish Turnip."

19. " As in every point of view this county appears from its soil and situation to be better adapted to *grass* than arable, it deserves enquiry, whether stock could not profitably be kept on *grass land alone*, without the aid of winter roots. The argument for ploughing arises from a wish of having straw to make manure, and turnips to support stock in the winter season.* But whenever the plough is put into the hand of the generality of farmers, the land is from that time in a state of degradation, and its value reduced at least 10s. per acre, in comparison with contiguous grass land.

" *Grass*, therefore, should be considered as the ultimate improvement of land in the Western part of the county of Somerset."

In those proposed improvements, men of reading will find nothing that is new or striking. Such of them, as are entitled to the name here assigned them, have long been before the public; and most or all of them have been repeatedly brought before the readers of the work which I am now concluding. Mr. Billingsley has remarked on most of them. But not in a way, I think, that would enhance the value of this abstract. Indeed, some of them are radically improper, and others doubtfully eligible.

In his " CONCLUSION," Mr. Billingsley has evidently employed a stronger effort of thought; and bestowed upon it more mature consideration.

P. 313. " This county does not raise grain sufficient for its consumption, nor are the climate and soil of many parts thereof favourable to corn farming; yet, were all the improvements

provements

* In p. 235, Mr. B. says—" arable land to a dairy farm"—" is certainly not only useful, but absolutely necessary."

provements before suggested to take place, there cannot be a doubt but that the produce of the soil might be increased at least one third.

" The advanced rent which might be produced by draining the marshes, and by inclosing and cultivating the common fields and waste lands, may, according to the most moderate calculation, be thus estimated :—

No. of Acres.	Description.	Increased Rent.			Total Increase.
		£.	s.	d.	£.
30,000	Marsh lands	0	15	0	22,500
20,000	Common field	0	5	0	5,000
65,000	Uncultivated waste	0	5	0	16,250 per ann.
					43,750

" To which may be added, a capacity of improvement in the arable and pasture lands *inclosed*, of at least five shillings per acre, amounting to more than 213,000*l*. per annum, which increased rent, at thirty years purchase, would exceed six millions.

" These blessed effects would be the natural consequence of that spirit of industry which publick encouragement would excite, would add greatly to the capital of the nation, and be much more valuable than any foreign conquest of treble the amount. Would to God that nations would learn wisdom, and instead of coveting distant territory, improve to the utmost *that* which they possess!"

I will not fastidiously suppress my gratification, on finding, that a passage so appropriate, and so consonant with my own sentiments, has spontaneously presented itself, to close my Review of the Reports to the Board of Agriculture.

THE

E N D

OF THE

FIVE VOLUMES

AND THE

SIX DEPARTMENTS.

THE FIVE

THE FIVE VOLUMES comprehend the COUNTY REPORTS, in manner following.

The NORTHERN DEPARTMENT

COMPRIZES,

NORTHUMBERLAND,   WESTMORELAND,
DURHAM,   LANCASHIRE,
CUMBERLAND,   YORKSHIRE,

and the
MOUNTAINOUS PARTS OF DERBYSHIRE.

The WESTERN DEPARTMENT

COMPRIZES,

CHESHIRE,   WORCESTERSHIRE,
FLINTSHIRE,   GLOCESTERSHIRE,
SHROPSHIRE,   NORTH WILTSHIRE, AND
HEREFORDSHIRE,   NORTH SOMERSETSHIRE.

The EASTERN DEPARTMENT

COMPRIZES,

LINCOLNSHIRE,   SUFFOLK, AND
NORFOLK,   NORTHEAST ESSEX;

WITH THE MARSHES AND FENS OF

YORKSHIRE,   HUNTINGDONSHIRE,
NORTH LINCOLNSHIRE,   CAMBRIDGESHIRE,
SOUTH LINCOLNSHIRE,   NORFOLK, AND
NORTHAMPTONSHIRE,   SUFFOLK.

The MIDLAND DEPARTMENT

COMPRIZES,

STAFFORDSHIRE,   NORTHAMPTONSHIRE,
DERBYSHIRE,   OXFORDSHIRE,
NOTTINGHAMSHIRE,   BUCKINGHAMSHIRE,
LEICESTERSHIRE,   BEDFORDSHIRE,
RUTLANDSHIRE,   and
WARWICKSHIRE,   a principal part of
HUNTINGDONSHIRE,   CAMBRIDGESHIRE.

The SOUTHERN and PENINSULAR DEPARTMENTS

COMPRIZE,

HERTFORDSHIRE,   HAMPSHIRE,
BERKSHIRE,   SURREY,
MIDDLESEX,   KENT,
SOUTH ESSEX,   SUSSEX,
SOUTH WILTSHIRE,   CORNWALL,
SOUTHEAST SOMERSET,   DEVONSHIRE, AND
DORSETSHIRE,   WEST SOMERSETSHIRE.

INDEX.

Thomas Wilson and Sons, Printers, High-Ousegate, York.

A GENERAL

TABLE OF CONTENTS,

OF

MR. MARSHALL'S REVIEW

OF

REPORTS

TO

The BOARD of AGRICULTURE;

𝔖𝔶𝔰𝔱𝔢𝔪𝔞𝔱𝔦𝔠𝔞𝔩𝔩𝔶 𝔞𝔯𝔯𝔞𝔫𝔤𝔢𝔡;

So that the whole of the useful information, concerning
each individual Subject of Rural Affairs, which has been collected
by the Board, in the several Counties of England, may be perused, or
consulted, with nearly the same facility, and with the very same advantage, as
if the Five Volumes were recast into one large Volume :—while the Intelligence which belongs, more especially, to each Department, is kept
entire, and distinct from what relates to the other
Agricultural Divisions of the Kingdom.

TOGETHER WITH

A GENERAL INDEX

TO THE FIVE VOLUMES.

———◆———

𝔜𝔬𝔯𝔨 :

Printed by Thomas Wilson and Sons, High-Ousegate;

FOR LONGMAN, HURST, REES, ORME, AND BROWN, PATER-
NOSTER-ROW, LONDON; AND FOR WILSON AND
SONS, YORK.

1818.

THE

HEADS

OF THE FOLLOWING

TABLE OF CONTENTS;

To give, at one view, a general idea of its arrangements; and to assist in referring to its individual subjects.

———

WOODLANDS.

AGRICULTURE.

GENERAL SUBJECTS.

CROPS in HUSBANDRY, and their MANAGEMENT.

LIVESTOCK, and their MANAGEMENT.

A GENERAL

TABLE OF CONTENTS

TO THE

FIVE VOLUMES OF REVIEW OF REPORTS.

PREFATORY SUBJECTS.

QUALI-

NATURAL ECONOMY.

SUB-

POLITICAL ECONOMY.

West

RURAL ECONOMY.

TENANTED ESTATES.

North

WOODLANDS.

AGRICULTURE.

GENERAL SUBJECTS.

West Yorkshire, 378.
North Yorkshire, 475.
East Yorkshire, 517.

II.

Cheshire, 24, 134.
Shropshire, 182, 242.
Herefordshire, 279, 327.
Worcestershire, 374.
Glocestershire, 407, 451.
North Somersetshire, 507.

III.

Lincolnshire, 57, 142.
Waterlands, 257.
Norfolk, 335, 371.
Suffolk, 430.
Essex, 517.

IV.

Stafford. 37.
Nottingham. 170.
Warwick. 295, 319.
Northampton. 353.
Huntingdon. 411, 422.
Oxford. 453, 479.
Buckingham. 503, 529.
Bedford. 561.
Cambridge. 618, 635.

V.

Hertfordshire, 13, 29.
Berkshire, 53, 83.
Middlesex, 105.
South Essex, 176.
South Wilts, 210.
Southeast Somerset, 234.
Dorsetshire, 248, 269.
Hampshire, 297, 336.
Surrey, 385.
Kent, 435.
Sussex, 476.

Cornwall, 525, 538.
Davonshire, 576.
West Somerset, 602.

IMPLEMENTS.

I.

Northumberland, 62.
Durham, 150.
Cumberland, 185.
Lancashire, 284.
West Yorkshire, 379.
North Yorkshire, 476.
East Yorkshire, 518.

II.

Cheshire, 134.
Herefordshire, 280, 328.
Glocestershire, 408.

III.

Lincolnshire, 57, 143.
Waterlands, 210.
Norfolk, 336, 371.
Suffolk, 432.
Essex, 517.
General Remarks, 517.

IV.

Stafford. 37.
Nottingham. 171.
Leicester. 189.
Rutland. 252.
Warwick. 296, 319.
Northampton. 353.
Oxford. 453.
Buckingham. 503, 530.
Bedford. 591.
Cambridge. 636.

V.

Hertfordshire, 29.
Berkshire, 53, 83.
Middlesex, 105, 131.
South Wilts, 212.
Dorsetshire, 270.
Hampshire, 293, 337.
Surrey, 386.
Kent, 435.
Sussex, 479.

Cornwall, 533.
Devonshire, 554, 576.

MANURES.

South

South Wilts, 215.
Southeast Somerset, 234.
Dorsetshire, 271.
Surrey, 386.
Kent, 438.
Sussex, 482.
Devonshire, 555.

SEMINATION.

I.
Northumberland, 71.
Cumberland, 191.

II.
Cheshire, 30. 147.
Shropshire, 245.
Herefordshire, 281.

III.
Lincolnshire, 57, 148.
Norfolk, 345, 376.
Suffolk, 436.
Essex, 484, 518.

IV.
Stafford. 40.
Leicester. 223.
Warwick. 298, 322.
Huntingdon. 411.
Oxford. 484.
Bedford. 594.

V.
Hertfordshire, 34.
Berkshire, 87.
Middlesex, 133.
Hampshire, 339.
Surrey, 390.

GROWING CROPS.

I.
Northumberland, 72.

Cumberland, 191.

II.
Cheshire, 148.
Shropshire, 246.
Herefordshire, 281.
Glocestershire, 452.

III.
Suffolk, 436.
Essex, 519.

IV.
Stafford. 41.
Nottingham. 172.
Warwick. 328.
Bedford. 597.

V.
Middlesex, 133.

HARVESTING.

I.
Northumberland, 73.

II.
Shropshire, 246.
North Somersetshire, 514.

III.
Lincolnshire, 149.
Norfolk, 347.

IV.
Northampton. 356.

HOMESTALL MANAGEMENT

I.
West Yorkshire, 407.*

II.
North Somersetshire, 514.

IV.
Warwick. 322.
Cambridge. 637.

---

* On the Winter Management or Store Cattle,—on the Thrashing or Dressing of Corn, on the Expenditure of Hay or Straw, or on the raising of Manure therefrom,—not a word! (excepting the item here referred to, and excepting what may have been incidentally mentioned under other heads). Indeed, those very important concerns of the arable Farmer, appear not to have been thought of, by the framer of the plan of the Board's Reports.

THE

South Wilts, 216.
Dorsetshire, 249, 271.
Hampshire, 340.
Surrey, 390.
Kent, 439.
Sussex, 482.
Cornwall, 526, 542.

MESLIN.
I.
Northumberland, 76.
II.
Herefordshire, 334.

RYE.
I.
Northumberland, 76.
III.
Norfolk, 382.
Suffolk, 438.
IV.
Nottingham. 172.
Bedford. 598.
V.
Surrey, 392.

BARLEY.
I.
Northumberland, 76.
Durham, 151.
Cumberland, 191.
West Yorkshire, 397.
II.
Cheshire, 150.
III.
Lincolnshire 151.
Norfolk, 349, 382:
Suffolk, 438.
Essex, 522.

IV.
Stafford. 42.
Nottingham. 173.
Leicester. 225.
Rutland. 272.
Northampton 357.
Oxford. 486.
Buckingham. 535.

Bedford, 598.

V.
Hertfordshire, 36.
Berkshire, 89.
Middlesex, 135.
South Wilts, 218.
Dorsetshire, 249.
Hampshire, 342.
Surrey, 393.
Kent, 439.
Sussex, 484.

OATS.
I.
Northumberland, 78.
Durham, 151.
Cumberland, 191.
North Yorkshire, 478,
II.
Cheshire, 150.
III.
Lincolnshire, 151.
IV.
Nottingham. 173.
Rutland. 273.
Northampton. 357.
Buckingham. 536.
Bedford. 599.
V.
Hertfordshire, 36.
South Wilts, 220.
Dorsetshire, 272.
Hampshire, 342.
Cornwall (naked) 542.

BEANS.
I.
Northumberland, 78.
Durham, 151.
West Yorkshire, 397.
North Yorkshire, 479.
II.
Cheshire, 150.
Glocestershire, 412.

III.

III.

Lincolnshire, 151.
Norfolk, 384.
Suffolk, 439.

IV.

Leicester. 225.
Rutland. 273.
Northampton. 357.
Oxford. 486.
Buckingham. 536.
Bedford. 599.

V.

Berkshire, 89.
Middlesex, 135.
South Essex, 177.
Kent, 440.

PEAS.

I.

Northumberland, 80.
Durham, 151.
Cumberland, 192.

III.

Norfolk, 384.

IV.

Rutland. 273.
Buckingham. 536.
Bedford. 599.

V.

Hertfordshire, 37.
Berkshire, 89
Middlesex, 136.
Hampshire, 342.
Surrey, 393.
Kent, 440.
Sussex, 484.

BUCKWEET.

II.

Cheshire, 150.

III.

Norfolk, 384.
Suffolk, 440.

V.

Sussex, 484.

RAPE SEED.

III.

Lincolnshire, 152.
Waterlands, 290.

IV.

Nottingham. 174.
Huntingdon. 434.
Bedford. 599.

V.

South Essex, 160.

HEMP.

II.

Shropshire, 249.

III.

Lincolnshire, 58, 153.
Waterlands, 259.
Norfolk, 385.
Suffolk, 441.

IV.

Huntingdon. 435.

V.

Dorsetshire, 272.

FLAX.

I.

West Yorkshire, 398.
North Yorkshire, 479.

II.

Glocestershire, 455.
Worcestershire, 376.

III.

Lincolnshire, 154.
Dorsetshire, v. 249, 273.

WELD.

III.

Lincolnshire, 150.
Norfolk, 347, 379.

V.

Surrey, 393.

TEASLES.

I.

North Yorkshire, 479.

II.

II.
Glocestershire, 456.
North Somersetshire, 515.

III.
North Essex, 486.

WOAD.
II.
North Somersetshire, 517.

III.
Lincolnshire, 58, 154.

IV.
Northampton. 387.

V.
Berkshire, 89.

HOPS.
II.
Shropshire, 183.
Herefordshire, 283, 335, 351.
Worcestershire, 376.
North Wiltshire, 491.
North Somersetshire, 529.

III.
Suffolk, 457.
Essex, 486, 525.

IV.
Nottingham. 174.

ORCHARD FRUIT.
I.
Durham, 152.
Lancashire, 310.

II.
Cheshire, 35.
Shropshire, 251.
Herefordshire, 288. 336.
Worcestershire, 383.
Glocestershire, 414, 463.
North Somersetshire, 523.

IV.
Stafford. 46.

Bedford. 601.

V.
Hertfordshire, 40.
Southeast Somerset, 235.
Dorsetshire, 249, 275.
Hampshire, 347.
Surrey, 402.
Kent, 445.
Cornwall, 544.
Devonshire, 577.
West Somerset, 602.

POTATOES.
I.
Northumberland, 80.
Lancashire, 292.
North Yorkshire, 480.

II.
Cheshire, 30, 151.
Shropshire, 249.
Herefordshire, 334.
Glocestershire, 458.
North Somersetshire, 519.

III.
Lincolnshire, 58, 159.
Suffolk, 445.

IV.
Leicester. 226.
Rutland. 274.
Northampton. 357.
Oxford. 486.
Buckingham. 536.
Bedford. 599.

V.
Middlesex, 136.
South Essex, 160, 178.
South Wilts, 220.
Dorsetshire, 274.
Hampshire, 342.
Sussex, 485.

TURNEPS.
I.
Northumberland, 80, 113.
Cumberland,

28   CROPS IN HUSBANDRY.

Cumberland, 192.
West Yorkshire, 399.

II.
Cheshire, 150.
Shropshire, 248.
Herefordshire, 283, 335.
Glocestershire, 459.

III.
Lincolnshire, 58, 160.
Norfolk, 349, 387.
Suffolk, 451.

IV.
Nottingham. 173.
Rutland. 274.
Northampton. 358, 387.
Huntingdon. 435.
Oxford. 453. 486.
Buckingham. 537.
Bedford. 599.
Cambridge. 638.

V.
Hertfordshire, 37.
Middlesex, 136.
South Wilts, 221.
Southeast Somerset, 235.
Dorsetshire, 274.
Hampshire, 342.
Surrey, 394.
Kent, 441.
Sussex, 485.

Cornwall, 543.

BULBOUS RAPE.

I.
North Yorkshire, 482.

II.
Herefordshire, 334.

III.
Lincolnshire, 162.

IV.
Leicester. 227.
Warwick. 325.
Oxford. 488.
Buckingham. 537.

Cambridge. 639.

V.
Hertfordshire, 37.
Berkshire, 90.
Dorsetshire, 275.
Surrey, 395.

CARROTS.

II.
Cheshire, 153.

III.
Lincolnshire, 160.
Suffolk, 445.
General Remarks, 450.

IV.
Leicester. 189.
Buckingham. 537.

CABBAGES.

II.
Cheshire, 150.

III.
Lincolnshire, 162.
Norfolk, 390.
Suffolk, 453.

IV.
Leicester. 226.
Buckingham. 538.

RAPE HERBAGE.

IV.
Northamptonshire, 358, 388.

V.
South Essex, 160.
South Wilts, 222.
Hampshire, 343.
Surrey, 396.
Kent, 442.
Sussex, 487.

TARE HERBAGE.

II.
Glocestershire, 412.

Lin-

III.
Lincolnshire, 152.
Norfolk, 384.

IV.
Buckinghamshire, 538.

V.
Hertfordshire, 39.
Middlesex, 137.
South Wilts, 222.
Sussex, 488.

MIXED HERBAGE.

I.
Northumberland, 88.
Durham, 151.
Cumberland, 192.
Westmoreland, 235.
Lancashire, 304.
West Yorkshire, 401.
North Yorkshire, 482.

II.
Cheshire, 154.
Glocestershire, 413, 460.
North Somersetshire, 520.

III.
Lincolnshire, 162.
Waterlands, 260.
Norfolk, 390.
Suffolk, 455.
Essex, 486.

IV.
Stafford. 42.
Nottingham. 177.
Northampton. 358, 388.
Huntingdon. 435.
Buckingham. 538.
Bedford. 600.

V
Hertfordshire, 39.
Berkshire, 90.
Middlesex, 137.
South Essex, 160, 179.
South Wilts, 222.
Hampshire, 343.

Surrey, 396.
Kent, 442.
Sussex, 487.
Cornwall, 543.

SAINFOIN.

II.
Glocestershire, 413.

III.
Norfolk, 351.

IV.
Rutland. 275.
Northampton. 358, 389.
Oxford. 488.
Buckingham. 539.
Cambridge. 639.

V.
Berkshire, 56.
Middlesex, 137.
South Wilts, 223.
Hampshire, 343.
Surrey, 397.
Kent, 442.

PERENNIAL GRASS LAND.

I.
Northumberland, 89.
Durham, 151.
Cumberland, 193.
Westmoreland, 236.
Lancashire, 305.
West Yorkshire, 402.
North Yorkshire, 484.

II.
Cheshire, 34, 154.
Shropshire, 183, 250.
Herefordshire, 288, 342.
Glocestershire, 463.
North Wiltshire, 486.
North Somersetshire, 523,

III.
Lincolnshire, 58, 166.
Waterlands, 55, 203, 138, 221, 260, 290.

Norfolk,

LIVESTOCK, AND THEIR MANAGEMENT.

Here

Herefordshire, 344.
Worcestershire, 391.
North Somersetshire, 524.

III.
Lincolnshire, 59, 176.
Waterlands, 211, 261.
Norfolk, 352.

IV.
Stafford. 47.
Leicester. 228.
Rutland. 254 278.
Warwick. 326.
Northampton. 359, 391.
Huntingdon. 403, 411, 436.
Oxford. 455.
Buckingham. 543.
Bedford. 562, 601.
Cambridge. 641.

V.
Berkshire, 57, 92.
Middlesex, 108.
Hampshire, 294, 348.

Cornwall, 544.

CATTLE.

I.
Northumberland, 91.
Durham, 153.
Cumberland, 195.
Westmoreland, 237.
Lancashire, 313.
West Yorkshire, 404.
North Yorkshire, 487.
East Yorkshire, 520.

II.
Cheshire, 35, 155.
Flintshire, 168.
Shropshire, 184, 252.
Herefordshire, 294, 344.
Worcestershire, 391.
Glocestershire, 415. 464.
North Wiltshire, 487.
North Somersetshire, 524.

III.
Lincolnshire, 60, 177.
Waterlands, 211, 261.
Norfolk, 352, 394.
Suffolk, 457.
Essex, 488.

IV.
Stafford. 48.
Nottingham. 178.
Leicester. 191, 229.
Rutland. 254, 278.
Warwick 300, 326.
Northampton. 359, 391.
Huntingdon. 403, 412, 436.
Oxford. 455, 491.
Buckingham. 505, 543.
Bedford. 562, 601.
Cambridge. 620, 641.

V.
Hertfordshire, 40.
Berkshire, 57, 92.
Middlesex, 108, 141.
South Essex, 162.
South Wilts, 226.
Southeast Somerset, 236.
Dorsetshire, 250, 277.
Hampshire, 348.
Surrey, 363, 407.
Kent, 447.
Sussex, 494.

Cornwall, 526, 545, 555.
Devonshire, 578.

DAIRY.
I.
Northumberland, 96.
Cumberland, 197.
Westmoreland, 238.
Lancashire, 314.
West Yorkshire, 405.
North Yorkshire, 488.

II.
Cheshire, 41, 157.
Shropshire, 184.

Here-

Herefordshire, 346.
Glocestershire, 415, 465.
North Wiltshire, 488.
North Somersetshire, 528.

III.
See Cattle, above.

IV.
Derby. 67.
Leicester. 193, 230.
Rutland. 254.
Warwick. 300, 327.
Northampton. 360, 394.
Huntingdon. 436.
Oxford. 491.
Buckingham. 505, 544.
Bedford. 563, 601.
Cambridge. 621, 642.

V.
Berkshire, 92.
Middlesex, 144.
South Essex, 150, 162, 182.
South Wilts, 227.
Southeast Somerset, 238.
Dorsetshire, 250, 278.
Hampshire, 294, 298, 349.
Sussex, 497.

Cornwall, 546.
Devonshire, 579.

SUCKLING.

IV.
Buckingham. 506, 548.
Cambridge. 642.

V.
South Essex, 163, 182.
Middlesex, 142.

SHEEP.

I.
Northumberland, 97, 115.
Durham, 153.
Cumberland, 197.
Westmoreland, 238.
Lancashire, 323.

West Yorkshire, 406.
North Yorkshire, 489.
East Yorkshire, 520.

II.
Cheshire, 35, 160.
Shropshire, 185, 256.
Herefordshire, 297, 347.
Worcestershire, 391.
Glocestershire, 416, 465.
North Somersetshire, 529.

III.
Lincolnshire, 62, 183.
Waterlands, 211, 261.
Norfolk, 353, 374, 397.
Suffolk, 465.
Essex, 489.
General Remarks, 68, 184,
195.

IV.
Stafford. 49.
Nottingham. 180.
Leicester. 193, 232.
Rutland. 254, 278.
Warwick. 300, 327.
Northampton. 361, 394.
Huntingdon. 403, 412, 487.
Oxford. 455, 492.
Buckingham. 506, 550.
Bedford. 563, 603.
Cambridge. 621, 642.

V.
Hertfordshire, 41.
Berkshire, 58, 94.
Middlesex, 110, 145.
South Essex, 165, 183.
South Wilts, 227.
Southeast Somerset, 239.
Dorsetshire, 251, 279.
Hampshire, 294, 298, 349.
Surrey, 363, 408.
Kent, 448.
Sussex, 498.
Cornwall, 526, 547.
Devonshire, 556, 581.
West Somerset, 604.

DEER.

II.

A GENERAL

A

GENERAL INDEX

FIVE VOLUMES OF REVIEW OF REPORTS.

Clark's

Potter's

THE END.

(Thomas Wilson and Sons, Printers, High-Ousegate, York.)